COMMON ELEMENTS

Name	Symbol	Approx. At. Wt.	Common Ox. Nos.	Name	Symbol	Approx. At. Wt.	Common Ox. Nos.
Aluminum	Al	27	$+3$	Magnesium	Mg	24	$+2$
Antimony	Sb	122	$+3,+5$	Manganese	Mn	55	$+2,+4,+7$
Arsenic	As	75	$+3,+5$	Mercury	Hg	201	$+1,+2$
Barium	Ba	137	$+2$	Nickel	Ni	59	$+2$
Bismuth	Bi	209	$+3$	Nitrogen	N	14	$-3,+3,+5$
Bromine	Br	80.	$-1,+5$	Oxygen	O	16	-2
Calcium	Ca	40.	$+2$	Phosphorus	P	31	$+3,+5$
Carbon	C	12	$+2,+4$	Platinum	Pt	195	$+2,+4$
Chlorine	Cl	35.5	$-1,+5,+7$	Potassium	K	39	$+1$
Chromium	Cr	52	$+2,+3,+6$	Silicon	Si	28	$+4$
Cobalt	Co	59	$+2,+3$	Silver	Ag	108	$+1$
Copper	Cu	63.5	$+1,+2$	Sodium	Na	23	$+1$
Fluorine	F	19	-1	Strontium	Sr	88	$+2$
Gold	Au	197	$0,+3$	Sulfur	S	32	$-2,+4,+6$
Hydrogen	H	1.0	$-1,+1$	Tin	Sn	119	$+2,+4$
Iodine	I	127	$-1,+5$	Titanium	Ti	48	$+3,+4$
Iron	Fe	56	$+2,+3$	Tungsten	W	184	$+6$
Lead	Pb	207	$+2,+4$	Zinc	Zn	65	$+2$

VALENCE OF COMMON IONS

Name	Symbol	Valence	Name	Symbol	Valence
Aluminum	Al^{+++}	$+3$	Lead(II)	Pb^{++}	$+2$
Ammonium	NH_4^+	$+1$	Magnesium	Mg^{++}	$+2$
Barium	Ba^{++}	$+2$	Mercury(I)	Hg_2^{++}	$+1$
Calcium	Ca^{++}	$+2$	Mercury(II)	Hg^{++}	$+2$
Chromium(III)	Cr^{+++}	$+3$	Nickel(II)	Ni^{++}	$+2$
Cobalt(II)	Co^{++}	$+2$	Potassium	K^+	$+1$
Copper(I)	Cu^+	$+1$	Silver	Ag^+	$+1$
Copper(II)	Cu^{++}	$+2$	Sodium	Na^+	$+1$
Hydronium	H_3O^+	$+1$	Tin(II)	Sn^{++}	$+2$
Iron(II)	Fe^{++}	$+2$	Tin(IV)	Sn^{++++}	$+4$
Iron(III)	Fe^{+++}	$+3$	Zinc	Zn^{++}	$+2$
Acetate	$C_2H_3O_2^-$	-1	Hydroxide	OH^-	-1
Bicarbonate	HCO_3^-	-1	Hypochlorite	ClO^-	-1
Bisulfate	HSO_4^-	-1	Iodide	I^-	-1
Bromide	Br^-	-1	Nitrate	NO_3^-	-1
Carbonate	$CO_3^=$	-2	Nitrite	NO_2^-	-1
Chlorate	ClO_3^-	-1	Oxide	O^-	-2
Chloride	Cl^-	-1	Permanganate	MnO_4^-	-1
Chromate	$CrO_4^=$	-2	Peroxide	O_2^-	-2
Fluoride	F^-	-1	Phosphate	$PO_4^\equiv$	-3
Hexacyanoferrate(II)	$Fe(CN)_6^\equiv$	-4	Sulfate	SO_4^-	-2
Hexacyanoferrate(III)	$Fe(CN)_6^\equiv$	-3	Sulfide	S^-	-2
Hydride	H^-	-1	Sulfite	SO_3^-	-2

THE HOLT SCIENCE PROGRAM

SCIENCE, *Observation and Experiment,* Davis, Burnett, and Gross

SCIENCE, *Experiment and Discovery,* Davis, Burnett, and Gross

SCIENCE, *Discovery and Progress,* Davis, Burnett, and Gross

LIFE SCIENCE, *The World of Living Things,* Davis, Burnett, and Gross

MODERN BIOLOGY, Moon, Otto, and Towle

MODERN CHEMISTRY, Dull, Metcalfe, and Williams

MODERN PHYSICS, Dull, Metcalfe, and Williams

LIVING THINGS, Fitzpatrick, Bain, and Teter

MODERN HEALTH, Otto, Julian, and Tether

HUMAN PHYSIOLOGY, Morrison, Cornett, and Tether

MODERN PHYSICAL SCIENCE, Brooks, Tracy, and Tropp

MODERN EARTH SCIENCE, Ramsey and Burckley

MODERN SPACE SCIENCE, Trinklein and Huffer

MATTER, ENERGY AND CHANGE, sponsored by Manufacturing Chemists' Assoc., Inc.

SUPERSTITION TO SUPERSONICS, sponsored by Manufacturing Chemists' Assoc., Inc.

LABORATORY AND FIELD STUDIES IN BIOLOGY, sponsored by National Academy of Sciences—National Research Council

GEOLOGY AND EARTH SCIENCES SOURCEBOOK, sponsored by National Academy of Sciences—National Research Council, under the guidance of a Committee of the American Geological Institute

CHEMISTRY PROBLEMS, Castka

SEMIMICRO CHEMISTRY, DeBruyne, Kirk, and Beers

SCIENTIFIC EXPERIMENTS IN CHEMISTRY, sponsored by Manufacturing Chemists' Assoc., Inc.

PHYSICS PROBLEMS, Castka and Lefler

SCIENTIFIC EXPERIMENTS IN PHYSICS, Lehrman

Charles E. Dull
H. Clark Metcalfe
John E. Williams

MODERN

NEW YORK

CHEMISTRY

HOLT, RINEHART AND WINSTON, INC.

H. Clark Metcalfe is Head of the Science Department in Wilkinsburg Senior High School, Wilkinsburg, Pennsylvania.

John E. Williams is a teacher of chemistry in the Newport Harbor High School, Newport Beach, California.

Charles E. Dull was Head of the Science Department in West Side High School and Supervisor of Science for the Junior and Senior High Schools, Newark, New Jersey.

Unit Opening Photographs. **1.** Pyrex glass laboratory equipment, *Corning Glass Works;* **2.** Field ion microscope picture of a tungsten crystal, *E. W. Müller;* **3.** Oxy-acetylene torches on a large-capacity cutting machine, *Union Carbide;* **4.** Ozone testing chamber, *Standard Oil (N.J.);* **5.** Giant tree ferns, *W. H. Hodge;* **6.** Chemist using a pH meter, *Beckman Instruments;* **7.** Mining of rock salt, *International Salt;* **8.** Spraying liquid sulfur, *Freeport Sulphur;* **9.** Book matches on an assembly line, *Diamond National;* **10.** Forest on the way to Yosemite Valley, California, *Philip Gendreau;* **11.** Thermite welding, *Thermit;* **12.** Steel rails being cut by hot saws, *United States Steel;* **13.** Nuclear core of Shippingport, Pennsylvania, nuclear reactor, *Westinghouse Electric;* **14.** Copper wheel engraving of glass bowl, *Steuben Glass;* **15.** Hortonspheres for butadiene storage and naphtha fractionating unit, *Humble Oil Refining.*

Title Page Photograph. Launching of a communications satellite, *U. S. Air Force.*

PREFACE

MODERN CHEMISTRY is an all-purpose textbook designed to meet the varying needs of the standard high school course in chemistry. Classroom-developed from its first edition, this revision carries forward the sound idea of classroom testing.

To present the study of chemistry in the light of modern theory and to keep the subject matter abreast of the latest developments in the field, this edition has been carefully revised. After an introduction to some fundamental terms and concepts of physical science which includes a detailed explanation of significant figures and scientific notation, the authors develop the topics of atomic structure, the Periodic Table, and chemical bonding. The concept of sublevels and sublevel notation is introduced in the discussion of atomic structure. The periodicity of atomic radii and of ionization potentials is explained in the discussion of the Periodic Table. Electronegativity and its importance in compound formation are described in connection with chemical bonding. The Stock system of nomenclature is introduced and used in this edition of MODERN CHEMISTRY. The remainder of the theoretical and descriptive material of the course is then based on the relationship between the structure of substances and the properties they exhibit.

In this revision of the text, the authors describe and explain the concept of equilibrium more extensively than in previous editions. Various types are included, such as physical, solubility, and ionic equilibria. Oxidation and reduction are treated entirely in terms of electron transfer. Acids and bases are defined in the modern sense and the hydronium ion is used exclusively instead of the hydrogen ion in explaining certain aspects of acid behavior. Many other significant changes have been made in the text at the suggestion of teachers and students who have used the previous edition, and from the authors' own secondary teaching experience. The areas of secondary-school chemistry which the authors consider to be fundamental are treated in detail. However, no attempt has been made to produce a text which is encyclopedic in nature or which includes a multiplicity of topics.

Teachers will find ample material in MODERN CHEMISTRY for an outstanding college-preparatory course. For those students who do not plan to go to college, there is sufficient elementary theory and interest-arousing descriptive material for a complete and thorough course. It has been the authors' purpose to include more material than can ever be covered in one school year, thus permitting a wide choice of topics and allowing for selectivity according to student, school, and community differences. Teachers should feel free to choose those topics which best meet their local needs. As a guide in the selection of material, some paragraphs, and certain questions and problems, have been marked with a star (★). These starred sections are intended only for the better students. The needs of the average student are amply provided for in the unstarred material which constitutes the major portion of the text.

Careful attention has been given to teaching and learning aids. The inductive approach, so helpful to teachers and students alike, has been used wherever possible. The language of chemistry has been made clear and meaningful. Chemical words and terms are defined and pronounced in a short glossary at the beginning of each chapter and again, when the word or term appears in the text, it is printed in *boldface italics* and defined. These words and terms are also listed at the end of each chapter in the material entitled *Test Yourself on These Terms*. In addition, an extensive *Glossary* appears at the back of the book and includes definitions of all words and terms presented in the text. The complete *Appendix*, also in the back of the book, contains tables of useful data.

The material for each chapter concludes with *Questions* which are based on the text itself, graded according to difficulty in *Groups* A and B. There are more *Problems* than in previous editions of this book, and these are also graded into *Group* A and *Group* B. All problems have been revised and edited so that the rules for significant figure computation may be meaningfully applied. The average student should master all the *Group* A questions and problems; the better students will be able to do both. Special activities appear under the title *Some Things for You to Do*.

At the end of each unit there appear two sets of more difficult exercises: *Check Your Progress in Chemistry* and *Challenging Your Knowledge*. The former contains an abundance of drill material in chemical equations and in all types of problems as a cumulative review, while the latter consists of questions and problems which will really challenge even the best students.

Because of their great learning value, line drawings are used extensively. The text is also illustrated with many fine photographs, chosen with great care for their teaching value.

The following teachers have been kind enough to read the entire manuscript or special parts of it, and have offered invaluable assistance by their helpful criticisms: Edward A. Kassig, head of the science department, Broad Ripple High School, Indianapolis, Indiana; Earl V. Good, head of the science department, Stamford High School, Stamford, Connecticut; Richard B. Williams, chairman of the science department, San Jose High School, San Jose, California; Mrs. Helen Crawley, Natick High School, Natick, Massachusetts; and Miss Marcile Hollingsworth, head of science department, Lamar Senior High School, Houston, Texas.

The authors also acknowledge with thanks the work of: Felix Cooper, who prepared the text illustrations; and Gabrielle Wunderlick, who obtained the photographs.

In this printing of the 1962 edition of MODERN CHEMISTRY all data in the body of the text and in supplementary tables has been changed where necessary to conform with the revision of the physical atomic mass scale and chemical atomic weight scale to the basis of a carbon atom, mass number 12, defined as exactly 12. The revised atomic weights appear in the Periodic Table, in the Complete Table of Elements inside the back cover, and in appropriate places throughout the text.

CONTENTS

Read this page before you read your textbook.

1. Keep your eyes and your mind continually open. In science we base each conclusion on known facts and nothing can be taken for granted. Your eyes must be trained to observe carefully and your mind must be equally trained to reason from observations, both printed and otherwise, so as to draw logical conclusions from the observed data. With open eyes and inquiring mind you will go far in your work.

2. Get your bearings by examining the Table of Contents on pages vii and viii. What is the scope of this book? Are certain words in the chapter titles unfamiliar? Possibly they are now but by the time your work is completed at the end of the course, you will be familiar with all of them. This over-all glance at the contents will give you a perspective necessary to understand what you will be reading.

3. After your teacher has made the assignment for which you will be responsible at the next class meeting, it's up to you to know what to do about preparing it. But first, be sure you understand exactly what is expected of you—what pages to read, what words to know, what questions, problems, projects or other activities to do, and whether the assignment is to be written or oral or both. If you are not sure, don't hesitate to ask. Write down all parts of the assignment in your notebook.

4. Skim over the assigned text material hastily to get a general idea what it is about, paying special attention to the paragraph headings in **boldface type.** These are key items in your textbook and form the basis for its organization.

5. Having obtained a general idea as to the subject matter of your assignment, go over the material carefully and give it your thorough concentration. Ask yourself repeatedly, Do I understand this? and if you cannot honestly answer yes, then read it again. As you read, study the drawings, tables, and photographs and read the captions which explain them. In the drawings, examine each label and learn the part of the drawing to which the label relates. Trace with a blunt object (not a pencil) the drawing of any process (such as flow of liquids and gases or movement of electrons) and understand what takes place, in which direction, and why.

6. In your reading, pay special attention to the scientific words and terms printed in **boldface italic type.** These are key words and are important to a clear understanding of the text. Many of them will be unfamiliar but you must know them and be able to define each one. Science is not a difficult subject if you learn its language, but you will never succeed unless you master this essential aspect of it. Each new word or term is printed in **boldface italics** the first time is appears, but it may and probably will be used again later. If you find that you do not understand the pronunciation and meaning of a new word, look it up immediately in the *Glossary*. Similarly, if you have forgotten such a word or term and can't remember on what page you originally met it, turn to the *Glossary* at the back of the book and look up its definition.

7. Having read the material assigned and learned the new scientific words and terms, turn to the questions at the end of the chapter which cover the text material you have completed. Answer each one fully and, if you are unable to do so, return to that part of the text which is still unclear. Reread it with the question in mind until you have the answer. Use the same procedure with the problems.

COMMON ELEMENTS

Name	Symbol	Approx. At. Wt.	Common Ox. Nos.	Name	Symbol	Approx. At. Wt.	Common Ox. Nos.
Aluminum	Al	27	$+3$	Magnesium	Mg	24	$+2$
Antimony	Sb	122	$+3,+5$	Manganese	Mn	55	$+2,+4,+7$
Arsenic	As	75	$+3,+5$	Mercury	Hg	201	$+1,+2$
Barium	Ba	137	$+2$	Nickel	Ni	59	$+2$
Bismuth	Bi	209	$+3$	Nitrogen	N	14	$-3,+3,+5$
Bromine	Br	80.	$-1,+5$	Oxygen	O	16	-2
Calcium	Ca	40.	$+2$	Phosphorus	P	31	$+3,+5$
Carbon	C	12	$+2,+4$	Platinum	Pt	195	$+2,+4$
Chlorine	Cl	35.5	$-1,+5,+7$	Potassium	K	39	$+1$
Chromium	Cr	52	$+2,+3,+6$	Silicon	Si	28	$+4$
Cobalt	Co	59	$+2,+3$	Silver	Ag	108	$+1$
Copper	Cu	63.5	$+1,+2$	Sodium	Na	23	$+1$
Fluorine	F	19	-1	Strontium	Sr	88	$+2$
Gold	Au	197	$0,+3$	Sulfur	S	32	$-2,+4,+6$
Hydrogen	H	1.0	$-1,+1$	Tin	Sn	119	$+2,+4$
Iodine	I	127	$-1,+5$	Titanium	Ti	48	$+3,+4$
Iron	Fe	56	$+2,+3$	Tungsten	W	184	$+6$
Lead	Pb	207	$+2,+4$	Zinc	Zn	65	$+2$

VALENCE OF COMMON IONS

Name	Symbol	Valence	Name	Symbol	Valence
Aluminum	Al^{+++}	$+3$	Lead(II)	Pb^{++}	$+2$
Ammonium	NH_4^+	$+1$	Magnesium	Mg^{++}	$+2$
Barium	Ba^{++}	$+2$	Mercury(I)	Hg_2^{++}	$+1$
Calcium	Ca^{++}	$+2$	Mercury(II)	Hg^{++}	$+2$
Chromium(III)	Cr^{+++}	$+3$	Nickel(II)	Ni^{++}	$+2$
Cobalt(II)	Co^{++}	$+2$	Potassium	K^+	$+1$
Copper(I)	Cu^+	$+1$	Silver	Ag^+	$+1$
Copper(II)	Cu^+	$+2$	Sodium	Na^+	$+1$
Hydronium	H_3O^+	$+1$	Tin(II)	Sn^{++}	$+2$
Iron(II)	Fe^{++}	$+2$	Tin(IV)	Sn^{++++}	$+4$
Iron(III)	Fe^{+++}	$+3$	Zinc	Zn^{++}	$+2$
Acetate	$C_2H_3O_2^-$	-1	Hydroxide	OH^-	-1
Bicarbonate	HCO_3^-	-1	Hypochlorite	ClO^-	-1
Bisulfate	HSO_4^-	-1	Iodide	I^-	-1
Bromide	Br^-	-1	Nitrate	NO_3^-	-1
Carbonate	$CO_3^=$	-2	Nitrite	NO_2^-	-1
Chlorate	ClO_3^-	-1	Oxide	$O^=$	-2
Chloride	Cl^-	-1	Permanganate	MnO_4^-	-1
Chromate	$CrO_4^=$	-2	Peroxide	$O_2^=$	-2
Fluoride	F^-	-1	Phosphate	$PO_4^{\equiv}$	-3
Hexacyanoferrate(II)	$Fe(CN)_6^{\equiv}$	-4	Sulfate	$SO_4^=$	-2
Hexacyanoferrate(III)	$Fe(CN)_6^{\equiv}$	-3	Sulfide	$S^=$	-2
Hydride	H^-	-1	Sulfite	$SO_3^=$	-2

Unit 1 · CHEMISTRY IN A MODERN WORLD

Chemistry: A Science of Matter and Energy
The Composition of Matter
Matter and Its Changes

1

Chapter 1 · CHEMISTRY: A SCIENCE OF MATTER AND ENERGY

1. AN INTRODUCTION TO CHEMISTRY

1. Chemistry is a physical science. Through the ages, man has learned many things about himself and his environment. However, it was not until he started to record his discoveries and observations that modern science, as such, began. Early scientists soon started to organize and classify their discoveries and observations. This organized knowledge has developed into the fundamental sciences with which we are familiar today. Each important discovery suggests new avenues of investigation, the result being the expansion of scientific knowledge at an ever-increasing rate.

All the sciences may be grouped into two large divisions: the *biological sciences,* which are concerned with living things, their structure, life processes, and environment; and the *physical sciences,* which deal with the natural relationships about us. An understanding of basic concepts in the sciences helps us to recognize and appreciate the orderliness in nature.

Chemistry is the science dealing with the structure and composition of materials and the changes in composition which these materials undergo.

Physics is concerned primarily with changes in materials which do *not* involve a change in composition. It deals with the laws and principles of the physical universe.

Mathematics is the science of our number system. It gives us a means of expressing the relationships we observe in nature and of performing useful and necessary computations. Mathematics is often called the *language of the sciences.*

During the present century it has become increasingly evident that chemistry holds the key to the life sciences. As a result, there is an increasing merger of chemical research with the other sciences. Substantial knowledge of more and more complex chemical structures has enabled chemists to make major contributions toward the ultimate understanding of the mysterious life processes. This is the realm of *biochemistry,* a blend of biology and chemistry.

2

2. Keystones of modern chemistry.
The initial concept of modern chemistry, *that elements are the basic stuff of which all things are made*, was under development in France at about the time of the American revolution. In 1778 **Antoine Lavoisier** (la-*vwah*-see-ay) demonstrated that oxygen was the active fraction of the air involved in ordinary combustion processes. This set the stage for a great search for chemical elements and finally, through the efforts of a long line of investigators, some ninety elements were recognized. By 1920 most of these had been isolated and their properties studied.

Lavoisier was followed closely by **John Dalton** of England who, in 1808, conceived elements as consisting of chemically indivisible particles he called *atoms*. In 1811 the Italian physicist, **Amadeo Avogadro**, formulated some general laws describing the behavior of combined atoms, or *molecules*. Then in 1852, Great Britain's **Sir Edward Frankland** proposed the first useful explanation of the manner in which these atoms combined to form molecules, a combining quality later to be called *valence*. Chemistry was soon to be recognized as the architecture of molecules.

The first great chemical architect was **Friedrich Kekulé** of Germany, who in 1858 determined the bases on which the carbon skeletons of long-chain and ring molecules of organic compounds are formed. From this beginning chemists went on to construct a great variety of useful molecules in the forms of drugs, dyes, explosives, fibers, plastics, and solvents.

The first Nobel Prize in chemistry was given to **Jacobus H. van't Hoff** of Holland in 1901 for his pioneering work in developing the laws of reactions and solutions. Germany's **Emil Fischer** received the second Nobel Prize in chemistry in 1902 for his work on the structure of sugars and proteins. Sweden's **Svante Arrhenius**, about whom you will learn more in Unit 6, was awarded the third Nobel Prize in 1903 for his theory explaining the behavior of electrolytes in solution.

Later, in 1909, the Nobel Prize went to the German chemist **Wilhelm Ostwald** for his work in catalysis, a technique of tremendous importance in industrial chemistry. Ostwald is sometimes referred to as the father of physical chemistry. The Swiss chemist, **Alfred Werner**, received the Prize in 1913 for

VOCABULARY

Active material. One which reacts vigorously with other materials.

Density. The mass of a material per unit volume.

Energy. The capacity for doing work.

Inactive material. One which reacts passively with other materials.

Inert material. One which does not react with other materials under the ordinary conditions of chemical reactions.

Inertia. Resistance of matter to change of position or motion.

Law. A statement of scientific fact concerning natural phenomena.

Mass. The measure of inertia of a body.

Matter. Anything which occupies space and has mass.

Phenomenon. An event or situation of scientific interest susceptible of scientific description and explanation.

his studies of the structure of complex compounds. Again in 1920 a German, **Walther Nernst,** was awarded the Nobel Prize for his discoveries in thermodynamics.

Marie Curie, whose discovery of the radioactive elements, radium and polonium, was probably the most important contribution to modern chemistry since Lavoisier introduced the modern concept of elements, was awarded the Nobel Prize in 1911. No longer was the atom to be considered impregnable; here were atoms of elements which burst apart giving off tiny particles and high-energy radiations. Thus a chemist opened up a whole new realm for exploration by physicists, the structure within the atom.

The list of Nobel Prizes, while not infallible, gives a rough indication of the creative effort in chemistry being put forth by scientists of the various nations of the world. Up to 1920 only one American chemist had been awarded this prize. Eight German, three French, and two British chemists had been selected. Since 1920, however, eight American chemists have become Nobel Prize winners. Meanwhile German scientists have won eleven, British scientists eight, and French and Russian scientists one each.

3. The methods of science. In some instances, important scientific discoveries have come about quite by accident. However, most of our scientific knowledge is the result of carefully planned investigations carried on by trained scientists. Their techniques, known as *scientific methods,* are simply *logical approaches to the solution of problems which lend themselves to investigation.* Scientific methods require strict honesty, the ability to withhold a decision until all the evidence is in, and the desire for truth.

Scientists believe implicitly in the or-

Fig. 1-1. **Curiosity is the beginning of discovery.** (Hedrich-Blessing)

derliness in nature—that everything in the universe behaves in an ordered way, and that man can discover and understand natural rules of behavior. Chemists, like other scientists, strive to explain a large number of related observations in terms of *broad principles* or *generalizations*. All basic scientific research is devoted to the discovery of these principles. *The generalizations which describe behavior in nature are called laws.* Natural laws tell us what relations *do* occur in nature; they *do not* tell us what relations *must* occur. The laws of science may be expressed by concise statements or by means of mathematical formulas.

One of the distinguishing qualities of man is his curiosity. This causes him to ask two important questions: *"what?"* and *"why?"* When an event or situation in nature, called a *phenomenon*, is observed by one trained in the methods of science, the answers to these questions are sought by carrying out systematic, disciplined, and persistent investigations.

We may recognize four distinct phases in the application of scientific methods: *observing, generalizing, theorizing, and testing.*

1. Observing. The scientist accumulates as much reliable data as possible about an observed phenomenon, his initial interest being in *what* actually occurs. These data may come from direct observations, from a search of scientific literature for information previously reported, and from well planned and skilfully executed experiments.

2. Generalizing. The scientist organizes the accumulated data and looks for relations between them. Relations he discovers may enable him to formulate a broad generalization describing what does occur. When well established by

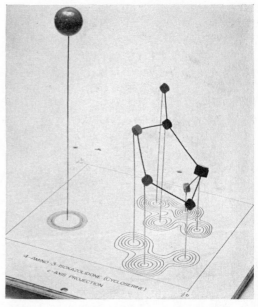

Fig. 1-2. **A physical model is often used by chemists to help them understand the behavior of matter.** (Ray Pepinsky, Crystal Research Laboratory)

abundant supporting data, this generalization may be recognized as a new law or principle which states what the behavior is.

3. Theorizing. When the scientist understands *what* occurs he is ready to move on to the more stimulating task of determining *why* the phenomenon occurs. A creative imagination may enable him to develop a plausible explanation and to construct a simple physical or mental model which will relate the observed behavior to familiar and well-understood phenomena. *A plausible explanation of an observed natural phenomenon in terms of a simple model which has familiar properties is called a theory.*

4. Testing. Once a seemingly satisfactory theory is developed, it must be tested and retested to establish its validity. In fact, the scientist continually tests observational and experimental data and predictions based on known

2. MATTER AND ENERGY

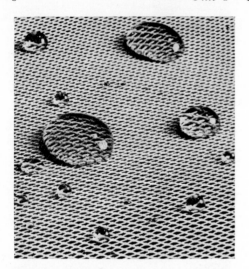

Fig. 1-3. This water-repellent, silicone-treated material is a product of chemical research. (Dow-Corning)

principles by subjecting them to new and ingenious experiments. A theory is retained only so long as it is useful and it may be discarded or modified as a result of new experimentation. A theory that stands up under scientific testing is a valuable asset to scientists because it stimulates the imagination and serves as a basis for predicting behavior not previously investigated. This is the heart of the scientific method and the real stimulus for the tremendous growth of science.

The principles of chemistry are studied most effectively and understood most easily when the laws and experimental evidence making up a body of related knowledge are brought together to form a general theory concerning the behavior of matter. In this way the term "theory" is often used by chemists in a broad sense. Some examples of chemical theories which you will soon study in this sense are the *kinetic theory*, the *atomic theory*, and the *theory of ionization*.

4. The concept of matter. All materials about us consist of matter. With our senses—sight, touch, taste, and smell—we recognize various kinds of matter. This book, your desk, the air you breathe, the water you drink are examples of matter. Some kinds of matter are easily observed. A stone or a piece of wood may be seen and held in the hand. Other kinds of matter are recognized less readily, such as the air or even water in a quiet pool. However, we ride on compressed air in automobile tires. We know of the tremendous damage which can be caused by rapidly moving air (see Fig. 1-4).

We say that *matter is anything which occupies space and has mass.* Matter possesses *inertia,* a resistance to change of position or motion. The concept of inertia as a property of matter is quite important in the study of physics. Imagine a basketball being used in a bowling alley as a substitute for a bowling ball. The effect on the pins would not be the same at all. Although they are approximately the same size, the bowling ball has a greater mass since it contains more matter than the basketball. Its inertia is correspondingly higher and thus its tendency to remain in motion, once set in motion, is greater.

Matter may be acted on by *forces* which may set it in motion, or change its motion. While all these statements are descriptive of matter, they do not provide us with a completely satisfactory definition. Scientists, with their great knowledge of the properties and behavior of matter, are not yet able to define it precisely. Many secrets of nature still challenge the minds of men.

5. Mass and weight. *The quantity of matter which a body possesses is known* *as its mass.* If we try to move something we notice that it resists our effort. Its mass is the measure of this resistance. Thus *mass is the measure of the inertia of the body* and is responsible for it.

Mass is also responsible for the *weight* of the body. *Weight is the measure of the earth's attraction for a body.* If we were to attach an object to a spring balance we would find that it weighs less when taken away from the center of the earth. On the other hand, its mass remains unchanged; *the mass of a body is constant.*

Mass is usually measured by comparison with known masses. If the masses of two bodies are the same they will have equal weights while in the same location. Thus the mass of a body, when determined by *weighing* it on a chemical balance, is sometimes referred to as its "weight." This practice is common throughout chemistry and should not be confusing if the meanings of the terms *mass* and *weight* are understood. Chemists are primarily concerned with measurements of mass, and we shall use the term *mass* in its proper meaning.

6. The density of matter varies. Matter occupies space and therefore has volume. From our everyday experiences we recognize that materials have different masses. We say that lead is heavy and that cork is light. This has little meaning unless we have in mind equal volumes of lead and cork. *The mass of a unit volume of a material is called its density,* which is expressed by the equation

$$D = \frac{m}{V}$$

Where m is the mass of a material and V is its volume, D is its density. The

Fig. 1-4. **Air is an example of matter in the gaseous state. When moving at high velocities, it can cause great destruction. This photograph shows damage caused by Hurricane Donna at Wakefield, Rhode Island, in September 1960.** (United Press International)

basic unit of mass in chemistry is the *gram* (g) and of volume is the *cubic centimeter* (cm³). Thus, density may have the dimensions g/cm³.

By comparing the masses of equal volumes of materials we are able to see that the density of different kinds of matter varies. Thus lead, with a mass of 11.34 grams for one cubic centimeter, is nearly 50 times denser than cork having a mass of 0.24 gram for one cubic centimeter (see Fig. 1-5).

7. **Three states of matter.** We call a block of ice a solid. It may melt and form a liquid. As it evaporates, liquid water changes into a vapor or gas. Iron, too, is a solid but it may be melted and converted into a liquid. When iron is boiled, it forms iron vapor. Materials exist either in the *solid, liquid,* or *gaseous* state and may undergo a change from one state to another under suitable conditions.

A block of wood placed on a table keeps its shape and its volume. To change its shape or its volume you would have to use considerable force on the block from the outside. A solid does not need lateral (side) support to prevent it from losing its shape. *Solids have both a definite volume and a definite shape.*

Suppose we pour a quart of water out on the top of a table. The water is not rigid but spreads out in all directions. A liquid must have lateral support to retain its shape. For that reason a liquid takes the shape of its container. We find, however, that a liquid has a definite volume if we try to put a quart of milk into a pint bottle. Therefore we conclude that **liquids have a definite volume, and that they take the shape of their containers.**

If we inflate an automobile tire, we find that the air takes the shape of the tire, which is its container. The tire is really full of air, but if a blow-out occurs, the escaping air expands in volume. A pint of liquid does not expand and form a quart if it is put into a quart bottle. However, a pint of air would expand and occupy all that space if it were placed in a really empty quart bottle. **Gases have neither a definite shape nor a definite volume.** This fact makes it difficult to measure the volume of gases. If they are warmed, they expand decidedly, but their volume is reduced when the pressure on them is increased. In measuring gas volumes, we must specify *both the temperature and the pressure* to which they are subjected.

Both liquids and gases are known as **fluids.** These are materials that flow readily and require vessels to contain them. We think of solids as being rigid yet none is perfectly rigid. Butter, for example, may not be very solid on a warm summer day. Similarly, there are no perfectly fluid materials. Molasses, water, and carbon dioxide may be ob-

Fig. 1-5. **Equal volumes of different materials do not necessarily have the same mass.**

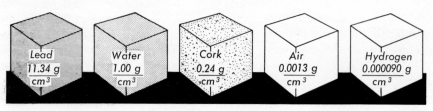

| Lead 11.34 g cm³ | Water 1.00 g cm³ | Cork 0.24 g cm³ | Air 0.0013 g cm³ | Hydrogen 0.000090 g cm³ |

served to flow, but certainly at different rates.

Liquids, having a definite volume, can have a free surface; that is, a surface unbounded by the container. Thus water may be contained in an open vessel. The free (upper) surface of a liquid lies in a plane perpendicular to the force acting on it. In the normal case of a liquid at rest, this force is gravity and the free surface of the liquid lies in the horizontal plane. Matter in the gaseous state must be bounded on all sides by the container. Gases are fluids which do not have a free surface.

Fluids which cannot exist as liquids having a free surface at ordinary conditions of temperature and pressure are correctly termed *gases*. **Vapor** *is the term used to denote the gaseous state of fluids which exist as liquids under normal conditions*. Thus we speak of water *vapor* and oxygen *gas*.

8. The properties of matter. We are able to identify matter and determine its usefulness by studying its properties. Chemists are concerned with the materials that compose matter. Many liquids, including water, are colorless. Some colorless liquids have distinctive odors; water is odorless. Water freezes at 0° Centigrade, boils at 100° Centigrade (at standard pressure), and has a density of 1 gram per cubic centimeter at 4° Centigrade. Since no other liquid exhibits exactly these same characteristics, liquid water is easily identified. *Properties of matter useful in identifying it are called* **specific** (*or characteristic*) **properties**. The most useful specific properties are those that lend themselves to quantitative measurements and can be expressed as a number of units. The specific properties of materials may be organized under two general headings: *physical*, and *chemical*.

Physical properties include *color, odor, solubility, density, hardness, melting* and *boiling points*, and *crystalline* or *amorphous forms*. These physical properties do not apply equally to all states of matter. For example, hardness and crystalline form are not properties of fluids. Similarly, odor is of little value in describing many solids. **Physical properties** *are those characteristics which can be determined without causing a change in the identity of a material*.

Under chemical properties we include *chemical activity*, or behavior with other materials. Some materials are *active*, reacting vigorously with others. Some other materials are *inactive*. These inactive materials do react, but not very readily, with others. Still other materials are *inert*. These do not react at all under ordinary conditions of chemical reactions. In our study of chemical properties, we shall be interested to know whether a material burns. We shall also inquire how it reacts with air, with water, with acids, and with alkalies. **Chemical properties** *are those characteristics which pertain to the behavior of a material in changes in which its identity is altered*.

9. The concept of energy. We find much the same difficulty in defining energy as we did in defining matter. Scientists know a great deal about energy and how it may be used but they cannot define it precisely. **Energy** *is usually defined as the capacity for doing work*. It is associated with matter but is not a form of matter. We have no knowledge of matter which does not possess energy.

10. Forms of energy. Our most common forms of energy are *mechanical energy* and *heat energy*. Mechanical energy may be of two types: **potential energy** *or the energy of position*, and **kinetic energy** *or the energy of motion*. Thus

Fig. 1-6. The Law of Conservation of Matter and Energy was demonstrated when the A-bomb was tested at Bikini. (U. S. Navy)

water at the brink of a waterfall has potential energy due to its elevated position. As the water descends it acquires kinetic energy due to its motion. Heat energy is released whenever fuels are burned. Practically all our industrial power is provided by heat energy from burning fuel and from the kinetic energy of falling water.

Other forms of energy are *electric energy, chemical energy, light energy,* and *nuclear energy.* Chemical energy is a basic concern of the chemical industry. Nuclear energy is being developed as a source of industrial power.

We may convert or *transform* one form of energy into another. As an example, suppose we burn coal to produce energy. Some of the chemical energy of the coal and the oxygen of the air is released as heat during the burning action. The heat energy may be transferred to water and convert it to steam. The steam can then drive a turbine to produce kinetic energy. A dynamo may be turned to generate electric energy. This may then be transformed into heat in an electric iron or in an electric toaster, or it may be transformed into light energy in an incandescent lamp or carbon arc. It may also be transformed into mechanical energy in an electric motor which drives a clock or a locomotive. It is the transformation of energy that is usually observed. Our means of measuring energy is to measure the *energy change* during an energy transformation.

11. The conservation of matter and energy. About 60 years ago Albert Einstein (1879–1955) suggested that matter and energy are related. This relationship is shown by his now famous equation $E = mc^2$. E represents the amount of energy, m the amount of matter, and c is a constant equal to the velocity of light. A great number of experiments during the last 30 years have established the truth of this relationship.

Matter can be converted to energy and energy to matter. The conversion factor, c^2, is involved in both transformations. Indeed, the amount of matter is changed if the amount of energy is changed. Thus matter and energy are not two different physical quantities, which we can define independently. Instead, *they may be considered to be two different forms of the same physical quantity.* The facts are formulated into a law of science known as the **Law of Conservation of Matter and Energy.** This law may be stated formally as follows: *matter and energy are interchangeable; and the total matter and energy in the universe is constant.*

Energy is either given up or absorbed whenever a material enters into a reaction. Only in nuclear reactions involving a tremendous quantity of energy, such as the explosion of a hydrogen bomb, does the amount of matter transformed into energy become significant. Ordinary chemical reactions which occur in the laboratory involve such small matter changes that there is no method of detecting them. For all ordinary purposes such changes of matter into energy may be ignored. We may then recognize the following generalization: *in an ordinary chemical change, the total mass of the reacting materials is equal to the total mass of the products.*

3. MEASUREMENTS IN CHEMISTRY

12. The Centigrade temperature scale. Scientific measurements of temperature are generally made on the **Centigrade scale.** This temperature scale was devised by a Swedish astronomer, Anders Celsius (1701–1744). It is officially referred to as the Celsius scale but this usage has not yet become very common. Two *fixed points*, the freezing and normal boiling points of water, are used to graduate the scale. On the Centigrade scale the two fixed points are called *0 degrees* (0° C) and **100** *degrees* (100° C). The space between them is

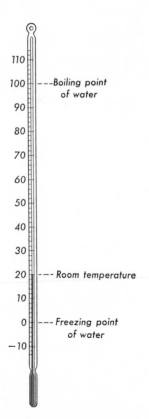

Fig. 1-7. The Centigrade thermometer is widely used in scientific work. Compare the temperatures shown here with those on the common Fahrenheit thermometer.

BRIEF TABLE OF METRIC EQUIVALENTS

Length	10 millimeters (mm)	= 1 centimeter (cm)
	100 centimeters	= 1 meter (m)
	1000 meters	= 1 kilometer (km)
Capacity	1000 milliliters (ml)	= 1 liter (l)
	1000 liters	= 1 kiloliter (kl)
Mass	1000 milligrams (mg)	= 1 gram (g)
	1000 grams	= 1 kilogram (kg)

divided into 100 equal intervals or 100 Centigrade degrees (100 C°).

13. The metric system. The study of science could not be precise without a suitable system of measurement. The English system, which we use in our daily activities, presents many disadvantages in scientific measurements. It is a system which, in a sense, just grew up. Its chief disadvantage is that there are no simple numerical relationships between the different units.

The *metric system*, with which you may already be familiar, was developed in France near the end of the eighteenth century. It is used in scientific work throughout the world and is in general use in practically all countries except the United States and Great Britain. Certain industries in the United States, particularly pharmaceutical manufacturers, are now adopting the metric system for general use. *It is a decimal system that has simple numerical relationships between units.* The disadvantage in its everyday usage lies in the fact that the basic units do not have the practical magnitudes of those of the English system. They do not lend themselves to the convenient custom of reducing by halves and quarters.

14. Units of the metric system. The metric system includes measures of *length, capacity,* and *mass.* The basic unit of length is the *meter* (m), of capacity is the *liter* (l), and of mass is the *gram* (g). Prefixes are used with these units to complete the system. Latin prefixes are employed to identify *descending* values. These are *deci–* (0.1), *centi–* (0.01), and *milli–* (0.001). Greek prefixes are used to identify *ascending* values; *deka–* (10), *hecto–* (100), and *kilo–* (1000). The prefixes shown in the brief table of metric equivalents with the three metric units will be used throughout your study of chemistry. It will be helpful to memorize them.

As originally conceived, the metric system was to be based on natural standards with the meter as the fundamental unit. The authors of the metric system

Fig. 1-8. **The centimeter is nearly 0.4 of an inch in length. One inch equals 2.54 centimeters.**

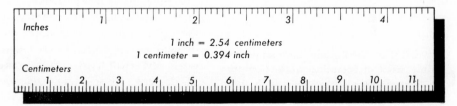

Inches

1 inch = 2.54 centimeters
1 centimeter = 0.394 inch

Centimeters

intended that the meter should be one ten-millionth of the north polar quadrant of the Paris meridian. However, they found later that they could compare two meter bars with each other with greater precision than they could relate them to the earth's quadrant. Accordingly, *the standard meter is commonly defined as the distance between two parallel lines engraved on a platinum-iridium bar which is preserved at the International Bureau of Weights and Measures near Paris.*

The standard-meter bar is a physical instrument and, if it should be damaged, lost, or destroyed, there would be no primary standard of this fundamental metric unit. Accordingly, the International Conference on Weights and Measures has defined a *non-destructible* standard meter which any laboratory that has the proper equipment can reproduce as a primary standard. By this new definition, the meter is described in terms of the orange-red spectral line of light emitted from excited atoms of an isotope of krypton (krypton 86), the meter being 1,650,763.73 times the wavelength of this line.

The meter is slightly longer than the English yard, being equal to 39.37 inches or 3.28 feet. One inch is 2.54 centimeters. This is now a defined relationship, being taken as 2.540000000 centimeters per inch.

One gram was intended to be the mass of 1 cubic centimeter (cm³) of water at 4° C, the temperature at which it is most dense. Again it was found that the masses of two metal cylinders weighing about one kilogram each could be compared with each other more precisely than either could be related to the mass of 1000 cubic centimeters of water. *The gram is now defined as one thousandth of the mass of the standard*

Fig. 1-9. **Some comparisons between the English and Metric systems. The liter is slightly larger than the U. S. liquid quart, and the kilogram is more than twice as heavy as the avoirdupois pound.**

kilogram resting in the International Bureau of Weights and Measures. The gram is an exceedingly small unit equal to 0.035 ounce. One pound is approximately 454 grams; one kilogram is approximately 2.2 pounds.

*The **liter** is defined as the volume of one kilogram of water at 4° C.* Because of a slight error, 1 kilogram of water having a volume of 1 liter does not measure precisely 1000 cm³, but is actually 1000.027 cm³. The error is so slight that, except for purposes of definition, it can be neglected. We shall

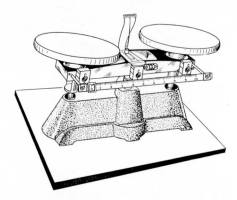

Fig. 1-10. A modern platform balance is used for ordinary weighing in the laboratory. It may have a sensitivity of 0.1 gram.

consider the cm^3 volume unit and the *ml* capacity unit as being equal. Because the volumes of liquids and gases are commonly measured in flasks and other containers graduated in capacity units, their measured volumes are most conveniently expressed in milliliter, liter, and kiloliter (capacity) units. This is a standard practice in chemistry and will be followed generally in this book. Since water is a universal standard, the remarkable simplicity of the metric system can be seen in the table of volume-mass relations at the bottom of this page.

The liter is slightly larger than the U.S. liquid quart. It is equal to 1.06 quarts. A liter, or 1000 cm^3, equals 61 in^3 or 33.8 fluid ounces.

15. Accuracy of measurements. Your work in chemistry will involve many different kinds of measurements. In some instances these will be rather precise, in others rather crude. Chemistry students generally tend to imply more accuracy

in their measurements than the instruments they use justify. The degree of accuracy of any measurement you make will depend on two factors, your ability to use the measuring device properly, and the precision of the device. Where measurements are used in computing results, *your final result is no more accurate than the least accurate measurement used.*

Laboratory measurements usually require that you estimate the fraction beyond the smallest division on the instrument. The accuracy of this estimated figure is doubtful. It is customary to retain *one* doubtful figure in the result of any measurement.

Suppose you wish to determine the volume of a metal block. Your measuring instrument is a meter stick having 1 mm divisions. You find the sides to be 3.54 cm, 4.85 cm, and 5.42 cm, estimating the last figure in each case. You may be reasonably sure of the one estimated figure in each of these measurements. However, you can have no idea of the digit which should occupy the next decimal place. Each measurement thus consists of two *certain figures* and one *doubtful figure*, or three *significant figures. The digits which represent the number of units counted with reasonable assurance in a measurement are called* **significant figures.**

The area of one surface is

$$3.54 \text{ cm} \times 4.85 \text{ cm} = 17.1690 \text{ cm}^2$$

Recognizing that the product of anything multiplied by a doubtful figure is also doubtful, and that only one such figure may be carried, the result is

TABLE OF VOLUME–MASS RELATIONS

1 liter of water has 1000 cm^3 volume and a mass of 1 kg
1 ml of water has 1 cm^3 volume and a mass of 1 g

rounded to 17.2 cm². The volume of the block then becomes

17.2 cm² × 5.42 cm = 93.224 cm³

Again the result is properly expressed as 93.2 cm³, the volume of the metal block. Had all of the doubtful figures been retained throughout the computation, the volume would be expressed as 93.055980 cm³. It is obvious that this degree of accuracy, millionths of a cubic centimeter, cannot be obtained with a meter stick graduated in tenths of a centimeter.

The greater the number of significant figures obtained when making a measurement, the more accurate is the measurement. Conversely, only a few significant figures do not provide much accuracy, although it may be the best measurement that can be made with the equipment in use. *Merely assuming more places does not improve the accuracy of the measurement.*

In the measurements and computations given, the number of significant figures is easily recognized since all figures used are nonzero digits. It is not so easy to determine when zeros appearing in an expression are significant. For example, the mean distance to the moon is known to six significant figures to be 238,854 mi. This distance is more commonly expressed as 239,000 mi, being accurate to *three* significant figures. The three zeros which follow the 9 merely serve to locate the (understood) decimal point. Similarly, a measured length of 0.00531 cm is accurate to *three* significant figures, the zeros being used to locate the decimal point. However, the measurements 104.06 m and 100.60 m contain *five* significant figures. The question naturally arises: when are zeros significant?

Of course, the person who reads an

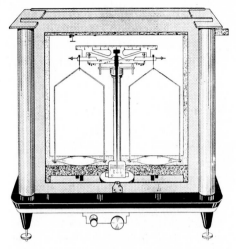

Fig. 1-11. **The analytical balance may have a sensitivity of 0.0001 gram.**

instrument while making a measurement knows whether a zero appearing in his expression is significant. He must follow accepted rules concerning significant figures if he is to communicate the information accurately to others who may use the data. In order to overcome the difficulties of communication where zeros are included in the expression of a measured quantity, the following rules for determining the number of significant figures have been established and will be used throughout this book:

1. *All nonzero digits are significant:* 127.34 g contains *five* significant figures.
2. *All zeros between two nonzero digits are significant:* 120.007 m contains *six* significant figures.
3. Unless specifically indicated by the context to be significant, *all zeros to the left of an understood decimal point but to the right of a nonzero digit are not significant:* 109,000 km contains *three* significant figures.
4. *All zeros to the left of an expressed decimal point and to the right of a*

nonzero digit *are significant:* 109,000. km contains *six* significant figures.

5. *All zeros to the right of a decimal point but to the left of a nonzero digit are not significant:* 0.00476 kg contains *three* significant figures. (The single zero conventionally placed to the left of the decimal point in such an expression is never significant.)

6. *All zeros to the right of a decimal point and to the right of a nonzero digit are significant:* 0.04060 cm and 30.00 mg contain *four* significant figures.

There is a limit of accuracy inherent in any experimental procedure. It depends on the precision of the measuring devices used. It is the aim of the chemist, and of the chemistry student as well, to perform the various operations and measurements with such skill that the experimental accuracy will be limited only by the apparatus used.

16. The scientific notation of numbers. In science we often meet numbers which are extremely large or exceedingly small. The speed of light is approximately 30,000,000,000 centimeters per second. The speed in a vacuum generally accepted as accurate to *seven* significant figures is 29,979,280,000 cm/sec. The mass of the earth is about 6,000,-000,000,000,000,000,000,000,000 grams. The mass of an electron is 0.000,000,000,-000,000,000,000,000,910,83 gram. The wavelength of yellow light is about 0.000059 cm. These numbers have little meaning in the ordinary sense. In *sci-*entific notation* we may write them conveniently and economically as a number having the form

$$M \times 10^n$$

where M is a number between 1 and 10 having one digit to the left of the decimal point and n is a positive or negative integer.

We may now write the unusual quantities already given in our new form as shown in the table at the bottom of this page.

To change a number into scientific-notation form:

1. Determine M by moving the decimal point so that you leave only one nonzero digit to the left of it.

2. Determine n by counting the number of places you have moved the decimal point; if moved to the left, n is positive; if to the right, n is negative. The laws of exponents apply in computations involving numbers expressed in scientific-notation form.

When a number is written in the form $M \times 10^n$ all the digits, zero and nonzero, expressed explicitly in M are significant. This enables us to tell at a glance the number of significant figures and the accuracy implied in an indicated measurement to a degree of certainty that may not be possible using the ordinary system of notation.

The distance from the earth to the sun, 93,005,000 mi, cannot be expressed in ordinary notation to three significant

NUMBERS IN SCIENTIFIC–NOTATION FORM

$$30,000,000,000 \text{ cm/sec} = 3 \times 10^{10} \text{ cm/sec}$$
$$29,979,280,000 \text{ cm/sec} = 2.997928 \times 10^{10} \text{ cm/sec}$$
$$6,000,000,000,000,000,000,000,000,000 \text{ g} = 6 \times 10^{27} \text{ g}$$
$$0.000,000,000,000,000,000,000,000,910,83 \text{ g} = 9.1083 \times 10^{-28} \text{ g}$$
$$0.000059 \text{ cm} = 5.9 \times 10^{-5} \text{ cm}$$

figures without confusion. However, using the scientific notation, this distance may be written to an accuracy of three significant figures as 9.30×10^7 mi with complete clarity.

17. Operations with significant figures. The results of mathematical operations involving laboratory measurements can be no more accurate than the measurements themselves. Accordingly, certain precautions must be observed when performing calculations in order to avoid implying greater accuracy in the results than was originally obtained in the measurements. The following rules, while not infallible, are valid for most practical purposes and should be adopted where the context does not indicate otherwise.

1. Addition and subtraction. Remembering that the rightmost significant figure in a measurement is of doubtful accuracy, *the rightmost significant figure in a sum or difference occurs in the leftmost place at which the doubtful figure occurs in any of the measurements involved.* If, for example, the leftmost place where a doubtful figure occurs is in the hundredths place (second place to the right of the decimal point), the sum or difference should be rounded to the nearest hundredth. When working with numbers expressed in scientific notation, all terms should be converted to the same power of ten before adding or subtracting.

2. Multiplication and division. Three points previously discussed in Section 15 must be remembered in operations involving multiplication and division: (*a*) The rightmost significant figure in a measurement is of doubtful accuracy. (*b*) The product of any number multiplied by a digit of doubtful accuracy is also uncertain. (*c*) Only one doubtful digit is retained in the result. Therefore,

the product or quotient is accurate to the number of significant figures contained in the least accurate factor. The result in either operation should be rounded to the same number of significant figures contained in the factor that has the least number of significant figures. In an expression in which both multiplications and divisions occur, the multiplications should be performed first. The result should be rounded to the proper number of significant figures on completing each multiplication or division operation.

In multiplication or division operations with numbers expressed in scientific-notation form, the M portions are handled as described above keeping in mind that all digits are significant. The laws of exponents govern the multiplication and division of the 10^n terms. In multiplication the exponents are added:

$$10^3 \times 10^4 = 10^7$$
$$10^6 \times 10^{-2} = 10^4$$
$$10^4 \times 10^{-6} = 10^{-2}$$

In division the exponent of the divisor is subtracted from the exponent of the dividend:

$$10^3 \div 10^2 = 10^1$$
$$10^4 \div 10^{-3} = 10^7$$
$$10^{-5} \div 10^2 = 10^{-7}$$

Number expressions that are not the result of measurements should not be interpreted as having limited accuracy. Such numbers, when involved in a computation with laboratory measurements, do not enter into the determination of the number of significant figures in the result. As an example, the freezing point of water is *defined* as 0° C. This is exactly zero and could be written with as many zero digits to the right of the decimal point as desired. A thermometer reading, of course, is a measurement and would have limited accuracy, being written with the number of significant figures the instrument is capable of yielding. Similarly, a triangle has *exactly* three sides. If one side of an equilateral triangle is measured to an accuracy of four significant figures and then multiplied by the number of sides, the number of significant figures in the product remains the same as that of the original measurement.

Measurements are always expressed as numbers of units: 12.5 g, 6.7 cm, 10.0 sec, 42.1° C, 0.09 g/l, etc. Both the number and the unit are essential parts of the expression since the choice of unit affects the magnitude of the number. A measurement determined to three significant figures to be 1.30 m would be written as 130. cm if the centimeter unit rather than the meter unit had been used.

$$1.30 \cancel{m} \times \frac{100 \text{ cm}}{\cancel{m}} = 130. \text{ cm}$$

Observe that the expression 100 cm/m is arrived at by definition, not by measurement. Thus, it is exactly 100 cm and does not affect the significance of the measurement. Had the measurement been determined to two significant figures to be 1.3 m, it would then be written as 130 cm when converted to the centimeter unit.

$$1.3 \cancel{m} \times \frac{100 \text{ cm}}{\cancel{m}} = 130 \text{ cm}$$

Thus 1.30 m is equivalent to 130. cm and 1.3 m is equivalent to 130 cm.

Because of the multiplicity of units and the fact that the expression of a physical measurement requires *both* a number and a unit, chemistry students will avoid confusion and errors in computations by adopting the practice of *always* writing the unit with the number to which it belongs. Usually the "cancellation" of units in an expression leads directly to the proper unit for the answer. This method of writing and solving expressions, illustrated in the following sample problems, will be used in all problem work in this book.

SAMPLE PROBLEM

A chemistry student was required to determine the density of an irregularly shaped sample of lead. He first weighed it on a balance sensitive to 0.01 g and found its mass to be 49.33 g. He then immersed the lead in water contained in a cylinder graduated in milliliters and observed that it displaced 4.35 ml of water (the 0.05 ml being estimated).

SOLUTION

The student recalled from his study of general science that a body immersed in a liquid displaces its own volume. Since the volume of a solid is normally expressed in cubic measure, the equivalency of the milliliter and the cubic centimeter is used to convert the volume to cubic centimeters.

$$1 \text{ cm}^3 = 1 \text{ ml}$$

$$4.35 \cancel{ml} \times \frac{1 \text{ cm}^3}{\cancel{ml}} = 4.35 \text{ cm}^3$$

By definition: $$D = \frac{m}{V}$$

$$D = \frac{49.33 \text{ g}}{4.35 \text{ cm}^3}$$

$$D = 11.34 \text{ g/cm}^3$$

Observe that the indicated division has been carried to the hundredths place and then rounded to the nearest tenth to give the proper number of significant figures in the answer.

A more appropriate way to set up this solution would be as follows:

$$D = \frac{m}{V}$$

$$D = \frac{49.33 \text{ g}}{4.35 \text{ ml} \times 1 \text{ cm}^3/\text{ml}}$$

$$D = 11.3 \text{ g/cm}^3$$

SAMPLE PROBLEM

What is the concentration of sodium chloride (table salt), in grams of salt per gram of solution, if 400. mg of the salt are dissolved in 100. ml of water measured at 65° C?

SOLUTION

The problem requires that the concentration be expressed in grams of salt per gram of solution. The mass of solution is the sum of the mass of the water used and the mass of the salt added. Thus, the volume of water must be converted to mass of water. To make this conversion the density of water at 65° C must be known.

The table in a chemistry handbook giving density of water over a range of temperatures shows that water has a density of 0.981 g/ml at 65° C.

By definition: $$D = \frac{m}{V}$$

Solving for *m:* $$m = DV$$

Substituting: $$m = 0.981 \frac{\text{g}}{\text{ml}} \times 100. \text{ ml} = 98.1 \text{ g}$$

(Observe that the ml units "cancel" leaving g which is the proper unit for the answer.)

The mass of the salt is given in milligrams and the mass of the water is in grams. Since milligrams and grams cannot be added, the milligrams of salt must be converted to grams.

By definition: $$1 \text{ mg} = 0.001 \text{ g}$$

$$400. \text{ mg} \times \frac{0.001 \text{ g}}{\text{mg}} = 0.400 \text{ g of salt added.}$$

(Observe that 0.001 g is an exact number derived by definition and is not a measurement accurate only to one significant figure.)

Mass of solution = 98.1 g + 0.400 g = 98.5 g

(Recall the rule for addition of significant figures to recognize that the sum is 98.5 g and *not* 98.500 g.)

Since 0.400 g of salt is present in 98.5 g of solution, there is

$$\frac{0.400}{98.5} \text{ g of salt in 1 g of solution}$$

or   0.00406 g salt/g solution

SUMMARY

Chemistry is the science dealing with materials, their composition, and the changes which they undergo. Scientific methods are logical approaches to the solution of problems which lend themselves to investigation. Four distinct phases in the application of scientific methods are: observing, generalizing, theorizing, and testing.

Matter is anything which occupies space and has mass. Matter possesses inertia. The measure of inertia of an object is called its mass. Weight is the measure of the earth's attraction for an object. The mass of a substance is determined indirectly by comparing its weight with that of a known mass.

There are three states of matter: solid, liquid, and gaseous. The state of any substance depends largely upon its temperature. Some substances exist as gases, others as liquids, and still others as solids, at ordinary temperatures. The properties of matter are classified as either physical or chemical.

Energy is the capacity for doing work. The Law of Conservation of Matter and Energy tells us that matter and energy are interchangeable and the sum total in the universe is constant.

The Centigrade (Celsius) temperature scale is used almost entirely in chemistry. The two fixed points are 0° C and 100° C.

The metric system is used in chemistry. The unit of length is the meter, of capacity is the liter, and of mass is the gram. Metric prefixes common in chemistry are milli– (0.001), centi– (0.01), and kilo– (1000). Metric units have all been standardized by the International Bureau of Weights and Measures.

The scientific notation form is convenient for expressing large and small numbers. Such numbers are in the general form $M \times 10^n$, where M is a number between 1 and 10 having one digit to the left of the decimal point, and n is a positive or negative integer.

There is a limit of accuracy inherent in any measuring device. The significant figures derived from any measurement should be known in order that computations may be carried out economically and results may show the extent of accuracy. Measurements are always expressed as numbers of units and both the number and the unit are essential elements of any expression including the measurements. Expression of both the numbers and the units aids considerably in the solution of problems.

TEST YOURSELF ON THESE TERMS

active material | inert material | milli–
amorphous | inertia | phenomenon
centi– | kilo– | physical property
Centigrade scale | kinetic energy | physical sciences
chemical property | law | potential energy
chemistry | Law of Conservation of | scientific method
crystalline | Matter and Energy | scientific notation
density | liquid | significant figure
energy | liter | solid
exact number | mass | theory
fluid | matter | unit of measure
gas | measurement | vapor
gram | meter | volume
inactive material | metric system | weight

QUESTIONS

Group A

1. Why is chemistry considered to be a fundamental science?
2. What distinguishes (*a*) a solid from a liquid? (*b*) a liquid from a gas?
3. What properties of materials are classed as physical properties?
4. What properties of materials are classed as chemical?
5. What are the three basic units of the metric system?
6. Name the six prefixes used in the metric system and indicate what each one means.
7. Why is the study of chemistry concerned with energy?
8. In scientific work what advantage does the metric system offer over the English system?

Group B

9. Prepare a list of new chemical products which you have read about in newspapers and magazines.
10. (*a*) List five common materials used in the kitchen in your home. (*b*) What properties does each have which makes it suitable for its particular use?
11. Why are both liquids and gases considered to be fluids?
12. What determines whether a certain property of a material is classed as physical or chemical?
13. Why does our sense of touch give us the most direct evidence of the existence of matter?
14. A weighing was made on a platform balance which was graduated in 0.1 g units and was sensitive to 0.01 g. The mass was recorded as 73.14 g. (*a*) How many significant figures are in this measurement? (*b*) Which digit would be called a doubtful figure?

15. Volume is a property of a material. (*a*) Is it a specific property? (*b*) Is mass a specific property? (*c*) Is the ratio of mass to volume a specific property? Explain.

16. Your laboratory partner was given the task of measuring the length of a box (approximately 5 in) as accurately as possible using a meter stick graduated in millimeters. He supplied you with the following measurements: 12.65, 12.6 cm, 12.65 cm, 12.655 cm, 126.55 mm, 12 cm. (*a*) State which one of the measurements you would accept, giving the reason. (*b*) Give your reason for rejecting each of the others.

17. Copy each of the following measurements and underscore all significant figures in each (do not mark in this book): (*a*) 127.50 km; (*b*) 1200 m; (*c*) 90027.00 cm³; (*d*) 0.0053 g; (*e*) 670. mg; (*f*) 0.0730 g; (*g*) 43.050 l; (*h*) 300900 kg; (*i*) 0.147 cm; (*j*) 6271.9 cm².

18. Explain why the unit of any measurement should be written in a mathematical expression with the number to which it belongs.

PROBLEMS

See Table 1, Appendix

Group A

1. How many millimeters are there (*a*) in 1 centimeter? (*b*) in 1 meter? (*c*) in 1 kilometer?

2. How many centimeters are there (*a*) in 1 foot? (*b*) in 2 meters? (*c*) How many inches are there in 1 meter?

3. How many milliliters are there in (*a*) 2 liters? (*b*) 10 liters? (*c*) How many liters are there in 1 m³?

4. Calculate the number of milligrams (*a*) in 0.4 kilogram; (*b*) in 1 pound. (*c*) How many grams are there in 2 kilograms?

5. (*a*) What is your height in meters? (*b*) What is your mass in kilograms?

6. A Florence flask has a capacity of 2.50×10^2 ml. (*a*) What part of a liter is this? (*b*) How many grams of water will the flask hold?

7. The distance to the sun is approximately 93,000,000 miles. Express this distance in scientific notation form.

8. The thickness of an oil film on water is about 0.0000005 cm. Express this thickness in scientific notation form.

Group B

9. A cubic box holds 1000. g of water. (*a*) What is the volume of the box in milliliters? (*b*) in cubic centimeters? (*c*) What is the length of one side in centimeters? (*d*) in meters?

10. A test tube in the laboratory is 125 mm long and 25.0 mm in diameter. (*a*) What is its capacity in milliliters? (*b*) How many grams of water will it hold?

11. Each member of a class of 24 students needs 8.600 g of sodium chloride for an experiment. The instructor sets out a new one-pound jar of the salt. How many grams should he have left to return to the stock room at the end of the laboratory period?

12. A 1-liter graduated cylinder has an inside diameter of 8.24 cm. There is a 52-mm ungraduated portion at the top. What is the total height of the cylinder in centimeters?

13. The density of mercury, when given to three significant figures, is 13.6 g/ml. (*a*) What is the mass of 8.20 ml of mercury? (*b*) What volume would 120. g of mercury occupy?

14. Express the distance 152.20 cm in each of the following units showing the conversion computation in each case: (*a*) meters; (*b*) millimeters; (*c*) kilometer; (*d*) inches.

15. Chemists have determined that 18.0 g of water consists of 6.02×10^{23} molecules. Assuming that a teaspoon holds 3.70 ml of water, determine the number of water molecules the teaspoon can hold.

16. Pretend that you are able to remove individual molecules of water from the teaspoon of Problem 15 at the rate of 1 molecule per second. How many years would be required to empty the spoon?

SOME THINGS FOR YOU TO DO

1. Make a collection of clippings from your daily newspaper which deal with chemical research, chemical industries, or new chemical products.

2. Prepare a list of reasons favoring the introduction of the metric system into the United States for general use. State the objections to its introduction.

3. See how many energy transformations you can list pertaining to the operation of an automobile on the highway.

Chapter 2 · THE COMPOSITION OF MATTER

1. Three general classes of matter.
We are familiar with many different kinds of materials. To study materials without first organizing them into similar groups would be difficult and would require much effort and time. Chemists have found that all forms of matter may be divided into three general groups on the basis of their properties. These three general classes into which all forms of matter may be divided are *elements, compounds,* and *mixtures.*

2. Mixtures. If we examine a piece of granite closely with a hand lens, we can see three different crystalline materials: quartz, feldspar, and mica. The properties of each differ greatly. A *material which has parts with different properties is said to be* **heterogeneous** (het-er-oh-*jee*-nee-us).

The properties of quartz are the same regardless of its source. One part of a piece of quartz has the same properties as every other part. This is also true of

VOCABULARY

Atom. The smallest part of an element that can enter into combination with other elements.

Compound. A substance which can be decomposed into two or more simpler substances by ordinary chemical means.

Element. A substance which cannot be further decomposed by ordinary chemical means.

Heterogeneous material. One which has parts possessing different properties.

Homogeneous material. One which has similar properties throughout.

Mixture. A material composed of two or more substances each of which retains its own characteristic properties.

Substance. A homogeneous material consisting of one particular kind of matter.

feldspar and mica. *A material which has similar properties throughout is said to be* **homogeneous** (hoh-muh-*jee*-nee-us). Heterogeneous materials are *mixtures* of homogeneous materials.

All mixtures are not heterogeneous, however. When sugar is dissolved in water, the solution which is formed has similar properties throughout. Thus the solution is homogeneous. We may increase the amount of sugar or water, but we still have a homogeneous mixture of the two materials. The solution has the sweet taste of the sugar it contains. The water may be removed by evaporation and the sugar recovered in its original form. Solutions are therefore homogeneous mixtures. Air is a gaseous solution. Alloys are usually solid solutions. *A* **mixture** *is a material consisting of two or more kinds of matter, each retaining its own characteristic properties.*

3. Substances include compounds and elements. It has already been stated that materials with similar properties throughout are homogeneous. In chemistry, *a* **substance** *is a homogeneous material consisting of one particular kind of matter.* Both the sugar and the water of a sugar-water solution are substances. Unlike the granite which has the different properties of quartz, feldspar, and mica, the properties of sugar cannot be attributed to anything but the sugar itself and are due to its particular composition. Furthermore, *a substance has a definite chemical composition.*

Suppose we were to place a small quantity of sugar in a test tube and heat it over a low flame. The substance would readily melt and change color. Finally a charred black mass would be deposited in the bottom of the test tube, and drops of a clear colorless liquid would

Fig. 2-1. **All matter is divided into three general classes: elements, compounds, and mixtures.**

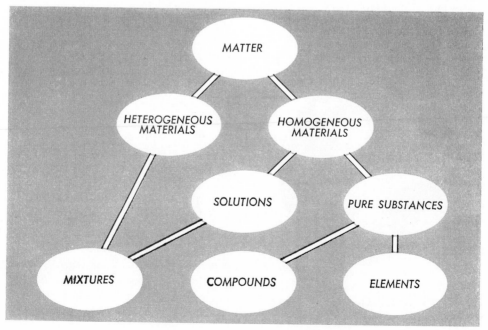

appear around the cooler open end. This black substance can be shown to be carbon and the liquid to be water. The properties of the sugar no longer exist. Instead we observe the properties of two different substances. Sugar may be recognized as a complex substance or *compound*. *A compound is a substance which may be decomposed into two or more simpler substances by ordinary chemical means.*

Chemists are able to decompose water into two simpler substances, hydrogen and oxygen. Thus water is a compound. Chemists have not succeeded, however, in decomposing carbon, hydrogen, or oxygen into any simpler substances. We conclude that these are elementary substances or *elements*. *Elements are substances which cannot be further decomposed by ordinary chemical means.* Elementary substances cannot be further broken down or simplified by the usual methods of carrying out chemical reactions—by application of heat, light, or electric energy.

4. There are relatively few elements in nature. One of the most fascinating facts of science is that all matter is composed of about 100 elements. Probably 90 different elements occur in a free or combined state in the earth's crust in detectable amounts. The atmosphere consists almost entirely of the two elements, nitrogen and oxygen. Water, which covers such a great portion of the surface of the earth, is a combination of hydrogen and oxygen. It is true, however, that natural water contains many dissolved substances.

Only about 30 elements are well known. The relative distribution of the 10 most abundant elements in the atmosphere, lakes, rivers, and oceans, and the earth's crust is:

Oxygen	49.5%	Sodium	2.6%
Silicon	25.8%	Potassium	2.4%
Aluminum	7.5%	Magnesium	1.9%
Iron	4.7%	Hydrogen	0.9%
Calcium	3.4%	Titanium	0.6%
	All other elements	0.7%	

A few elementary substances such as gold, silver, copper, and sulfur, have been known since ancient times. During the Middle Ages and the Renaissance which followed, more elements were discovered. Through the years, scientists have added even more elements to the list as a result of improved research techniques.

There are 103 known elements at the time of this writing. The theoretical possibility of eventually extending the number to 118, or even beyond 137, has been suggested. However, present evidence indicates that the number may not exceed 110.

The 92 elements ranging from hydrogen to uranium are traditionally known as *natural elements*. They constitute the pre-Atomic Age list of elements. Atomic bomb research during World War II led to the synthesis of *neptunium* named

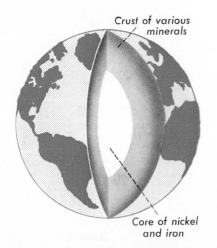
Crust of various minerals

Core of nickel and iron

Fig. 2-2. The core of the earth is believed to be composed of nickel and iron.

94-Plutonium
95-Americium - 63-Europium
96 - Curium - 64-Gadolinium
97 - Berkelium- 65-Terbium
98 - Californium 66-Dysprosium

Fig. 2-3. Glenn T. Seaborg is the 1951 Nobel laureate in chemistry. He and his associates are credited with the discovery of plutonium and eight other artificial radioactive elements. He won the Fermi Award in 1959. (Wide World)

for the planet Neptune, and *plutonium* named for Pluto. These were followed by *americium* (am-er-*ih*-see-um) named for America, *curium* (*ku*-ree-um) named in honor of Madame Curie, *berkelium* (*berk*-lee-um) for Berkeley (the site of the University of California), and *californium* for the university and the state. More recently *einsteinium* named for Albert Einstein, *fermium* named for Enrico Fermi, *mendelevium* (men-del-*ev*-ee-um) named for Dimitri Mendeleyev (men-deh-*lay*-eff) brought the total to 101.

In the summer of 1957 a team of American, British, and Swedish scientists working at the Nobel Institute in Sweden announced the discovery of element 102 and suggested the name *nobelium*. Careful experiments by other scientists have failed to confirm this discovery and so the name *nobelium* is in doubt.

In 1958 a research group at the Lawrence Radiation Laboratory of the Uni-

versity of California produced element 102 and identified it by chemical means. These scientists may be expected to propose a new name for this element. In 1961, element 103 was produced by scientists at this same laboratory. The name *lawrencium* has been proposed for element 103 in honor of Dr. Ernest O. Lawrence, the inventor of the cyclotron, and the founder of the laboratory in which the element was produced.

5. Two general classes of elements. Elements differ enough in their properties so that chemists recognize two general classes, *metals* and *nonmetals*. *1. Metals.* Some elements have a luster similar to that of steel or silver. They reflect heat and light readily and conduct heat and electricity remarkably well. Some are ductile and can be drawn into wire, or malleable and can be hammered into thin sheets. Elements which have such properties are known as **metals.** Some examples of metals are: gold, silver, copper, iron, zinc, tin, lead, magnesium, calcium, and aluminum. Mercury is a liquid metal.

2. *Nonmetals*. These are usually poor conductors of heat and electricity. They cannot be hammered into sheets or drawn into wire because they are usually too brittle. Sulfur is an example of such a nonmetal. Some nonmetals such as iodine, carbon, and phosphorus are solid at room temperatures. Bromine is a liquid nonmetal. Others are gaseous, as oxygen, nitrogen, and chlorine.

Some borderline elements have certain properties characteristic of metals and other properties characteristic of nonmetals. Arsenic and antimony are two examples of this type. They are sometimes called **metalloids.**

6. **The chemical symbol.** Jöns Jakob Berzelius (1779–1848), a Swedish chemist, was the first to use letters as symbols for elements to replace the crude picture system used by the alchemists in the Middle Ages. Berzelius used the first letter of the name of an element as its symbol. For example, the letter **O** represents oxygen, and the letter **H** represents hydrogen.

Since there are over 100 elements known, and there are only twenty-six

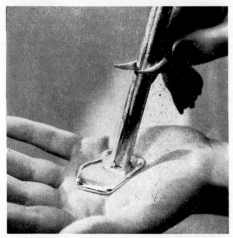

Fig. 2-4. **Sulfur (top) is a non-metallic element that occurs as yellow rhombic crystals in its ordinary form. The metallic element gallium (center) will melt in your hand but will not boil until heated to about 2000° C. Mercury (right) is the only metallic element that is liquid at room temperature.**

letters in our alphabet, the names of several elements must begin with the same letter. In this event, Berzelius suggested using the second letter of the name of the element with the first letter, or the first letter with some other letter whose sound is conspicuous when the name of the element is pronounced. For example, the symbol for carbon is **C**; for calcium, **Ca**; for chlorine, **Cl**; for chromium, **Cr**; and for cobalt, **Co**. The first letter of a symbol is *always* a capital, but the second letter of a symbol is *never* capitalized. For example, **Co** is the symbol for cobalt, but **CO** is the formula for the compound *carbon monoxide*, composed of the two elements carbon and oxygen.

In several cases, the symbol for an element is derived from the Latin name of the element. For example, the symbol for iron is **Fe**, from the Latin *ferrum*. **Pb**, the symbol for lead, comes from the Latin word *plumbum*. The symbols for silver, **Ag**, and sodium, **Na**, come from the Latin words, *argentum* and *natrium*.

7. The significance of a symbol. A chemical symbol is more than an abbreviation; it has quantitative significance. When we use the symbol **O**, it first of all means oxygen. More than that, it means *one atom* of oxygen. The expression **2 O** means 2 atoms of oxygen; **5 O** means 5 atoms of oxygen. Similarly **Fe** means 1 atom of iron; **3 Fe**, 3 atoms of iron; and **10 Fe**, 10 atoms of iron. *The atom is the smallest particle of an element that can enter into combination with other elements.* Just as a mason uses different kinds of bricks to build houses, so the chemist uses different kinds of atoms to build chemical compounds. The symbol of an element will acquire additional significance as the study of chemistry progresses.

8. Compounds differ from mixtures. When matter is made up of two or more elements, they may either be mixed mechanically or combined chemically. The material is either a *mixture* or a *compound* depending on what happened to the elements. If it is a mixture, the properties of each of the elements present can be recognized. On the other hand, if the elements are chemically combined, a complex substance with its own characteristic properties is observed.

Suppose some powdered sulfur and some iron powder are mixed thoroughly on a sheet of paper. There is no evidence of chemical action, no light is produced and no heat is given off. The two substances may be mixed in any proportion. It is possible to use a large amount of iron and a small amount of sulfur or a large portion of sulfur and a small portion of iron.

If the paper containing this mixture is moved back and forth over a strong magnet, the iron particles can be separated from the sulfur. When a small portion of the mixture is put in hydrochloric acid, the iron reacts with the acid and disappears from view leaving the sulfur unaffected. When another portion of the mixture is put in carbon disulfide, the sulfur dissolves leaving the iron powder unchanged.

In each of these tests the properties of iron and sulfur persist. This is typical of a mixture; the components do not lose their identity. They may be mixed in any proportion without evidence of chemical activity.

It is possible to cause the iron and sulfur to unite chemically to form a compound. Suppose iron and sulfur are mixed intimately in the ratio of 7 g to 4 g respectively and the mixture is heated in a test tube over a Bunsen flame. With a rise in temperature the

DIFFERENCES BETWEEN A MIXTURE AND A COMPOUND

MIXTURE	COMPOUND
1. In a mixture, the components may be present in any proportion.	1. A compound always has a definite composition by weight.
2. In the preparation of a mixture, there is no evidence of any chemical action taking place.	2. In the preparation of a compound, evidence of chemical action is usually apparent (light, heat, etc.)
3. In a mixture, the components do not lose their identity. The components of a mixture may be separated by mechanical means.	3. In a compound, the constituents lose their identity. The constituents of a compound can be separated by chemical means only.

mixture begins to glow. Even after its removal from the flame, the mixture continues to react and the whole mass soon becomes red hot. *Both heat and light are produced during the chemical action which causes the sulfur to unite chemically with the iron to form a compound.*

After the reaction has ceased and the product has been removed, careful examination shows that it no longer resembles either the iron or the sulfur; each element has lost its characteristic properties. The iron cannot be removed by a magnet. The sulfur cannot be dissolved out of the product with carbon disulfide. Hydrochloric acid acts on the mixture of iron and sulfur to produce hydrogen, an odorless gas. It acts on this new product to produce hydrogen sulfide, a gas with a distinctive (rotten egg) odor. *A new substance with a new set of properties has been formed.*

Chemical analysis of this new product shows that it is made up of seven parts by weight of iron to four parts by weight of sulfur. *A compound is always made up of the same elements in a definite proportion by weight.* For example, the new compound, which may be called *iron sulfide,* is composed of 63.5% iron and 36.5% sulfur. That does not mean that this sulfide could not be made by

starting with eight parts of iron and four parts of sulfur. It does mean that in such a case, one part by weight of iron would remain as an unused surplus after the seven parts of iron had combined with four parts of sulfur to form iron sulfide.

The differences between a mixture and a compound are summarized in the table above.

9. The Law of Definite Composition. Louis Proust (1755–1826), a French chemist, was one of the first to observe that elements always combine with one another in a definite ratio by weight. About fifty years later, Jean Servais Stas, a Belgian chemist, performed a series of precise experiments which confirmed the observations of Proust. We now recognize the work of Proust as the *Law of Definite Composition: every compound has a definite composition by weight.*

Because the Law of Definite Composition is true, a manufacturer of chemical compounds can find out just how much of each constituent to use in making each compound.

10. Some common examples of mixtures and compounds. Air is a mixture. Its composition varies somewhat in different localities. Other familiar examples of mixtures include such well-known substances as baking powders, concrete, and various kinds of soil. There is practically no limit to the number of possible mixtures. They may be made up of two or more elements, of two or more compounds, or of both elements and compounds. For example, brass is a mixture of two elements, copper and zinc. Common gunpowder is a mixture of two elements, carbon and sulfur, with a compound, potassium nitrate. A solution of common salt is a mixture of two compounds, sodium chloride and water.

Some of our large dictionaries define almost a half-million words, all formed from one or more of the 26 letters that make up our alphabet. Try to imagine the number of compounds it would be possible to make from 100 or more elements. However, some elements do not unite readily with others to form compounds. Half a dozen are known which never form compounds. There are enough elements that do combine, however, to form the *several hundred thou-*

sand compounds known to chemists. Water, table salt, sugar, marble, alcohol, baking soda, ether, glycerol, turpentine, starch, cellulose, nitric, hydrochloric, and sulfuric acids are examples of some common compounds.

The simplest compounds are made up of two different elements; iron sulfide is such a compound. Carbon dioxide is composed only of carbon and oxygen. Table salt consists of the element sodium combined with the element chlorine. Sodium is an active metallic element which must be protected from contact with air and water. Chlorine is a poisonous gas. But when combined chemically, the two form common table salt.

Many compounds are composed of no more than three different elements. Carbon, hydrogen, and oxygen are the constituents of sugar. These same three elements, combined in different proportions, form many other compounds having decidedly different properties.

SUMMARY

Matter is classed either as a mixture or a pure substance. Pure substances are either compounds or elements. Compounds are substances which may be decomposed into two or more simpler substances by ordinary chemical means. Elements are substances which may not be further decomposed by ordinary chemical means. Mixtures are materials composed of two or more substances each of which retains its own characteristic properties.

While over 100 elements are known, no more than 90 exist outside of the scientist's laboratories. These make up all of the world that we know. Only about 30 elements are well known. Ten elements form about 99% of the earth's crust. Oxygen is the most abundant element, silicon ranks second in abundance. Elements may be classed as metals and nonmetals; however, some are called metalloids.

Symbols are used to represent elements. The symbol of an element stands for one atom of that element. The atom is the smallest particle of an element that can enter into combination with other elements.

The Law of Definite Composition states that every compound has a definite composition by weight.

TEST YOURSELF ON THESE TERMS

atom	heterogeneous	metalloid
chemical symbol	homogeneous	mixture
compound	Law of Definite Composition	nonmetal
element	metal	substance

QUESTIONS

Group A

1. What are the three general classes of matter?
2. Distinguish between matter and a substance.
3. Distinguish between a complex substance and an elementary substance.
4. (*a*) What are the two general classes of elements? (*b*) Do all elements fit definitely into one of these classes?
5. Distinguish between a compound and a mixture.
6. What are the five most abundant elements?
7. (*a*) What are the properties of metals? (*b*) of nonmetals?
8. (*a*) How many elements are known? (*b*) How many were known prior to the atomic-bomb research of World War II?
9. What is the meaning of a chemical symbol?
10. (*a*) List five familiar substances which you recognize to be elements. (*b*) List five which are compounds. (*c*) List five familiar mixtures.

Group B

11. What difference in the properties of white sand and sugar would enable a mixture of the two substances to be separated?
12. How would you carry out the separation of the sand-sugar mixture of Question 11?
13. Why is a solution recognized as a mixture?
14. What is the meaning of the phrase "definite composition by weight"?
15. Why is the Law of Definite Composition very important to chemists?
16. Consult the complete list of known elements appearing on the inside of the back cover of this book and compile a list of those about which you already have some knowledge. Give the name, symbol, and the pertinent bit of knowledge in column form.
17. Given two liquids, one a solution and the other a compound, how would you distinguish the solution from the compound?
18. Suppose you heat three different solids in open vessels and then allow them to cool. The first gains weight, the second loses weight, and the third remains the same. How can you reconcile these facts with the generalization that, in an ordinary chemical change, the total mass of the reacting materials is equal to the total mass of the products?

19. How can you explain the fact that gold, silver, and copper were known long before such metals as iron and aluminum?
20. Suppose you were given a sample of iodine crystals, a sample of antimony metal, and a sample of a mixture of iodine and antimony which had been ground together to form a fine powder of uniform consistency. Look up the physical and chemical properties of both iodine and antimony and list those for each element that you believe would be useful in effecting their separation and recovery from the mixture supplied. On the basis of these properties devise a procedure which would enable you to separate the two elements from the mixture and recover the separate elements.

SOME THINGS FOR YOU TO DO

1. New uses are being found for some of the less common elements. Consult a recent advanced chemistry text to find the uses which are now being made of selenium, titanium, zirconium, iridium, gallium, and indium.
2. Look up the words from which the symbols for antimony, copper, gold, mercury, potassium, tin, and tungsten are taken or derived.
3. Devise an experiment and a series of arguments which will enable you to demonstrate the fact that an ordinary solution is a homogeneous mixture.
4. Develop a mineral collection that illustrates the forms in which the common elements of the earth's crust are found in nature.
5. Visit your local museum and examine the extensive mineral collections that may be found there to determine which elements are found in abundance in your own locality.

Chapter 3 · MATTER AND ITS CHANGES

1. THE NATURE OF MATTER

1. Particles composing matter. When you crush a lump of sugar you can see that it is made up of many small particles of sugar. You may go further and grind these particles into the finest of powders, but each tiny piece is still sugar. Now suppose you dissolve the sugar in water. The tiny particles disappear completely. Even a microscopic examination of the solution does not reveal their presence. However, your sense of taste tells you that sugar is present in the water solution. Similarly, the odor of gas escaping from an open gas valve tells you of its presence. You cannot see gas particles in the air of the room, even if you use the most powerful microscope. These and many similar experiments have led scientists to believe that the *ultimate particles* of matter must be exceedingly small.

Greek philosophers, as early as 400 B.C., believed that matter was indestructible. They also thought that it could be divided into smaller and smaller particles until a point was reached beyond which no further subdivision was possible. These were the ultimate particles of the philosophers. Democritus (deh-*mock*-rih-tus) (460–370 B.C.) referred to such particles as *atoms*, from a Greek word meaning indivisible. This ancient philosopher derived his fundamental knowledge almost entirely from his own thinking. The modern scientific method uses experiments to reveal fundamental truths. Thus the ideas the early philosophers had about matter have very little resemblance to our present knowledge of the nature of matter.

The English chemist John Dalton (1766–1844) spoke of ultimate particles of matter and referred to them as *atoms*. He sometimes tried to distinguish between elementary and complex substances by using the term *complex atom*. Count Amadeo Avogadro (1776–1856), an Italian chemist and physicist, used the term *molecules* for the ultimate particles.

Today we recognize that pure substances exist either as compounds or elements. We have seen that compounds consist of different elements which are chemically combined. In Chapter 2 we defined the smallest particle of an element that can enter into combination with other elements as an atom. Chemical elements are made up of such minute particles. *All atoms of a particular element are essentially alike but are different from those of all other elements.*

Any sample of a compound has the same composition as every other sample of that compound. A particular compound is always composed of the same elements in the same proportion by weight (Law of Definite Composition). The simplest kind of compound is composed of particles from two different elements chemically linked or *bonded* together. More complex compounds are formed from particles of several different elements.

The characteristic properties by which a substance is recognized are those exhibited by it in mass quantities, that is, in measurable amounts commonly encountered. Chemists now use the term *molecule to denote the smallest portion of a substance that retains the properties exhibited by that substance in mass.*

When atoms of elements exist singly, there is no distinction between the meaning of the terms "atom" and "molecule." The atoms of some elements combine naturally to form pairs and exist as simple diatomic (two-atom) molecules. Atmospheric oxygen and nitrogen are examples, their molecules being represented respectively as O_2 and N_2. Observe that O_2 means *2 atoms of oxygen bonded together to form 1 oxygen molecule*, while $2\,O$ means 2 separate unbonded oxygen atoms; $3\,O_2$ *means 3 molecules of oxygen, each of which consists of 2 oxygen atoms bonded together.* Other elements may form larger atom groups. Phosphorus has a molecular particle organization consisting of four atoms and is written P_4.

VOCABULARY

Boiling point. The temperature at which equilibrium vapor pressure of a liquid is equal to prevailing atmospheric pressure.

Catalyst. An agent which affects a chemical action without itself being permanently altered.

Diatomic. Consisting of two atoms.

Endothermic. Pertaining to a reaction which occurs with the absorption of heat.

Equilibrium vapor pressure. The pressure exerted by a vapor in equilibrium with its liquid.

Exothermic. Pertaining to a reaction which occurs with the evolution of heat.

Molecule. The smallest portion of an element or a compound that retains the properties exhibited by the substance in mass.

Monatomic. Consisting of one atom.

Physical equilibrium. A dynamic state in which two opposing physical processes in the same system proceed at equal rates.

Precipitate. A substance, usually a solid, which separates from a solution as a result of some physical or chemical change.

Fig. 3-1. **The electron microscope is capable of magnifications to 200,000 diameters.** (Goodyear News Service)

Sulfur molecules may be eight-atom particles or S_8. The metallic elements generally exhibit crystalline structures in which the atoms are closely packed in regular patterns that show no simple molecular units. In these instances, each individual crystal can be considered to be a single giant molecule.

Some compounds have distinct unit structures composed of simple molecules. Water is a familiar example, the molecules consisting of two hydrogen atoms and one oxygen atom represented as H_2O. Other substances may show complex unit structures formed by groups of molecules or molecular aggregates. Still others may have no molecular organization at all. Ordinary table salt, sodium chloride, consists of electrically charged atoms of sodium and chlorine (called ions) which are dis-

tributed in a regular crystalline lattice pattern that is continuous to each crystal face. Simple molecules of sodium chloride do not exist except in the vapor state at very high temperatures.

2. The size of molecules. Molecules vary greatly in size. It has been estimated that if a drop of water could be magnified until it became as large as the earth, the molecules composing it would be about one meter in diameter. The simple molecules of gases, consisting of one, two, or three atoms, have diameters of approximately 3×10^{-8} cm. Some virus protein molecules, consisting of approximately 7.5×10^5 atoms and having diameters of about 2.3×10^{-6} cm, have been photographed with an electron microscope. Using a more suitable scale for atoms and molecules, the *Ångström scale,* this range of molecular diameters is from 3 Å to 230 Å. ($1 Å = 1 \times 10^{-8}$ cm).

The forces that hold the atoms of different elements together to form molecules of compounds may also cause atoms of a single element to combine. Free and isolated atoms are rarely found in nature. Instead, atoms of most elements are combined with one another at ordinary temperatures to form larger structural particles. Notable exceptions are the inert elements: helium, argon, neon, krypton, xenon (*zee*-non), and radon. The atoms of these inert gases do not combine with each other to form larger particles. There is no distinction, therefore, between the atoms and molecules of these gases. We may say that a molecule of helium consists of a single atom.

The molecules of the ordinary gaseous elements, oxygen, nitrogen, hydrogen, fluorine, and chlorine are made up of two atoms. The nonmetal bromine, a liquid at ordinary temperatures, exists as diatomic molecules. Its sister element, iodine, forms molecular crystals in which each molecular particle is diatomic. Mention has already been made of the fact that phosphorus and sulfur form four- and eight-atom molecules, and that molecules of compounds may range from a minimum of two atoms to extremely large numbers of atoms.

3. Forces between molecules. The atoms of all elements are bound together by strong forces. These forces are electric in nature and will be discussed in Chapter 6. The attracting forces between molecules are much weaker. In gases they are practically negligible because gas molecules are relatively far apart from one another. Gas molecules are therefore essentially independent particles and fill whatever space is available to them.

Many liquids are known to have molecular structure similar to that of their gaseous state. Iodine vapor and liquid iodine both have diatomic molecules, but the molecules of liquid iodine are much closer together than those in gaseous iodine. Such liquid molecules are subject to attracting forces strong enough to form a free surface (definite volume) but too weak to hold them in any fixed order (no definite shape).

Solids may be separated into two general groups, *crystalline solids* and *amorphous solids.* **Crystalline solids** have a regular arrangement of particles. **Amorphous solids** are those which have a completely random particle arrangement and are, in a literal sense, *shapeless.* Many solids which scientists once thought were amorphous have been found to have a minute crystalline structure.

Some solids are made up of simple molecules. Solid iodine consists of diatomic molecules arranged in systematic order forming *molecular crystals.* Other solids show no molecular structure at all. Most crystalline salts are of this sort. The crystals consist of an orderly pattern of ions bound together by strong electric forces.

4. The formulas of compounds. A chemical symbol stands for one atom of a particular element. The **monatomic** (single-atomed) **molecules** of the inert

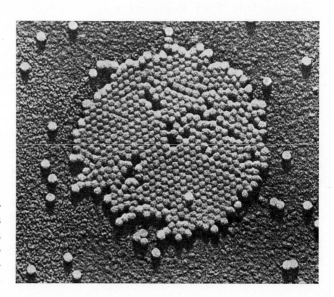

Fig. 3-2. **Very large molecules, like these polio virus molecules, can be seen with the aid of the electron microscope.** (The National Foundation)

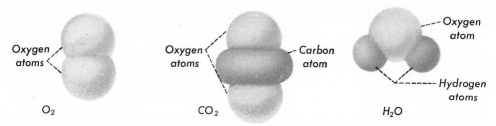

Fig. 3-3. **The oxygen molecule is diatomic. The carbon dioxide molecule is composed of one carbon atom and two oxygen atoms. The two hydrogen atoms of the water molecule are on the same side of the oxygen atom, the angle H–O–H being 105°.**

elements are therefore represented by just their symbols. If a molecule is more complex, the number of atoms in the molecule is shown by means of a numerical subscript following the symbol. Thus the diatomic molecules of the ordinary elementary gases are represented by H_2, O_2, N_2, F_2, and Cl_2. Bromine is represented by Br_2, and iodine by I_2. *It is customary to represent the elements other than those known to have diatomic molecules as monatomic.*

Chemists use chemical symbols and numerical subscripts in a shorthand method of representing the composition of compounds. Such shorthand notations are called *formulas.* The formula for water, H_2O, represents *one molecule* of water and indicates that the water molecule consists of *two atoms* of hydrogen and *one atom* of oxygen. The formula for water is read *H-two-O.* The expression 2 H_2O represents *two molecules* of water, each containing two atoms of hydrogen and one atom of oxygen. Similarly, 5 H_2O signifies *five molecules of water.* When no other coefficient is used ahead of a formula, it is understood that the coefficient should be 1.

If the structure of a substance has been determined experimentally to be molecular, the formula may truly represent a molecule of that substance. Thus hydrogen peroxide has the formula H_2O_2 rather than HO, since it is known that the molecule contains two atoms of hydrogen and two atoms of oxygen. Whenever a formula is written with subscripts *not* in the simplest whole number ratio we may safely assume that it is a *molecular formula.*

Many compounds do not have simple molecular structures or, as in the case of sodium chloride, do not contain molecules at all. Formulas for such substances cannot stand for molecules. They do, however, express the constituent elements and the relative number of atoms of each. Such formulas are usually expressed in the simplest whole number ratio and are known as *empirical formulas.* The formula for sodium chloride, **NaCl**, is empirical.

2. THE KINETIC THEORY

5. The molecules of gases have motion. Many observations show us that molecules of gases are constantly in motion. If tiny smoke particles are suspended in air and properly illuminated under a microscope, they are seen to be buffeted about in a kind of vibratory fashion. This continuous motion is produced by the numerous collisions with moving gas molecules.

If the stopper is removed from a container of ammonia, its irritating properties soon become evident throughout the room. When the chemistry class makes the foul-odored hydrogen sulfide gas in the laboratory, objections frequently come from other students and teachers in all parts of the building. The gases are said to *diffuse* (or scatter) throughout the laboratory and throughout the building.

6. Moving molecules have kinetic energy. A gas under normal conditions occupies roughly 1000 times the volume of its liquid or solid state. The molecules of a gas are, therefore, widely separated. Each moving molecule continues in a given direction until it collides either with another molecule or with the wall of the container. It has been estimated that some molecules move in random directions at speeds of the order of 5×10^5 mm/sec and travel average distances of 1×10^{-4} mm between collisions with other molecules or the walls of the container. We may expect such

molecules to experience 5×10^9, or 5 billion collisions per second. The collisions with the vessel walls are responsible for the *pressure* of gases.

As you already know, objects in motion have kinetic energy. This is equally true of molecules of gases or automobiles moving along a highway. All molecules of a gas do not have the same kinetic energy. However, most of them at any time may be expected to have an energy value near the average kinetic energy of all the molecules. *An increase in the temperature increases the rate at which the molecules move.* Thus the temperature of a gas provides an indication of the average kinetic energy of the molecules.

A container of gas may stand indefinitely under constant conditions without change of temperature or pressure. This would indicate that the gas molecules do not give up any portion of their kinetic energy when they collide. Instead, they rebound, taking all their energy with them. Molecules of gases are said to be *perfectly elastic* and their motions are entirely random.

7. The diffusion of gases. Recognizing these characteristics of gas molecules, let us now consider the way in which gases diffuse. If the air is pumped out of a container and a gas is then allowed to enter it, we observe that the container is instantly filled with the gas. We would expect this to occur because of the great speed of the molecules and the lack of collisions.

Molecules of a gas escaping into a room already occupied by other gases do, of course, experience frequent collisions, perhaps as many as 5 billion per second. The resulting random directions of motion delay the scattering of the molecules of the new gas throughout the other gases. Eventually, random motion

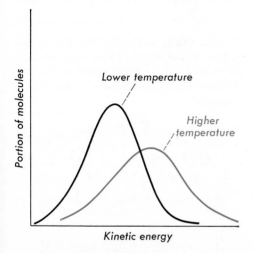

Fig. 3-4. Energy distribution in a gas at different temperatures.

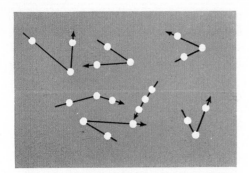

Fig. 3-5. **This enlarged diagram shows the movement of particles of paint as they are bombarded by invisible molecules of the liquid in which they are suspended.**

of all of the gas molecules results in their uniform distribution throughout the room. *This process of spreading out spontaneously to fill a space uniformly is characteristic of all gases and is known as diffusion.* Gaseous diffusion is slowed down, but not prevented, by the presence of other gases.

8. All gases do not diffuse at the same rate. All gases existing at the same temperature have the same average kinetic energy. Should we then expect their molecules to have the same average velocities? The kinetic energy of a particle is dependent on both its mass and velocity.

$$\text{K.E.} = \tfrac{1}{2} mv^2$$

where K.E. is kinetic energy, m is the mass of the particle, and v is its velocity. Thus molecules of different gases having the same kinetic energy move at different rates if their masses are different. The lighter molecules move more rapidly, the heavier molecules more slowly. The rates of diffusion of such gases are in proportion to their molecular velocities. Indeed, hydrogen, which is the least dense of all gases, diffuses more rapidly than other gases under similar condi-

tions. At room temperature the velocity of hydrogen molecules is about one mile per second. This is four times the velocity of oxygen molecules under similar conditions.

9. Motion in liquids and solids. There is abundant evidence that the particles of liquids and solids are in motion. Finely divided particles of a solid suspended in water or other liquids and viewed through a microscope, may be observed to move about in a helter-skelter manner. The motion is increased by using lighter or smaller particles and by higher temperatures. This is in agreement with the **Kinetic Theory** and we may conclude that the observed random motion is caused by collisions with molecules of the liquid.

The molecules of the vapors of liquids and solids have properties similar to those which we have attributed to gases. As stated previously, there is no distinction between a vapor and a gas other than the temperatures at which they normally exist. On cooling, gases may become liquids, and with further cooling, may become solids.

The molecules of gases, being rela-

Fig. 3-6. **Water molecules escape at the surface of the liquid. Some rebound into the surface after colliding with molecules of gases in the air or with water vapor molecules.**

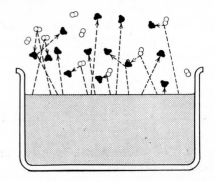

tively far apart and having high kinetic energy, are practically independent of each other. The particles of liquids and solids are close together and the forces between them are therefore much stronger. In liquids, the kinetic energy of the particles is still sufficient to partially overcome these forces. Motion is random, but greatly restricted. The particles of solids are still further restricted in their motion. The forces are sufficient to cause the unit particles to occupy fixed positions in the crystal structure and vibratory motion occurs about these fixed positions. In contrast to gases, liquids and solids form free surfaces, and solids have rigid structures.

X-ray photographs of crystals become less distinct as the crystal temperature is increased. The fixed positions of the particles within the crystal structure become less certain as their kinetic energy rises.

Water and other liquids, such as perfume, *evaporate* because molecules continually escape from the surface. The odors of solids like camphor and naphthalene (moth balls) give evidence of the motion of molecules of these substances. The vapor molecules of solids or liquids in closed containers exert pressure as do all confined gases. This *vapor pressure* reaches some maximum value depending on the temperature of the substance.

★ **10. Dynamic equilibrium.** When a cover is placed over a container partially filled with a liquid it appears that evaporation of the liquid continues for a while and then ceases. Let us examine this apparent situation in light of the Kinetic Theory. The temperature of the liquid is proportional to the average kinetic energy of all the molecules of the liquid. Most of these molecules have energies very close to the average; some

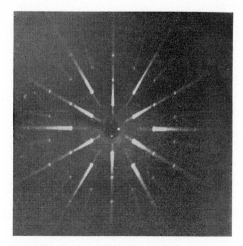

Fig. 3-7. X-ray diffraction photograph of ice. Chemists use X-ray diffraction in their study of crystal structure. (Polytechnic Institute of Brooklyn)

have very high energies and a few have very low energies at any particular time. The motions of all are random.

High energy molecules near the surface and moving toward the surface may overcome the attractive forces of the surface molecules completely and escape or evaporate. Some of these may collide with molecules of gases in the air or other vapor molecules and rebound into the liquid. As the evaporation continues, the concentration of vapor molecules continues to increase. Consequently, the chance of collisions of escaping molecules with vapor molecules increases and the number rebounding into the liquid increases.

Eventually the number of vapor molecules returning to the liquid equals the number of liquid molecules evaporating. Beyond this point there will be no *net* increase in the concentration of vapor molecules. The motions of the molecules do not cease and so the two actions, evaporation and condensation, do not cease; both merely continue at

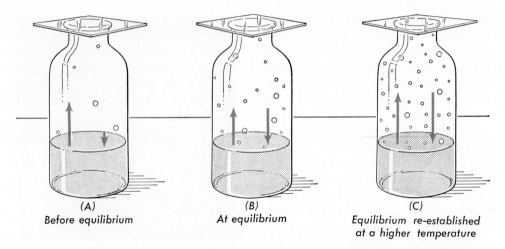

(A)   (B)   (C)
Before equilibrium   *At equilibrium*   *Equilibrium re-established
                                                        at a higher temperature*

Fig. 3-8. **An example of physical equilibrium and the influence of temperature. The different sizes of the arrows indicate the relative rates of evaporation (up) and condensation (down). The pressure exerted by the vapor molecules at equilibrium is known as the equilibrium vapor pressure of that
particular liquid.**

equal rates. We may conclude that an *equilibrium* is attained between the rate of liquid molecules evaporating and the rate of vapor molecules condensing. It is obvious that this is a dynamic condition in which *opposing* processes are proceeding at *equal* rates. Since this dynamic equilibrium involves purely physical activity, it is referred to as *physical equilibrium: a dynamic state in which two opposing physical processes in the same system proceed at equal rates.*

We might represent the evaporation process in the following manner:

liquid → vapor

The condensation process would be accordingly,

vapor → liquid

We could then represent this state of dynamic equilibrium occurring in a confined space as

liquid ⇄ vapor

Freezing and melting are physical changes and the freezing and melting points of pure crystalline substances coincide. For pure water, both processes occur at 0° C, that is, ice melts at 0° C to form liquid water and water freezes at 0° C to form ice. If ice gradually disappears in a mixture of ice and water, it is evident that the melting process is proceeding at a rate faster than the freezing process. If, however, the relative amounts of ice and water remain unchanged in the mixture, both processes must be proceeding at equal rates and a state of physical equilibrium is indicated.

liquid ⇄ solid

You will encounter many examples of equilibrium in your study of chemistry. ⋆ **11. Equilibrium vapor pressure.** The vapor molecules of solids or liquids in closed containers exert pressure as do all confined gases. When equilibrium is reached there is no net change in the system and the concentration of vapor molecules in the space above the liquid surface remains constant. Thus, at equilibrium, there is a vapor pressure characteristic of the liquid present in the system. It is known as the *equilibrium vapor pressure* of the liquid. **Equilibrium vapor pressure is the pressure exerted by a vapor in equilibrium with its liquid.**

What is the effect on a liquid-vapor equilibrium system if the temperature of the liquid is raised? Again, let us examine this situation in terms of the Kinetic Theory. The rise in temperature means that the average kinetic energy of the liquid molecules has been raised. A relatively larger number of liquid molecules now possess sufficient energy to escape through the liquid surface; the rate of evaporation is increased.

liquid ⇌ vapor

Thus, the liquid-vapor equilibrium is *disturbed* and the concentration of vapor molecules above the liquid surface is increased. This, in turn, increases the chances of collisions with escaping molecules causing an increase in the rate of condensation. Soon the equilibrium is re-established, but at a *higher equilibrium vapor pressure.*

All liquids have characteristic forces of attraction between their molecules. Where the attractive forces are strong, there is less tendency for the liquid to evaporate. The equilibrium vapor pressure of such a liquid is correspondingly low. Glycerol is an example of a liquid with a low equilibrium vapor pressure. Conversely, where the attractive forces between liquid molecules are weak, the liquid tends to evaporate readily with a resulting high equilibrium vapor pressure. Ether is such a liquid. The magnitude of the equilibrium vapor pressure

of a liquid depends on *the nature of the liquid* and *its temperature.*

★ **12. The boiling point of liquids.** An understanding of the nature of equilibrium phenomena, and in particular the manner in which equilibrium vapor pressures are established, leads one naturally to an understanding of the phenomenon of *boiling.* From physics we know that any pressure exerted anywhere on the surface of a confined liquid is transmitted undiminished in every direction throughout the liquid (Pascal's law).

Consider the beaker of water being heated over a Bunsen flame in Fig. 3-9. When vapor bubbles first appear at the bottom of the beaker where the water is hottest, they diminish in size and disappear completely as they rise into the cooler layers of the water. Atmospheric pressure acts on the surface of

Fig. 3-9. A liquid boils when its equilibrium vapor pressure becomes equal to the prevailing atmospheric pressure.

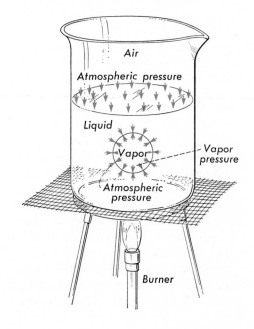

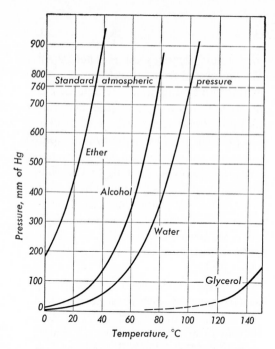

Fig. 3-10. **The equilibrium vapor pressures of some common liquids as a function of temperature.**

the vapor **bubble**, according to Pascal's law, to collapse it. Only when the equilibrium vapor pressure exerted by the vapor molecules on the liquid at the surface of the bubble is equal to the atmospheric pressure can the vapor bubble be maintained.

As the temperature of the water rises with its attendant rise in vapor pressure, *a temperature is reached where the equilibrium vapor pressure becomes equal to the pressure of the atmosphere acting on the surface of the liquid.* At this temperature the vapor bubbles maintain themselves in the liquid and present to the liquid a greatly increased liquid-vapor surface allowing evaporation (a surface **phenomenon**) to occur at a greatly increased rate and we say that the liquid *boils.* The **boiling point** of a *liquid is the temperature at which the equilibrium vapor pressure of the liquid is equal to the prevailing atmospheric pressure.* If the pressure on the surface

of a liquid is increased, as in a pressure cooker, the boiling point of the liquid rises. If the pressure is decreased, as in vacuum pans used in sugar refining, the boiling point of the liquid lowers.

The boiling point of water is exactly 100° C at *standard* atmospheric pressure, the average pressure of the air at sea level. This is known as the *standard* (or *normal*) *boiling point of water.*

Pressure of gases or vapors is commonly measured by means of a mercury barometer and is expressed in terms of the height of the column of mercury it will support. **Standard pressure is de-** *fined as the pressure required to support a column of mercury 760 mm high at 0° Centigrade.* When the boiling points of liquids are given, standard atmospheric pressure conditions are understood.

Ether, which has a high equilibrium vapor pressure, boils at 34.6° C. The boiling point of glycerol, mentioned for its low equilibrium vapor pressure, is 290° C. The vapor-pressure characteristics of several liquids are shown in Fig. 3-10.

3. CHANGES IN MATTER

13. Physical changes. Ice melts, water boils, liquids freeze, glass breaks, and sugar dissolves in water. We may heat a piece of platinum wire until it glows. In all these cases matter undergoes some change. Its form may be different or it may have experienced a change of state or energy level. However, in no case has the matter lost its identity. Sometimes by a reversal of the action which caused the change, the material may be restored to its original form and the same identifying properties are again readily recognized.

These are examples of *physical*

changes. In such changes only alterations in physical properties are apparent; the composition of the material is not changed. *Physical changes are those in which the identifying properties of substances remain unchanged.*

Modern ideas concerning solutions suggest that some types of physical changes may involve intermediate processes which are not physical in nature. These ideas will be treated in Chapter 19.

14. Chemical changes. You know that wood burns, iron rusts, silver tarnishes, milk sours, plants decay, and acids react with metals. In each of these actions the identifying properties of the original substance are altered; new substances with different properties are recognized. Changes occur which alter the composition of matter. *Chemical changes are those in which new substances with new properties are formed.*

Chemical action may involve the combining of atoms of elementary substances to form compounds. Complex substances may be broken down into simpler compounds or into the elements which compose them. Compounds may react with other compounds or elements to form new and different compounds. *The science of* **chemistry** *is concerned specifically with the chemical changes of substances and with methods of controlling these changes.*

15. Chemical changes involve energy. Chemical changes are always accompanied by energy changes. Substances possess energy because of their composition and structure. This is a kind of potential energy which chemists generally refer to as *chemical energy.* The products of chemical changes are different in composition and structure from the original substances and thus will have larger or smaller amounts of chemical energy. If the amount is smaller, energy will be *liberated* during the change, usually in the form of *heat* and sometimes *light* or *electricity.* If the amount of chemical energy is larger, energy will be *absorbed* during the change.

Calcium carbide is produced in the intense heat of the electric furnace. Carbon disulfide is formed when hot sulfur vapor is passed over white-hot carbon in an electric furnace. Heat energy is absorbed continuously while such chemical actions are taking place. *Any chemical change which absorbs heat energy as it progresses is said to be* **endothermic.**

Some chemical changes are of importance because of their products. Others are carried out because of the energy which is released. In the burning of fuels, large amounts of heat energy are released rapidly. Many similar changes occur in nature, but take place so slowly that the evolution of heat is not noticed. *Any chemical change which liberates heat energy as it proceeds is said to be* **exothermic.** The majority of chemical changes which occur in nature are exothermic.

In the burning of fuels, light energy usually accompanies the release of heat. A photoflash lamp is designed to release a maximum amount of energy as light. The final proof of a chemical change rests with the analysis of the products. However, the evolution of heat and light offers evidence that chemical action is taking place.

The explosion of dynamite or gunpowder produces *mechanical energy.* Similarly, the explosion of gasoline vapor mixed with air in the cylinder of an automobile engine is an example of chemical action.

In the flashlight cell the zinc cylinder is acted on chemically when the cell is

Fig. 3-11. **The energy set free by chemical reactions is utilized to propel rockets to great heights.** (U. S. Air Force)

in use. *Electric energy* is produced by this action and indicates that the chemical change is taking place within the cell.

The *evolution of a gas* is often used as evidence that chemical action is taking place. We must be careful, however, to avoid mistaking the boiling of a liquid or the escaping of a dissolved gas from solution for chemical action.

In many cases an insoluble solid is formed by adding one solution to another. The *formation of an insoluble solid, called a* **precipitate**, may show that a chemical change has taken place as the solutions are mixed.

Chemists use several agents to bring about chemical changes or to control those which have already started. Some type of energy is often used.

1. *Heat energy.* A match is kindled by rubbing it over a rough surface to warm it by friction. By holding the lighted match to a piece of paper we may start the paper burning. The heat from the burning match is used to start this chemical change. It is, however, an exothermic action and we do not need to continue furnishing heat in order to keep the paper burning. Many chemical actions which occur in the preparation of foods are endothermic. Heat is supplied to keep these reactions going. As a rule, increasing the temperature hastens the speed of chemical changes. *Each increase in temperature of 10 C° approximately doubles the speed of chemical action.*

2. *Light energy.* The process of photosynthesis, by which green plants manufacture food, requires light energy. When we open the shutter of a camera for only a fraction of a second, light falls on the sensitive film. This starts a chemical change in the film which enables us to develop a picture.

3. *Electric energy.* If a direct current of electricity is passed through water containing a little acid, the water will be decomposed by the electric current into hydrogen and oxygen. We use this method of bringing about a chemical change when a storage battery is charged. Electricity is also used commercially to produce changes, as in the electric furnace. Electric energy is used in plating one metal on another, in the extracting of aluminum and other metals

from their ores, and in purifying some metals.

4. Solution in water. Baking powder is a mixture of two or more compounds. No chemical action occurs as long as the powder is kept *dry*. However, when water is added to baking powder, chemical action begins immediately and a gas is evolved. Many chemicals which do not react in the *dry* state begin to react as soon as they are dissolved in water.

5. Catalysis (kuh-*tal*-uh-sis). Some chemical changes may be brought about by *catalysts* (*kat*-uh-lists). These are specific agents which enable changes to occur that would otherwise be difficult or impractical to carry out. You will soon be preparing oxygen in the laboratory by heating a mixture of potassium chlorate and manganese dioxide. Without the manganese dioxide the preparation would have to be carried out at a higher temperature. Also, the gas would be produced more slowly. The manganese dioxide aids the action by its presence. It could be recovered in its original form at the conclusion of the experiment. *A catalyst is an agent which affects a chemical action without itself being permanently altered.*

Many chemical processes, such as the production of vegetable shortening, the manufacture of synthetic rubber, and the preparation of high-octane gasoline, depend on catalysis for their successful operation.

16. Nuclear changes. New substances are produced during a chemical change by the rearrangement of the atoms of the original substances. In a *nuclear change* new substances with new properties are also produced. *However, in a nuclear change, the new substances are formed by changes in the identity of the atoms themselves.*

In nature some nuclear changes take place spontaneously. Radium atoms disintegrate in successive stages, finally becoming lead. Scientists are able to bring about many important nuclear changes. The synthetic elements named in Chapter 2 are products of nuclear changes. Nuclear reactions will be discussed at greater length in Unit 13.

SUMMARY

Molecules are the smallest particles of a substance which normally exist in nature and retain the properties that characterize the substance in mass quantities. Gases consist of simple molecules. Some liquids and solids are known to be made up of simple molecules. Some crystalline solids do not have molecular structure, but are composed of ions. Molecules of elements are made up of one or more like atoms. Molecules of compounds are made up of two or more unlike atoms.

A formula is used by chemists to represent the composition of a substance. A molecular formula shows what atoms are present in each molecule, and the number of each. An empirical formula expresses the constituent elements in the compound and the relative number of atoms of each.

The particles of matter have motion and thus possess kinetic energy. Many indirect observations of molecular motion led to the formulation of the Kinetic Theory of Matter. Temperature is an indication of the average kinetic energy of the particles of matter. The molecules of gases are relatively far apart and are practically independent of each other. Particles of liquids are much more restricted but do experience random motion. Particles of solids are still more restricted in their motion and vibrate about fixed positions.

Changes in matter are of three kinds: *1.* physical; *2.* chemical; and *3.* nuclear. Physical changes do not alter the composition of matter. Chemical changes result in the formation of new substances with new properties. In nuclear changes new substances result from changes in the identity of atoms. If heat energy is released during a chemical change it is said to be exothermic. If heat energy is absorbed it is endothermic. The energy involved in chemical changes is usually in the form of heat, light, or electricity.

Heat, light, electricity, solution in water, and catalysts are agents which aid in producing and controlling chemical changes.

Nuclear changes result in the formation of new substances by changes in the identity of the atoms themselves. Such changes release tremendous amounts of energy.

TEST YOURSELF ON THESE TERMS

amorphous solid	empirical formula	kinetic theory
Ångström scale	endothermic	molecular formula
boiling point	equilibrium vapor	molecule
catalyst	pressure	monatomic molecule
chemical change	evaporation	nuclear change
condensation	exothermic	physical change
crystalline solid	formula	physical equilibrium
diatomic molecule	inert element	precipitate
diffusion	kinetic energy	symbol

QUESTIONS

Group A

1. Distinguish between an atom and a molecule.
2. What is the difference between a symbol and a formula?
3. (*a*) What gaseous elements have diatomic molecules? (*b*) How is each represented?
4. (*a*) What gaseous elements have monatomic molecules? (*b*) How is each represented?
5. How many atoms of each element are represented by the following formulas: sugar, $C_{12}H_{22}O_{11}$; sand, SiO_2; salt, $NaCl$; hydrogen peroxide, H_2O_2; soap, $C_{17}H_{35}COONa$?
6. What is the difference between a physical change and a chemical change?
7. What is the meaning of (*a*) molecular formula? (*b*) empirical formula?
8. How can a chemist usually increase the speed of a chemical change?
9. What information is given by the following: HCl, $2\,H_2SO_4$, $4\,CCl_4$, CO, Co, and $3\,H_2O$?

Group B

10. Explain the following: (*a*) solids have definite shape and definite volume; (*b*) liquids have definite volume but no definite shape; (*c*) gases have neither definite volume nor definite shape.

11. (*a*) How may we account for the pressure of a gas in a closed vessel? (*b*) Why does this pressure remain constant indefinitely under constant conditions?

12. Which of the following changes are physical and which are chemical? (*a*) burning coal; (*b*) tarnishing silver; (*c*) magnetizing steel; (*d*) exploding gunpowder; (*e*) boiling water; (*f*) melting shortening.

13. Which of the chemical changes listed in Question 12 are also exothermic?

14. Ammonia (density 0.77 g/l) and chlorine (density 3.21 g/l) have distinct but different odors. If equal quantities of the two gases are released in the laboratory under exactly similar conditions, which gas will first be detected by students on the far side of the laboratory? Explain.

15. Show by example how each of the following produces chemical changes: (*a*) heat energy; (*b*) light energy; (*c*) electric energy.

16. What evidence usually indicates chemical action?

17. Water standing in a covered flask experiences a drop in temperature of 10 C°. How is the liquid-vapor equilibrium disturbed? Explain.

18. Would you expect an equilibrium vapor pressure to be reached in the space above a liquid in an open container? Why?

19. (*a*) Using the curves of Fig. 3-10, determine the temperature at which water in an open vessel will boil when the atmospheric pressure is reduced to 600 mm. (*b*) What is the boiling point of alcohol at this pressure? (*c*) of ether?

20. While camping on top of Pike's Peak you boil a three-minute egg for breakfast. What is likely to be the condition of the egg when served? Explain.

SOME THINGS FOR YOU TO DO

1. Blow up a toy balloon until it is about half its maximum size. Hold it over a hot steam radiator or an electric hot plate. Explain the increase in size.

2. Look up the melting points of several substances which are known to be molecular as solids, and of several substances which are known to have no simple molecular structure as solids. What can you infer concerning the structure of the solid state of substances which exist as liquids or gases at ordinary temperatures?

3. Drop a small crystal of potassium permanganate into a tall cylinder full of water. Set the cylinder aside where it will not be disturbed. Examine daily for a week. Explain.

4. Pour some perfume into an evaporating dish placed at the rear of your classroom. How much time elapses before its odor can be detected in the front of the room? A perfume molecule may travel approximately 100 feet per second. How do you explain the delay?

CHECK YOUR PROGRESS IN CHEMISTRY

1. Name several substances that exist in all three states of matter.
2. List the common physical and chemical properties.
3. What do you understand by the term *law* in science?
4. Give two uses of the term *theory* which are common in chemistry.
5. Give some examples of kinetic and potential energy.
6. Why is it easy to convert units in the metric system?
7. What prefixes are commonly used for units in the metric system and what does each represent?
8. What metric unit would you use to represent each of the following: (*a*) the area of the cover of this book; (*b*) a family's daily milk supply; (*c*) your own weight; (*d*) the length of the eye of a darning needle; (*e*) the speed of a moving automobile?
9. What disadvantage would we encounter in the everyday use of the metric system in place of our English system of weights and measures?
10. Where is the metric system commonly used?
11. How many chemical elements are there?
12. Name the 10 most abundant elements in the earth's crust.
13. What two things does a chemical symbol represent?
14. If two or more elements have symbols beginning with the same letter, how do we distinguish them?
15. If a symbol has two letters, (*a*) what is always true of the first letter? (*b*) what is always true of the second letter?
16. State the Law of Definite Composition.
17. What is the significance of a molecule of sugar?
18. Explain the gradual disappearance of water from a saucer.
19. The formula for sulfuric acid is H_2SO_4. What information does it convey?
20. Give (*a*) two examples of gases which have monatomic molecules; (*b*) three examples of gases which have diatomic molecules.
21. Give examples of familiar (*a*) physical changes; (*b*) chemical changes.
22. Give three ways in which energy may bring about a chemical change.

CHALLENGING YOUR KNOWLEDGE

1. Give one reason why the metric system is not established by law for general use in this country.
2. (*a*) How many of the elements are metals? (*b*) How many are nonmetals? (Consult the Periodic Table in Chapter 5.)
3. What do you think is the reason why iron and sulfur unite in definite proportions to form iron sulfide?
4. How do you decide whether a certain change is physical or chemical?
5. Carbon dioxide has simple molecular structure in all three states. Make three drawings representing your idea of solid carbon dioxide (Dry Ice), liquid carbon dioxide, and gaseous carbon dioxide.
6. Assuming the relative masses of oxygen and hydrogen molecules to be 32 and 2 respectively, prove that the velocity of hydrogen molecules is 4 times the velocity of oxygen molecules under the same conditions.

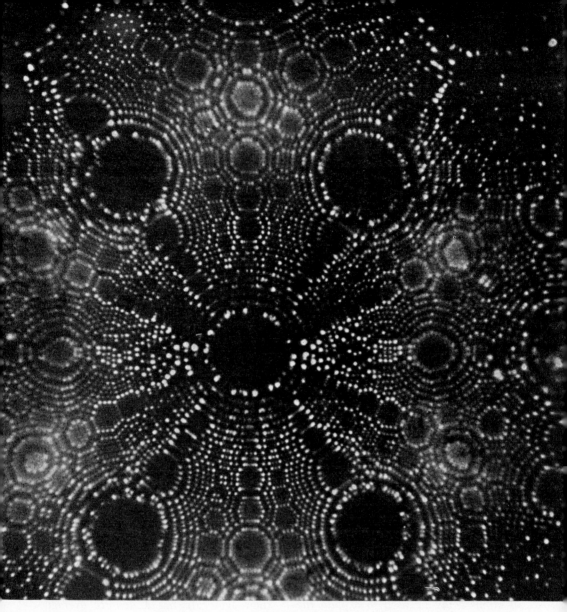

Unit 2 · THE ORGANIZATION OF CHEMISTRY

Atomic Theory and Atomic Structure
The Periodic Law
Chemical Bonds and Formula Writing

Chapter 4 · ATOMIC THEORY AND ATOMIC STRUCTURE

1. Dalton proposed the atomic theory. We have already described the ancient idea, first expressed by such Greek philosopers as Democritus, that matter is composed of very small ultimate particles. This concept of ultimate particles, or atoms of matter, was of little value to the development of science until the beginning of the nineteenth century. However, between 1803 and 1808 in England, John Dalton performed many chemical experiments, particularly with gases. He greatly extended the usefulness of man's ideas about atoms. Dalton was the first to realize that *the nature and properties of atoms could be used to explain the Law of Definite Composition of all substances* developed earlier by Proust *and the way and the proportions in which substances react with one another.* These are the fundamental ideas of Dalton's *atomic theory.* Since Dalton's day many discoveries have been made which give a more detailed picture of how the atomic theory explains the chemical phenomena in the world about us. However, Dalton's two basic ideas remain unchanged.

2. The modern atomic theory. The atomic theory today is described by several statements concerning the nature of matter. While no one has ever directly observed atoms, the chemical and physical properties of matter lead scientists to believe that the following statements about atoms and their properties are true.

1. All matter is made up of very small particles called *atoms.*

2. Atoms of the *same element* are *chemically alike;* atoms of *different elements* are *chemically different.*

3. While individual atoms of a given element may not all have the same mass, their aggregate has a *definite average mass* which is *characteristic of the element.*

4. While individual atoms of different elements may have nearly identical masses, the *aggregates of atoms of different elements* have *different average masses.*

5. Atoms are not subdivided in *chemical reactions.*

3. The structure of the atom. For almost three quarters of a century scientists have been accumulating evidence about the structure of atoms. Some of this evidence has come from the study of radioactive elements like radium and uranium. The cyclotron, the X-ray tube, and other modern electric devices for studying the structure of atoms have given additional information. At the present time scientists recognize that atoms are not simple indivisible particles. Instead, they are known to be composed of several different kinds of still smaller particles arranged in a rather complex way.

An atom consists of two main parts. *The positively charged central part is called the nucleus.* It is very small and very dense. Its diameter is about 10^{-13} cm, or 10^{-5} Å. This is about one one-hundred-thousandth of the diameter of the atom itself, since atoms range from 1 Å to 5 Å in diameter.

Negatively charged particles, called *electrons*, move about the nucleus in more or less definite regions called *shells* or *energy levels.* About 1913 the Danish scientist Niels Bohr (1885–) pictured the movement of electrons about the nucleus of an atom as similar to the rotation of the planets around the sun. However, the paths of the electrons are now known to be much less definite than the orbits of the planets. Electrons move about the nucleus of an atom much as bees move about in the area near their hive. Sometimes the electrons are near the nucleus, sometimes they are farther away. By this seemingly haphazard motion the electrons effectively occupy the relatively vast empty space around the nucleus. These electrons form an electronic field about the nucleus which gives the atom its volume and excludes other atoms. Each atom is electrically neutral, since the total positive charge of the nucleus is equaled by the total negative charge of the electrons in the shells or energy levels.

VOCABULARY

Atomic mass. The mass of an atom as expressed in atomic mass units of 1.660×10^{-24} g.

Atomic number. The number of protons in the nucleus of an atom.

Atomic weight. The average relative weight of the atoms of the naturally-occurring mixture of isotopes of an element based on the weight of the atoms of the isotope of carbon with mass number 12 as exactly 12.

Electron. A negatively-charged particle found in an atom.

Isotope. One of two or more forms of atoms with the same atomic number but with different atomic masses.

Mass number. The whole number closest to the atomic mass of an atom.

Neutron. A neutral particle found in the nucleus of an atom.

Nucleus. The positively-charged, dense central part of an atom.

Proton. A positively-charged particle found in the nucleus of an atom.

Shell. A region about the nucleus of an atom in which electrons may be considered to move.

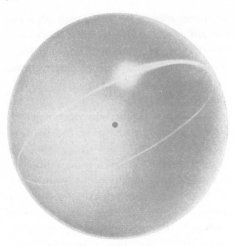

Fig. 4-1. **A hydrogen atom has a nucleus consisting of one proton. One electron moves about this nucleus in the K shell.**

4. The characteristics of electrons. *Electrons are negatively charged particles with a mass of* 9.108×10^{-28} *g.* This is 1/1837 of the mass of an atom of hydrogen—the atom of lowest mass. Each electron has one unit of negative electric charge. Electrons were discovered as a result of investigations of the flow of electricity through an evacuated glass tube, made by an English scientist, J. J. Thomson (1856–1940), in 1897.

The electron is a very small particle. Its diameter is believed to be about 2 $\times 10^{-12}$ cm or 2×10^{-4} Å. Regardless of the atom of which an electron is a part, all electrons are identical.

5. The nucleus of the atom. The nuclei of atoms of different elements are different. They always have different amounts of positive charge, and have different masses, although the difference in mass between atoms of two different elements is sometimes very slight. A nucleus is made up of two kinds of particles, *protons* and *neutrons.*

Protons are positively charged particles with a mass of 1.672×10^{-24} *g,* which is 1836/1837 of the mass of an atom of hydrogen. Thus, the proton accounts for most of the mass of a hydrogen atom because the hydrogen atom has a nucleus consisting of a single proton which has a single electron revolving about it. While a proton has much more mass than an electron, it is believed to be somewhat smaller. A proton has one unit of positive electric charge.

Protons were discovered in the early years of this century during the investigation of "positive rays" which appear when electricity flows through specially designed evacuated glass tubes. In a particular atom there are an equal number of protons and electrons. Since these have equal though opposite electric charges, each atom is electrically neutral.

Neutrons are neutral particles with a mass of 1.675×10^{-24} *g,* which is about the same mass as a proton. They have no electric charge. The English scientist, James C. Chadwick (1891–   ), discovered neutrons in 1932.

6. The hydrogen atom is the simplest atom. An atom of hydrogen consists of a nucleus composed of one proton, with one electron moving about it. This electron moves about the nucleus at a most probable distance corresponding to the innermost shell or lowest energy level which an electron can have. This shell or energy level is called the **K shell** or **1st energy level.** The sizes and distances between the particles of a hydrogen atom may be better understood if we picture the nucleus (a proton) as being the size of a pinhead, 0.25 centimeter in diameter. Comparatively speaking, the electron, which is somewhat larger, would revolve about the nucleus at an average distance of about 12 meters away. This electron does not follow any definite path about the nucleus but moves rapidly in a random fashion about the nucleus, effectively occupying the surrounding space.

7. The mass of an atom. Because atoms and the particles composing them have small masses which are inconvenient to express in gram units, scientists find it helpful to use an *atomic mass unit (a.m.u.)* of 1.660×10^{-24} g for expressing such masses. This unit is one-twelfth the mass of the most abundant type of carbon atom. The mass of a proton is 1.672×10^{-24} g. Dividing this by the value of the atomic mass unit, 1.660×10^{-24} g, the *atomic mass* of a proton is found to be 1.007 a.m.u. By the use of a mass spectrograph, the more accurate value of 1.007278 a.m.u. for the atomic mass of a proton is obtained. Similarly, the atomic mass of a neutron is 1.008666 a.m.u. and the atomic mass of an electron is 0.0005484 a.m.u. The *atomic mass of a particle or atom is the ratio between the mass of the particle or atom and the atomic mass unit, 1.660 $\times 10^{-24}$ g.*

The atomic mass of the hydrogen atom consisting of one proton and one electron is 1.007825 a.m.u. This is slightly less than the combined atomic masses of one proton and one electron. This difference in atomic mass is released as *binding energy* according to Einstein's equation $E = mc^2$ when a proton and an electron combine to form a hydrogen atom. Thus a hydrogen atom is more stable than a separated proton and electron, and energy must be used to separate the electron from the proton in a hydrogen atom. This is true of all atoms: the atomic mass of any atom is less than the combined atomic masses of its constituent particles by an amount of matter equivalent to the binding energy.

Frequently it is also convenient to use *"rounded-off"* integral (whole number) *values of atomic masses.* These are called *mass numbers.* Thus the mass number of an electron is zero, while the mass numbers of the proton, neutron, and hydrogen atom are each one. Since the atomic masses of the proton and neutron are both so nearly one, *the mass number of any atom equals the sum of the number of protons and neutrons in that atom.*

8. The atomic number of an atom. *The atomic number of an atom is the number of protons in the nucleus of that atom.* This is one aspect of the structure of an atom which definitely identifies an element. (The arrangement of electrons about the nucleus of a neutral atom also identifies an element.) For example, the element hydrogen consists of atoms with one proton in their nuclei. Their atomic number, therefore, is 1. Any nucleus having the atomic number 1 contains one proton, and is a hydrogen nucleus. As this is written there are 103 different elements with atomic numbers ranging from 1 to 103. It is possible to arrange the elements according to the order of increasing atomic number. This

PARTICLES IN AN ATOM

Name	Mass	Atomic Mass	Mass Number	Charge
Electron	9.108×10^{-28} g	0.0005484 a.m.u.	0	−1
Proton	1.672×10^{-24} g	1.007278 a.m.u..	1	+1
Neutron	1.675×10^{-24} g	1.008666 a.m.u.	1	0

simplifies the understanding of atomic structure. If the elements are arranged in this way, the nuclei of the atoms of one element differ from the nuclei of the atoms of the element preceding it by the addition of one proton.

9. The helium atom. The second element in order of complexity is helium. The atomic number of helium atoms is 2, indicating that helium nuclei contain two protons. The atomic mass of the helium atom is 4.002687 a.m.u.; thus, its mass number is 4. Since helium nuclei contain two protons and the mass number, 4, equals the sum of the number of protons and neutrons in the nuclei, each helium nucleus must also contain two neutrons. *The number of neutrons in the nucleus of any atom may be determined by subtracting the atomic number from the mass number* (for helium, $4 - 2 = 2$). Moving about the helium nucleus are two electrons, both in the K shell. These two electrons are all that can occupy this shell. Thus

Fig. 4-2. **A helium atom has a nucleus consisting of two protons and two neutrons. Two electrons move about this nucleus in the K shell.**

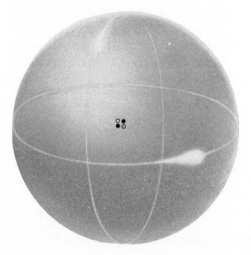

hydrogen and helium constitute a first series of elements. In this first series electrons enter the K shell one at a time until it is filled with two electrons.

10. The lithium atom. Lithium atoms have atomic number 3 and mass number 7. Thus a lithium nucleus will contain three protons and $(7 - 3 = 4)$ four neutrons. Surrounding the nucleus there must be three electrons, since the number of protons and the number of electrons in any uncharged atom is the same. Two of these three electrons move in the K shell. The third electron moves about the nucleus at a greater distance and with higher energy than the other two. It moves in the next larger shell or next higher energy level, which is called the **L shell** or **2nd energy level.** The K shell can contain no more than two electrons. When it reaches this maximum of two electrons, additional electrons must enter other shells at greater distances from the nucleus.

11. Other atoms of the second series. The element having atoms with atomic number 4 is beryllium. The mass number of a beryllium atom is 9. Beryllium nuclei are composed of four protons and five neutrons. The four electrons are distributed with two in the K shell and two in the L shell. Next in order of atomic structure are the elements boron, carbon, nitrogen, oxygen, fluorine, and neon. Each successive element has one additional proton and may have one or two additional neutrons in its nucleus. Each has one additional electron in the L shell. The element neon has a total of eight electrons in the L shell. Since eight is the maximum number of electrons which the L shell can contain, this element completes the second series.

The table opposite provides information about the structure of the atoms in the second series.

Sometimes scientists illustrate the structure of atoms by using electron-dot symbols. Such symbols usually show only the electrons in the outermost shell of an atom. We may write such symbols for the atoms of the first and second series as follows:

H·   He:

Li·   Be·   ·B·   ·C·

·N: ·O: :F: :Ne:

Unlike the K shell which has only one general region, or orbit, in which the two electrons move, the L shell has four possible electron orbits, grouped into two sublevels. These possible electron orbits are called *orbitals.* The L shell has one orbital in its lower energy sublevel and three orbitals in its higher energy sublevel. Each orbital may be unoccupied, may be occupied by one electron, or may be occupied by two electrons. An orbital is never occupied by more than two electrons. Two electrons which occupy the same orbital are called an *electron pair.* Neon has an outer shell of four electron pairs. This is an *octet of electrons.*

12. The atoms of the third series. The elements in the third series are

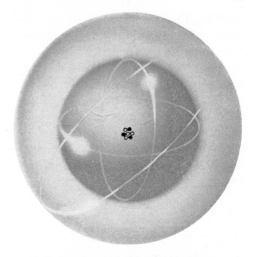

Fig. 4-3. **A lithium atom has a nucleus consisting of three protons and four neutrons. Two electrons are in the K shell and one is in the L shell. This is the first element in the second series.**

sodium, magnesium, aluminum, silicon, phosphorus, sulfur, chlorine, and argon. Each of the atoms of these elements has a complete K shell of two electrons and a complete L shell of eight electrons. Electron-dot symbols show the entry of successive electrons into the first *four* orbitals of the next higher energy level, the *M shell* or *3rd energy level*. Like the L shell, these first four orbitals of

STRUCTURE OF ATOMS IN THE SECOND SERIES

Name	Symbol	Atomic Number	Mass Number	Number of Protons	Number of Neutrons	Number of K Electrons	Number of L Electrons
Lithium	Li	3	7	3	4	2	1
Beryllium	Be	4	9	4	5	2	2
Boron	B	5	11	5	6	2	3
Carbon	C	6	12	6	6	2	4
Nitrogen	N	7	14	7	7	2	5
Oxygen	O	8	16	8	8	2	6
Fluorine	F	9	19	9	10	2	7
Neon	Ne	10	20	10	10	2	8

the M shell are grouped into two sublevels. The lower energy sublevel has one orbital while the higher energy sublevel has three orbitals. There is, however, a total of *nine* orbitals in the M shell. The five remaining M-shell orbitals comprise a third sublevel of still higher energy which is unoccupied in the atoms of the third series of elements. Argon, which completes the series, has an octet of electrons.

Na· Mg· ·Al· ·Si·

·P: ·S: :Cl: :Ar:

★ **13. The atoms of the fourth series.**
The atoms of the first two elements in the fourth series, potassium and calcium, have the same electron configuration or arrangement in the K, L, and M shells as argon does. Electron-dot symbols for these elements appear as follows:

K· 　　　　 Ca·

They show the entry of electrons into the single orbital which comprises the lowest energy sublevel of the **N** *shell or 4th energy level.* In the atoms of the next ten elements of this fourth series, successive electrons usually enter one of the five yet-unfilled orbitals of the highest energy sublevel of the M shell. This highest energy sublevel of the M shell has a higher energy than the lowest energy sublevel of the N shell. The distribution of M- and N-shell electrons in the most stable form of these atoms is given in the table below. Irregularities are caused by the slightly lower energy of the form actually most stable as compared with the form predicted by theory.

With the element zinc, the M shell is completely filled, and there are two electrons in the N shell. The remaining six elements in the fourth series, gallium, germanium, arsenic, selenium, bromine, and krypton, have completely filled K,

STRUCTURE OF ATOMS IN THE FOURTH SERIES

Name	Symbol	Atomic Number	Number of M Electrons	Number of N Electrons
Potassium	K	19	8	1
Calcium	Ca	20	8	2
Scandium	Sc	21	9	2
Titanium	Ti	22	10	2
Vanadium	V	23	11	2
Chromium	Cr	24	13	1
Manganese	Mn	25	13	2
Iron	Fe	26	14	2
Cobalt	Co	27	15	2
Nickel	Ni	28	16	2
Copper	Cu	29	18	1
Zinc	Zn	30	18	2
Gallium	Ga	31	18	3
Germanium	Ge	32	18	4
Arsenic	As	33	18	5
Selenium	Se	34	18	6
Bromine	Br	35	18	7
Krypton	Kr	36	18	8

L, and M shells. The N-shell electrons for the first two sublevels are shown in these electron-dot symbols:

$$\cdot\overset{\cdot}{G}a\cdot \quad \cdot\overset{\cdot}{G}e\cdot \quad \cdot\overset{\cdot}{A}s\colon$$

$$\cdot\overset{\cdot\cdot}{\underset{\cdot}{S}e}\colon \quad \colon\overset{\cdot\cdot}{\underset{\cdot}{B}r}\colon \quad \colon\overset{\cdot\cdot}{\underset{\cdot\cdot}{K}r}\colon$$

Krypton, the last member of the fourth series, has an octet of electrons in its N shell. The N shell, however, has two higher energy sublevels of 5 and 7 orbitals respectively, all of which are unoccupied in the atoms of the fourth series of elements.

★ **14. The atoms of the fifth series.** The fifth series of elements, like the fourth, consists of eighteen elements. The first two of these, rubidium and strontium, have inner shells like krypton and successive electrons in the lowest energy sublevel of the *O shell or 5th energy level.* Their K, L, M, and N shell electron configuration is the same as that of krypton.

$$Rb\cdot \quad S\overset{\cdot\cdot}{r}\cdot$$

The atoms of the next ten elements have successive electrons usually entering the next five orbitals (third sublevel) of the N shell, since this is the group of orbitals with the next higher energy. In atoms of the fifth series, there are still seven unoccupied orbitals (fourth sublevel) of the N shell.

The atoms of the element cadmium have completely filled K, L, and M shells, 18 electrons in the N shell (three sublevels filled), and 2 electrons in the O shell. The atoms of the remaining six elements of the fifth series, indium, tin, antimony, tellurium, iodine, and xenon, have K, L, M, and N shells like cadmium, but successive electrons enter the second sublevel orbitals of the O shell having the next higher energy.

$$\cdot\overset{\cdot}{I}n\cdot \quad \cdot\overset{\cdot}{S}n\cdot \quad \cdot\overset{\cdot}{S}b\colon$$

$$\cdot\overset{\cdot\cdot}{\underset{\cdot}{T}e}\colon \quad \colon\overset{\cdot\cdot}{\underset{\cdot}{I}}\colon \quad \colon\overset{\cdot\cdot}{\underset{\cdot\cdot}{X}e}\colon$$

STRUCTURE OF ATOMS IN THE FIFTH SERIES

Name	Symbol	Atomic Number	Number of N Electrons	Number of O Electrons
Rubidium	Rb	37	8	1
Strontium	Sr	38	8	2
Yttrium	Y	39	9	2
Zirconium	Zr	40	10	2
Niobium	Nb	41	12	1
Molybdenum	Mo	42	13	1
Technetium	Tc	43	14	1
Ruthenium	Ru	44	15	1
Rhodium	Rh	45	16	1
Palladium	Pd	46	18	0
Silver	Ag	47	18	1
Cadmium	Cd	48	18	2
Indium	In	49	18	3
Tin	Sn	50	18	4
Antimony	Sb	51	18	5
Tellurium	Te	52	18	6
Iodine	I	53	18	7
Xenon	Xe	54	18	8

Thus the entry of electrons into orbitals of two different shells proceeds in the fifth series of atoms in a manner similar to that of the fourth series. Xenon, the last member of the series, has an octet of electrons in its O shell, and 9 of the 16 orbitals of the N shell filled.

★ **15. The atoms of the sixth series.** The sixth series of atoms is much longer than the others. It consists of thirty-two elements. The atoms of the first two, cesium and barium, have inner shells like xenon and successive electrons in the lowest sublevel orbital of the P shell.

Cs·   Ba·

In the atoms of the next fourteen elements of the sixth series, successive electrons usually enter the highest energy group of seven orbitals (fourth sublevel) of the N shell. In atoms of the element ytterbium, the N shell has all of its 16 orbitals filled with 32 electrons.

The atoms of the next ten elements of the sixth series have successive electrons entering the group of 5 orbitals (third sublevel) of the O shell with next higher energy.

The atoms of the remaining six elements of this series, thallium, lead, bismuth, polonium, astatine, and radon, have 2 electrons in the K shell, 8 in the L shell, 18 in the M shell, 32 in the N shell, and 18 in the O shell. The **P shell, or 6th energy level** electrons are shown in these electron-dot symbols:

·Tl·   ·Pb·   ·Bi:

·Po: :At: :Rn:

Radon, the last member of the sixth series, has an octet of electrons in its P shell and nine orbitals (three sublevels) of the O shell filled.

★ **16. The atoms of the seventh series.** The seventh series of elements is an incomplete series of which only 17 elements are known. The arrangement of electrons in the O, P, and Q shells is believed to be as shown in the table on the opposite page.

★ **17. A summary of the pattern of atomic structure.** From a study of the

ATOMIC STRUCTURE OF THE LANTHANIDE SERIES

Name	Symbol	Atomic Number	Number of N Electrons	Number of O Electrons	Number of P Electrons
Lanthanum	La	57	18	9	2
Cerium	Ce	58	20	8	2
Praseodymium	Pr	59	21	8	2
Neodymium	Nd	60	22	8	2
Promethium	Pm	61	23	8	2
Samarium	Sm	62	24	8	2
Europium	Eu	63	25	8	2
Gadolinium	Gd	64	25	9	2
Terbium	Tb	65	27	8	2
Dysprosium	Dy	66	28	8	2
Holmium	Ho	67	29	8	2
Erbium	Er	68	30	8	2
Thulium	Tm	69	31	8	2
Ytterbium	Yb	70	32	8	2

STRUCTURE OF SOME ATOMS IN THE SIXTH SERIES

Name	Symbol	Atomic Number	Number of O Electrons	Number of P Electrons
Lutetium	Lu	71	9	2
Hafnium	Hf	72	10	2
Tantalum	Ta	73	11	2
Tungsten	W	74	12	2
Rhenium	Re	75	13	2
Osmium	Os	76	14	2
Iridium	Ir	77	15	2
Platinum	Pt	78	16	2
Gold	Au	79	18	1
Mercury	Hg	80	18	2

configuration of electrons in the atoms of the chemical elements, it is apparent that the electron shells are complex, having a varying number of sublevels of different energy. Furthermore, the lowest energy sublevel of a large shell has a lower energy than some of the higher energy sublevels of the next smaller shell. This produces an overlapping of shells and determines the order of entry of successive electrons into these sublevels. While there are some elements which appear to be exceptions, there is a general pattern to atomic structure.

There are seven shells or energy levels,

STRUCTURE OF ATOMS IN THE SEVENTH SERIES

Name	Symbol	Atomic Number	Number of O Electrons	Number of P Electrons	Number of Q Electrons
Francium	Fr	87	18	8	1
Radium	Ra	88	18	8	2
Actinium	Ac	89	18	9	2
Thorium	Th	90	18	10	2
Protactinium	Pa	91	20	9	2
Uranium	U	92	21	9	2
Neptunium	Np	93	23	8	2
Plutonium	Pu	94	24	8	2
Americium	Am	95	24	9	2
Curium	Cm	96	25	9	2
Berkelium	Bk	97	27	8	2
Californium	Cf	98	28	8	2
Einsteinium	Es	99	29	8	2
Fermium	Fm	100	30	8	2
Mendelevium	Md	101	31	8	2
		102	32	8	2
Lawrencium	Lw	103	32	9	2

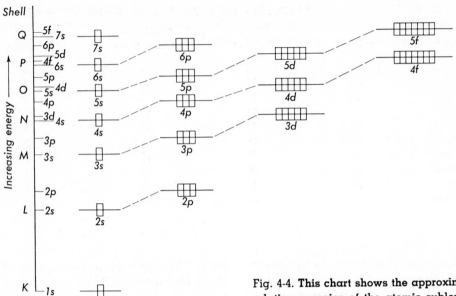

Fig. 4-4. **This chart shows the approximate relative energies of the atomic sublevels.**

designated by letters from K to Q or by numbers from 1 to 7. The K shell or 1st energy level has *one* sublevel, the L shell or 2nd energy level has *two* sublevels, the M shell or 3rd energy level has *three* sublevels, and so on. The sublevels are designated, in order, the *s* sublevel, the *p* sublevel, the *d* sublevel, the *f* sublevel, the *g* sublevel, the *h* sublevel, etc. The first four of these symbols were given by spectroscopists studying atomic structure who described the various series of spectral lines emitted by the elements as "sharp," "principal," "diffuse," and "fundamental." Thus the K shell has an *s* sublevel; the L shell has

an *s* sublevel and a *p* sublevel; the M shell has an *s* sublevel, a *p* sublevel, and a *d* sublevel; and the N shell has an *s* sublevel, a *p* sublevel, a *d* sublevel, and an *f* sublevel. An *s* sublevel has 1 orbital and can be occupied by a maximum of 2 electrons. A *p* sublevel has 3 orbitals and can be occupied by a maximum of 6 electrons. A *d* sublevel has 5 orbitals and can be occupied by a maximum of 10 electrons. An *f* sublevel has 7 orbitals and can be occupied by a maximum of 14 electrons. The following chart summarizes these conditions.

It has already been pointed out that there is some overlapping of sublevels of

MAXIMUM NUMBER OF ELECTRONS IN SHELLS

Shells or Energy Levels	Sublevels				Total
	s (1 orbital)	*p* (3 orbitals)	*d* (5 orbitals)	*f* (7 orbitals)	
K or 1	2				2
L or 2	2	6			8
M or 3	2	6	10		18
N or 4	2	6	10	14	32

different shells with regard to energy requirements. Thus the 4s sublevel (the s sublevel in the 4th energy level) has a lower energy requirement than the 3d sublevel, and is filled with electrons first. Potassium and calcium have 1 and 2 electrons respectively in the 4th energy level before the 3rd energy level fills from 8 to 18 electrons in the elements from scandium to zinc. Figure 4-4 shows the approximate relative energy values for the various sublevels. A complete tabulation showing the electron configurations in the atoms of the elements is in the Appendix, Table 4.

18. Isotopes of the elements. In the statements of the modern atomic theory, it was recognized that individual atoms of a given element might not all have the same mass, yet their aggregate has a definite average mass which is characteristic of the element. Dalton assumed that all the atoms of a given element were identical in all respects—in mass, in size, and in chemical properties. About 1916 two chemists, T. W. Richards (1868–1928) and Frederick Soddy (1877–1956), working independently, were investigating samples of the el-

ement lead from radioactive materials. They found that the average atomic mass of these samples did not correspond with the average atomic mass of lead taken from mines. They concluded, after careful analysis, that *not all atoms of a given element have the same mass.*

All elements exist in several forms having different masses. They may be of natural occurrence or may be artificially prepared. *These forms of the atoms of a single element do not differ in chemical properties, but do differ slightly in atomic mass.* Such forms of an element are called *isotopes*. The atoms of the isotopes of a particular element have the same number of protons and electrons; their nuclei differ because they contain different numbers of neutrons.

There are three known isotopes of hydrogen. The commonest isotope is the hydrogen atom which consists of one proton and one electron. A second isotope is present in naturally occurring hydrogen to the extent of one part in 6900. Its atoms consist of one proton and one neutron in the nucleus, with one electron in the K shell. The atoms of this isotope have atomic number 1 because

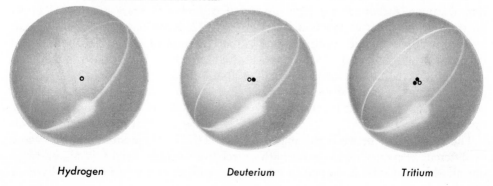

Fig. 4-5. The three isotopes: hydrogen, deuterium, and tritium. Notice that the only structural difference between them is the number of neutrons in the nucleus of each atom.

Hydrogen   *Deuterium*   *Tritium*

there is one proton in their nuclei, but they have mass number 2 since their nuclei contain one proton and one neutron. This isotope of hydrogen is called *deuterium* (dyoo-*teer*-ee-um). The third isotope of hydrogen is called *tritium* (*trit*-ee-um). The atoms of this isotope have a nucleus containing one proton and two neutrons. The single electron is in the K shell. Tritium atoms have atomic number 1, characteristic of hydrogen, but they have mass number 3.

19. Atomic weights are relative average weights. So far, the masses of individual atoms have been indicated on an arbitrary scale of atomic mass units. This scale was set up using one-twelfth of the mass of the most abundant carbon isotope as one atomic mass unit. On this scale, hydrogen atoms have a mass of 1.007825 a.m.u. Deuterium atoms have a mass of 2.014102 a.m.u. The most abundant isotope of carbon has a mass of exactly 12 a.m.u., since this is the isotope used in defining the atomic mass unit. The most abundant oxygen isotope has a mass of 15.99491 a.m.u. Other examples we might give are one isotope of sulfur, 31.97206 a.m.u., and an isotope of silver, 107.9301 a.m.u. Note that these values are not the actual masses of these atoms, but they do give the *relationship* between the masses of these atoms. They are *relative masses*. We observe from these relative masses that common carbon atoms have approximately 12 times as much mass as hydrogen atoms. Some sulfur atoms have about twice as much mass as oxygen atoms. Certain silver atoms have almost 108 times as much mass as hydrogen atoms and 9 times as much mass as carbon atoms.

The relationship between the masses of different elements which react with one another is of extreme importance to the chemist. It enables him to predict the quantities of materials which will be involved in chemical reactions. However, the actual masses of atoms are very small. The most common oxygen isotope, for example, has a mass of 2.65×10^{-23} g. The actual mass of a hydrogen atom is 1.67×10^{-24} g. It would be difficult for a scientist to use such inconveniently small numbers in calculations!

Long before chemists were able to calculate the actual mass of an atom, or even set up a scale of atomic mass units, they had worked out a system of *relative weights* for the atoms, based solely on the results of chemical reactions. This system is much simpler than using the actual masses, and for most of the chemist's work it is sufficient. Oxygen was the original standard on which the atomic weight scale was based. However, in 1961, the world organizations of chemists and physicists, in order to unify slightly different scales, redefined both the atomic mass and atomic weight scales in terms of the carbon isotope of mass number 12. This isotope is defined as having a mass of exactly 12 a.m.u. and all other atomic masses and atomic weights are evaluated to this standard. Thus the *atomic weight of an element is the average relative weight of the atoms of the naturally occurring mixture of isotopes of the element based on the weight of the atoms of the isotope of carbon with mass number 12 as exactly* 12. Since naturally occurring carbon consists of 98.89% carbon-12 and 1.11% carbon-13, 13.00336 a.m.u., its atomic weight is 12.01115.

Then the relative average weight of hydrogen atoms, which actually is about $\frac{1}{12}$ as much as that of carbon atoms will be 1.00797. Magnesium atoms, whose relative average weight is about twice as much as carbon atoms, will have an atomic weight of 24.312. In the same way the relative average weights of the atoms of the other elements are compared with the weight of carbon atoms with mass number 12, and relative weight values determined.

The existence of isotopes explains why so many atomic weights are nearly, but not exactly, whole numbers. The atomic weight of hydrogen is 1.00797. This is the average of one deuterium atom (atomic mass, 2.014102 a.m.u.) to every 6900 hydrogen atoms (atomic mass, 1.007825 a.m.u.). Similarly, there are two isotopes of chlorine. One has an atomic mass of 34.9609 a.m.u., the other an atomic mass of 36.9658 a.m.u. They are mixed, however, in such proportion that the atomic weight is 35.453. In naturally occurring compounds the percentage of each isotope of a given element is nearly always the same. Only through this fortunate circumstance is the average relative weight of the isotopic forms (the atomic weight) a useful quantity. Minor variations are noted in the Table of Atomic Weights inside the back cover.

20. The determination of atomic weights. For many years chemists carried out very precise analyses of carefully prepared chemical compounds to determine the relative weights of elements which combined in order to establish the table of atomic weights. At the present time, the values given in the Table of Atomic Weights, on the inside of the back cover of this book, are about the most precise which chemical analysis can yield. As a result, very little of this type of research is now being conducted. A newer, more accurate method of determining and verifying atomic weights has been developed by nuclear research. This method consists of adding the weights of the individual particles which make up the isotopes of the element whose weight is being calculated. A correction in this total weight must be made for the binding energy of each isotope. Since the relative percentage of the various isotopes in the naturally occurring elements is known, an atomic weight may be calculated. Such calculated atomic weights are in many cases more accurate than can be determined by the best chemical analysis. This method is now being used to verify the accuracy of chemical atomic weight determinations.

The Table of Atomic Weights on the inside of the back cover of this book includes the most recent accurate figures. They are still revised occasionally. You need not memorize them. The approximate atomic weights given on the inside of the front cover are sufficiently accurate for use in solving problems in high school chemistry. Your instructor may wish you to memorize some or all of these approximate values. For accurate chemical analysis, the precise atomic weights must always be used.

SUMMARY

The modern atomic theory states that: *1.* all matter is made up of very small particles called atoms; *2.* atoms of the same element are chemically alike; atoms of different elements are chemically different; *3.* while individual atoms of a given element may not all have the same mass, their aggregate has a definite average mass which is characteristic of the element; *4.* while individual atoms of different elements may have nearly identical masses, the aggregates of atoms of different elements have different average masses; *5.* atoms are not subdivided in chemical reactions.

Atoms are composed of positively charged particles—protons; negatively charged particles—electrons; and neutral particles—neutrons. Protons and neutrons are found in the central nucleus of an atom. Electrons move about this nucleus in regions called shells or energy levels.

The atomic mass of an atom is the ratio between the mass of the atom and the atomic mass unit, 1.660×10^{-24} g. The "rounded-off" integral value of the atomic mass is the mass number, which is also the total number of protons and neutrons in the nucleus. The atomic number of an atom is the number of protons in its nucleus.

The atoms of all the elements may be classified according to the order in which the shells or energy levels become filled with electrons. Isotopes are forms of the same element, with the same chemical properties, but with atoms which differ slightly in mass.

The atomic weight of an element is the average relative weight of the atoms of the naturally occurring mixture of isotopes of an element based on the weight of the atoms of the isotope of carbon with mass number 12 as exactly 12.

TEST YOURSELF ON THESE TERMS

atom	electron	neutron
atomic mass	electron configuration	nucleus
atomic mass unit	electron-dot symbol	octet
atomic number	electron pair	orbital
atomic theory	energy level	proton
atomic weight	isotope	shell
deuterium	mass number	tritium

QUESTIONS

Group A

1. What is the modern atomic theory?
2. (*a*) What are the main parts of an atom? (*b*) What particles are found in each part? (*c*) Describe each type of particle.
3. How does the size of the nucleus of an atom compare with the size of an atom?
4. What is a shell or energy level?
5. Describe the movement of electrons about the nucleus of an atom.
6. Describe a hydrogen atom.
7. (*a*) What is an atomic mass unit? (*b*) If you know the number and kinds of particles in an atom, how can you calculate its mass number?
8. What is the atomic number of an atom?
9. How do you calculate the number of neutrons in the nucleus of an atom?
10. An atomic nucleus contains 6 protons and 6 neutrons. About the nucleus move 6 electrons, 2 in the K shell and 4 in the L shell. (*a*) What is the atomic number of this atom? (*b*) What is its mass number? (*c*) What is the name of the atom?
11. How are shells or energy levels designated?
12. (*a*) What is an orbital? (*b*) How many electrons may occupy an orbital? (*c*) What is an electron pair?

13. What are isotopes?
14. What is the atomic weight of an element?
15. What element is the standard for the atomic weight scale?
16. From the Table of Atomic Weights given inside the back cover of this book, find the atomic numbers and atomic weights of: (*a*) silver; (*b*) gold; (*c*) copper; (*d*) sulfur; (*e*) uranium.

Group B

17. What did Dalton believe could be explained by knowledge of the nature and properties of atoms?
18. If you arrange the elements in order of increasing atomic number, how do successive elements differ in: (*a*) number of protons? (*b*) number of electrons? (*c*) number of neutrons?
19. How many shells are partially or fully occupied in the mendelevium atom?
20. Describe the electron configurations of the elements in the second series.
21. Draw electron-dot symbols for the elements in the third series.
22. Why do the fourth and fifth series of elements contain 18 elements, rather than 8 as in the second and third series?
23. The element bromine exists as two isotopes, Br-79 and Br-81. Its atomic weight is 80. What must be the approximate proportion of these two isotopes to give this average weight?
24. By means of diagrams show the difference between the third isotope of hydrogen, tritium, and an isotope of helium with mass number of 3.
25. What is the atomic weight of an element whose atoms are approximately 12 times as heavy as those of carbon? Consult the Table of Atomic Weights inside the back cover to find which element this is.
★ 26. (*a*) What designations are given to the sublevels? (*b*) How many orbitals are there in each type of sublevel? (*c*) How many electrons are there in a completed sublevel of each type?
27. In what two ways may atomic weights be determined?
28. Why does the chemist use a system of relative atomic weights rather than the actual masses of atoms?
★ 29. How many orbitals are there in: (*a*) the K shell? (*b*) the L shell? (*c*) the M shell? (*d*) the N shell? (*e*) the O shell?
★ 30. Which M-shell sublevels are filled: (*a*) in the element argon? (*b*) in the element krypton?

SOME THINGS FOR YOU TO DO

1. Look up the accounts of the discovery of protons, electrons, and neutrons, and describe the experiments which resulted in these discoveries to the class.
2. From a table of isotopes in a handbook, find the number and mass of the naturally-occurring stable isotopes of: (*a*) carbon; (*b*) sulfur; (*c*) iron; (*d*) copper; (*e*) silver.
3. Make a model of a carbon atom using different colored beads for protons, neutrons, and electrons. Use stiff wire, such as from coat hangers, to represent orbitals and support the electrons.

Chapter 5 • THE PERIODIC LAW

1. Classification makes the study of chemical elements easier. If you had to study the properties of each of the 103 chemical elements to have even an elementary knowledge of chemistry, the task would be great. However, if some elements had similar properties, and if they could be grouped together, it would not be too difficult to remember the distinguishing properties of the group. It might even be possible to remember some of the variations in properties among the members of the group, if the variations were to occur fairly regularly.

During the late eighteenth and early nineteenth centuries, chemists began to identify certain substances as chemical elements. They also recognized that there were similarities in the properties of some of these elements. They discovered that sodium and potassium were soft, silvery metals. They found that calcium, barium, and strontium could be prepared as elements by similar chemical changes; that sulfur, selenium, and tellurium formed similar chemical compounds; and that chlorine, bromine, and iodine were colored nonmetallic

elements. But such isolated discoveries did not offer much promise of classifying all the known chemical elements into any unifying system.

2. Early attempts to classify elements. About 1800, chemists began to determine the atomic weights of some elements with fair accuracy. Attempts were soon made to classify the elements on this basis. As early as 1817, Johann Wolfgang Döbereiner (*doh*-ber-eye-ner) (1780–1849), made an interesting observation. He noticed that the atomic weight of bromine was almost equal to the average of the atomic weights of iodine and chlorine.

$$(127 + 35.5) \div 2 = 82, \text{ average}$$

(The atomic weight of bromine is 79.9.) He also observed that the atomic weight of strontium, 87.6, was close to the average of the atomic weights of calcium and barium.

$$(40 + 137) \div 2 = 88$$

In a like way he found that the atomic weight of selenium, 79.0, was not too different from the average of the atomic weights of sulfur and tellurium.

$$(32 + 127.6) \div 2 = 80.$$

Such groups of elements were called **triads.**

In 1864 John A. Newlands (1838–1898) arranged all the known elements in the order of their atomic weights. He then divided them into series of seven elements each. He made this division because the eighth element was found to have chemical properties similar to the first element of the preceding series. Hence, he made that element the first one in a second series. He talked incessantly to the chemists of his time about his *law of octaves,* but they merely laughed at his ideas. They made so much fun of him that he lost interest and stopped his efforts to classify elements.

Lothar Meyer (1830–1895) plotted a graph showing an attempt to group elements according to atomic weights.

3. Mendeleyev's Periodic Table. By 1869 Dmitri Mendeleyev (men-deh-*lay*-eff) (1843–1907)—the name is spelled in a variety of ways—had worked out a *Periodic Table of the Elements.* In this table the different elements were arranged in the order of their atomic weights. In Mendeleyev's system of classification, the first two series or periods contained *seven elements* each. The next three periods contained *seventeen elements* each. The Periodic Tables we use today are largely based on the pioneer work done by Mendeleyev.

When Mendeleyev first prepared his Periodic Table, he realized that all the elements were probably not yet discovered. For example, scandium, gallium, and germanium were unknown in Mendeleyev's day. Mendeleyev carefully studied the properties of those elements he knew. From this study he learned where to leave gaps in his table for those to be discovered later, and predicted that new elements would be discovered to fit these gaps. He also

VOCABULARY

Electron affinity. The energy released when an electron is added to a neutral atom.

Group. A vertical column of elements in the Periodic Table.

Ion. An atom or a group of atoms with an unbalanced electrostatic charge.

Ionization energy. The energy required to remove an electron from an atom.

Period. A horizontal row of elements in the Periodic Table.

Periodic Table. A tabular arrangement of the chemical elements based on their atomic structure.

Rare earth element. An element which differs in electronic configuration from that of next lower or higher atomic number only in the number of electrons in the second-from-outermost shell.

Transition element. An element which differs in electronic configuration from that of next lower or higher atomic number only in the number of electrons in the next-to-the-outermost shell.

predicted the properties of these new elements. His predictions were later found to be quite accurate when compared with the actual properties of the elements.

Mendeleyev noticed, just as Newlands had, that the chemical properties of the elements recur at definite intervals. Therefore, he concluded that the chemical properties of elements are periodic functions of their atomic weights.

In Mendeleyev's table, the first two periods, or series, had seven elements before there was a recurrence of properties. In the third period, Mendeleyev found there were seventeen elements before there was recurrence of properties. Periods 4 and 5 were long series, too. The discovery of the inert gases, neon, argon, krypton, and xenon, by Sir William Ramsay (1852–1916) during the 1890's, together with the earlier discovered element, helium, added an additional element to each period in Mendeleyev's table.

Fig. 5-1. **Dmitri Mendeleyev, a Russian chemist, worked out the first Periodic Table of the Chemical Elements.** (Science Service)

4. Moseley determines atomic numbers. About 45 years after Mendeleyev's work on the Periodic Table, another important discovery was made which gave further aid to the problem of classifying the elements. In Chapter 4 it was stated that the atomic number of an element indicates the number of protons in the nucleus of its atoms. Henry Gwyn-Jeffreys Moseley (1887–1915), a brilliant young English scientist, used X rays to determine the atomic numbers of the elements.

X rays are radiations similar to light or radio waves except that they have higher frequencies and shorter wavelengths. X rays are produced when high-speed electrons strike the metal target in an evacuated tube. Moseley found that the wavelengths of the X rays produced in such tubes depend on the kind of metal used as a target. Therefore, he used as targets various metals ranging in atomic weight from aluminum to gold. He found that the wavelengths of X rays became shorter as he used elements which have more of what are now recognized as protons in their nuclei. The higher the atomic number of an element, the shorter the wavelength of X rays will be when that element is used as a target within the X-ray tube.

Moseley found in some cases an unusual variation in the wavelengths of X rays between two successive elements. The variation was twice as great as his calculations justified. He concluded that in such cases an element was missing from the Periodic Table. Several elements have since been discovered which fill the gaps that Moseley had indicated.

5. The Periodic Law. When the elements in a Periodic Table are placed in the order of their atomic numbers instead of in the order of their atomic weights, some of the problems of arrangement disappear. Arranged according to increasing atomic weights, potassium precedes argon. Yet, when arranged according to properties in the table, potassium follows argon. This is in agreement with the atomic numbers, argon 18, and potassium 19. A similar case is that of tellurium (atomic number 52) and iodine (atomic number 53).

As stated in Section 3, Mendeleyev concluded that the chemical properties of elements are periodic functions of their atomic weights. Today with evidence that atomic numbers are better criteria for establishing the order of the elements Mendeleyev's conclusion is restated as the **Periodic Law**: *The chemical properties of elements are periodic functions of their atomic numbers.* In other words, the chemical properties of elements recur after certain intervals, provided the elements are arranged in a table in the order of their atomic numbers.

6. **The arrangement of the modern Periodic Table.** The modern Periodic Table is shown on pages 72–73. Frequent reference to these pages as you study this section will help you to understand the Periodic Table and its importance in chemistry.

Each element is assigned a separate block in the table. In the center of the block is the chemical symbol for the element. Below the symbol is the atomic number of the element. Above the symbol is the atomic weight. To the right of each symbol are numbers which indicate the distribution of electrons in the shells of the atoms of this element. A horizontal row of blocks on the table is called a *period* or *series.* A vertical column is called a *group* or *family.*

Hydrogen, atomic number 1, is placed at the top of the table by itself because of its many unique properties. It is in the

Fig. 5-2. **Henry Gwyn-Jeffreys Moseley, an English physicist, used X-rays to determine the atomic numbers of the elements.** (Brown Brothers)

first column at the left of the table because it has 1 electron in its outermost shell. Helium, atomic number 2, is at the top of the extreme right-hand column as the simplest member of the group of elements known as the *inert gases.* Note that helium has 2 electrons in its K shell, and that with these 2 electrons, the K shell is complete. Hydrogen and helium comprise the first period of elements.

The second period consists of eight elements: *lithium*, a soft, silvery, active metal, whose atoms have 1 electron in their outer shell, the L shell; *beryllium*, a silvery metal, less active than lithium, whose atoms have 2 electrons in their L shell; *boron*, a black solid with few metallic properties, whose atoms have 3 electrons in their L shell; *carbon*, a solid element with very distinctive chemical properties intermediate between those of metals and nonmetals, 4 electrons in the L shell; *nitrogen*, a colorless gas,

PERIODIC TABLE

METALS

TRANSITION ELEMENTS

PERIOD

	I	II								
1	1.00797 **H** 1 (1)									
2	6.939 **Li** 3 (2,1)	9.0122 **Be** 4 (2,2)								
3	22.9898 **Na** 11 (2,8,1)	24.312 **Mg** 12 (2,8,2)								
4	39.102 **K** 19 (2,8,8,1)	40.08 **Ca** 20 (2,8,8,2)	44.956 **Sc** 21 (2,8,9,2)	47.90 **Ti** 22 (2,8,10,2)	50.942 **V** 23 (2,8,11,2)	51.996 **Cr** 24 (2,8,13,1)	54.9380 **Mn** 25 (2,8,13,2)	55.847 **Fe** 26 (2,8,14,2)	58.9332 **Co** 27 (2,8,15,2)	
5	85.47 **Rb** 37 (2,8,18,8,1)	87.62 **Sr** 38 (2,8,18,8,2)	88.905 **Y** 39 (2,8,18,9,2)	91.22 **Zr** 40 (2,8,18,10,2)	92.906 **Nb** 41 (2,8,18,12,1)	95.94 **Mo** 42 (2,8,18,13,1)	[99*] **Tc** 43 (2,8,18,13,2)	101.07 **Ru** 44 (2,8,18,15,1)	102.905 **Rh** 45 (2,8,18,16,1)	
6	132.905 **Cs** 55 (2,8,18,18,8,1)	137.34 **Ba** 56 (2,8,18,18,8,2)	Lanthanide Series 174.97 **Lu** 71 (2,8,18,32,9,2)	178.49 **Hf** 72 (2,8,18,32,10,2)	180.948 **Ta** 73 (2,8,18,32,11,2)	183.85 **W** 74 (2,8,18,32,12,2)	186.2 **Re** 75 (2,8,18,32,13,2)	190.2 **Os** 76 (2,8,18,32,14,2)	192.2 **Ir** 77 (2,8,18,32,15,2)	
7	[223] **Fr** 87 (2,8,18,32,18,8,1)	[226] **Ra** 88 (2,8,18,32,18,8,2)	Actinide Series [257] **Lw** 103 (2,8,18,32,32,9,2)							

Lanthanide Series

138.91 **La** 57 (2,8,18,18,9,2)	140.12 **Ce** 58 (2,8,18,20,8,2)	140.907 **Pr** 59 (2,8,18,21,8,2)	144.24 **Nd** 60 (2,8,18,22,8,2)	[147*] **Pm** 61 (2,8,18,23,8,2)	150.35 **Sm** 62 (2,8,18,24,8,2)	151.96 **Eu** 63 (2,8,18,25,8,2)

Actinide Series

[227] **Ac** 89 (2,8,18,32,18,9,2)	232.038 **Th** 90 (2,8,18,32,18,10,2)	[231] **Pa** 91 (2,8,18,32,20,9,2)	238.03 **U** 92 (2,8,18,32,21,9,2)	[237] **Np** 93 (2,8,18,32,23,8,2)	[242] **Pu** 94 (2,8,18,32,24,8,2)	[243] **Am** 95 (2,8,18,32,24,9,2)

INERT GASES

VIII

| 4.0026 He 2 | 2 8 |

NONMETALS

III	IV	V	VI	VII	VIII
10.811 **B** 5 (2,3)	12.01115 **C** 6 (2,4)	14.0067 **N** 7 (2,5)	15.9994 **O** 8 (2,6)	18.9984 **F** 9 (2,7)	20.183 **Ne** 10 (2,8)
26.9815 **Al** 13 (2,8,3)	28.086 **Si** 14 (2,8,4)	30.9738 **P** 15 (2,8,5)	32.064 **S** 16 (2,8,6)	35.453 **Cl** 17 (2,8,7)	39.948 **Ar** 18 (2,8,8)

			III	IV	V	VI	VII	VIII
58.71 **Ni** 28 (2,8,16,2)	63.54 **Cu** 29 (2,8,18,1)	65.37 **Zn** 30 (2,8,18,2)	69.72 **Ga** 31 (2,8,18,3)	72.59 **Ge** 32 (2,8,18,4)	74.9216 **As** 33 (2,8,18,5)	78.96 **Se** 34 (2,8,18,6)	79.909 **Br** 35 (2,8,18,7)	83.80 **Kr** 36 (2,8,18,8)
106.4 **Pd** 46 (2,8,18,18,0)	107.870 **Ag** 47 (2,8,18,18,1)	112.40 **Cd** 48 (2,8,18,18,2)	114.82 **In** 49 (2,8,18,18,3)	118.69 **Sn** 50 (2,8,18,18,4)	121.75 **Sb** 51 (2,8,18,18,5)	127.60 **Te** 52 (2,8,18,18,6)	126.9044 **I** 53 (2,8,18,18,7)	131.30 **Xe** 54 (2,8,18,18,8)
195.09 **Pt** 78 (2,8,18,32,16,2)	196.967 **Au** 79 (2,8,18,32,18,1)	200.59 **Hg** 80 (2,8,18,32,18,2)	204.37 **Tl** 81 (2,8,18,32,18,3)	207.19 **Pb** 82 (2,8,18,32,18,4)	208.980 **Bi** 83 (2,8,18,32,18,5)	[210*] **Po** 84 (2,8,18,32,18,6)	[210] **At** 85 (2,8,18,32,18,7)	[222] **Rn** 86 (2,8,18,32,18,8)

RARE EARTH ELEMENTS

157.25 **Gd** 64 (2,8,18,25,9,2)	158.924 **Tb** 65 (2,8,18,27,8,2)	162.50 **Dy** 66 (2,8,18,28,8,2)	164.930 **Ho** 67 (2,8,18,29,8,2)	167.26 **Er** 68 (2,8,18,30,8,2)	168.934 **Tm** 69 (2,8,18,31,8,2)	173.04 **Yb** 70 (2,8,18,32,8,2)

[247] **Cm** 96 (2,8,18,32,25,9,2)	[249*] **Bk** 97 (2,8,18,32,27,8,2)	[251*] **Cf** 98 (2,8,18,32,28,8,2)	[254] **Es** 99 (2,8,18,32,29,8,2)	[253] **Fm** 100 (2,8,18,32,30,8,2)	[256] **Md** 101 (2,8,18,32,31,8,2)	[254] 102 (2,8,18,32,32,8,2)

A value given in brackets denotes the mass number of the isotope of longest known half-life, or for those marked with an asterisk, a better known one.

nonmetallic properties, 5 electrons in its L shell; *oxygen,* a colorless gas, strong nonmetallic properties, 6 electrons in the L shell; *fluorine,* a pale-yellow gas, very strong nonmetallic properties, 7 electrons in its L shell; and *neon,* a colorless, inert gas, 8 electrons in its L shell. In this brief description of the properties of these elements, it should be noted that they range from an active metallic element to an active nonmetallic element, the last element in the period being inert. This variation in properties from metallic to nonmetallic is accompanied by an increase in the number of L-shell electrons from 1 to 7. The inert element neon has 8 electrons, an octet of electrons, in the L shell.

The third period also consists of eight elements: *sodium,* a soft, silvery, active metal similar to lithium, 1 electron in its outermost shell, the M shell; *magnesium,* a silvery metal similar in properties to beryllium, 2 electrons in its M shell; *aluminum,* a silvery metal with some nonmetallic properties, 3 electrons in the M shell; *silicon,* a dark-colored nonmetallic element with some properties resembling carbon, 4 electrons in the M shell; *phosphorus,* a nonmetallic solid element which forms compounds similar to those of nitrogen, 5 electrons in its M shell; *sulfur,* a yellow nonmetallic solid element, 6 electrons in its M shell; *chlorine,* a yellow-green gas with strong nonmetallic properties resembling those of fluorine, 7 electrons in the M shell; and *argon,* a colorless, inert gas, 8 electrons in its M shell. Again, the elements range from strong metallic to strong nonmetallic properties as the number of electrons in the outer shell varies from 1 to 7. The element with an octet of electrons in its outer shell is an inert gas.

Notice that elements with similar properties have a similar number of electrons in their outer shells. They fall into the same group in the Periodic Table.

In Group I in the Periodic Table, we find the Sodium Family, a group of six similar, very active, metallic elements. Their atoms all have only 1 electron in the outermost shell. *Francium* is the most complex member of the Sodium Family. Its position in the Periodic Table indicates that it is probably the most active metal. Group II consists of six active metals whose chemical properties are very much alike. The atoms of each have 2 electrons in their outer shell. This is the Calcium Family. The most chemically active member of this family is *radium.*

The properties of elements in Group III vary from nonmetallic to metallic as the atoms become more complex. The atoms of this group have 3 electrons in their outer shell. The elements of Group IV vary in a similar fashion; their atoms have 4 electrons in their outer shell. Atoms of elements of both of these groups have very stable inner shells.

Group V is the Nitrogen Family. *Nitrogen* and *phosphorus,* the elements in this family at the top of the table, are nonmetallic. The element *bismuth* at the bottom of the table is metallic. *Arsenic* and *antimony* exhibit both metallic and nonmetallic properties. Each of these atoms has 5 electrons in the outer shell, and has very stable inner shells.

Group VI is the Oxygen Family. The properties of the elements of this family vary from active nonmetallic to metallic as the atoms become more complex. The atoms of each element have 6 electrons in the outer shell and have very stable inner shells. The elements in Group VII, the Halogen Family, are very active nonmetals. Their atoms each have

7 electrons in the outer shell, and have very stable inner shells. The most active member of the Halogen Family is its simplest element, *fluorine.* Thus we see that the activity of the elements ranges from the most active metal at the lower left corner of the Periodic Table to the most active nonmetal at the upper right corner.

Group VIII is the Inert Gas Family. With the exception of *helium* atoms, which have a pair of electrons as their outer shell, atoms of these elements have an octet of electrons as their outer shell. This is the greatest number of electrons found in an outer shell. These elements were, until recently, believed to be chemically inert.

The fourth period of elements is the first long period. In addition to the eight elements in Groups I to VIII, there are also ten **transition elements.** These are metallic elements whose atoms have 1 or 2 electrons in the outer shell. Successive electrons usually enter the group of 5 orbitals of the 3*d* sublevel.

The fifth period of elements also includes ten transition elements, in which successive electrons enter the group of 5 orbitals of the 4*d* sublevel. These elements are all metals.

The sixth period consists of thirty-two elements. In addition to the ten transition elements, there is a group of fourteen **rare earth elements.** These elements have almost identical chemical properties. They are called the *Lanthanide Series.* The *two* outer shells of these atoms are almost the same. Successive electrons enter the group of 7 orbitals of the 4*f* sublevel, as the number of electrons in this energy level increases from 18 to 32.

The seventh period of elements is at present an incomplete period. It is assumed to be similar to the sixth period.

The rare earth elements in this period are called the *Actinide Series.* At present, seventeen members of the seventh period are known.

In the Periodic Table the elements are roughly divided into metals, nonmetals, and inert gases. The line separating the metals from the nonmetals is a zigzag line running diagonally down and to the right near the right end of the table. The elements which border this zigzag line are the *metalloids,* which show both metallic and nonmetallic properties under different conditions.

7. **The size of atoms is a periodic property.** It was recognized in Chapter 4 that an atom consists of a central nucleus with electrons moving about it. Since the nucleus has a diameter which is about one one-hundred-thousandth that of the atom, most of the volume of an atom is attributable to the complex motion of the electrons. By their motion and their negative charge, the electrons effectively occupy the space around the nucleus by forming a spherical electric field which gives the atom its volume and excludes other atoms.

The volume of an atom is not a completely definite quantity because the boundary of an atom's electronic field is not a distinct surface, but is somewhat fuzzy and indefinite. An atom may be rather easily distorted when it combines with other atoms, but very great force must be used if it is to be compressed appreciably.

The apparent size of an atom varies somewhat with the method used to measure it. Scientists however have measured the distance between adjacent nuclei in the crystalline forms of elements and in the molecules of gaseous elements, and these distances have been taken, with some slight corrections, as indicating the diameter of identical atoms. The diameter of an atom, and thus its radius and volume, does not increase regularly with atomic number as might be expected from the regular addition of an electron in successive elements. Atomic size varies in a periodic fashion as shown in Fig. 5-3, which is a miniature Periodic Table with element symbols in black and atomic numbers in blue. Above the symbols are the radii of atoms of the elements in Ångströms. Figure 5-4 shows the atomic radius plotted as a function of the atomic number.

From this chart and graph two conclusions about the relationship between atomic radius and the Periodic Table may be drawn.

1. The atomic radius increases with atomic number in a particular group or family of elements. Each element in a group has one more shell or energy level than the element above it. Even though the nuclear charge increases and tends to decrease the radii of the electron shells by drawing them closer, the addition of a shell more than counteracts this effect.

2. In a series or period, the atomic radius *generally* decreases from Group I to Group VII. The inert gas in Group VIII has a larger radius, but not as great a one as that of the elements of Groups I and II of the same period. The decrease in atomic radius across a period is due to the greater attraction of the increasing

PERIODIC TABLE OF ATOMIC RADII

0.30 H 1																	VIII
																	0.93 He 2
I	II											III	IV	V	VI	VII	
1.23 Li 3	0.89 Be 4											0.80 B 5	0.77 C 6	0.70 N 7	0.66 O 8	0.64 F 9	1.12 Ne 10
1.57 Na 11	1.36 Mg 12											1.25 Al 13	1.17 Si 14	1.10 P 15	1.04 S 16	0.99 Cl 17	1.54 Ar 18
2.02 K 19	1.74 Ca 20	1.44 Sc 21	1.32 Ti 22	1.22 V 23	1.19 Cr 24	1.18 Mn 25	1.17 Fe 26	1.16 Co 27	1.15 Ni 28	1.18 Cu 29	1.21 Zn 30	1.25 Ga 31	1.22 Ge 32	1.21 As 33	1.17 Se 34	1.14 Br 35	1.69 Kr 36
2.16 Rb 37	1.91 Sr 38	1.62 Y 39	1.45 Zr 40	1.34 Nb 41	1.30 Mo 42	1.27 Tc 43	1.25 Ru 44	1.25 Rh 45	1.28 Pd 46	1.34 Ag 47	1.38 Cd 48	1.42 In 49	1.42 Sn 50	1.39 Sb 51	1.37 Te 52	1.33 I 53	1.90 Xe 54
2.35 Cs 55	1.98 Ba 56	1.56 Lu 71	1.44 Hf 72	1.34 Ta 73	1.30 W 74	1.28 Re 75	1.26 Os 76	1.26 Ir 77	1.30 Pt 78	1.34 Au 79	1.39 Hg 80	1.44 Tl 81	1.50 Pb 82	1.51 Bi 83	1.65 Po 84	At 85	2.2 Rn 86
Fr 87	2.20 Ra 88	Lw 103															

1.69 La 57	1.65 Ce 58	1.64 Pr 59	1.64 Nd 60	1.63 Pm 61	1.62 Sm 62	1.85 Eu 63	1.62 Gd 64	1.61 Tb 65	1.60 Dy 66	1.58 Ho 67	1.58 Er 68	1.58 Tm 69	1.70 Yb 70
2.0 Ac 89	1.65 Th 90	Pa 91	1.43 U 92	Np 93	Pu 94	Am 95	Cm 96	Bk 97	Cf 98	Es 99	Fm 100	Md 101	102

Fig. 5-3. Periodic Table showing radii of the atoms of the elements in Ångström units.

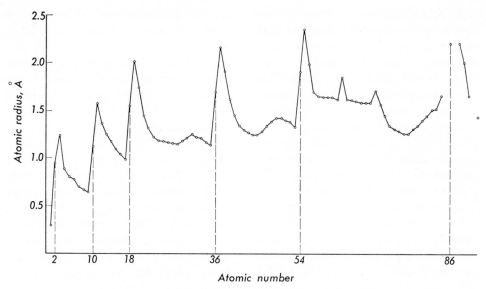

Fig. 5-4. Graph showing atomic radius plotted as a function of atomic number.

nuclear charge for electrons entering the same shell, thus pulling them closer to the nucleus. The irregularities may be due to the shell-enlarging effect of the mutual repulsion of electrons entering the same subshell. The greater size of the inert gas atoms is due to the structural stability of an outer shell consisting of an octet.

8. Ionization energy. An electron is held in an atom by the electrostatic force of the positively-charged protons in the nucleus and the negative charge of the electron. By supplying energy, it is possible to remove an electron from an atom. Using **A** as a symbol for an atom of any element, this electron removal may be shown in equation form:

$$A + energy \rightarrow A^+ + e^-$$

The particle **A**$^+$ remaining after the removal of an electron, e^-, is a singly-charged ion. *An **ion** is an atom* (or sometimes a group of atoms) *with an un-*

balanced electrostatic charge resulting from an unequal number of positively-charged protons and negatively-charged electrons. *The energy required to remove an electron from an atom is ionization energy,* and is usually expressed in electron-volts (an electron-volt is the energy acquired by an electron in falling through a potential difference of one volt). The chart, Fig. 5-5, shows the ionization energy required to remove the first electron from an atom of each element. Figure 5-6 is a graph showing ionization energy plotted as a function of atomic numbers. From these data the following conclusions may be drawn.

1. Low ionization energy is characteristic of a metal, while high ionization energy is characteristic of a nonmetal. An intermediate ionization energy is characteristic of a metalloid. The inert gases have unusually high ionization energies because of the stability of the outer shell octet.

2. Within groups of elements, the ionization energy generally decreases with increasing atomic number. In a group, increasing atomic number is accompanied by increasing atomic radius. Thus the outer-shell electrons of the elements of higher atomic number within a group are farther from the nucleus and will be attracted less by it. The ionization energy for removal of one such electron will therefore be less the greater the atomic number of the atom.

3. Ionization energy does not vary uniformly from atom to atom within a series, but is a periodic property. In each series or period, the ionization energy increases from Group I to Group VIII,

but the increase is not regular. There is a decrease between Group II and III in Periods 2 and 3 as the *s* sublevel is filled and the *p* sublevel is started. In these periods there is also a decrease between Groups V and VI as the *p* sublevel becomes half-filled. In Periods 4, 5, and 6, there is a sharp decrease in the ionization energy between the last transition element and Group III, where the *d* sublevel has become filled and the *p* sublevel is started. These apparent irregularities are due to the extra stability of completed and half-completed sublevels.

9. **Electron affinity.** Some neutral atoms have a tendency to acquire additional electrons. The measure of this

PERIODIC TABLE OF IONIZATION ENERGIES

13.6 H 1																	24.6 He 2
I	**II**											**III**	**IV**	**V**	**VI**	**VII**	**VIII**
5.4 Li 3	9.3 Be 4											8.3 B 5	11.3 C 6	14.5 N 7	13.6 O 8	17.4 F 9	21.6 Ne 10
5.1 Na 11	7.6 Mg 12											6.0 Al 13	8.1 Si 14	11.0 P 15	10.4 S 16	13.0 Cl 17	15.8 Ar 18
4.4 K 19	6.1 Ca 20	6.6 Sc 21	6.8 Ti 22	6.7 V 23	6.8 Cr 24	7.4 Mn 25	7.9 Fe 26	7.9 Co 27	7.6 Ni 28	7.7 Cu 29	9.4 Zn 30	6.0 Ga 31	8.1 Ge 32	10.5 As 33	9.7 Se 34	11.8 Br 35	14.0 Kr 36
4.2 Rb 37	5.7 Sr 38	6.6 Y 39	7.0 Zr 40	6.8 Nb 41	7.2 Mo 42	Tc 43	7.5 Ru 44	7.7 Rh 45	8.3 Pd 46	7.6 Ag 47	9.0 Cd 48	5.8 In 49	7.3 Sn 50	8.6 Sb 51	9.0 Te 52	10.4 I 53	12.1 Xe 54
3.9 Cs 55	5.2 Ba 56	5.0 Lu 71	5.5 Hf 72	6 Ta 73	8.0 W 74	7.9 Re 75	8.7 Os 76	9.2 Ir 77	9.0 Pt 78	9.2 Au 79	10.4 Hg 80	6.1 Tl 81	7.4 Pb 82	8.0 Bi 83	Po 84	At 85	10.7 Rn 86
Fr 87	5.3 Ra 88	Lw 103															

5.6 La 57	6.9 Ce 58	5.8 Pr 59	6.3 Nd 60	Pm 61	5.6 Sm 62	5.7 Eu 63	6.2 Gd 64	6.7 Tb 65	6.8 Dy 66	Ho 67	Er 68	Tm 69	6.2 Yb 70
Ac 89	Th 90	Pa 91	4 U 92	Np 93	Pu 94	Am 95	Cm 96	Bk 97	Cf 98	Es 99	Fm 100	Md 101	102

Fig. 5-5. **Periodic Table showing ionization energies of the elements in electron volts.**

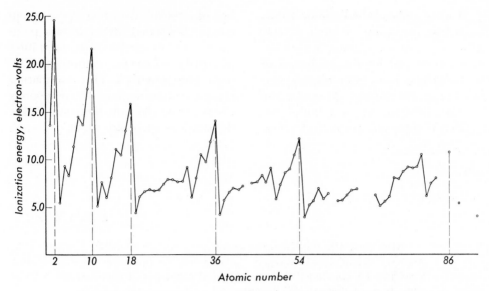

Fig. 5-6. Graph showing ionization energy plotted as a function of atomic number.

tendency is the *electron affinity, the energy released when an electron is added to a neutral atom.* When an electron is added to a neutral atom a singly-negatively-charged ion is formed, and an amount of energy, the electron affinity, is released. In equation form,

$$A + e^- \rightarrow A^- + \text{energy}$$

Like ionization energy, electron affinity may be measured in electron-volts. The electron affinity indicates how tightly an additional electron is bound to an atom. If the electron affinity is low, the electron is weakly bound; if the electron affinity is high, the electron is strongly bound. The table below gives the electron affinities for four members of the Halogen Family.

Element	Electron Affinity (electron-volts)
Fluorine	3.62
Chlorine	3.79
Bromine	3.56
Iodine	3.28

The Halogens would be expected to have high electron affinities, since the addition of one electron to these atoms gives them a stable outer shell consisting of an octet. It would also be expected that the electron affinities would decrease with increasing atomic number, because the added electron enters shells which are increasingly farther from the nucleus. There is no simple explanation for the low electron affinity of fluorine, but because of their relatively small size many second period elements show irregularities in properties from those of the rest of their group. Unfortunately, too, the determination of electron affinity is complex, and data are available for only a few elements.

The concepts of ionization energy and electron affinity are helpful in understanding the methods by which compounds are formed from atoms of metallic and nonmetallic elements. This topic is discussed in greater detail in Chapter 6.

10. The value of the Periodic Table. In former years the Periodic Table served as a check on atomic weight determinations and for the prediction of new elements. These uses are now outdated. For the present, however, the Periodic Table serves as a useful systematic, though not perfect, classification of elements according to their properties. The periodicity of certain properties such as atomic size, ionization potential, and electron affinity have already been described. This information helps determine the types of compounds which certain elements form, and makes the study of chemistry easier.

SUMMARY

After early attempts by other scientists to classify elements as triads, or in octaves, Mendeleyev arranged the elements in the order of their atomic weights. He concluded that the chemical properties of elements are periodic functions of their atomic weights.

Moseley found that X rays could be used to determine the atomic number of an element. An increase in the number of protons in the nucleus of a metal used as the target in an X-ray tube decreases the wavelength of the X rays it produces. When elements are arranged in the order of their atomic numbers, some discrepancies in Mendeleyev's arrangement disappear. As a result of this discovery, the Periodic Law is now stated: the chemical properties of elements are periodic functions of their atomic numbers.

In the modern Periodic Table the families of elements with similar properties, or groups, are in vertical columns. Each element in a family has a similar number of electrons in its outer shell. At the left of the table the most active elements are at the bottom. At the right of the table, they are at the top. A row of elements is called a period. In a given period, the properties of the elements gradually pass from strong metallic to strong nonmetallic nature, with the last member of a period being an inert gaseous element. Atomic size, ionization energy, and electron affinity vary from element to element in a periodic fashion.

TEST YOURSELF ON THESE TERMS

Actinide Series	ionization energy	Periodic Law
Calcium Family	Lathanide Series	Periodic Table
electron affinity	law of octaves	rare earth element
family	Mendeleyev	series
group	metalloid	Sodium Family
Halogen Family	Nitrogen Family	transition element
Inert Gas Family	Oxygen Family	triad
ion	period	X rays

Group A

1. (*a*) On what basis did Mendeleyev arrange the elements in his Periodic Table? (*b*) On what basis are they arranged today?
2. What use did Mendeleyev make of his Periodic Table?
3. How are X rays used to determine the atomic number of an element?
4. What is the Periodic Law?
5. (*a*) What information is given in each block of the Periodic Table? (*b*) How are these data arranged in each block?
6. (*a*) What is a group or family of elements? (*b*) What position does one occupy in the Periodic Table?
7. (*a*) What is a series or period of elements? (*b*) What position does one occupy in the Periodic Table?
8. (*a*) Name the elements in the second period. (*b*) How does the number of electrons in the outer shell vary in these elements? (*c*) How do their properties compare?
9. What is similar about the electron configurations of elements with similar properties?
10. How do the elements at the left of the Periodic Table vary in activity?
11. How do the elements in Group VII vary in activity?
12. What name is given to the elements which border the line dividing the metals from the nonmetals?
13. Why is the radius of an atom not a definitely fixed quantity?
14. (*a*) How do the atomic radii of the Group I elements compare with the radii of other elements of their period? (*b*) Why?
15. (*a*) Write an equation to represent the removal of the single outer shell electron from a sodium atom. (*b*) Write an equation to represent the addition of an electron to a neutral chlorine atom. (*c*) What particles are produced from the neutral atoms by these reactions?
16. (*a*) Why do metals have low ionization energies? (*b*) Why are the ionization energies of nonmetals high?

Group B

17. How are the elements in Döbereiner's triads related?
18. What was the basis for Newlands' *law of octaves?*
19. What family of elements was missing from Mendelelyev's Periodic Table?
20. (*a*) What are X rays? (*b*) How are they produced?
21. (*a*) How did Mendeleyev know where to leave gaps for undiscovered elements in his Periodic Table? (*b*) How did Moseley know where to leave gaps for undiscovered elements?
22. (*a*) Why is hydrogen placed separately in the Periodic Table? (*b*) Why is it placed above Group I?
23. (*a*) What are transition elements? (*b*) In which periods of elements do they appear?
24. (*a*) What are rare earth elements? (*b*) In which periods of elements do they appear?

25. (*a*) How does atomic size vary with atomic number within a family of elements? (*b*) Why does it vary this way?
26. (*a*) How does atomic size generally vary with atomic number within a period of elements? (*b*) Why does it vary this way?
27. (*a*) How would you expect the ionization energies of two atoms of about equal size but different atomic number to compare? (*b*) Why?
28. (*a*) If energy must be supplied to remove an outer shell electron from an atom, which is more stable, the atom or the resulting ion? (*b*) If energy is released during the addition of an electron to a neutral atom, which is more stable, the atom or the resulting ion?
29. What determines the number of elements in each period of the Periodic Table?
30. What is the probable electron configuration that element 106 would have?
31. How many O-shell orbitals would be filled theoretically in element 118?
32. What is the present value of the Periodic Table?

SOME THINGS FOR YOU TO DO

1. Look up in a history of chemistry or a college textbook of chemistry the predictions that Mendeleyev made for "ekaboron," "ekaluminum," and "ekasilicon," and compare them with the properties of scandium, gallium, and germanium, respectively.
2. Make a spiral model of the Periodic Table. Use a large-size can for the cylinder. Cut white paper the proper size to encircle the can. Lay out the table on this paper, remembering to make the periods slant so that helium and lithium, neon and sodium, argon and potassium, etc., follow one another in a spiral.

Chapter 6 · CHEMICAL BONDS AND FORMULA WRITING

1. CHEMICAL BONDS

1. Elements combine to form compounds. In Chapter 3 it was stated that elements *could* combine during a chemical change to form compounds. Now that the structure of the atoms of the elements has been described, we are ready to learn *how* atoms combine.

2. Atoms of different elements have different combining capacity. The following series of formulas shows that different numbers of hydrogen and chlorine atoms can combine with single atoms of other elements.

HCl	$NaCl$
H_2O	$CaCl_2$
NH_3	$AlCl_3$
CH_4	CCl_4

One atom of hydrogen combines with one atom of chlorine. One atom of sodium also combines with one atom of chlorine. To form a molecule of a compound of hydrogen and oxygen, two atoms of hydrogen are needed for each oxygen atom. Likewise, two chlorine atoms are required for each calcium

atom when a compound of calcium and chlorine is formed. One atom of nitrogen combines with three hydrogen atoms, while one atom of aluminum combines with three chlorine atoms. One atom of carbon combines with either four hydrogen atoms or four chlorine atoms. Why is there this difference in the number of hydrogen and chlorine atoms which will combine with a single atom of another element? Is there any relation between the structure of an atom and the number of other atoms with which it will combine?

3. Valence means "combining capacity." It would be rather awkward for chemists to talk about the "combining capacity" of an element. Instead, they have coined a special, shorter word which means "combining capacity." That word is *valence*. In Section 10 of this chapter we will give a more accurate definition of valence, but for the present, let us realize that *valence means the combining capacity of an element.*

4. Valence electrons and chemical bonds. The electrons in the outermost shell of an atom play a very active part in the formation of compounds. For this reason the electrons in an *incomplete* outer shell are called the **valence electrons.** The remainder of the atom, excluding the valence electrons, is called the **kernel** of the atom. In the formation of chemical compounds from the elements, the *valence electrons are either transferred from the outer shell of one atom to the outer shell of another atom, or shared among the outer shells of the combining atoms.* This produces **chemical bonds.**

Electron transfer results in **ionic bonding** *while electron sharing produces* **covalent bonding.** When an atom of one element enters into chemical combination with an atom of another element, both atoms usually attain a stable outer shell consisting of an octet of electrons. (Hydrogen either shares its single electron or attains a stable outer shell of two electrons. Lithium loses its single L-shell electron to attain a stable outer shell of two electrons.) *This particular kind of electronic structure, resembling that of the inert gases, has chemical stability.*

Energy changes are always involved in the process of electron transfer or electron sharing. In *most* cases when compounds are formed from the elements, energy is liberated—the process of electron transfer is always exothermic and that of electron sharing is usually exothermic. In *a few* cases of compound formation by electron sharing, energy is absorbed—the process of electron sharing may sometimes be endothermic.

5. Ionic bonding (electrovalence). In the formation of a compound by ionic bonding, electrons are actually transferred from the outer shell of one atom to the outer shell of a second atom. By this process both atoms usually attain outer shells containing eight electrons.

VOCABULARY

Anion. A negative ion.

Binary compound. A compound consisting of only two elements.

Cation. A positive ion.

Chemical bond. The linkage between atoms produced by transfer or sharing of electrons.

Covalent bonding. Bonding in which atoms share a pair of electrons.

Electronegativity. The tendency of an atom to attract the shared electrons forming a bond between it and another atom.

Ionic bonding. Bonding in which one or more electrons are transferred from one atom to another.

Polar covalent bond. A covalent bond in which there is an unequal attraction for the shared electrons and a resulting unbalanced distribution of charge.

Polar molecule. A molecule containing one or more unsymmetrically arranged polar covalent bonds, and as a whole having regions of positive and negative charge.

Radical. A group of atoms which usually behaves as if it were a single atom.

Valence. The number of electrons gained, lost, or shared by an atom in bonding with one or more atoms.

For example, when sodium reacts with chlorine to form sodium chloride, the single electron in the M shell of the sodium atom is transferred to the M shell of the chlorine atom. The sodium atom, now deficient in one electron, has the stable electronic configuration of neon. The chlorine atom, now with one excess electron, has the stable electronic configuration of argon. Since only 1 atom of each element is required for the electron transfer which produces these stable electronic configurations, the empirical formula of the compound is **NaCl**. The particles which are produced by this transfer of an electron are no longer electrically neutral atoms of sodium and chlorine. They are an electrostatically-charged *sodium ion* with a single excess positive charge and an electrostatically-charged *chloride ion* with a single excess negative charge. These ions are found in crystals of sodium chloride in the ratio of 1 sodium ion to 1 chloride ion. The table below shows the number of protons and electrons in these atoms and ions, their resultant electrostatic charges, their electrovalent symbols, and their radii in Ångströms. Also see Fig. 6-1.

Using only the M-shell electrons, the electron-dot symbol for an atom of sodium is

Na∘

while that for an atom of chlorine is

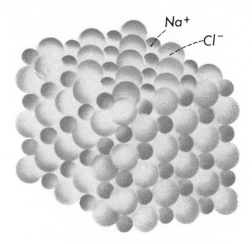

Fig. 6-1. **This diagram shows the arrangement of the sodium and chloride ions in sodium chloride.**

·C̈l:

After reaction, the formula for sodium chloride may be represented by an electron-dot formula as

Na+ ∘C̈l:−

or by a simpler ionic formula as Na^+Cl^-. (The symbols for electrons, ∘ and · , which are used here and in other electron-dot formulas in this chapter, are only to show the origin of the electrons in the completed shells. They *do not mean* that electrons from different atoms are different from each other. All electrons, regardless of the atom from which they originate, are identical.)

	Sodium Atom	Sodium Ion	Chlorine Atom	Chloride Ion
Number of Protons	11	11	17	17
Number of Electrons	11	10	17	18
Net Charge	0	+1	0	−1
Symbol	Na^0	Na^+	Cl^0	Cl^-
Radius, Å	1.57	0.95	0.99	1.81

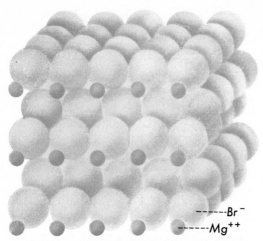

-------Br$^-$

-------Mg^{++}

Fig. 6-2. This diagram shows the arrangement of the magnesium and bromide ions in magnesium bromide.

The formation of sodium ions and chloride ions in a common salt crystal may be assumed, for a study of the energy change involved, to consist of three separate reactions. The first, the removal of an electron from a sodium atom forming a sodium ion, is endothermic. The amount of energy required is the ionization energy of sodium.

$$Na^0 + energy \rightarrow Na^+ + e^-$$

The second reaction is the addition of an electron to a neutral chlorine atom. This reaction is exothermic, the energy evolved being the electron affinity of chlorine.

$$Cl^0 + e^- \rightarrow Cl^- + energy$$

The third reaction is the movement of the oppositely-charged sodium ion and chloride ion into their equilibrium positions in the sodium chloride crystal. This reaction is also exothermic.

$$Na^+ + Cl^- \rightarrow Na^+Cl^- + energy$$

Since the energy required for the first of these three reactions is less than that evolved in the second and third, the over-all effect is the evolution of energy. This is true of all ionic compound formation. The process of electron transfer is exothermic.

In another example, the formation of magnesium bromide, the 2 outer M-shell electrons of the magnesium are transferred. *Both* M-shell electrons must be transferred in order for the magnesium atom to acquire the stability of the electronic configuration of the inert gas, neon. But the N shell of the bromine atom already contains seven electrons, and eight is the number needed for a stable octet of electrons. So 1 bromine atom has place for only 1 of the 2 electrons which the magnesium atom transfers. This means that 2 bromine atoms are needed to react with 1 magnesium atom. Each bromine atom gains 1 electron. The formula for magnesium bromide is **MgBr$_2$**. The particles which compose this compound are magnesium ions, each with two excess positive charges, and bromide ions, each with a single excess negative charge. These particles are found in crystals of mag-

	Magnesium Atom	Magnesium Ion	Bromine Atom	Bromide Ion
Number of Protons	12	12	35	35
Number of Electrons	12	10	35	36
Net Charge	0	+2	0	−1
Symbol	Mg^0	Mg^{++}	Br^0	Br$^-$
Radius, Å	1.36	0.65	1.14	1.95

nesium bromide in the ratio of 2 bromide ions to 1 magnesium ion (see the table on page 86 and also Fig. 6-2).

The electron-dot symbol for an atom of magnesium is

$$\overset{\circ}{Mg}\circ$$

while that for an atom of bromine is

$$\cdot \overset{\cdot\cdot}{\underset{\cdot\cdot}{Br}}:$$

The electron-dot formula for magnesium bromide is then

$$:\overset{\cdot\cdot}{\underset{\cdot\cdot}{Br}}:^{-}\quad Mg^{++}\quad \circ\overset{\cdot\cdot}{\underset{\cdot\cdot}{Br}}:^{-}$$

and the ionic formula is $Mg^{++}Br_2{}^{-}$.

Since the energy required to remove two electrons from one magnesium atom is less than the electron affinity of two bromine atoms plus the energy released when one magnesium ion and two bromide ions move into their equilbrium positions in a magnesium bromide crystal, the formation of magnesium bromide is another example of the exothermic nature of electron transfer.

6. The relative sizes of atoms and ions. In the tables accompanying Section 5, the radii of the atoms and ions of sodium, magnesium, chlorine, and bromine are given. Notice the great difference in radius between an atom and the ion formed from it.

It is characteristic of metals to form positive ions. *Positive ions are called cations.* It is to be expected that metallic ions would be smaller than the corresponding metallic atoms since the outer shell electrons are no longer present and the remaining electrons are attracted more strongly to the nucleus by the unbalanced positive charge.

Nonmetallic elements form negative ions. *Negative ions are called anions.* Nonmetallic ions are larger than the corresponding nonmetallic atoms since electrons have been added to make the outer shell an octet, and the excess negative charge weakens the attraction of the nucleus for the surrounding electrons.

The accompanying table shows the sizes of representative atoms and ions. From these data, in addition to the generalizations given above, it will be seen that:

1. Within a group or family of elements, the ion size increases with atomic number.

2. Within a period of elements, greater

RADII OF REPRESENTATIVE ATOMS AND IONS

Ångströms

	Group I		Group II		Group III		Group VI		Group VII	
Period 2	Li^0	1.23	Be^0	0.89	B^0	0.80	O^0	0.66	F^0	0.64
	Li^+	0.60	Be^{++}	0.31	B^{+++}	0.20	$O^=$	1.40	F^-	1.36
Period 3	Na^0	1.57	Mg^0	1.36	Al^0	1.25	S^0	1.04	Cl^0	0.99
	Na^+	0.95	Mg^{++}	0.65	Al^{+++}	0.50	$S^=$	1.84	Cl^-	1.81
Period 4	K^0	2.02	Ca^0	1.74	Ga^0	1.25	Se^0	1.17	Br^0	1.14
	K^+	1.33	Ca^{++}	0.99	Ga^{+++}	0.62	$Se^=$	1.98	Br^-	1.95
Period 5	Rb^0	2.16	Sr^0	1.91	In^0	1.42	Te^0	1.37	I^0	1.33
	Rb^+	1.48	Sr^{++}	1.13	In^{+++}	0.81	$Te^=$	2.21	I^-	2.16
Period 6	Cs^0	2.35	Ba^0	1.98	Tl^0	1.44				
	Cs^+	1.69	Ba^{++}	1.35	Tl^{+++}	0.95				

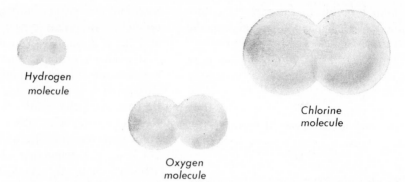

Fig. 6-3. **The molecules of the common gases, such as those of hydrogen, oxygen, and chlorine represented here, consist of two atoms joined by covalent bonding.**

positive charge produces markedly smaller cations while greater negative charge produces only slightly larger anions. This is due to the fact that greater positive ionic charge is accompanied by greater nuclear charge, while greater negative ionic charge is accompanied by a lower nuclear charge.

Figures 6-1 and 6-2 show the arrangement of ions in crystals of sodium chloride and magnesium bromide. It is apparent that the arrangement of ions in a crystal depends on the relative numbers of each kind of ion present (which depends on their charge) and on the relative sizes of the ions. Crystals are described in more detail in Chapter 19.

7. **Covalent bonding (covalence).** In covalent bonding, electrons are not transferred from one atom to another, but two atoms each share one of their electrons with the other. These two shared electrons effectively fill an orbital in each element and thus form a covalent electron pair. This constitutes the bond between these two atoms.

The atoms of the common gases form diatomic molecules by covalent bond-

ing. For instance, in the diatomic hydrogen molecule, each hydrogen atom shares its single valence electron with the other. These electrons revolve about both nuclei, so that each atom has two electrons revolving about it. Each atom, in effect has the *s* orbital of its K energy level filled. This means that each hydrogen atom has, in effect, the stable K-shell configuration of a helium atom. The electron-dot formula for a molecule of hydrogen is

$$H{:}H$$

Diatomic chlorine molecules are formed in the same way. Each atom shares one electron with the other, filling, in effect, an incomplete orbital in the M level of each. This gives both the stable electron arrangement of the inert gas argon, with an octet of electrons in the M shell. The electron-dot formula for a molecule of chlorine is

$$\overset{\circ\circ}{\underset{\circ\circ}{\text{Cl}}}{:}\overset{\bullet\bullet}{\underset{\bullet\bullet}{\text{Cl}}}{:}$$

Oxygen also exists as diatomic molecules. But an atom of oxygen is represented as

$$\cdot \overset{\cdot\cdot}{\underset{\cdot}{O}} :$$

so a molecule of oxygen has the electron-dot formula

$$\overset{\circ\,\circ}{\underset{\circ\,\circ}{O}} : \overset{\cdot\cdot}{O} :$$

Unlike atoms also combine by covalent bonding. Several simple compounds formed by covalent bonding are hydrogen chloride, water, ammonia, and methane. Their electron-dot structures are shown in the table at the bottom of the page. Notice that a pair of shared electrons constitutes the bond between two atoms, and that each atom acquires a stable outer shell of two or eight electrons.

There are some situations in which both electrons which form a covalent bond between two atoms come from only one of the bonded atoms. The ammonium ion, NH_4^+, is an example.

$$\left[\begin{array}{c} H \\ \overset{\circ}{\underset{\circ}{}} \\ H \overset{\cdot}{\underset{\circ}{N}} : H \\ \overset{\cdot\cdot}{\underset{\circ}{}} \\ H \end{array} \right]^+$$

In this ion three of the covalent nitrogen-hydrogen bonds consist of 1 shared nitrogen electron and 1 shared hydrogen electron. The other covalent nitrogen-hydrogen bond consists of 2 electrons, both of which are supplied by the nitrogen atom. The hydrogen atom thus bonded lacks its own electron and produces the single positive charge of the ion.

Frequently chemists indicate a shared pair of electrons—a covalent bond—by a dash (—) instead of by two dots (:). Thus the formula for hydrogen chloride may be written

$$H : \overset{\cdot\cdot}{\underset{\cdot\cdot}{Cl}} : \quad \text{or} \quad H - \overset{\cdot\cdot}{\underset{\cdot\cdot}{Cl}} :$$

or omitting the electrons which are not involved in the bonding, simply

$$H - Cl$$

Similarly, the formula for methane,

$$\begin{array}{c} H \\ \overset{\cdot}{\underset{\circ}{}} \\ H \overset{\circ}{\underset{\circ}{C}} \overset{\cdot}{\underset{\circ}{}} H \\ \overset{\circ}{\underset{\circ}{}} \\ H \end{array}$$

becomes

$$\begin{array}{c} H \\ | \\ H - C - H \\ | \\ H \end{array}$$

or the formula for the ammonium ion

	Hydrogen Chloride	Water	Ammonia	Methane
Individual Atoms	$H\circ, \ \cdot \overset{\cdot\cdot}{\underset{\cdot\cdot}{Cl}} :$	$H\circ, \ H\circ, \ \cdot \overset{\cdot\cdot}{\underset{\cdot}{O}} :$	$H\circ, \ H\circ, \ H\circ, \ \cdot \overset{\cdot}{\underset{\cdot}{N}} :$	$H\circ, \ H\circ, \ H\circ, \ H\circ, \ \cdot \overset{\cdot}{\underset{\cdot}{C}} \cdot$
Molecules	$H\overset{\cdot\cdot}{\underset{\cdot\cdot}{Cl}} :$	$H \overset{\cdot\cdot}{\underset{\circ\,\circ}{O}} :$ H	$H \overset{\cdot}{\underset{\circ\,\circ}{N}} :$ H with top H	$H \overset{\cdot}{\underset{\circ\,\circ}{C}} H$ H

becomes

$$\left[\begin{array}{c} H \\ | \\ H-N-H \\ | \\ H \end{array} \right]^+$$

In each of the examples of covalent bonding illustrated, the bonded atoms are more stable due to filled orbitals and have lower energy than the unbonded atoms. Thus these molecules are all formed from the atoms by exothermic processes.

The covalent compound carbon disulfide, CS_2,

$$:\!\overset{..}{S}\!\overset{\circ}{\underset{\circ}{:}}\!C\!\overset{\circ}{\underset{\circ}{:}}\!\overset{..}{S}\!:$$

is an example of a compound which is less stable than the uncombined atoms. It can be made only by an endothermic process. Its instability may be due to the two double carbon-sulfur bonds in the molecule. (Two pairs of electrons shared by two atoms constitute a double bond between the atoms. Similarly three pairs of electrons shared by two atoms constitute a triple bond between the atoms. Double and triple bonds are usually less stable than single bonds.)

8. Electronegativity. In ionic bonding electrons are completely transferred from the outer shells of metallic atoms to the outer shells of nonmetallic atoms. In covalent bonding, electrons are shared in the outer shells of the bonded atoms. If two covalently bonded atoms are alike, their attractions for the shared electrons are equal, and the electrons are distributed equally about both atoms. Each atom remains electrically neutral even though they are bonded together. If two covalently bonded

atoms are unlike, the attraction of one of the atoms for the shared electron pair may be stronger than the attraction of the other atom for them. Then, the electrons will not be equally shared, but will be more closely held by the atom with stronger attraction. This atom will not be electrically neutral, but will be slightly negative, though not as negative as a singly-charged anion. The other atom will then be left slightly positive, though not as positive as a singly-charged cation. *A covalent bond in which there is an unequal attraction for the shared electrons and a resulting unbalanced distribution of charge is called a polar covalent bond.* Polar covalent bonds thus are intermediate in nature between ionic bonds in which electron transfer is complete and pure covalent bonds in which electron sharing is equal.

Ionization energy is a measure of the strength with which an outer shell electron is held by a neutral atom. Electron affinity indicates the strength of the attraction between a neutral atom and an additional electron. By considering these two values, together with certain propties of molecules, chemists have derived an arbitrary scale to indicate *the attraction of an atom for the shared electrons forming a bond between it and another atom. This property is called electronegativity.* Atoms with high electronegativity have a strong attraction for shared electrons. Atoms with low electronegativity have a weak attraction for shared electrons. The relative electronegativities of two atoms give an indication of the type of bonding which may exist between them.

The chart, Fig. 6-4, gives values of the electronegativity for the elements. A study of this chart leads to the following conclusions.

1. Low electronegativity is characteristic

PERIODIC TABLE OF ELECTRONEGATIVITIES

I	II											III	IV	V	VI	VII	VIII
2.1 H 1																	He 2
1.0 Li 3	1.5 Be 4											2.0 B 5	2.5 C 6	3.0 N 7	3.5 O 8	4.0 F 9	Ne 10
0.9 Na 11	1.2 Mg 12											1.5 Al 13	1.8 Si 14	2.1 P 15	2.5 S 16	3.0 Cl 17	Ar 18
0.8 K 19	1.0 Ca 20	1.3 Sc 21	1.5 Ti 22	1.6 V 23	1.6 Cr 24	1.5 Mn 25	1.8 Fe 26	1.8 Co 27	1.8 Ni 28	1.9 Cu 29	1.6 Zn 30	1.6 Ga 31	1.8 Ge 32	2.0 As 33	2.4 Se 34	2.8 Br 35	Kr 36
0.8 Rb 37	1.0 Sr 38	1.2 Y 39	1.4 Zr 40	1.6 Nb 41	1.8 Mo 42	1.9 Tc 43	2.2 Ru 44	2.2 Rh 45	2.2 Pd 46	1.9 Ag 47	1.7 Cd 48	1.7 In 49	1.8 Sn 50	1.9 Sb 51	2.1 Te 52	2.5 I 53	Xe 54
0.7 Cs 55	0.9 Ba 56	1.2 Lu 71	1.3 Hf 72	1.5 Ta 73	1.7 W 74	1.9 Re 75	2.2 Os 76	2.2 Ir 77	2.2 Pt 78	2.4 Au 79	1.9 Hg 80	1.8 Tl 81	1.8 Pb 82	1.9 Bi 83	2.0 Po 84	2.2 At 85	Rn 86
0.7 Fr 87	0.9 Ra 88	Lw 103															

1.1 La 57	1.1 Ce 58	1.1 Pr 59	1.1 Nd 60	1.1 Pm 61	1.1 Sm 62	1.1 Eu 63	1.1 Gd 64	1.1 Tb 65	1.1 Dy 66	1.1 Ho 67	1.1 Er 68	1.1 Tm 69	1.1 Yb 70
1.1 Ac 89	1.3 Th 90	1.5 Pa 91	1.7 U 92	1.3 Np 93	1.3 Pu 94	1.3 Am 95	1.3 Cm 96	1.3 Bk 97	1.3 Cf 98	1.3 Es 99	1.3 Fm 100	1.3 Md 101	1.3 102

Fig. 6-4. Periodic Table showing the electronegativities of the elements on an arbitrary scale.

of metals. The lower the electronegativity, the more active the metal. Thus the lowest electronegativities are found at the lower left of the Periodic Table.

2. High electronegativity is characteristic of nonmetals. Thus the highest electronegativities are found at the upper right of the Periodic Table. Fluorine is the most electronegative element. Oxygen is second.

3. Since they do not form compounds by usual bonding mechanisms, the inert gases are not assigned electronegativity values.

4. Electronegativity generally decreases within the numbered groups or families with increasing atomic number.

In the transition element groups there is usually only a slight variation in electronegativity.

5. Electronegativity increases within a period or series through the middle of the Periodic Table, decreases slightly in the remaining metals, and then increases to usually a maximum in Group VII.

9. Electronegativity difference and chemical bonding. The table on page 92 gives values for a useful approximate relationship between the difference of electronegativity of two elements and the percentage of ionic character of a single bond between the two atoms.

Bonds with more than 50% ionic character are considered to be essentially

Electronegativity Difference	Percentage of Ionic Character
0.2	1
0.4	4
0.6	9
0.8	15
1.0	22
1.2	30
1.4	39
1.6	47
1.8	55
2.0	63
2.2	70
2.4	76
2.6	82
2.8	86
3.0	89
3.2	92

ionic. Thus it is evident that the bonds between metallic elements and the distinctly nonmetallic elements are largely ionic. Sodium chloride, $NaCl$, electronegativity difference $3.0 - 0.9 = 2.1$, is a compound with ionic bonds. Similarly $CaBr_2$ and BaO are examples of compounds with ionic bonds.

Since the nonmetallic elements have rather similar electronegativity values, the bonding between nonmetallic elements is predominantly covalent. The hydrogen-oxygen bonds in water, electronegativity difference $3.5 - 2.1 = 1.4$, are 39% ionic. Thus these are polar covalent bonds, with the oxygen being somewhat negative and the hydrogen being somewhat positive. Since the water molecule contains two such bonds unsymmetrically arranged, *the water molecule as a whole shows regions of positive and negative charge and is a polar molecule.* Likewise the nitrogen-hydrogen bonds in ammonia are polar, and since the molecule is geometrically unsymmetrical, it, too, is a polar molecule. While the carbon-hydrogen bonds in methane are slightly polar, the symmetry of the molecule causes the methane molecule as a whole to be nonpolar.

Bonds between like atoms, such as are found in the oxygen molecule or the chlorine molecule, have no ionic character since the electronegativity difference is zero.

While we have classed chemical bonds as ionic bonds or covalent bonds, it is now apparent that these are not clear, distinct classifications. On the Periodic Table, the type of bonding gradually changes from essentially ionic, as between the active metals of Groups I and II and oxygen or the halogens, to covalent bonding in the metalloids and between nonmetals. A third type of bonding, metallic bonding, which occurs between atoms of metals, will be described in Chapter 24.

The Inert Gases have electronic configurations which are chemically very stable. It has been found possible, however, to produce at least one stable compound of xenon and fluorine. Under certain unusual conditions, unstable "compounds" have also been prepared from some of these inert elements.

10. The chemical definition of valence. Now that ionic and covalent bonding have been described, a more complete definition of the term valence can be given. *Valence is the number of electrons which an atom gains, loses, or shares in bonding with one or more atoms.* Valence is shown by atoms only when they are combined. It is not shown by uncombined atoms. That is why the valence of a single atom of an element is said to be 0. An atom of the element sodium has 0 valence. Sodium in sodium chloride has a valence of +1, since the sodium atom has lost 1 electron and the resulting sodium ion has an excess of 1 positive charge. An atom of the element chlorine has 0 valence. But in sodium chloride, the chlorine has a valence of –1, since the chlorine atom gained 1 electron and the resulting chloride ion has 1 excess negative charge.

The valence of atoms in covalent compounds is an absolute (unsigned) number, since there is only electron sharing. In hydrogen chloride, the valence of both the hydrogen and the chlorine is 1, since they each share 1 of their electrons. In water, the valence of hydrogen is again 1, but the valence of oxygen is 2. Each hydrogen atom shares 1 of its electrons with the oxygen, but the oxygen atom shares 2 of its electrons—1 with each hydrogen. In sulfur trioxide, the valence of sulfur is 6, while the valence of each oxygen atom is 2. The sulfur atom shares all 6 of its electrons with the oxygen atoms, while each oxygen atom either shares 2 of its electrons with the sulfur or completes its octet of electrons with 2 electrons from the sulfur atom.

It is also important to note that while atoms transfer or share electrons to form chemical bonds, there is still an equal number of protons and electrons in the group of atoms forming a molecule or forming the relative proportions indicated by an empirical formula. Consequently, molecules or the relative proportions of atoms indicated by an empirical formula have the same electrical balance or electrical neutrality found in single uncombined atoms.

The table below summarizes structural and valence data for some of the simple elements of Groups I, II, VI, VII, and VIII of the Periodic Table.

★ 11. **The structure of crystalline solids.** Crystalline solids may be *molecular, macromolecular, or ionic.* Some solids are made up of simple molecules. Solid iodine consists of diatomic molecules arranged in systematic order forming *molecular crystals.* The melting points of such solids are usually low since the forces binding the molecules into the crystal structure are relatively weak. Other solids have unit structures which are somewhat more complex than the simplest molecular form would provide.

STRUCTURAL AND VALENCE DATA

	Element	Hydrogen	Helium	Oxygen	Neon	Sodium	Magnesium	Chlorine
Atomic Structure	Nuclear charge	+1	+2	+8	+10	+11	+12	+17
	Number of electrons	1	2	2, 6	2, 8	2, 8, 1	2, 8, 2	2, 8, 7
Kernel Structure	Nuclear charge	+1	+2	+8	+10	+11	+12	+17
	Number of electrons	0	2	2	2, 8	2, 8	2, 8	2, 8
Valence Structure	Number of electrons	1	0	6	0	1	2	7
Valence Notation	Electrovalence	H^+	He^0	$O^=$	Ne^0	Na^+	Mg^{++}	Cl^-
	Covalence	H·	He:	·O̤:	:Ne:	Na·	Mg·	:C̤l:

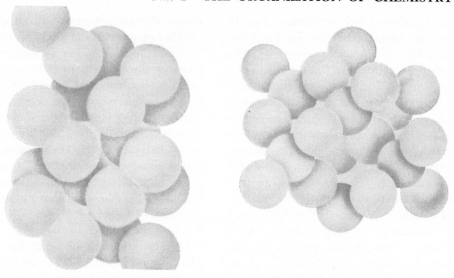

Fig. 6-5. **Solid iodine (left) forms molecular crystals. Compare its molecular structure with that of the diamond (right) which forms molecular groups called macromolecules.**

They may be composed of specific molecular groups or aggregates of these groups regularly arranged throughout the solid. Such molecular groups or aggregates are called *macromolecules.* They may be very complex and quite large when compared to simple molecules. A diamond is such a crystalline solid. A cut and polished diamond is a macromolecule. Still other solids show no molecular structure at all. The ions composing such substances are arranged in a characteristic pattern which is repeated in each dimension to the faces of the crystal. Sodium chloride crystals are of this sort. Macromolecular and ionic solids have high melting points since the covalent bonds in macromolecules and the electrovalent bonds in ionic compounds are quite strong. Molecules of sodium chloride do not exist except at very high temperatures.

12. Elements may show several valences. Many elements exhibit more than one valence. Some differences in the valence shown by an element depend on the kind of bond which it forms with other elements. However, another factor is important. Some transition elements, with four or five electronic sublevels, can transfer the electrons in the outermost sublevel and sometimes with very little additional energy transfer one or two electrons from the next-to-outermost sublevel. The electrons in excess of an octet in the next-to-outermost sublevel are those available for transfer. Iron is such a transition element. In forming compounds, it can transfer two *s* sublevel electrons from the N shell, and sometimes, in more energetic reactions, an additional electron can be transferred from the *d* sublevel of the M shell. Thus its valence can be +2, or +3. This accounts for the variable valence which is characteristic of many of the transition metals.

13. Radicals. Some groups of atoms act like single atoms in forming compounds. These groups of atoms are called *radicals.* Some of the common radicals are the sulfate ion, $SO_4^=$, the nitrate ion, NO_3^-, and the phosphate ion, $PO_4^≡$. The bonds within these radicals are predominantly covalent, but the groups of atoms have an excess of electrons when combined, and thus are negative ions. There is only one common positive radical, the ammonium ion NH_4^+, produced when a molecule of ammonia, NH_3, acquires a proton. Electron-dot representations of these radicals are:

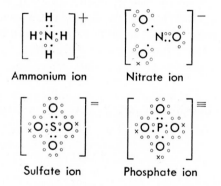

Ammonium ion　　　Nitrate ion

Sulfate ion　　　Phosphate ion

In the ammonium radical there are 11 protons (7 in the nitrogen nucleus and 1 in each of four hydrogen nuclei) and 10 electrons (2 in the K shell of the nitrogen atom, and the 8 valence electrons shown). With 11 protons and only 10 electrons, the radical has a net charge, or valence, of +1. The valences of the other radicals may be worked out in similar fashion. The electrons represented by small crosses are acquired by the radical from other elements through electron transfer.

14. The Table of Valences of Elements and Radicals. A knowledge of the ionic valences of common elements and radicals is very important in chemistry. They are given in the table on the next page. Cations other than ammonium have names which are the same as the elements from which they are formed. If a metal has more than one common valence, the name of the ion includes its valence in Roman numerals in parentheses. Before proceeding further, *this table must be thoroughly memorized.*

Since an older system of naming metallic ions is still frequently used, the following table of name equivalents will be helpful if you have to convert the name of a compound given in the older system to the new system used in this book.

Old System	New System
Cuprous, Cu^+	Copper(I), Cu^+
Mercurous, Hg^+	Mercury(I), Hg^+
Cupric, Cu^{++}	Copper(II), Cu^{++}
Ferrous, Fe^{++}	Iron(II), Fe^{++}
Mercuric, Hg^{++}	Mercury(II), Hg^{++}
Chromic, Cr^{+++}	Chromium(III), Cr^{+++}
Ferric, Fe^{+++}	Iron(III), Fe^{+++}

2. FORMULA WRITING

15. Valences are used in writing formulas. The valence of an element indicates how many electrons it gains, loses, or shares in forming compounds. The formulas for many compounds can be easily derived by means of the table of valences without becoming involved with the details of atomic structure and chemical bonding. First let us try sodium chloride. Sodium has a valence of +1, while chlorine as the chloride ion has a valence of −1. When formulas for compounds are written, *the total valence of the first, or positive, part of the compound must be equal but opposite in charge to the total valence of the* *second, or negative part of the compound. The total valence of an element is found by multiplying the valence of the element by the number of atoms of that element taken.* Since the valence of 1 atom of sodium is equal but opposite in charge to the valence of 1 atom of chlorine, the formula for sodium chloride, NaCl, indicates 1 atom of each element.

Next we shall try calcium chloride. Calcium has a valence of +2. Chlorine as the chloride ion has a valence of −1. In order that the total valence of the positive part of the compound be equal but opposite in charge to that of the negative part of the compound, 2 chlorine atoms will be needed. One calcium atom has a valence of +2, while the total valence of 2 chlorine atoms is −2, thus the formula is $CaCl_2$. The sub-

script $_2$ indicates that 2 atoms of chlorine combine with 1 atom of calcium in forming calcium chloride.

What is the formula for aluminum bromide? Aluminum has a valence of +3. Bromine as the bromide ion has a valence of −1. To make the total valence of each part of the compound equal but opposite in charge to the other, 3 bromide ions will be needed. They will have a total valence of −3, which will match the +3 of the aluminum. The formula is $AlBr_3$.

Observe that this method of formula writing yields only an empirical formula which shows the simplest whole-number ratio of atoms in the compound.

16. Writing the formulas for other compounds. In the case of lead(II) sulfate, the work is easy. Lead(II) has a valence of +2. Sulfate radical has a

VALENCES SHOWN BY COMMON ELEMENTS AND RADICALS

+1	+2	+3
Ammonium, NH_4^+	Barium, Ba^{++}	Aluminum, Al^{+++}
Copper(I), Cu^+	Calcium, Ca^{++}	Chromium(III), Cr^{+++}
Mercury(I), Hg_2^{++}	Copper(II), Cu^{++}	Iron(III), Fe^{+++}
Potassium, K^+	Iron(II), Fe^{++}	
Silver, Ag^+	Lead(II), Pb^{++}	
Sodium, Na^+	Magnesium, Mg^{++}	
	Mercury(II), Hg^{++}	
	Nickel(II), Ni^{++}	
	Zinc, Zn^{++}	

−1	−2	−3
Acetate, $C_2H_3O_2^-$	Carbonate, $CO_3^=$	Phosphate, $PO_4^{\equiv}$
Bicarbonate, HCO_3^-	Chromate, $CrO_4^=$	
Bisulfate, HSO_4^-	Oxide, $O^=$	
Bromide, Br^-	Peroxide, $O_2^=$	
Chlorate, ClO_3^-	Sulfate, $SO_4^=$	
Chloride, Cl^-	Sulfide, $S^=$	
Fluoride, F^-	Sulfite, $SO_3^=$	
Hydroxide, OH^-		
Iodide, I^-		
Nitrate, NO_3^-		
Nitrite, NO_2^-		

valence of -2. Since the valences are already equal but opposite in charge, only 1 lead atom and 1 sulfate radical are needed to form the compound whose formula is $PbSO_4$.

In writing the formula for magnesium hydroxide, a radical must be used more than once in a formula. The symbol for magnesium with a valence of $+2$ is Mg^{++}. Hydroxide with a valence of -1 is written OH^-. Two hydroxide radicals are needed in order to have a negative valence which is equal but opposite in charge to the positive valence of magnesium. In writing this formula parentheses are used to enclose the hydroxide radical, (OH). Then, the subscript $_2$ is written outside the parentheses, $(OH)_2$. This shows that it is the *entire* OH radical which is taken twice. The complete formula for magnesium hydroxide is $Mg(OH)_2$. This formula must *not* be written $MgOH_2$. If the formula were so written, it would indicate that there are 2 hydrogen atoms and 1 oxygen atom, not 2 hydroxide radicals. Chemists put the subscript number outside the parentheses to indicate that the radical inside the parentheses is found that number of times in the formula. Parentheses are not used when a radical is found only once in a formula.

Let us try another similar formula, that for lead(II) acetate. Lead(II) has the symbol Pb with a valence of $+2$. The acetate radical is $C_2H_3O_2$ with a valence of -1. One atom of lead and two acetate radicals are needed for the formula. Following the same system used for writing the formula for magnesium hydroxide, the formula for lead(II) acetate becomes $Pb(C_2H_3O_2)_2$. Note that in order to show that there are two acetate radicals in the formula, the $C_2H_3O_2$ is enclosed in parentheses, and the subscript $_2$ is placed outside.

Ammonium sulfate has two radicals in its formula. The ammonium radical is NH_4 with a valence of $+1$. The sulfate radical is SO_4 with a valence of -2. In order to make the total valences equal but opposite in charge, 2 ammonium radicals must be used. To represent these in the formula, the NH_4 is enclosed in parentheses, with the subscript $_2$ outside. The formula is then written $(NH_4)_2SO_4$.

Finally, let us write the formula for iron(III) carbonate. Iron(III) has a valence of $+3$. The valence of the carbonate radical is -2. In order to make the total valence of the positive part of the formula equal but opposite in charge to the total valence of the negative part of the formula, 2 atoms of iron and 3 carbonate radicals must be used. A total of six electrons is transferred—three from each of two iron atoms to two to each of three carbonate radicals. The formula is $Fe_2(CO_3)_3$.

17. Naming compounds from their formulas. For many types of compounds all that is necessary is to give the name of the first part of the formula and then follow it with the name of the second part. $BaSO_4$ is called barium sulfate (Ba^{++} is the barium ion, $SO_4^{=}$ is the sulfate radical). $FeCl_3$ is iron(III) chloride. Notice that there are two possible valence states for iron. One is iron(II) with a valence of $+2$; the other is iron(III), with a valence of $+3$. Since there are 3 chlorine atoms associated with the iron in this formula, the iron has a valence of $+3$, and the compound is *iron(III) chloride*. $FeCl_2$ is *iron(II) chloride*.

Another system is sometimes used to name certain binary covalent compounds. **Binary compounds** are those which consist of only two elements. They are named by the following steps.

1. The first word of the name is made up of: *a.* a prefix to indicate the number of atoms of the first element appearing in the formula, if more than one; and *b.* the name of the first element in the formula.
2. The second word of the name is made up of: *a.* a prefix to indicate the number of atoms of the second element appearing in the formula, if there exists more than one compound of these two elements; *b.* the root of the name of the second element; and *c.* the suffix *–ide*, which means that *only* the elements named are present.

Carbon monoxide is written CO. Only one atom of the first element appears in the formula, so no prefix is used with the first word; it consists only of the name of the first element, *carbon*. The prefix *mon–* is used in the second word of the name because there is only one atom of oxygen in this formula, but there is more than one compound of carbon and oxygen. *Ox–* is the root of the name of the element oxygen. Then comes the suffix *–ide*.

In like manner, CO_2 is carbon dioxide. The prefix denoting three is *tri–*; for four it is *tetra–*; and for five it is *pent–* or *penta–*. These prefixes are used with both the first and second words in the name. Examples are $SbCl_3$, antimony trichloride; CCl_4, carbon tetrachloride; and As_2S_5, diarsenic pentasulfide.

18. The significance of a formula. A formula written by the valence system may give only an indication of the simplest proportion which may exist between the atoms of combining elements. This simplest formula may be only an empirical formula. The actual molecule which is formed may be the same as the empirical formula, or it may be a multiple of the unit indicated in the empiri-

cal formula. For compounds which do not exist as molecules, a formula is empirical and merely indicates the relative numbers of atoms of each element.

As a beginner in chemistry you must be warned against expecting too much from the valence scheme. A formula can give no more information than that required to write it. It is possible to write the formula for a compound and then learn that such a compound just does not exist! There are many formulas, too, for compounds which do exist but which do not follow the rules of ionic valence. You will be unable to explain the formulas of any of these well-known compounds by the ionic valence scheme: H_2O_2, C_2H_2, CaC_2, C_2H_4, CO, or Fe_3O_4. Some of these apparent discrepancies are explained by covalent chemical bonding in the molecule:

Others are the result of oversimplification of the formula. Fe_3O_4, for instance, is a formula which is oversimplified. It actually should be written $FeO \cdot Fe_2O_3$.

19. Valence explains the Law of Definite Composition. We are now able to understand the real significance of the Law of Definite Composition. It is very easily explained by the principles of valence which we have just learned. The fact that atoms share, or transfer, or receive certain numbers of electrons when they combine controls the proportion in which those elements can combine. Only 1 hydrogen atom can combine with 1 chlorine atom. The hydrogen atom can share only 1 electron and the chlorine atom needs only 1 electron to complete its octet of M-shell electrons. The ratio of the two atoms which combine can be only 1 to 1. It cannot be 1 to 2, or 3 to 2, or some other ratio. Consequently, hydrogen chloride is always HCl, 1 atom of hydrogen to 1 atom of chlorine. The reason for other compounds being formed with very definite proportions depends on valence— the combining power of the individual atoms.

SUMMARY

Valence means the combining capacity of an element. Chemical bonds are produced when valence electrons are either transferred from the outer shell of one atom to the outer shell of another atom, or are shared with electrons in the outer shell of another atom. The formation of chemical bonds usually enables an atom to acquire a chemically stable outer shell.

There are two types of chemical bonding. 1. Ionic bonding, in which electrons are actually transferred from the outer shell of one atom to the outer shell of a second atom. The resulting particles are ions. 2. Covalent bonding, in which two atoms share a pair of electrons and form molecules.

Electronegativity is the tendency of an atom to attract the electrons which form a bond between it and another atom. Bonds between atoms having an electronegativity difference greater than about 1.7 are essentially ionic. Bonds between atoms having a smaller electronegativity difference are polar covalent, while bonds between atoms of equal electronegativity are pure covalent bonds.

Valence is the number of electrons which an atom gains, loses, or shares in bonding with one or more atoms. Elements may show several valences in compounds. Uncombined elements have no valence.

Radicals are groups of atoms which act like single atoms in forming compounds.

When formulas for compounds are written using the Table of Valences, the total valence of the first part of the compound must equal the total valence of the second part of the compound. (The total valence of a part of a compound is found by multiplying the valence of the part by the number of those parts taken.) The number of atoms or radicals taken is adjusted so the total valences are equal, and subscripts are used to indicate the number of atoms or radicals taken. These compounds are named by giving the names of the two parts of the compound.

When binary compounds, those containing only two elements, are named: 1. the first word consists of (*a*) a prefix to indicate the number of atoms of the first element appearing in the formula, if more than one, and (*b*) the name of the first element in the formula; 2. the second word consists of (*a*) a prefix to indicate the number of atoms of the second element, if there is more than one compound of these two elements, (*b*) the root of the name of the second element, and (*c*) the suffix –*ide*.

Valence explains the Law of Definite Composition. The number of electrons which can be gained, lost, or shared controls the proportions in which atoms can combine.

TEST YOURSELF ON THESE TERMS

anion
binary compound
cation
chemical bond
chemical stability
complete shell
covalence
covalent bonding

diatomic
electronegativity
electrovalence
formula
ionic bonding
ionic crystal
kernel
macromolecule

molecular crystal
polar covalent bond
polar molecule
radical
subscript
total valence
valence
valence electrons

QUESTIONS

Group A

1. What is valence?
2. (*a*) What part of the atom is involved in the production of a chemical bond? (*b*) How are such bonds formed?
3. (*a*) What are the types of chemical bonding? (*b*) What particles result from each type of bonding?
4. (*a*) What is an ion? (*b*) How does it differ from an atom?
5. What is the valence of: (*a*) sodium ion; (*b*) copper(I) ion; (*c*) iron(III) ion; (*d*) nickel(II) ion; (*e*) hydrogen in the water molecule?
6. What are the names of the following radicals: (*a*) NH_4; (*b*) SO_4; (*c*) NO_3; (*d*) CO_3; (*e*) $C_2H_3O_2$?
7. What is the valence of each of the following as ions: (*a*) HCO_3; (*b*) Br; (*c*) CrO_4; (*d*) SO_3; (*e*) PO_4?
8. Write formulas for these compounds: (*a*) barium chloride; (*b*) calcium oxide; (*c*) magnesium sulfate; (*d*) silver bromide; (*e*) zinc carbonate.
9. What are the names of the following compounds: (*a*) $NaHCO_3$; (*b*) H_2O_2; (*c*) $HgCl_2$; (*d*) $Fe(OH)_3$; (*e*) $Ni(C_2H_3O_2)_2$?
10. Write the formulas for the following compounds: (*a*) ammonium nitrate; (*b*) aluminum sulfide; (*c*) copper(II) hydroxide; (*d*) lead(II) phosphate; (*e*) iron(III) sulfate.
11. Name these compounds: (*a*) CuCl; (*b*) CaS; (*c*) $KHSO_4$; (*d*) $NaNO_2$.
12. Write the formulas for the following compounds: (*a*) chromium(III) fluoride; (*b*) nickel(II) chlorate; (*c*) potassium bicarbonate; (*d*) calcium chromate; (*e*) mercury(II) iodide.
13. What are the names of the following compounds: (*a*) Na_2O_2; (*b*) NH_4NO_2; (*c*) $Mg_3(PO_4)_2$; (*d*) $FeSO_4$; (*e*) Ag_2CO_3?
14. Write formulas for: (*a*) sodium bisulfate; (*b*) lead(II) chromate; (*c*) copper(I) chloride; (*d*) mercury(I) nitrate; (*e*) iron(II) oxide.
15. Name the following: (*a*) K_2SO_3; (*b*) $BaCrO_4$; (*c*) $Cr(OH)_3$; (*d*) $PbBr_2$.
16. What is electronegativity?
17. What electronegativity difference is there between atoms which form (*a*) ionic bonds? (*b*) polar covalent bonds? (*c*) bonds with no ionic character?
18. How does valence explain the Law of Definite Composition?

Group B

19. (*a*) What kind of outer electronic shell does an atom usually attain when it combines with other atoms? (*b*) Why is this electronic structure chemically stable?
20. Describe the types of energy changes which may occur: (*a*) in electron transfer; and (*b*) in sharing of electrons.
21. Draw an electron-dot symbol for: (*a*) a potassium atom; (*b*) a potassium ion.
22. Draw an electron-dot symbol for (*a*) a sulfur atom; (*b*) a sulfide ion.
23. Write the names for these compounds according to the system for naming binary compounds: (*a*) SO_3; (*b*) $SiCl_4$; (*c*) PBr_3; (*d*) As_2O_5; (*e*) PbO.
24. Write the formulas for these compounds: (*a*) sulfur dioxide; (*b*) bismuth trichloride; (*c*) manganese dioxide; (*d*) arsenic pentiodide; (*e*) carbon tetraiodide.
25. Explain why copper shows valences of +1 and +2.
26. (*a*) How is a radical similar to a molecule? (*b*) How does a radical differ from a molecule?
27. For each of the following bonds give the percent ionic character and indicate whether the bond is essentially ionic, polar covalent, or pure covalent. (*a*) K—Br; (*b*) C—O; (*c*) Na—O; (*d*) C—H; (*e*) Br—Br.
28. Classify each of the following as ionic crystal, polar covalent molecule, or nonpolar covalent molecule. (*a*) $MgCl_2$; (*b*) CCl_4, consisting of a central carbon atom and four symmetrically arranged chlorine atoms; (*c*) HCl; (*d*) CO_2, consisting of an oxygen atom, a carbon atom, and a second oxygen atom arranged linearly; (*e*) P_4.
29. Naphthalene crystals melt at 80° C, while sodium bromide crystals melt at 755° C. Which crystals are ionic and which are molecular?
30. Nitrogen atoms are joined in N_2 molecules by a triple covalent bond. Draw the electron-dot formula for a nitrogen molecule.

CHECK YOUR PROGRESS IN CHEMISTRY

1. What are the steps in the application of the scientific method?
2. What generalization did Einstein make which has contributed to our understanding of matter and energy?
3. Define the following terms: (*a*) matter; (*b*) heterogeneous material; (*c*) homogeneous material; (*d*) mixture; (*e*) element; (*f*) compound.
4. What is the meaning of the chemical symbol Na?
5. On the basis of the Kinetic Theory, how are the following observations explained: (*a*) gases are compressible; (*b*) gases exert pressure; (*c*) gases have a lower density than solids or liquids; (*d*) gases will completely fill any container into which they are admitted; (*e*) gases can be liquefied by compression?
6. What methods may be used to bring about chemical changes?
7. Give five statements to summarize the atomic theory.
8. Nitrogen has an atomic number of 7 and a mass number of 14. Explain how a nitrogen atom is made up.

9. What is the significance of the Roman numeral group designations, I, II, III, etc., on the Periodic Table?
10. Draw electron-dot symbols for the elements of the second series.
11. What is a probable electron distribution for element 104?
12. Why are the Inert Gases usually considered inert?
13. How do you explain the fact that chlorine has an atomic weight of 35.453, yet there are no atoms of chlorine that weigh this amount?
14. When we say that magnesium has an atomic weight of 24.312, what do we mean?
15. What similarities are there in the elements of Group I?
16. How do the properties of the elements change across period four of the Periodic Table?
17. Which family of elements on the Periodic Table has 6 electrons in the outermost shell?
18. Why does sodium have a valence of +1 in compounds and sulfide have a valence of −2?
19. How does ionic bonding differ from covalent bonding?
20. What is the formula for: (*a*) aluminum hydroxide; (*b*) copper(I) oxide; (*c*) ammonium sulfide; (*d*) lead(II) acetate; (*e*) iron(III) bromide; (*f*) magnesium bicarbonate; (*g*) silver sulfide; (*h*) mercury(II) iodide; (*i*) potassium sulfite; (*j*) nickel(II) phosphate?
21. Give the names of the following compounds: (*a*) CO; (*b*) CO_2; (*c*) SO_2; (*d*) SO_3; (*e*) N_2O_3; (*f*) N_2O_5.
22. Draw an electron-dot formula for (*a*) barium chloride; (*b*) sulfur dioxide.

CHALLENGING YOUR KNOWLEDGE

1. Write formulas for the following compounds: (*a*) cesium bromide; (*b*) hydrogen selenide; (*c*) radium carbonate; (*d*) indium hydroxide; (*e*) rubidium chromate.
2. Why is 6 a possible valence for chromium?
3. How was the magnitude of an atomic mass unit decided upon?
4. Why are tellurium and iodine in proper position in the Periodic Table according to atomic numbers but not according to atomic weights?
5. Naturally-occurring copper consists of the following percentages of two isotopes: 69.09% Cu-63 and 30.91% Cu-65. Cu-63 has an atomic mass of 62.930, and Cu-65 has an atomic mass of 64.929. What is the calculated atomic weight of copper? How does it compare with the accepted value for the atomic weight of copper?

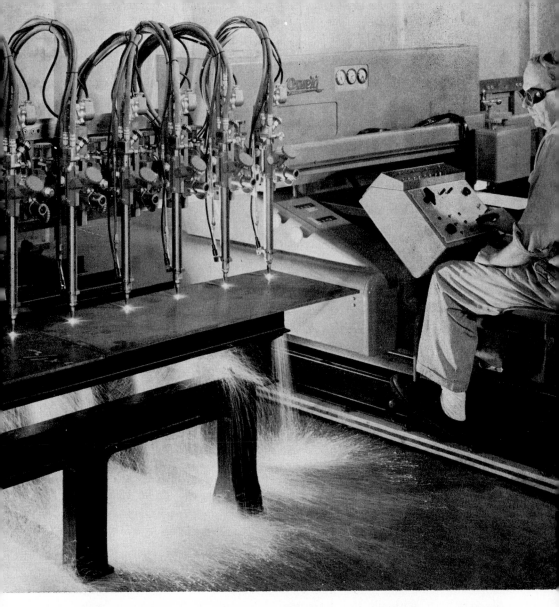

Unit 3 · WATER AND ITS ELEMENTS

Oxygen
Hydrogen
The Gas Laws
Water

Chapter 7 · OXYGEN

1. OXYGEN

1. Oxygen is the most important element. Oxygen, atomic number 8, has several characteristics which make it the most important element. It is the most abundant element in the earth's crust. In fact, it has been estimated that even if the composition of the entire earth is considered, there are more oxygen atoms in the earth, the waters on the earth, and in the atmosphere surrounding the earth, than atoms of any other single element. Oxygen is necessary for the support of plant and animal life. Oxygen combines with all the other elements except the inert gases.

2. Oxygen is found in the land, sea, and air. About one fifth of the atmosphere is oxygen. Animals living in water get their oxygen from the small amount that is dissolved in water. Oxygen in the air and oxygen that is dissolved in water are examples of *free* or *elementary oxygen.* As the free element, oxygen consists of diatomic covalent molecules, O_2. Oxygen that has united with other elements to form compounds is called

combined oxygen, and is much more plentiful than free oxygen. Water contains almost 89% oxygen by weight in combination with hydrogen. Such minerals as clay, sand, and limestone contain a large percentage of combined oxygen. In fact, oxygen is one of the elements present in most of the rocks and minerals of the earth's crust.

3. Joseph Priestley is credited as the discover of oxygen. Priestley (1733–1804) was an English clergyman and scientific experimenter. His greatest discovery came in 1774 when he used a lens to focus the sun's rays on mercury(II) oxide, a red powder. When this oxide is heated strongly, the bond between the atoms is broken, oxygen comes off as a gas, and mercury remains. The equation for this chemical change is:

$$2\ HgO \rightarrow 2\ Hg + O_2 \uparrow$$

A chemist uses an equation like this to show what happens during a chemical reaction. He writes the formulas of the material, or materials, he starts with (in this case mercury(II) oxide, HgO) on the left. Instead of an equals sign (=), he uses a yields sign (→). The materials produced in the reaction are written at the right of the yields sign. This reaction produces mercury, Hg, and oxygen, O_2. If the product is a gas, as oxygen is in this case, an arrow pointing upward is placed beside its formula to show that it is a gas. A word interpretation of this equation would be: Two molecules of mercury(II) oxide, when heated, yields two atoms of mercury and a molecule of oxygen gas. The writing of chemical equations will be discussed in more detail in Chapter 12.

Priestley did not use the name *oxygen* for the gas which he discovered. He described it as "perfect air" or "very active air." He was delighted to find that a candle would continue to burn brightly in the gas. Priestley inhaled some of the gas and said that he felt peculiarly light and easy for some time. The gas was later named *oxygen* by the French chemist Lavoisier.

It is remarkable that Karl Wilhelm Scheele (*shay*-luh) (1742–1786), a Swed-

Fig. 7-1. **Joseph Priestley, an English scientific experimenter, was a co-discoverer of oxygen.** (Brown Brothers)

ish chemist, also discovered oxygen about the same time. His results were not published until several years after his discovery, and by that time Priestley had been generally acknowledged as the discoverer of oxygen. Scheele should be given equal credit as its co-discoverer.

VOCABULARY

Allotrope. One of the two or more different forms of an element.

Combustion. Any chemical action which occurs so rapidly that both noticeable heat and light are produced.

Electrolysis. Separation of a compound into simpler substances by electricity.

Kindling temperature. The lowest temperature at which a substance takes fire and continues to burn.

Oxidation. Any chemical action in which an atom, a group of atoms, or an ion loses electrons.

Oxide. A compound consisting of oxygen and usually one other element.

Resonance. The shifting of the electronic structure of a molecule between two or more different patterns.

Spontaneous combustion. A combustion started by the accumulation of heat from slow oxidation.

Volatile. Easily vaporized.

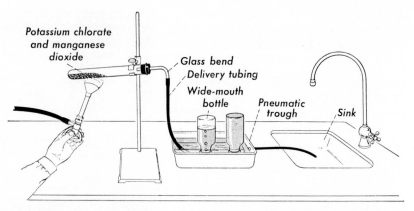

Fig. 7-2. Apparatus for the laboratory preparation and collection of oxygen.

4. The preparation of oxygen. There are several ways of preparing this element.

1. By heating potassium chlorate. This is the laboratory method most commonly used. Potassium chlorate is a white, crystalline solid composed of potassium, chlorine, and oxygen. When this compound is heated, it decomposes. Oxygen is given off and potassium chloride is left as a residue.

$$2 \; KClO_3 \rightarrow 2 \; KCl + 3 \; O_2 \uparrow$$

Manganese dioxide is usually mixed with the potassium chlorate in this labo-

ratory preparation. It acts as a catalyst or catalytic agent, therefore we do not include it in the equation (see Chapter 3, Section 15, Subsection 5).

Figure 7-2 shows the generation and collection of oxygen in the laboratory. The oxygen gas produced in the large test tube passes through the delivery tube into an inverted bottle that has previously been filled with water. As the oxygen rises in the bottle, it displaces the water. This method of collecting gases, known as *water displacement*, is used for gases which are not appreciably soluble in water.

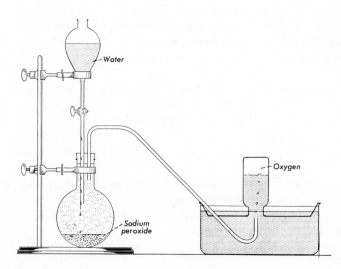

Fig. 7-3. Oxygen may also be prepared in the laboratory by adding water to sodium peroxide.

2. By the addition of water to sodium peroxide. Sodium peroxide, Na_2O_2, is prepared by burning sodium in air. If water is allowed to drop onto sodium peroxide in a generator like that shown in Fig. 7-3, oxygen is liberated.

$$2\ Na_2O_2 + 2\ H_2O \rightarrow 4\ NaOH + O_2 \uparrow$$

This is a convenient laboratory method for preparing small quantities of oxygen since it does not require heat, but sodium peroxide is a more expensive source of oxygen than potassium chlorate.

3. By the electrolysis of water. Figure 7-4 represents a laboratory apparatus in which water may be electrolyzed or decomposed by electric energy. Direct current electricity is passed through the water. Oxygen gas collects at the positive terminal, and hydrogen gas at the negative terminal. Sulfuric acid is added to make the water a better conductor of electricity.

$$2\ H_2O \rightarrow 2\ H_2 \uparrow + O_2 \uparrow$$

Large quantities of electric energy are needed to decompose the water. Industrially, this method yields oxygen of the highest purity. The hydrogen, which is produced simultaneously, may be sold as a by-product.

4. From liquid air. This is the common industrial method for preparing oxygen. Air can be changed to a liquid if it is compressed greatly at the same time that it is being cooled to a very low temperature ($-200°$ C). The liquid air which results consists largely of oxygen and nitrogen. Liquid nitrogen ($-195.8°$ C) has a boiling point about thirteen degrees lower than that of liquid oxygen ($-183.0°$ C). Hence, if liquid air is permitted to stand, the nitrogen will soon boil away and leave nearly pure liquid oxygen. The oxygen which then boils away is pure enough for industrial purposes. The raw material for this method of preparing oxygen costs nothing, but the machinery used is very expensive. Other gases are obtained from the liquid air and are sold as by-products.

5. The physical properties of oxygen. Pure oxygen is a colorless, odorless, tasteless gas which is slightly denser than air. At standard conditions of temperature ($0°$ C) and pressure (760 mm), one liter of oxygen has a mass of 1.43 g. Under the same conditions, one liter of air has a mass of 1.29 g. Oxygen is slightly soluble in water. The colder the water is, the greater is the volume of oxygen that can be dissolved in it. About five liters of oxygen can be dissolved in 100 liters of water at $0°$ C, but the same volume of water at $20°$ C can dissolve only three liters.

Any gas may be converted into a liquid if it is compressed under a high enough pressure, and cooled sufficiently at the same time. Liquid oxygen is pale-blue in color, and boils at $-183.0°$ C. It is slightly attracted by a magnet. This effect of a magnet on liquid oxygen leads

Fig. 7-4. An apparatus of this type may be used to decompose water by electrolysis.

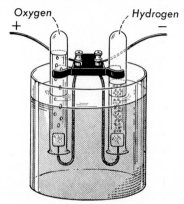

us to believe that there are unpaired electrons in an oxygen molecule. That is why

$$:\overset{..}{\underset{.}{O}}:\overset{..}{\underset{.}{O}}:$$

is a more accurate electron-dot formula for an oxygen molecule than

$$:\overset{..}{O}::\overset{..}{O}:$$

Further cooling of liquid oxygen results in its freezing to a pale-blue crystalline solid at $-218.4°$ C.

6. The chemical properties of oxygen. Oxygen is one of the most active elements. This is to be expected since oxygen is highly electronegative, ranking second only to fluorine, the most active nonmetal. Oxygen combines with other elements, forming compounds called *oxides*. An **oxide** *is a compound consisting of oxygen and (at least) one other element*. All oxides are formed by exothermic reactions and are usually very stable compounds. Pure oxygen is much more active than air, which contains one volume of oxygen diluted with about four volumes of nitrogen and other gases.

When the electronegativity difference between oxygen and another element is large, as it is with the metals of Groups I and II, the reaction between the two frequently occurs spontaneously and rapidly at room temperature. The following reactions are of this type, and the oxides formed are ionic compounds.

$$4\ Na + O_2 \rightarrow 2\ Na_2O$$
$$2\ Ba + O_2 \rightarrow 2\ BaO$$

The reactions of nonmetals and oxygen, where the electronegativity difference is small, generally occur at elevated temperatures. The resulting oxides contain covalent bonds and exist as molecules. These reactions are examples of this type of oxide formation.

$$S + O_2 \rightarrow SO_2$$
$$C + O_2 \rightarrow CO_2$$
$$2\ H_2 + O_2 \rightarrow 2\ H_2O$$

The electronegativity difference between oxygen and the metals other than those of Groups I and II is of intermediate value, about 0.8—1.8. Reactions between oxygen and these metals may occur slowly at room temperature, and will occur, sometimes quite rapidly, if the temperature is elevated. Iron, at room temperature and in the presence of moisture, unites slowly with oxygen. The resulting product is iron(III) oxide, commonly called iron rust.

$$4\ Fe + 3\ O_2 \rightarrow 2\ Fe_2O_3$$

A strand of steel picture wire or a small bundle of steel wool, heated red hot and plunged into pure oxygen, burns brilliantly and gives off bright sparks. Molten drops of another oxide of iron, Fe_3O_4, are formed in this reaction.

$$3\ Fe + 2\ O_2 \rightarrow Fe_3O_4$$

Such metals as tin, lead, copper, and zinc unite with oxygen to form oxides, slowly when cold, and more rapidly when heated. Oxides of metals such as gold and platinum are formed only at high temperatures. The oxides of metals of intermediate electronegativity difference are usually macromolecular in structure.

7. The test for oxygen. A blazing splint continues to burn in air, but it burns more vigorously in pure oxygen. If a *glowing* splint is lowered into a bottle of pure oxygen, it bursts into flame immediately. *This is commonly used as the test to identify oxygen.*

8. The uses of oxygen.

1. Oxygen is a prime essential for life. In higher animals and in man, oxygen enters the lungs with the inhaled air. It diffuses through thin membranes of the lungs into the blood stream from which it passes into the tissues and fluids of the body.

Fish and other animals that breathe by gills get their oxygen from air that is dissolved in the water.

All plants, except some of the simplest bacteria, require oxygen.

2. Oxygen tents are used in hospitals. Pure oxygen, or air to which more oxygen has been added, is sometimes given to persons suffering from pneumonia or other diseases. It is also administered to persons who may be too weak to inhale a normal quantity of air, such as persons who have experienced heart attacks. For these purposes the patient is placed in an oxygen tent. An electric motor keeps the tent supplied with air to which oxygen is added in any desired proportion.

In cases of asphyxiation from inhaling smoke or suffocating gases, from apparent drowning, or from electric shock, oxygen may be administered by means of an inhalator or a resuscitator.

3. Oxygen aids in the purification of water and sewage. Sunlight and oxygen are excellent agents for destroying harmful bacteria. Rivers containing sewage are purified by flowing considerable distances in contact with the oxygen of the air, which dissolves in the water and supports the life of organisms which decompose the polluting materials. In the sewage disposal plants of some cities, sewage is sprayed into the air in tiny jets in order to increase the amount of dissolved oxygen and thus hasten the purification process.

Fountains, cascades, and other devices are used to aid in city water purification. By exposing water to contact with air, disease bacteria are destroyed, and the water also becomes more palatable for drinking.

4. Oxygen is used in torches for welding. The oxyhydrogen torch was invented in 1801 by Robert Hare (1781–1858), an American chemist. Essentially it consists of two concentric tubes. Hydrogen from a storage cylinder passes through the outer tube and is lighted at the tip. The oxygen from a separate cylinder passes through the inner tube. It unites chemically with the hydrogen and produces a

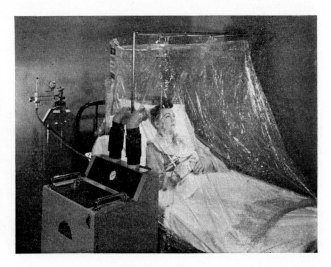

Fig. 7-5. An oxygen tent is used in the treatment of persons who are suffering from respiratory diseases or who are too weak to inhale a normal quantity of air. An electric motor keeps the tent supplied with air to which oxygen in any desired proportion is added.

flame with a temperature of about 2300° C. Oxyhydrogen torches are used for melting platinum and quartz, as well as to fuse aluminum oxide in making artificial rubies. For many purposes today, the oxyacetylene torch is more popular. As shown in Fig. 7-7, acetylene is used instead of hydrogen as the flammable gas. (Acetylene is the common name for the gas; its chemical name is *ethyne.*) The flame of this torch has a very high temperature, estimated at about 3400° C to 3700° C. It is used extensively in the cutting and welding of metals.

5. *Oxygen has several industrial uses.* Pure oxygen is reacted with coal, natural gas, or liquid fuels to produce a mixture of hydrogen and carbon monoxide which is then used in the production of synthetic gasoline, methanol, ammonia, and other important compounds. Oxygen is used in the steel industry to speed up steel production. In the glass industry, oxygen provides hotter, more intense flames for working high melting point glasses. Liquid oxygen is used in many rockets and missiles to burn the high-energy fuel.

2. OXIDATION AND COMBUSTION

9. Oxidation. The surface of a piece of sheet lead which has been scraped until it is bright and lustrous becomes dull and tarnished in a few days. The oxygen in the air unites slowly with the lead to form this tarnish, which is lead (II) oxide. The carbon of glowing charcoal in an outdoor grill combines with oxygen to form a gaseous compound, carbon dioxide. In both of these cases an element combines with oxygen and in the process is oxidized. Both reactions are exothermic; the one with carbon produces enough heat to be useful for cooking.

In reactions with all of the elements except fluorine, oxygen is the more highly electronegative element. Thus an atom of each such element when combining with an oxygen atom *loses its valence electrons either partially or completely*, depending on the percent of ionic character of the bond which is formed. While the term oxidation was originally used to describe the reaction of oxygen with some other substance, it

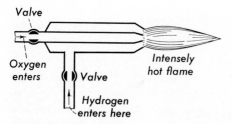

Fig. 7-6. **The oxyhydrogen torch, above, produces a flame with a temperature of about 2300° C.**

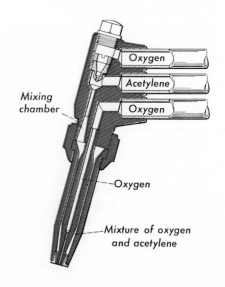

Fig. 7-7. **The oxyacetylene torch, at the right, is used for cutting and welding metals.**

Fig. 7-8. **An oxygen furnace for the production of steel in operation. The vigor of the reaction may be judged by the brightness of the waste gases being drawn off through the hood over the furnace.** (Jones and Laughlin)

now has a much broader meaning. *Oxidation is defined as any reaction in which an atom, a group of atoms, or an ion loses electrons.* Thus, while the reaction of an atom of an element (other than fluorine) with oxygen causes the atom to lose electrons and thus undergo oxidation, the process of oxidation is not limited to reactions involving oxygen. In the reaction

$$2\ Na + Cl_2 \rightarrow 2\ Na^+Cl^-$$

the sodium atoms lose electrons to the chlorine atoms and thus undergo oxidation.

In oxidations involving oxygen, the oxygen is usually supplied from the air. If a more vigorous oxidizing action is needed, pure oxygen gas may be used. A compound which is particularly rich in oxygen, and which readily gives up some of that oxygen, is said to be a good *oxidizing agent.* Examples of good oxidizing agents are hydrogen peroxide, H_2O_2, nitric acid, HNO_3, and potassium chlorate, $KClO_3$. However, since oxygen is not required for all oxidations, some good oxidizing agents, such as chlorine or bromine, contain no oxygen.

10. **Combustion.** A piece of magnesium ribbon held in the flame of a burner ignites and burns with an intense white light. It unites with oxygen so rapidly that both light and noticeable heat are produced. *Combustion or burning is defined as any chemical action which occurs so rapidly that both noticeable heat and light are produced.* When wood burns, the carbon and hydrogen of the wood unite chemically with the oxygen of the surrounding air. Just as oxidation may occur without

oxygen, so combustion may also take place without oxygen. Hydrogen burns in chlorine gas with a pale white flame which evolves noticeable heat. This reaction, too, is a combustion.

Ordinary burning, or ordinary combustion, *involving oxygen*, requires two materials. We must have both a combustible material and oxygen. Materials burn more rapidly in oxygen than they do in air, and some burn in oxygen which do not burn in air at all. Magnesium burns in air, but it burns almost explosively in oxygen. Finely divided iron burns in oxygen, giving off dazzling white sparks.

11. Burning was misunderstood until modern times. In early days, fire and burning were so mysterious that fire worship was not uncommon. Scientists through the ages pondered over this mysterious process and proposed theories to explain it. When substances burned,

Fig. 7-9. **Combustion is any chemical reaction which occurs so rapidly that both noticeable heat and light are produced. The burning of this building in air is an example of combustion.** (National Board of Fire Underwriters)

they seemed to lose something as the flames rose skyward. One theory of burning, which was popular during the 18th century, was the *phlogiston theory* of combustion. According to this theory, a combustible material was rich in a substance called *phlogiston*. When the material burned, the phlogiston escaped. No one had ever seen phlogiston, of course, but scientists assumed that it was there. Priestley was a firm believer in the phlogiston theory, even to the time of his death. The theory was wrong, and progress in chemistry was delayed until the discovery of the correct explanation of burning. We are indebted to Lavoisier, a French scientist, for correctly explaining burning and oxidation.

12. Lavoisier's twelve-day experiment. Antoine Laurent Lavoisier (1743–1794), the brilliant French scientist, had been studying the rusting of metals in air when he learned of Priestley's experiments with "perfect air." He came to the conclusion that the "perfect air" was really a part of ordinary air. To prove his point, he devised the following experiment, now considered one of the classic experiments of chemistry.

The retort, shown in Fig. 7-10, *contained a weighed quantity of mercury,* and the bell jar *contained a measured volume of air* at the beginning of the experiment. The pneumatic trough also contained mercury. When Lavoisier heated the mercury in the retort at a rather low temperature, some of it changed to a red powder. At the same time, the volume of air in the bell jar was reduced. After 12 days no further action took place. *The mercury in the retort had acquired a coating of red powder* and *the volume of the air in the bell jar had been reduced to four fifths of its former volume.* Thus Lavoisier proved that one fifth of the air is a gas

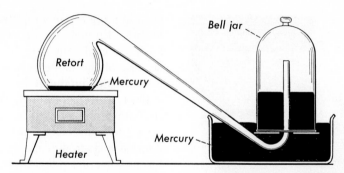

Fig. 7-10. **By using apparatus such as this, Lavoisier proved that Priestley's "perfect air" was a part of ordinary air. Lavoisier gave "perfect air" its present name of oxygen.**

that is capable of uniting with mercury to form a red powder. He named the gas *oxygen*. Today we recognize the red powder as mercury(II) oxide, and represent the reaction which took place between the mercury and the oxygen of the air by the following equation:

$$2 \text{ Hg} + \text{O}_2 \rightarrow 2 \text{ HgO}$$

After the first part of the experiment was completed, Lavoisier heated the red powder which had been formed, but more strongly than at first. He found that the gas which was liberated was exactly like Priestley's "perfect air." In fact, this part of Lavoisier's experiment is the same as the reaction by which Priestley discovered oxygen:

$$2 \text{ HgO} \rightarrow 2 \text{ Hg} + \text{O}_2 \uparrow$$

13. Kindling temperature. Before wood or other combustible material can begin to burn, heat must be applied to warm it to its *kindling temperature. The lowest temperature at which a substance takes fire, and continues to burn, is called its* **kindling temperature.**

Different substances have different kindling temperatures. The warmth of your hand is sufficient to kindle phosphorus, but you must not try it, because phosphorus produces painful burns. The head of a match is made of some material with a low kindling temperature. When the head is scratched, the friction develops enough heat to kindle the matchstick (see Fig. 7-11).

14. Increasing the surface area increases the rate of combustion. Combustion occurs only at the surface of a

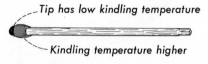

Tip has low kindling temperature

Kindling temperature higher

Fig. 7-11. **Why is a match made this way?**

Fig. 7-12. **In this experiment, the unburned match shows that combustion occurs only at the surface where the gases are uniting with oxygen.**

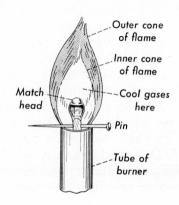

Outer cone of flame

Inner cone of flame

Match head

Cool gases here

Pin

Tube of burner

Fig. 7-13. **A dust explosion started the fire in these grain elevators.** (National Fire Protection Association)

burning material. A match head can be supported on the tube of a lighted burner, as shown in Fig. 7-12. The fact that the match is not kindled shows that burning takes place only at the surface of the flame where the gas comes into contact with the air. This may also be shown by momentarily thrusting a sheet of paper down on the flame. The charred spot on the paper will be circular, with an uncharred center.

A block of wood, split into two pieces, furnishes two new surfaces at which combustion can take place. Such pieces will burn faster than the original block. If these pieces are split again, more new surfaces are exposed to the oxygen in the air, and combustion is still more rapid. Excelsior and paper burn rapidly because they have such large surface areas at which combustion can occur.

15. Dust explosions. A powdered combustible substance, loose enough so that oxygen can mix with it readily, will burn in a practically instantaneous combustion throughout the entire mass. Such an explosion may be destructive because of the sudden expansion of the heated gases produced by the burning.

Dust scattered through the air of a coal mine, or tiny particles of cork dust in a linoleum factory, or particles of flour in a flour mill may explode with terrific force if kindled by an accidental spark. Such an explosion is called a *dust explosion* (see Fig. 7-13).

16. Fire extinguishing. Three requirements for ordinary combustion are: a supply of combustible material; a supply of oxygen; and enough heat to warm the combustible material to its kindling temperature.

The elimination of any one of these three requirements will extinguish a fire. All the known methods of extinguishing fires make use of at least one of the following principles: removing the combustible material; shutting off the supply of oxygen; and cooling the burning substance below its kindling temperature.

Some examples of each principle will emphasize each requirement. The scattering of the burning embers of a campfire and turning off the gas on a range are examples of removing the combustible material. Water lowers the tem-

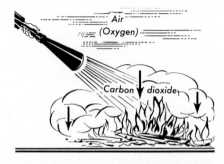

Fig. 7-14. **The carbon dioxide "snow" from a CO_2 extinguisher cools the burning material to below its kindling temperature. It forms a dense gas that blankets the fire.**

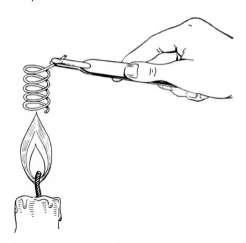

Fig. 7-15. **When the copper spiral is lowered into the candle flame, it conducts heat away so rapidly that the flame is cooled to below its kindling temperature. As a result, the candle is extinguished.**

perature of a burning substance, and as the water evaporates, its vapor shuts off the supply of oxygen. The effect of lowering the temperature may also be shown by holding a spiral of heavy copper wire in a candle flame. The copper conducts heat away so rapidly that the temperature falls below the kindling point, and the flame is extinguished. Dry sand is often effective for extinguishing oil fires because it cools the burning oil below its kindling temperature, and also shuts off the supply of oxygen.

17. **Spontaneous combustion.** *Spontaneous combustion* produces fires which seem to start themselves. Slow oxidation of a combustible material in a confined space liberates heat. If the heat cannot escape easily, it accumulates and increases the temperature of the combustible material. Eventually the kindling point is reached and burning results.

Spontaneous combustion can be dem-onstrated by placing a piece of white phosphorus about as large as a pinhead on an asbestos board. White fumes which rise from the phosphorus are good evidence that slow oxidation is taking place. If the phosphorus is now covered with a little powdered boneblack, it takes fire and burns vigorously because the boneblack holds in most of the heat of oxidation until the kindling temperature of phosphorus is reached.

Many fires start from spontaneous combustion. This often occurs in piles of bituminous coal, particularly if powdered coal covers a mass of lump coal in the center of the pile. The curing of hay is another process of oxidation. If hay is put into a barn before it is properly dried, oxidation will continue within the confined space and spontaneous combustion may result. Many barns are set on fire in this manner. Paint "dries"

Fig. 7-16. **Oily rags, such as those used to wipe up spilled paint, should be put in a metal can to prevent fires from starting by spontaneous combustion.** (National Safety Council)

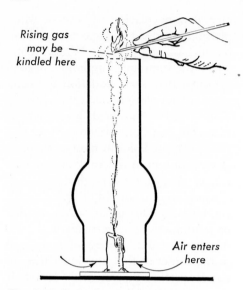

Rising gas
may be
kindled here

Air enters
here

Fig. 7-17. **A flame is a burning gas.**

Materials that are easily changed to a gas, or vaporized, are said to be volatile. Gasoline is an extremely volatile liquid. If some gasoline is poured into an open dish, the vapors are easily ignited, and the gasoline burns with a large flame. Kerosene is less volatile than gasoline. Hence, the flames from burning kerosene do not rise as high as those from gasoline. Charcoal and coke glow as they burn, but produce little or no flame. They are nearly pure carbon, a solid that does not change to a gas easily. Anthracite does not produce much flame because it contains little volatile matter. Many volatile substances are not combustible. Carbon tetrachloride, often used as a nonflammable cleaning fluid, is an example.

19. The operation of a laboratory burner. To secure better combustion, a laboratory burner is designed to mix some air with the gas before it is ignited.

A burner of the type shown in Fig. 7-18 was devised by the German chemist, Robert W. Bunsen (1811–1899). The laboratory burners used today have been somewhat improved over Bunsen's design. In the laboratory burner the gas enters the tube or barrel through a small opening called the tip or *spud.* The flow of gas through the tip is controlled by the needle valve. Air enters through the holes in the lower end of the barrel or tube. This air mixes with the gas in the tube before it reaches the top of the tube where it is ignited and burns. The tube can be turned to regulate the amount of air that enters. The complete operation of a burner will be explained in the laboratory by your instructor.

20. The parts of a burner flame. An examination of the flame of a properly adjusted laboratory burner shows that it consists of two distinct cones (see Fig. 7-18). The outer cone is called the

because the linseed oil which it contains absorbs oxygen from the air, forming an elastic solid. It is a form of oxidation, and heat is liberated as the paint "dries." For this reason cloths that have been used to wipe spilled paint are especially dangerous. They should first be hung outdoors where there is a good circulation of air, and then, if they must be kept, stored in a closed metal can as a precaution in preventing fires.

18. The nature of a flame. A candle burns with a yellow flame, but before the flame is produced, the wax of the candle must be melted and then changed into a vapor. If a glass cylinder is placed over a burning candle so that only a little air enters at the bottom, as shown in Fig. 7-17, we find that it is possible to extinguish the flame and then relight it by bringing a lighted taper just inside the top of the cylinder. The burning taper does not touch the wick, but it ignites the gas which is rising from the wick. This demonstration shows that a flame is a burning gas.

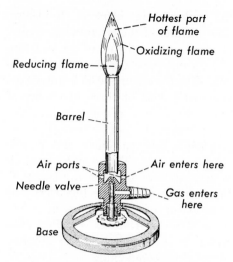

Fig. 7-18. A laboratory gas burner, showing the parts of the flame.

oxidizing flame. A piece of copper held in such a flame quickly becomes covered with a black layer of copper(II) oxide. If we hold the oxide of some metal, copper(II) oxide for example, in the inner cone of the burner flame, a process occurs that is the opposite of oxidation. The copper(II) oxide is soon *reduced* to the metallic state in the inner cone. The inner cone is called the *reducing flame.* The flame of the laboratory burner has a temperature of about 1600° C in the hottest part, just above the tip of the inner cone.

21. Some substances do not burn. Some substances burn readily and are said to be **flammable.** Other substances are **nonflammable** and do not burn under ordinary conditions. Nearly all oxides are nonflammable. Water and carbon dioxide make excellent fire extinguishers because they are nonflammable. Similarly, the oxides of calcium, magnesium, and silicon make good materials for lining furnaces. These substances are already fully oxidized, and therefore are incombustible.

3. OZONE

22. The occurrence of ozone. A peculiar odor is often noticed where static electricity machines are operating. This odor is due to the presence of ozone, a more active form of oxygen. Electric discharges through the air, such as sparks from a static electricity machine or a lightning flash, convert some of the oxygen of the air into ozone. The ultraviolet rays from the sun change some of the oxygen in the upper layers of the atmosphere into ozone.

23. The preparation of ozone. Ozone is produced by passing oxygen through an apparatus like that shown in Fig. 7-19, which consists of glass tubes that are partially covered with layers of tinfoil. The inner layers of tinfoil are connected with one terminal of an induction coil or static machine. The outer layers are connected to the other terminal. The discharge of electricity from one layer to the other provides the energy to convert some oxygen to ozone.

24. There is a difference between oxygen and ozone. Several chemical elements exist in two or more different forms. Oxygen is one such element. We shall learn later that other elements, such as carbon, sulfur, and phosphorus, may also occur in different forms. *The different forms of such elements are*

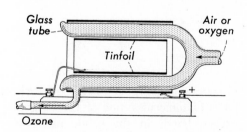

Fig. 7-19. Oxygen can be converted to ozone by an electric discharge in this apparatus.

Oxygen molecule   Ozone molecule

Fig. 7-20. A molecule of oxygen consists of two atoms of oxygen while a molecule of ozone consists of three atoms of oxygen. Oxygen and ozone are allotropes.

called *allotropes*. Ordinary oxygen and ozone are thus allotropes of oxygen. Allotropes are generally given different names, such as oxygen and ozone, or graphite and diamond, two allotropes of carbon.

In converting oxygen to ozone, energy is absorbed. Ozone, therefore, has greater energy than oxygen, and consequently is less stable and more active. Three volumes of oxygen form two volumes of ozone, because oxygen, O_2, has 2 atoms per molecule, while ozone, O_3, has 3 atoms per molecule.

$$3 \ O_2 + \text{energy} \rightarrow 2 \ O_3 \uparrow$$

25. The structure of the ozone molecule illustrates resonance. If we attempt to write an electron-dot formula for the ozone molecule, we see that there are two possible formulas which provide each oxygen atom with an octet of electrons:

$$\ddot{\text{O}}: \qquad \qquad :\ddot{\text{O}}:$$
$$:\ddot{\text{O}}\cdot \quad \text{or} \quad :\text{O}.$$
$$\ddot{\text{O}}: \qquad \qquad \ddot{\text{O}}:$$

If ozone actually consisted of these types of molecules, one of the oxygen-oxygen bonds in the ozone molecule should show properties different from the other. However, the properties of ozone indicate that the two bonds in

the molecule are identical. Evidently, then, neither of the electron-dot formulas shows a true picture of the structure of an ozone molecule. The actual molecule shows properties which are an average or *hybrid* of these two types of molecules. The oxygen-oxygen bonds in ozone molecules are intermediate in properties between single and double covalent bonds. The double bond is said to *resonate* between the two positions. *The shifting of the electronic structure of a molecule between two or more different patterns is called resonance.* It is quite a common property of covalent compounds.

26. The properties of ozone. Ozone is a blue gas with an irritating odor. It is denser than oxygen and considerably more soluble in water. Because ozone molecules have more energy than oxygen molecules, ozone is one of the most vigorous oxidizing agents known. It destroys bacteria, and it causes many colors to fade rapidly.

27. Ozone has several important uses. It has been used to some extent for bleaching wood pulp, textile fibers, oils, and waxes. Attempts have been made to use ozone in ventilating systems of buildings to purify the air. Unfortunately, ozone is irritating to the nasal passages and cannot be used in sufficient quantity to destroy the bacteria in the air. It is useful, however, for destroying the odors in slaughter houses, cold-storage rooms, and restaurant kitchens, because the oxides of many organic odor-causing substances are odorless gases. Ozone has been used for many years as an excellent water purifying agent. In concentrations of less than one part per million, it completely sterilizes the water, deodorizes it, and removes certain objectionable impurities such as iron and manganese compounds.

SUMMARY

Oxygen, the most abundant element, is found in the air, in water, and in many rocks of the earth's crust. Priestley and Scheele first prepared oxygen by heating mercury(II) oxide. In the laboratory, it is usually prepared by heating a mixture of potassium chlorate and manganese dioxide. The manganese dioxide acts as a catalyst. Commercially, oxygen is prepared by the electrolysis of water, or from liquid air.

Oxygen is a colorless, odorless, tasteless gas, which is slightly denser than air, and slightly soluble in water. It is a highly electronegative element which combines with other elements to form oxides.

Oxygen is an absolute necessity for life. Patients who have difficulty in breathing are sometimes administered oxygen. Oxygen aids in the purification of water and sewage. Oxyhydrogen and oxyacetylene torches are used to produce high temperatures. Oxygen is used in the production of methanol and other important carbon compounds, in the steel and glass industry, and to oxidize rocket and missile fuels.

Oxidation is any chemical action in which an atom, a group of atoms, or an ion loses electrons. Combustion is rapid oxidation in which noticeable heat and light are produced. Lavoisier was the first to correctly explain the nature of burning. For ordinary combustion to occur, we must have a combustible substance; it must be heated to its kindling temperature; and a supply of oxygen must be available. Conversely, to put out a fire, the combustible material must be removed; or it must be cooled below its kindling temperature; or the supply of oxygen must be shut off.

A flame is a burning gas. Easily vaporized materials are said to be volatile. Laboratory gas burners are designed to mix some air with the gas before it is burned. Gas flames have an outer cone, called the oxidizing flame, and an inner cone, called the reducing flame.

Ozone is a more active form of oxygen that is produced by an electric discharge. Ordinary oxygen and ozone are allotropic forms of oxygen. The ozone molecule is a resonance hybrid of two types of structure. Resonance is the property of an atom or molecule of shifting its electronic structure between two or more different patterns. Ozone is a vigorous oxidizing agent, destroying bacteria and causing colors to fade.

TEST YOURSELF ON THESE TERMS

allotrope	kindling temperature	oxyacetylene torch
burning	Lavoisier	oxyhydrogen torch
catalyst	liquid air	ozone
combined oxygen	meaning of →	phlogiston theory
combustion	meaning of ↑	Priestley
dust explosion	nonflammable	reducing flame
electrolysis	oxidation	resonance
elementary oxygen	oxide	volatile
flame	oxidizing agent	water displacement
flammable	oxidizing flame	method

QUESTIONS

Group A

1. Why is oxygen the most important element?
2. Distinguish between: (*a*) elementary oxygen, and (*b*) combined oxygen. Give an example of the occurrence of each.
3. Why is manganese dioxide used in the laboratory preparation of oxygen?
4. (*a*) What method of gas collection is used for oxygen? (*b*) What property must a gas have so that it may be collected by this method?
5. What are the physical properties of oxygen gas?
6. What type of compound is formed when oxygen combines with another element?
7. (*a*) Write a word equation for the reaction between potassium and oxygen which yields K_2O. (*b*) Will K_2O be ionic, molecular, or macromolecular? (*c*) Why?
8. (*a*) Write a word equation for the reaction between selenium and oxygen which yields the solid, SeO_2, which melts at about 340° C. (*b*) Will SeO_2 be ionic, molecular, or macromolecular? (*c*) Why?
9. How can an old battleship be divided into pieces of steel scrap?
10. Distinguish between oxidation and combustion.
11. In ordinary burning, what is the oxidizing agent?
12. Why do we use crumpled paper, sticks of wood, and finally coal, in starting a coal fire?
13. Why does a pile of magazines burn poorly in a rubbish burner?
14. What are the three requirements for ordinary combustion to occur?
15. Give three examples of fires that are sometimes started by spontaneous combustion. How may they be prevented?
16. Draw a diagram and explain the operation of a laboratory burner.
17. (*a*) What is an allotrope? (*b*) Give two examples of elements which exist in allotropic forms.
18. (*a*) What advantages does ozone possess for air purification? (*b*) Why, then, is it not extensively used in air-conditioning systems?

Group B

19. Describe Priestley's discovery of oxygen.
20. Interpret the equation, $2 H_2 + O_2 \rightarrow 2 H_2O$, in words.
21. Which has the lower boiling temperature, oxygen or nitrogen?
22. How can you test a colorless, odorless, and tasteless gas to determine whether it is oxygen or not?
23. Why do we drown in water, and yet fishes die in air?
24. (*a*) Describe Lavoisier's Twelve-Day Experiment. (*b*) What significance was it to the development of chemistry?
25. Why do dust explosions sometimes occur in flour mills?
26. Give examples of each of the three methods for extinguishing fires.
27. Oxygen and fluorine combine indirectly to form OF_2. In this reaction which element is oxidized and why?
28. By means of electron-dot formulas illustrate resonance in the ozone molecule.
29. Why do we believe that an oxygen molecule contains unpaired electrons?

PROBLEMS

Group A

1. Water is 88.89% oxygen. How many grams of oxygen can be obtained by the electrolysis of 100. grams of water?
2. How many liters of oxygen will be produced in Problem 1? One liter of oxygen has a mass of 1.43 g.
3. Iron rust is 30.0% oxygen and 70.0% iron. What weight of iron rust can be formed from 50.0 lb of iron?

Group B

4. When 12.0 g of carbon are burned, 44.0 g of carbon dioxide are produced. How much carbon dioxide goes up the chimney during a season when 10.0 tons of coal is burned, if the coal contains 80.0% carbon?
5. Potassium chlorate contains 39.2% oxygen, and mercury(II) oxide contains 7.39% oxygen. How many grams of mercury(II) oxide would have to be heated to give the same amount of oxygen as that obtained from the heating of 100. g of potassium chlorate?
6. What volume will 100. g of oxygen occupy at 0° C and 760 mm pressure?

SOME THINGS FOR YOU TO DO

1. Look up the basic ideas of the phlogiston theory in a history of chemistry or an encyclopedia. Find out how an experiment such as the burning of magnesium ribbon in air would have been explained by this theory. What data would you need concerning this experiment to prove the theory false?
2. Spread a little lycopodium powder on an asbestos square and try to ignite it with a Bunsen burner. Note how difficult it is to get a compact mass to burn. Now spread some of the lycopodium powder on a cardboard. Shake the cardboard about two feet above a Bunsen burner flame in such a way that the lycopodium powder falls as a dust cloud. A flash of flame similar to a dust explosion results.
3. Crumple some paper towels into a loose paper wad, and support the wad on an iron tripod. Dissolve a tiny piece of phosphorus in 10 ml of carbon disulfide, and pour the solution over the paper wad. Spontaneous combustion should occur within a few minutes. CAUTION: *Dispose of all residues in such a way as to avoid accidental fires later.*
4. Visit an automobile repair shop where oxyacetylene welding is done.
5. If you live near or travel during vacation time through Sunbury, Pennsylvania, visit the Priestley Museum in nearby Northumberland. Here you will see some of the actual apparatus used by Priestley, together with many other relics and personal papers preserved from the days after Priestley moved to the United States.

Chapter 8 · HYDROGEN

1. The occurrence of hydrogen. Hydrogen, the simplest element, is, like oxygen, a gas at ordinary temperatures. It ranks ninth in abundance by weight among the chemical elements, but it ranks in second or third place if actual numbers of atoms are considered. Hydrogen is usually combined with other elements in a variety of compounds. There are more compounds of hydrogen than of any other element. Free, or elementary hydrogen, which exists as covalent diatomic molecules, H_2, is much less common because of its flammability. Very small traces of hydrogen, probably derived from volcanoes and coal mines, do exist in the air. However, such small amounts are present that it is not listed as one of the important gases of the atmosphere. One ninth of water by weight is hydrogen, and all acids contain this element. Hydrogen is present in nearly all plant and animal tissues. Nearly all fuels—natural gas, wood, coal, and oil—contain hydrogen.

2. The early history of hydrogen. In the sixteenth century it was observed that a combustible gas was produced when sulfuric acid reacted with iron. Henry Cavendish (1731–1810), an English scientist, is usually credited as the discoverer of hydrogen, because in 1766 he first prepared a quantity of the gas and observed its properties. Cavendish observed that hydrogen burns. He called the gas "inflammable air." In 1781, as a

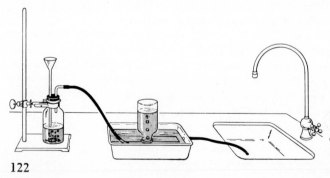

Fig. 8-1. The laboratory preparation and collection of hydrogen.

result of experiments, he proved that water is the only product of the combustion of hydrogen in air. Lavoisier in 1783 suggested the present name *hydrogen*, a word derived from two Greek words meaning "water producer."

3. The preparation of hydrogen. *1. From acids by replacement.* This is the usual laboratory method. All acids contain hydrogen, which usually may be set free by reaction with certain metals. Several different acids and several different metals can be used. For example, iron, zinc, or magnesium will react with either hydrochloric acid or sulfuric acid to produce hydrogen. The rate at which hydrogen is evolved in such reactions depends upon several factors: the amount of metal surface exposed to the acid; the temperature; the strength and kind of acid used; the kind of metal used; and the purity of the metal.

Figure 8-1 shows one type of apparatus commonly used for the laboratory preparation of hydrogen. Zinc is put into the bottle and either dilute sulfuric or hydrochloric acid is then added through the funnel tube. The hydrogen is collected by water displacement. The equations for the chemical reactions of zinc with sulfuric acid, H_2SO_4, and hydrochloric acid, HCl, are:

$$Zn + H_2SO_4 \rightarrow ZnSO_4 + H_2 \uparrow$$
$$Zn + 2\ HCl \rightarrow ZnCl_2 + H_2 \uparrow$$

During these reactions it looks as though the zinc dissolves in the acid, but this is not so. These are *chemical reactions* in which the metal *reacts* with the acid and forms free hydrogen gas and a zinc compound. The zinc sulfate or zinc chloride is dissolved in the excess water, but either may be recovered as a white solid by evaporating the water. We see, then, that new substances with new properties are formed. This is definite evidence of a chemical reaction and not of a mere physical change. If the formulas of the acids are compared with the formulas of the zinc compounds produced, we can easily see that an atom of zinc has taken the place of two atoms of hydrogen.

VOCABULARY

Absorption. A soaking up of one substance through the entire mass of another.

Adsorption. The acquisition of one substance by the surface of another.

Diffusion. The process by which two or more originally separate kinds of atoms or molecules mix because of their atomic or molecular motion.

Hydride. A compound of hydrogen and at least one other element of lower electronegativity.

Hydrogenation. The chemical addition of hydrogen to a material.

Oxidizing agent. The atom, group of atoms, or ion which takes up electrons during a chemical reaction.

Reducing agent. The atom, group of atoms, or ion which supplies electrons during a chemical reaction.

Reduction. Any chemical action in which an atom, a group of atoms, or an ion gains electrons.

2. From water by replacement. Sodium is a silvery metal, soft enough to be easily cut with a knife, and of low enough density to float on water. It is so active chemically that it reacts vigorously with water and liberates hydrogen gas from it. Each sodium atom replaces one of the hydrogen atoms in a molecule of water. To show this reaction more clearly, the formula for water is written as HOH, instead of the usual H_2O.

$$2 \text{ Na} + 2 \text{ HOH} \rightarrow 2 \text{ NaOH} + H_2 \uparrow$$

Each water molecule has had *one* of its hydrogen atoms replaced by a sodium atom. The sodium hydroxide produced may be recovered as a white, crystalline solid if the excess water is evaporated.

Potassium is a metal which is similar to sodium. It is below sodium in the same family in the Periodic Table and is more reactive. It liberates hydrogen from water with such vigor that the heat of the reaction is sufficient to ignite the hydrogen. The equation for the reaction of potassium and water is:

$$2 \text{ K} + 2 \text{ HOH} \rightarrow 2 \text{ KOH} + H_2 \uparrow$$

Magnesium decomposes *boiling* water slowly. Calcium, in the same family as magnesium, but below it in the Periodic Table, and thus more reactive, will liberate hydrogen slowly from cold water. At a high temperature, iron will liberate hydrogen from steam.

All the methods of preparing hydrogen from water by replacement by metals are laboratory methods.

3. From water by electrolysis. In the electrolysis of water, hydrogen as well as oxygen is produced. Commercially, if oxygen is the main product, hydrogen becomes a by-product which can also be sold. This method is used in the United States for producing pure hydrogen in

areas where cheap electricity is available. It is also a laboratory method of preparing hydrogen.

4. From water by hot carbon. This is a common industrial process for producing hydrogen. When steam is passed over red-hot coal or coke, a mixture of gases called *water gas* is formed. It consists mainly of hydrogen and carbon monoxide. When the mixture is cooled and compressed, the carbon monoxide liquefies, and the remaining hydrogen gas is then compressed into steel cylinders. The equation for the reaction is:

$$C + H_2O \rightarrow CO \uparrow + H_2 \uparrow$$

Frequently the carbon monoxide is converted to carbon dioxide by passing the water gas with additional steam over a catalyst, such as iron oxide, at a temperature below 500° C.

$$CO + H_2O \rightarrow CO_2 \uparrow + H_2 \uparrow$$

Thus additional hydrogen is produced from the steam, and the resulting carbon dioxide is separated by dissolving it in water under moderate pressure.

5. From hydrocarbons. Hydrocarbons are compounds of hydrogen and carbon which are commonly derived from petroleum or natural gas. If a hydrocarbon, such as propane, C_3H_8, reacts with steam in the presence of a nickel catalyst at a temperature of about 850° C, hydrogen and carbon dioxide are produced.

$$C_3H_8 + 6 H_2O \rightarrow 3 CO_2 \uparrow + 10 H_2 \uparrow$$

The carbon dioxide may be separated from the hydrogen by dissolving it in water under pressure.

Hydrogen may also be obtained by heating hydrocarbons in the absence of oxygen to decompose them. If methane, CH_4, is so decomposed the equation for the reaction is:

$$CH_4 \rightarrow C + 2\,H_2 \uparrow$$

The carbon produced is in the form of lampblack.

4. The physical properties of hydrogen. Hydrogen gas is colorless, odorless, and tasteless. It is the gas of lowest density, its density being only one fourteenth that of air. One liter of hydrogen at standard temperature (0° C) and standard pressure (760 mm) has a mass of 0.09 gram. It is less soluble in water than oxygen.

In 1898 James Dewar (1842–1923) succeeded in converting hydrogen into a liquid by cooling the gas to a *very low temperature*, and at the same time subjecting it to *very high pressure*. Liquid hydrogen is clear and colorless, and only one fourteenth as dense as water. Thus liquid hydrogen, the liquid of lowest density, has a mass of about 70 grams per liter. Under atmospheric pressure, liquid hydrogen boils at −252.7° C. When a part of the liquid is evaporated, the remainder freezes to an icelike solid whose melting point is −259.1° C. It is the solid of lowest density, having a mass of 88 grams per liter.

An interesting property of hydrogen is its *adsorption* by certain metals, such as platinum and palladium. **Adsorption is an acquisition of one substance by the surface of another, whereas absorption is a soaking up of one substance through the entire mass of another,** as in the case of a sponge and water. A piece of platinum *adsorbs*, or *occludes*, hydrogen gas, liberating heat in the process. Adsorption is physically similar to condensation. In both processes widely separated gas molecules are brought into the closer proximity characteristic of liquids. During such a change the molecules evolve energy which appears as heat. Finely divided platinum offers a larger surface,

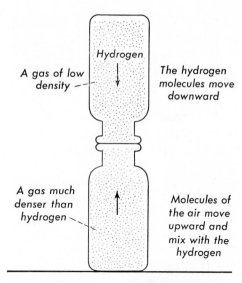

A gas of low density

Hydrogen

The hydrogen molecules move downward

The hydrogen molecules move downward

A gas much denser than hydrogen

Molecules of the air move upward and mix with the hydrogen

Fig. 8-2. **Although air is 14 times as dense as hydrogen, the light, fast hydrogen molecules move downward and intermingle with the slower, heavier molecules of the gases in the air.**

adsorbing the gas so rapidly that the hydrogen gas may be raised to the kindling temperature. Some gas burners use this principle for igniting the gas.

Hydrogen diffuses rapidly because hydrogen molecules move about with greater velocity than the heavier molecules of other gases at the same temperature (see Chapter 3, Sections 7 and 8). The diffusion of hydrogen can be demonstrated by placing a bottle filled with hydrogen gas above another bottle filled with air, as shown in Fig. 8-2. After a few minutes, the mouth of each bottle is held in the flame of a laboratory burner. The resulting explosions show that the hydrogen molecules moved so that there were some in both bottles.

Even if two gases are separated by a porous barrier, such as a membrane or an unglazed porcelain cup, diffusion takes place through the pores, as shown

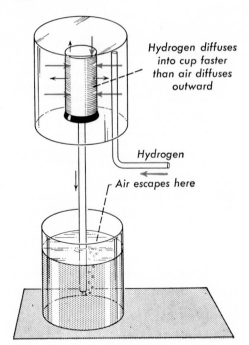

Fig. 8-3. **Hydrogen diffuses into the cup faster than air diffuses outward. As a result, some of the air in the cup is forced down the tube and bubbles through the liquid.**

in Fig. 8-3. An unglazed porcelain cup is closed by a rubber stopper through which a piece of glass tubing has been inserted. When a large beaker filled with hydrogen is placed over the porcelain cup, hydrogen molecules diffuse into the cup faster than the molecules of the gases in air diffuse into the beaker. This creates a pressure in the cup which forces gas out the end of the tube.

The rapid diffusion of hydrogen makes it difficult to store in thin-walled containers. Rubber balloons filled with hydrogen collapse in a short time because the hydrogen escapes through the rubber.

5. The chemical properties of hydrogen.

1. Reactions with nonmetals. Since the electronegativity of hydrogen (2.1) equals or is less than the electronegativity of other nonmetals, hydrogen reacts with nonmetals to form molecular compounds with covalent bonds whose polarity depends on the electronegativity of the nonmetal. Such bonds range in polarity from the almost nonpolar H — C bond to the highly polar H — F bond.

Hydrogen burns in air or oxygen with a very hot, pale-blue, nearly invisible flame. Water is the only product of combustion (see Fig. 8-4).

$$2\ H_2 + O_2 \rightarrow 2\ H_2O$$

Hydrogen does not support combustion. If a bottle of hydrogen is held mouth downward while a blazing splint is thrust slowly upward into the bottle, the hydrogen ignites and burns at the mouth of the bottle, but the splint does not burn inside the bottle in an atmosphere of hydrogen. (See Fig. 8-5.) Hydrogen is not a very active element at ordinary temperatures. A mixture of hydrogen and oxygen must be heated to 800° C or ignited at a lower temperature by an electric spark to make the gases combine. Then they combine explosively.

Hydrogen and chlorine do not combine when they are mixed in the dark, but in the presence of direct sunlight they unite explosively forming hydrogen chloride. A jet of hydrogen will burn in chlorine. The equation for these chemical changes is the same:

$$H_2 + Cl_2 \rightarrow 2\ HCl \uparrow$$

Under suitable conditions, hydrogen may be made to unite with nitrogen to form ammonia, NH_3, a very important compound.

$$3\ H_2 + N_2 \rightarrow 2\ NH_3 \uparrow$$

2. *Reactions with metals.* Hydrogen reacts with many nontransition metals to form binary compounds called *hydrides*. In these compounds hydrogen is the more electronegative element. The hydrides of Group I metals and of the Group II metals, calcium, strontium, and barium, are ionic compounds which at room temperature are white crystalline solids. In these compounds hydrogen is present as the H⁻, hydride ion. They may be produced by heating the free metal in an atmosphere of hydrogen.

$$2 \, Na + H_2 \rightarrow 2 \, Na^+H^-$$
$$Ba + H_2 \rightarrow Ba^{++}H_2^-$$

6. Reduction. When a piece of sheet copper is heated in air, a black scale of copper(II) oxide forms on the surface. In this reaction,
Equation 1

$$2 \, Cu + O_2 \rightarrow 2 \, CuO$$

the copper partially *loses electrons* to the oxygen when copper(II) oxide is formed, and thus undergoes *oxidation*.

If this copper(II) oxide is put in a Pyrex glass tube, as shown in Fig. 8-6, and a stream of dry hydrogen passed over it while the copper(II) oxide is being heated, the hydrogen combines with the oxygen from the copper(II) oxide and forms water, leaving elementary copper.
Equation 2

$$CuO + H_2 \rightarrow Cu + H_2O$$

In this reaction the copper *regains the electrons* it partially lost to the oxygen in the reaction represented by Equation 1. The copper is said to have undergone *reduction*. While reduction originally meant only the removal of oxygen from a compound, **reduction is now defined**

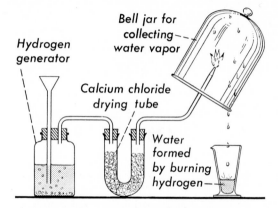

Fig. 8-4. When hydrogen is burned in air, water vapor is the only product of combustion.

as any chemical action in which an atom, a group of atoms, or an ion gains electrons. Reduction is thus the opposite of oxidation, and the two processes must occur simultaneously.

We have already stated that in Equation 1 the copper underwent oxidation, or was oxidized. Since in combining with the copper, the oxygen partially gained electrons from the copper, the oxygen underwent reduction, or was reduced. In an oxidation-reduction reaction *the*

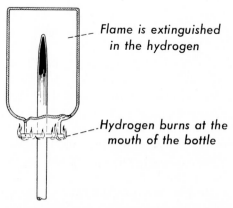

Fig. 8-5. When a blazing splint is thrust upward into a bottle of hydrogen, the hydrogen is ignited and burns at the mouth of the bottle, but the splint does not burn inside the bottle in an atmosphere of hydrogen.

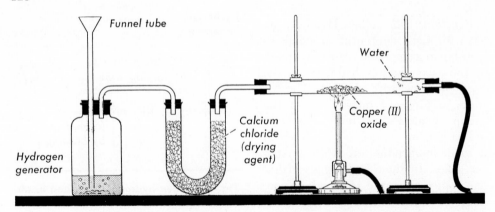

Fig. 8-6. When hydrogen is passed over hot copper(II) oxide, the combined copper is reduced to elementary copper. The calcium chloride is used to dry the hydrogen by absorbing any water the hydrogen bubbles may have carried over from the generator. Thus the water that condenses on the cool walls of the long Pyrex tube beyond the hot copper(II) oxide must be the result of the combination of hydrogen and the oxygen from the oxide.

atom, group of atoms, or ion which takes up electrons is the **oxidizing agent** —in Equation 1 oxygen was the oxidizing agent. Similarly, the atom, group of atoms, or ion which loses electrons is known as the **reducing agent**—in Equation 1 copper was the reducing agent. Note that in such reactions the substance oxidized acts as the reducing agent and the substance reduced acts as the oxidizing agent.

In Equation 2 the copper gained electrons and was reduced. The hydrogen partially lost electrons to the oxygen when water was formed, and so it was oxidized. The oxygen experienced neither oxidation nor reduction. Copper is the oxidizing agent and hydrogen is the reducing agent.

7. The test for hydrogen. Suppose you have been given a colorless gas which you wish to prove to be hydrogen. If the gas burns in air and forms water, you know that it contains hydrogen. If a gas burns in air or oxygen with a nearly colorless flame and produces only water

as the product, we have a conclusive test for hydrogen.

8. The uses for hydrogen.

1. For its low density. Because hydrogen is the gas of lowest density, it has been used for filling both toy balloons for children and large gas bags for airships. What is called the "lifting power" of hydrogen is really the difference between the weight of a given volume of air and that of the same volume of hydrogen. To lift heavy weights, balloons filled with hydrogen must be large in order that they displace a large volume of air. However, the tendency of hydrogen to leak through tiny openings and its flammability have caused some terrible disasters. Helium, the inert gas with about 93% as much "lifting power" as hydrogen, is much safer. Since it is chemically inert, it is, of course, not flammable. Military balloons of the United States are inflated with helium. The Weather Bureau sends hydrogen-filled balloons aloft to observe air currents and weather conditions in the upper air.

2. As a reducing agent. Hydrogen can remove oxygen from the oxides of some metals, such as copper, tin, lead, zinc, and iron, which are found in nature as oxides. Hydrogen is sometimes used as a reducing agent to extract metals from their oxides, but more often carbon in the form of coke is used because it is usually less expensive and more convenient.

Some metals need to be worked in an atmosphere free of oxygen, or in what is called a *reducing atmosphere.* Tungsten, a metal which is used for making the filaments of electric lamps, is worked in a reducing atmosphere. By surrounding the tungsten with hydrogen in a closed furnace, the oxidation of the metal is prevented.

3. As a fuel. Nearly all our fuels contain hydrogen, either free or combined with other elements. Coal gas and oil gas contain hydrogen in quantity. Methane, CH_4, is a major component of natural gas. Hydrogen is used as a fuel for the oxyhydrogen torch. Pure hydrogen makes an excellent fuel, but is somewhat more expensive than other available gaseous fuels.

4. For making hydrogen compounds. The greatest use for hydrogen today is in making ammonia, NH_3, by direct union of nitrogen and hydrogen. The ammonia is then used as the starting point for making fertilizers, explosives, dyestuffs, and many other valuable and useful compounds.

Increased amounts of gasoline are obtained from petroleum by reacting hydrogen with some of the higher boiling portions of the oil. High pressures and a catalyst are necessary in this *hydrogenation* of petroleum.

Methanol, or wood alcohol, which is used as an ingredient in antifreeze for automobiles and also as a solvent, is made from hydrogen and carbon monoxide. A catalyst is used to speed up the reaction. Increasing quantities of hydrochloric acid are being produced by direct combination of the elements hydrogen and chlorine.

5. For hardening oils. Millions of pounds of cottonseed oil are changed each year from liquid oil to solid fat by hydrogenation, using finely divided nickel as a catalyst. Some of the molecules in the liquid oil combine with additional hydrogen atoms in the process, producing a substance that is a solid fat at room temperature, but still a liquid fat at body temperature. Most vegetable shortenings found on, the market today are examples of such hydrogenated oil.

Peanut, corn, soybean, and coconut oil are also hardened by hydrogenation to make margarine. Some fish oils lose their objectionable odor when they are hydrogenated, and thus become suitable for making soap. Lard is sometimes hydrogenated to produce a whiter, firmer product.

6. In the atomic hydrogen torch. Molecules of hydrogen are diatomic at ordinary temperatures. Dr. Irving Langmuir (1881–1957), an American scientist, found that it is possible to break up hydrogen molecules into their atoms by passing hydrogen gas through an electric arc. Tungsten electrodes are used, as shown in Fig. 8-7. The bond between hydrogen atoms in a hydrogen molecule is probably the strongest covalent bond. Therefore, tremendous energy must be used to overcome the forces binding the atoms into molecules. Accordingly, the combustion of atomic hydrogen beyond the arc yields not only the heat evolved as water vapor is formed, but also a much larger amount of heat, equal to the energy expended in breaking up the

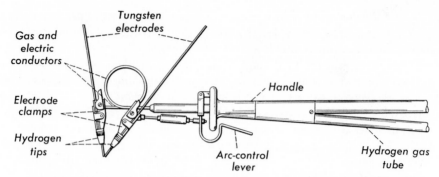

Fig. 8-7. The atomic hydrogen torch produces heat from the combustion of atomic hydrogen to form water vapor.

hydrogen molecules into atoms. The temperature produced by the atomic hydrogen torch is estimated at 4000° C. It is used for cutting and welding metals which cannot be fused by other torches at lower temperatures.

7. In the hydrogen bomb. The large amount of energy produced by a hydrogen bomb is a result of nuclear reactions taking place between the isotopes of hydrogen, deuterium, and tritium. These reactions are discussed in Chapter 39.

SUMMARY

Hydrogen is found in water and in all acids. It was discovered by Cavendish in 1766. In the laboratory it is prepared by reacting an acid with a metal such as zinc, or by adding an active metal such as sodium to water. Commercially, it is prepared from water by electrolysis, by separating the hydrogen from water gas, or from hydrocarbons.

Hydrogen is a colorless, odorless, tasteless gas that has the lowest density of any material known. It is very slightly soluble in water. Platinum and palladium adsorb hydrogen. Hydrogen diffuses readily and can pass through very tiny openings. It burns with a very hot flame that is nearly invisible. Hydrogen is not active at ordinary temperatures. A mixture of hydrogen and oxygen, when ignited, produces an explosion and forms water vapor as the product. Hydrogen and chlorine react to form hydrogen chloride. Hydrogen and nitrogen can be made to unite, forming ammonia.

Reduction is any chemical action in which an atom, a group of atoms, or an ion gains electrons. In oxidation-reduction reactions, the atom, group of atoms, or ion which takes up electrons is the oxidizing agent; while the atom, group of atoms, or ion which loses electrons is the reducing agent.

Hydrogen is used for filling balloons because of its low density, but its flammable nature makes such use somewhat dangerous. Hydrogen is sometimes used as a reducing agent in the extraction of metals from oxides. Some gaseous fuels contain elementary hydrogen, while many fuels contain combined hydrogen. Tremendous volumes of hydrogen are used to make ammonia and methanol. The yield of gasoline from petroleum is increased by hydrogenation. Hydrogen is used to convert liquid oils into solid fats for cooking.

TEST YOURSELF ON THESE TERMS

absorption	hydride	oxidizing agent
adsorption	hydrocarbon	reducing agent
atomic hydrogen torch	hydrogen	reduction
Cavendish	hydrogenation	test for hydrogen
diffusion	occlusion	water gas

QUESTIONS

Group A

1. (*a*) What substances are used for the ordinary laboratory preparation of hydrogen? (*b*) What products are formed?
2. Give five physical properties of hydrogen.
3. What happens when a burning splint is thrust into and out of a bottle of hydrogen?
4. (*a*) What product is formed when hydrogen combines with chlorine; (*b*) with nitrogen? (*c*) What type of bond does hydrogen form with these two elements? (*d*) Of what type of particle do these compounds consist?
5. (*a*) What product is formed when hydrogen combines with potassium; (*b*) with strontium? (*c*) What type of bond does hydrogen form with these two elements? (*d*) Of what type of particle do these compounds consist?
6. Why must all the air be expelled from a hydrogen generator before the gas is lighted at the end of the delivery tube?
7. Why do toy balloons, even when tied tightly, gradually collapse?
8. What happens when sodium is added to water?
9. What solid has the lowest density?
10. Distinguish between *adsorption* and *absorption*.
11. Explain the statement: Oxidation and reduction are opposite processes.
12. Give a use for hydrogen which depends on its: (*a*) low density; (*b*) reducing action; (*c*) combustibility.
13. Describe two commercial methods for preparing hydrogen.
14. In testing bottles of hydrogen gas, should the bottles be held mouth *upward*, or mouth *downward*?
15. How are liquid oils changed to solid fats for cooking purposes?

Group B

16. What reasons can you give for the fact that only very small traces of free hydrogen are present in the atmosphere near the earth's surface?
17. Why is Cavendish credited with the discovery of hydrogen, even though the gas had been known much earlier?
18. What factors determine the rate at which hydrogen is evolved from hydrochloric acid by reaction with coarse iron filings?
19. From its position in the Periodic Table, would you expect cesium to react with water more or less vigorously than potassium?

20. What is the chief operating expense in the production of hydrogen by electrolysis of water?
21. What is a hydrocarbon?
22. In the reaction of steam on hot coke for producing water gas, which substance is: (*a*) the oxidizing agent; (*b*) the reducing agent; (*c*) the substance oxidized; (*d*) the substance reduced?
23. Describe an experiment to show the diffusion of hydrogen.
24. How may hydrogen be used in the petroleum industry?
25. What happens when a blazing splint is lowered into: (*a*) a bottle of hydrogen; (*b*) a bottle of oxygen; (*c*) a bottle of hydrogen mixed with oxygen; (*d*) a bottle of hydrogen mixed with air? How do the reactions differ in the two latter cases?
26. Would you use: (*a*) sand; or (*b*) water; or (*c*) either of them for extinguishing the flames from burning potassium? Give a reason for your answer.
27. Draw an electron-dot symbol for a hydride ion.
28. Tin(II) oxide reacts with hydrogen to form tin and water vapor. In this reaction, which substance is: (*a*) the oxidizing agent; (*b*) the reducing agent; (*c*) oxidized; (*d*) reduced?
29. (*a*) Which will be the more ionic compound, BaH_2 or MgH_2? (*b*) Why?
30. Suppose that the clay cup and the inverted beaker of Fig. 8-3 are both filled with hydrogen and that the beaker is removed: (*a*) describe the movement of the liquid in the beaker; (*b*) explain why such movement occurs.

PROBLEMS

Group A

1. Sulfuric acid contains 2.04% hydrogen. How many grams of hydrogen can be prepared from 200. g of sulfuric acid?
2. Water contains 11.11% hydrogen. How many grams of hydrogen can be obtained by the electrolysis of 500. g of water?
3. What will be the volume in liters of the hydrogen produced in Problem 2, if hydrogen has a density of 0.0900 g/l?

Group B

4. While water contains 11.11% hydrogen, only one-half of it may be replaced when sodium reacts with water. What mass of hydrogen could be obtained from 2.00 g of water if it is completely reacted with sodium?
5. What volume in milliliters will the gas obtained in Problem 4 occupy?
6. In producing water gas from the reaction of steam on red-hot coke, 12.0 g of carbon from the coke react with 18.0 g of steam. What volume of hydrogen at 0° C and 760 mm pressure can be obtained from the reaction of 1.00 metric ton of coke, 90.0% carbon, by complete reaction with steam? Steam is 11.11% hydrogen.

SOME THINGS FOR YOU TO DO

1. Fill a toy rubber balloon with hydrogen from a cylinder of hydrogen gas. Tie the opening securely. If a tank of hydrogen is not available, the laboratory gas supply may be used as a substitute. Leave the balloon in the room for several days, and note how the gas diffuses through the pores of the rubber.

2. Connect a clay pipe by means of rubber tubing with a hydrogen generator. Prepare a bowl of soapy water and add a few drops of glycerol. Now use the stream of hydrogen to blow soap bubbles. Shake the soap bubbles loose, and note how they rise to the ceiling. As they rise, ignite them with a candle attached to a long stick.

3. Prepare some "reduced iron" by heating an iron pipe in which some iron(III) oxide has been placed, and then passing a stream of hydrogen through the pipe. Support the pipe horizontally. Fit a one-hole cork stopper to the end of the pipe nearer the hydrogen generator. Use glass tubing and rubber tubing to connect the generator with the iron pipe.

4. Prepare a biographical sketch of the life of Henry Cavendish and read it to the class.

Chapter 9 · THE GAS LAWS

1. PRESSURE CHANGES AFFECT GAS VOLUMES

1. The volume of a gas depends on its temperature and pressure. When you buy a gallon of gasoline or some other liquid, you buy a definite volume of the liquid. If the liquid is very cold, you receive a slightly greater number of molecules in a gallon than if it is warm. Expansion and contraction with temperature changes may cause the volume of large quantities of liquid, such as a

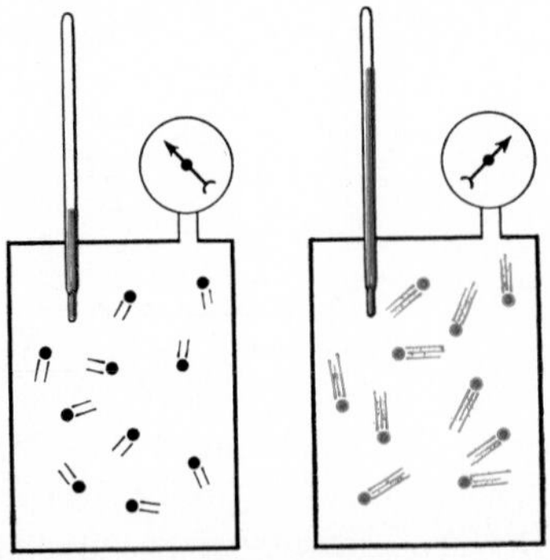

Fig. 9-1. At constant volume, as the temperature of a gas increases, the pressure it exerts increases.

tank truck of gasoline, to vary five gallons or more. When dealing with smaller volumes of liquids, such variations are not particularly noticeable, unless precise measurements are made.

In the case of gases, however, the same number of molecules can occupy widely different volumes. The expression "a cubic foot of air" means little unless the temperature and pressure at which it is measured are also known. A cubic foot of air can be compressed to a few cubic inches in volume; it can also expand to fill a high school auditorium. Steel cylinders of oxygen and hydrogen with an internal volume of two cubic feet are widely used in industry. When such cylinders are returned "empty" they still contain two cubic feet of gas, although when they were delivered "full" they may have had 100 times as many molecules of the gas compressed within the cylinder.

According to the Kinetic Theory (Chapter 3), gas molecules are essentially independent particles. They are at relatively great distances from each other, but move rapidly in a random fashion and fill whatever space is available to them. Scientists have computed that if the molecules of the gases in the atmosphere could be magnified until they were as big as baseballs, the average distance between them would be about 0.6 meter. This gives an idea of the relative distances between the tiny molecules that make up all gases. It also explains why so many more molecules of a gas can be crowded into a given space already occupied by gas molecules.

We have already stated that the temperature of a gas is an indication of the average energy of the gas molecules. The higher the temperature of a gas, the more energy its molecules possess, and the more rapidly they move about. As gas molecules strike the walls of a container they exert a pressure against it. If the volume which a certain number of gas molecules occupies remains constant, we should expect the pressure exerted by the gas to increase if its temperature is raised. We should also expect the pressure exerted by this same number of gas molecules to decrease if the temperature is lowered (see Fig. 9-1).

Furthermore, if the pressure exerted by this number of gas molecules is to remain the same as the temperature is increased, the volume which the gas

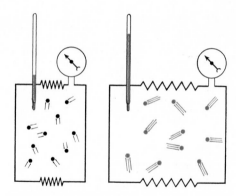

Fig. 9-2. **At constant pressure, as the temperature of a gas increases, the volume it occupies increases.**

occupies must increase. Since the molecules move faster at higher temperatures they strike the walls of the container more frequently and with more force. Only if the area which they strike becomes greater will the force of the molecules striking a unit area remain the same, and the pressure remain the same. The area which they strike can become larger if the volume of the container is larger. In a similar fashion, with pressure remaining constant, and the temperature decreased, the volume which a certain number of gas molecules occupies must become less (see Fig. 9-2).

Finally, if the temperature of these gas molecules remains constant, we

VOCABULARY

Boyle's Law. The volume of a certain amount of dry gas is inversely proportional to the pressure, provided the temperature remains constant.

Charles' Law. The volume of a certain amount of dry gas varies directly with the Kelvin temperature, provided the pressure remains constant.

Ideal gas. A theoretical gas which conforms exactly to the Gas Laws.

Standard pressure. The pressure exerted by a column of mercury exactly 760 mm high at 0°C.

Standard temperature. 0°Centigrade.

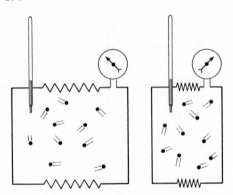

Fig. 9-3. **At constant temperature, as the volume of a gas decreases, the pressure it exerts increases.**

should expect the pressure exerted by the gas to be greater if the volume which the gas occupies becomes smaller. And similarly, the pressure exerted by these gas molecules would be less if the volume available to the gas were larger (see Fig. 9-3). As a result of these consequences of the Kinetic Theory, it can readily be seen that gas volumes are related to the temperature and pressure of the gas. Accordingly, both temperature and pressure must be considered when measuring the volume of a gas.

2. Standard temperature and pressure. Variations in gas volumes make it necessary to select some standard temperature and pressure for use when measuring the volumes, or when comparing them. *Standard temperature is exactly zero degrees Centigrade.* It is the temperature of melting ice, and was selected because it is a convenient and precise temperature. *Standard pressure is the pressure exerted by a column of mercury exactly 760 millimeters high.* We use 760 millimeters of mercury as the standard pressure because that is the average pressure of the atmosphere at sea level. Temperatures are easily measured with an accurate thermometer.

The pressure of a gas is measured by means of a barometer. *Standard temperature and pressure is commonly abbreviated as S.T.P.*

3. Measuring the pressure of a gas collected over mercury. Suppose some hydrogen is delivered into a gas measuring tube called a eudiometer (yoo-dih-om-eh-ter), which was previously filled with mercury. As hydrogen enters the

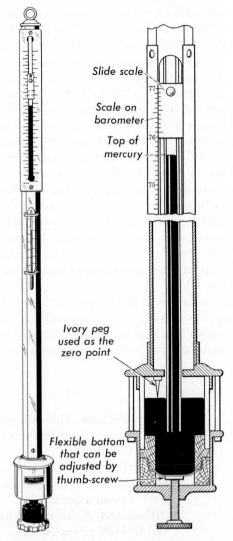

Fig. 9-4. **A barometer is used to measure air pressure.**

tube, it bubbles to the top, and pushes the mercury down. Suppose enough hydrogen is added to make the level of the mercury inside the tube just the same as that of the mercury in the bowl (see 1, Fig. 9-5). *When these two levels are equal, the pressure of the hydrogen is the same as that of the atmosphere.* This pressure can be determined by reading the barometer.

★ Suppose, however, that not enough hydrogen is delivered into the eudiometer to make the levels equal, and the level inside the tube is above that outside the tube (see 2, Fig. 9-5). The pressure of the gas inside the tube is less than the pressure of the air outside; otherwise, the enclosed gas would push the mercury down to the same level. To determine the pressure of the hydrogen, the difference between the level of the mercury inside the tube and outside the tube, must be *subtracted* from the barometer reading.

★ If so much hydrogen is delivered into the eudiometer that the mercury level inside the tube drops below that outside, the gas inside the tube will be under a greater pressure than that of the air outside (see 3, Fig. 9-5). To determine the pressure of the gas in this case, the difference between the level of the

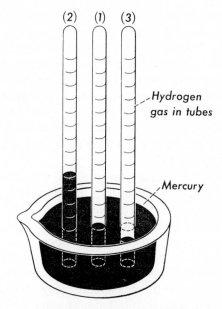

Fig. 9-5. In (1) the pressure of the hydrogen is the same as that of the atmosphere. In (2) the pressure of the hydrogen is less than that of the atmosphere. In (3) the pressure of the hydrogen is greater than that of the atmosphere.

mercury inside the tube and outside the tube must be *added* to the barometer reading.

★ Since these corrections are somewhat inconvenient to make, we usually try to adjust the mercury levels inside and

★SAMPLE PROBLEM

What is the pressure of the gas in a eudiometer tube when the mercury level in the tube is 18 mm higher than that outside? The barometer reads 735 mm.

SOLUTION

Since the mercury level inside is higher than that outside, the pressure on the gas in the eudiometer tube must be less than atmospheric pressure. Accordingly, the difference in levels is subtracted from the barometric pressure to obtain the pressure of the gas. 735 mm − 18 mm = 717 mm, the pressure of the gas.

outside the tube to the same level by moving the eudiometer up or down in the bowl of mercury. Then the gas pressure inside will be the same as that read on the barometer. Occasionally the bowl of mercury may not be deep enough to make this possible, then the corrections we have just noted have to be applied. See the Sample Problem at the bottom of page 137.

★ **4. Measuring the pressure of a gas collected over water.** In elementary work, gases are usually collected over water rather than over mercury. Since mercury is 13.6 times as dense as water, a given pressure will support a column of water 13.6 times as high as an equivalent column of mercury (Fig. 9-6). When a gas is collected over water, pressure corrections similar to those just noted for differences in mercury level must be applied. But since mercury is 13.6 times as dense as water, *a difference in water levels must be divided by 13.6 to convert it to its equivalent length in terms of a column of mercury.*

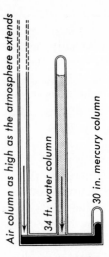

Fig. 9-6. The pressure of the atmosphere supports a column of water 13.6 times higher than the column of mercury it supports.

The advantage of collecting a gas over mercury is that mercury does not evaporate appreciably at room temperatures. When a gas is bubbled through water, however, the collected gas always has some water vapor mixed with it. Water

★ **SAMPLE PROBLEM**

Oxygen is collected in a eudiometer tube over water. The water level inside the tube is 27.2 mm higher than that outside. The temperature is 20.°C. The barometric pressure is 740.0 mm. What is the pressure of the dry oxygen?

SOLUTION

To convert the difference in water levels to an equivalent difference in mercury levels, the difference in water levels is divided by 13.6. 27.2 mm ÷ 13.6 = 2.0 mm, the equivalent difference in mercury levels. Since the level inside the tube is higher than that outside, the difference in levels must be subtracted from the barometric pressure. 740.0 mm − 2.0 mm = 738.0 mm. To correct for the water vapor pressure, Table 5 in the Appendix indicates that the water vapor pressure at 20.°C is 17.5 mm. This must be subtracted from the pressure corrected for difference in levels. 738.0 mm − 17.5 mm = 720.5 mm, the pressure of the dry oxygen.

vapor, like other gases, exerts pressure. Thus the pressure of a gas enclosed in a tube over water is the combined pressure of the gas itself and the pressure of the water vapor (see Chapter 3, Section 9). Table 5 in the Appendix gives the pressure of water vapor at different temperatures. *To determine the pressure of the dry gas* (unmixed with water vapor), *the vapor pressure of water at the given temperature is subtracted from the total pressure of the gas within the tube.* See the Sample Problem on the opposite page.

5. The variation of gas volume with pressure; Boyle's Law. A rubber ball filled with air is very elastic or "springy." If the ball is squeezed, the volume of the gas inside is decreased, but it expands again when the pressure is released.

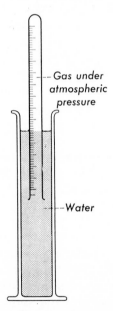

Fig. 9-7. **Even though the liquid levels inside and outside this eudiometer are the same, a correction for water vapor pressure must be made when determining dry gas pressure because the gas was collected over water.**

Robert Boyle (1627–1691) first made careful measurements to show the relationship between pressures and volumes of gases. He found that doubling the pressure on a gas would reduce its volume by one half. Boyle formulated the results of his experiments on what he called the "springiness of the air" in a law that bears his name. We may state **Boyle's Law:** *The volume of a certain amount of dry gas is inversely proportional to the pressure, provided the temperature remains constant.*

This law may be stated mathematically as

$$\frac{V}{V'} = \frac{p'}{p}$$

where V is the original volume, V' the new volume, p the original pressure, and p' the new pressure. Solving the expression for V', we obtain this frequently more useful mathematical statement of Boyle's Law,

$$V' = V\frac{p}{p'}$$

6. Using Boyle's Law. Suppose 200. ml of a gas such as hydrogen are collected over mercury on a day when the barometer reads 740. mm. The mercury level inside the tube is adjusted so that it is the same as that outside. The pressure on the confined gas is thus the same as atmospheric pressure, 740. mm. If the tube is permitted to stand until the next day, we may find that the temperature of the gas is unchanged, but that the pressure has risen to 750. mm. When the tube is lowered into the bowl of mercury to make the mercury level inside the tube the same as that outside, we find that the volume of gas has decreased. The new volume of gas V' is $\frac{p}{p'}$ or $\frac{740.\,mm}{750.\,mm}$ of its volume V, 200. ml,

Fig. 9-8. Robert Boyle, an English scientist, was the first to make careful measurements to show the relationship between pressures and volumes of gases. (New York Public Library)

on the first day. Substituting in the Boyle's Law formula, and solving, we obtain

$$V' = V p/p'$$
$$V' = 200. \text{ml} \times 740. \text{mm}/750. \text{mm}$$
$$V' = 197 \text{ ml}$$

It is possible that by the third day the pressure may have fallen to 720. mm. When the mercury levels are adjusted so that they are the same inside the tube and out, we find that the volume V' of the gas is

$$V' = 200. \text{ml} \times 740. \text{mm}/720. \text{mm}$$
or $$V' = 205 \text{ ml}$$

The Sample Problems which appear on the opposite page give other examples of the use of Boyle's Law. The problem-solving techniques of Chapter 1 should be applied. Write the appropriate formula, solve for the required unknown quantity, substitute the problem values and units, and calculate the numerical answer.

2. TEMPERATURE CHANGES AFFECT GAS VOLUMES

7. The variation of gas volume with temperature. Bread dough rises when it is placed in a hot oven. The increase in temperature causes the bubbles of carbon dioxide gas within the dough to expand. The rather large increase in the volume of the dough as it is baked into bread shows that the gas must expand considerably as the temperature is increased. In fact this gas, as well as other gases, expands many times as much per degree rise in temperature as do liquids and solids.

Jacques Charles (1746–1823), a French scientist, first made careful measurements of the changes in volume of gases with changes in temperature. His experiments revealed that:

1. All gases expand or contract at the same rate with changes in temperature, provided the pressure is unchanged.

2. The change in volume amounts to $\frac{1}{273}$ of the original volume at $0°$ C for each Centigrade degree the temperature is changed.

We may start with a definite volume of a gas at $0°$ C and experiment by heating it. Just as the whole of anything may be considered as made up of two halves, $\frac{2}{2}$, or three thirds, $\frac{3}{3}$, so we can consider this volume as $\frac{273}{273}$. If we warm the gas one Centigrade degree, it expands $\frac{1}{273}$ of its original volume. Its new volume is $\frac{274}{273}$. In the same manner, the gas expands $\frac{100}{273}$ when it is heated 100 C°. Such expansion, added to the original volume, makes the new volume $\frac{373}{273}$. Any gas warmed 273 Centigrade degrees expands $\frac{273}{273}$, or its volume is just doubled, $\frac{546}{273}$.

A gas whose volume is measured at

0° C contracts by $\frac{1}{273}$ of its volume if it is cooled 1 C°. Its new volume is $\frac{272}{273}$ of its former volume. Cooling this gas to −100.° C reduces the volume $\frac{100}{273}$. In other words the gas shrinks to $\frac{173}{273}$ of its former volume. At this rate, if we cooled the gas to −273° C, it would lose $\frac{273}{273}$ of its volume, and its volume would become zero. Such a situation cannot occur, however, because all gases become liquids before such a low temperature is reached. This rate of contraction with cooling applies only to gases.

8. The Kelvin temperature scale. Scientists believe that −273.16° C is the lowest possible temperature. At this temperature a body would have lost all the heat that it is possible for it to lose. Scientists have come very close to this lowest possible temperature, but theoretically it is impossible to reach.

The physicist Sir William Thomson (1824–1907), better known by his title, Lord Kelvin, invented the Kelvin temperature scale which measures absolute temperature or the average kinetic energy of the particles of a substance. In this scale, 0° K (zero degrees Kelvin) is the lowest possible temperature, −273.16° C. In most calculations this temperature is rounded off to −273° C. A Kelvin degree represents the same

SAMPLE PROBLEM

A 500. ml sample of hydrogen is collected when the pressure is 800. mm of mercury. What volume will the gas occupy when the pressure is 760. mm of mercury?

SOLUTION

$$V' = V\,p/p'$$
$$V' = 500.\ \text{ml} \times 800.\ \text{mm}/760.\ \text{mm}$$
$$V' = 526\ \text{ml, the new volume}$$

★SAMPLE PROBLEM

The volume of oxygen in a eudiometer tube is 40.0 ml. The water level inside the tube is 20.4 mm higher inside than outside. The barometer reading is 730.0 mm. The temperature is 22°C. What will be the volume of the dry oxygen at 760.0 mm pressure, if the temperature remains unchanged?

SOLUTION

1. Correction for difference in levels.

730.0 mm − (20.4 mm ÷ 13.6) = 728.5 mm.

2. Correction for water vapor pressure. Water vapor pressure at 22°C is 19.8 mm. 728.5 mm − 19.8 mm = 708.7 mm.

3. Correction for change in pressure.

$$V' = V\,p/p'$$
$$V' = 40.0\ \text{ml} \times 708.7\ \text{mm}/760.0\ \text{mm}$$
$$V' = 37.3\ \text{ml, volume at 760.0 mm and 22°C}$$

Fig. 9-9. **The experiments of Jacques Charles, a French scientist, concerning the effect of temperature changes on gas volumes resulted in Charles' Law.** (Bettmann Archive)

temperature change as a Centigrade degree. The following table will help you in comparing the Kelvin and Centigrade temperature scales.

If you observe the corresponding temperatures on the Centigrade and Kelvin scales, you will note that Kelvin temperatures are just 273 degrees higher than Centigrade temperatures.

Kelvin temperature =
  Centigrade temperature + 273°

Centigrade	Kelvin
100.°	373°
50.°	323°
20.°	293°
0.°	273°
−100.°	173°
−273°	0.°

9. Charles' Law. Thermometers are not graduated to give Kelvin scale readings, but the scale makes it easy to solve problems dealing with the changes in gas volumes as temperatures vary. It eliminates the use of zero and of negative numbers. Using the Kelvin temperature scale, *Charles' Law* can be stated: *The volume of a certain amount of dry gas varies directly with the Kelvin temperature, provided the pressure remains constant.*

Charles' Law may be stated mathematically:

$$\frac{V}{V'} = \frac{T}{T'}$$

where V is the original volume, V' the new volume, T the original *Kelvin* temperature, and T' the new *Kelvin* temperature. Solving the expression for V'

$$V' = V\frac{T'}{T}$$

SAMPLE PROBLEM

A 500. ml volume of gas is measured at 20.° C. If the pressure remains unchanged, what will be the volume of the gas at 0.° C?

SOLUTION

Change the Centigrade temperatures to Kelvin temperatures:
$20.° C + 273° = 293° K$. $0.° C + 273° = 273° K$.

$$V' = V\, T'/T$$
$$V' = 500.\ ml \times 273° K/293° K$$
$$V' = 466\ ml, \text{ the new volume}$$

The Sample Problem opposite illustrates the use of this formula in solving problems involving Charles' Law.

10. Combined use of Boyle's and Charles' Laws. The calculation of the new volume of a gas when both temperature and pressure are changed involves no new principles. We merely multiply the original volume first by a ratio of the pressures to determine the new volume corrected for pressure alone. Then we multiply this answer by a ratio of the Kelvin temperatures to calculate the new volume corrected for both pressure and temperature.

Expressed mathematically,

$$V' = V \times \frac{p}{p'} \times \frac{T'}{T}$$

The Sample Problems below illustrate the use of this formula. You will find it much easier to solve Gas-Law problems if you use logarithms or a slide rule in making your calculations.

* 11. The behavior of real gases. Boyle's and Charles' Laws describe the behavior of an *ideal* gas. An *ideal gas* would consist of infinitely small molecules which exert no forces on each other.

SAMPLE PROBLEM

Some gas measures 200. ml at 20°. C and 750. mm pressure. What will be the volume of the gas at 15° C and 735 mm pressure?

SOLUTION

20.° C = 293° K; 15° C = 288° K.

$$V' = V \times p/p' \times T'/T$$
$$V' = 200. \text{ ml} \times 288° \text{K}/293° \text{K} \times 750. \text{ mm}/735 \text{ mm}$$
$$V' = 201 \text{ ml, the new volume}$$

*SAMPLE PROBLEM

A gas-measuring tube holds 25.0 ml of air. The air was collected over water when the temperature was 20.° C. The water level inside the eudiometer is 68.0 mm higher than that outside. The barometer reading is 740.0 mm. Calculate the volume of dry air at S.T.P.

SOLUTION

1. Correction for difference in levels. 68.0 mm ÷ 13.6 = 5.0 mm. Since the water level inside is higher than that outside, the air is under pressure less than atmospheric, and the correction is subtracted. 740.0 mm − 5.0 mm = 735.0 mm.

2. Correction for water vapor pressure. Table 5 in the Appendix indicates that the water vapor pressure at 20.° C is 17.5 mm. This correction is subtracted. 735.0 mm − 17.5 mm = 717.5 mm.

3. Correction for pressure and temperature changes.

$$V' = V \times p/p' \times T'/T$$
$$V' = 25.0 \text{ ml} \times 717.5 \text{ mm}/760.0 \text{ mm} \times 273° \text{K}/293° \text{K}$$
$$V' = 22.0 \text{ ml, volume of dry air at S.T.P.}$$

Real gases within the normal ranges of temperatures and pressures conform very well to the behavior of an ideal gas, even though they consist of molecules of finite size which do exert forces on each other. Under normal temperatures and pressures, the spaces separating the molecules are large enough so that the actual size of the molecules and forces between them have little effect.

Boyle's Law applies to real gases with a fairly high degree of accuracy, but it does not apply to gases under such high pressure that the molecules are close enough together to attract each other. Under this condition the gas is almost at the point at which it condenses into a liquid.

Charles' Law holds for real gases with considerable accuracy, except at low temperature. Under this condition, gas molecules move more slowly and molecular attraction occurs. Thus, at temperature conditions near the point where the gas condenses into a liquid, Charles' Law does not apply.

SUMMARY

If the volume which a certain number of gas molecules occupies remains constant, the pressure exerted by the gas increases if its temperature is raised. If the pressure exerted by this number of gas molecules remains the same as the temperature is increased, the volume the gas occupies increases. If the temperature of these gas molecules remains constant, the pressure exerted by the gas increases if the volume occupied by the gas becomes smaller. Gas volumes are related to the temperature and pressure of the gas.

Standard temperature is zero degrees Centigrade. Standard pressure is the pressure exerted by a column of mercury exactly 760 millimeters high. The temperature of a gas is measured by means of a thermometer, and its pressure is measured with a barometer. When a gas is collected over water, some water vapor becomes mixed with the gas. The amount of pressure due to water vapor varies according to the temperature.

Boyle's Law: The volume of a certain amount of dry gas is inversely proportional to the pressure, provided the temperature remains constant. Jacques Charles found that all gases expand or contract at the same rate. Gases expand $\frac{1}{273}$ of the volume at $0°$ C for each Centigrade degree the temperature is raised. The lowest possible temperature is $-273°$ C. The Kelvin temperature scale has its $0°$ K reading at $-273°$ C. The readings on the Kelvin scale are 273 degrees higher than on the Centigrade scale. Charles' Law: The volume of a certain amount of dry gas varies directly with the Kelvin temperature, provided the pressure remains constant. Boyle's Law and Charles' Law may be combined in the Gas-Law formula $V' = V \times p/p' \times T'/T$.

TEST YOURSELF ON THESE TERMS

barometer	Gas-Law formula	standard pressure
Boyle's Law	Ideal gas	standard temperature
Charles' Law	Kelvin temperature	S.T.P.
eudiometer	Kinetic Theory	water vapor pressure

QUESTIONS

Group A

1. Why is the term "a cubic foot of air" unsatisfactory?
2. (*a*) What is standard temperature? (*b*) What is standard pressure?
★ 3. If some hydrogen gas is enclosed in a eudiometer, what are three possibilities concerning its pressure compared with that of the air in the room?
4. State Boyle's Law.
5. (*a*) What is the Centigrade temperature corresponding to 0° K? (*b*) How does any Centigrade temperature compare with the corresponding Kelvin temperature?
6. What is Charles' Law?

Group B

7. How is a gas described by the Kinetic Theory?
8. At constant volume, how is the pressure exerted by a gas related to the temperature?
9. At constant pressure, how is the volume occupied by a gas related to the temperature?
10. At constant temperature, how is the volume occupied by a gas related to its pressure?
★11. (*a*) What is meant by the vapor pressure of water? (*b*) What effect does it have on the observed pressure of a gas collected over water? (*c*) How is the observed pressure corrected to obtain the pressure of the dry gas?
★12. What corrections are applied to the barometer reading: (*a*) gas measured over mercury, level inside the eudiometer the same as that outside; (*b*) gas measured over mercury, level inside eudiometer higher than that outside; (*c*) gas measured over water, level inside eudiometer same as that outside; (*d*) gas measured over water, level inside eudiometer higher than outside?

PROBLEMS

Group A

Use cancellation whenever possible

1. Some oxygen occupies 250. ml when the barometer reads 720. mm. What will be the volume the following day when the barometer reads 750. mm?
2. A gas collected when the pressure is 800. mm has a volume of 380. ml. What volume will the gas occupy at standard pressure?
3. A gas has a volume of 100. ml when the pressure is 735 mm. What volume will the gas occupy at 700. mm pressure?
4. A gas has a volume of 240.0 ml at 70.0 cm pressure. What pressure is needed to reduce the volume to 60.0 ml?
5. Change the following temperatures to Kelvin scale: (*a*) 20.° C; (*b*) 85° C; (*c*) −15° C; (*d*) −190.° C.

6. Given 90.0 ml of hydrogen gas collected when the temperature is 27° C. What volume will the hydrogen occupy at 42° C?

7. A gas has a volume of 180. ml when its temperature is 43° C. To what temperature must the gas be lowered to reduce its volume to 135 ml?

8. A gas measures 500 ml. at a temperature of −23° C. Find its volume at 23° C.

9. A sample of gas occupies 50.0 l at 27° C. What is the volume of the gas at standard temperature?

10. Convert to standard conditions: 2280. ml of gas measured at 30.° C and 808 mm pressure.

11. Convert to standard conditions: 1000. ml of gas at −23° C and 700. mm pressure.

12. Convert to standard conditions: 1520. ml of gas at −33° C and 720. mm pressure.

13. A gas collected when the temperature is 27° C and the pressure is 80.0 cm measures 500 ml. Find the volume at −3° C and 75.0 cm.

14. Given 100. ml of gas measured at 17° C and 380. mm pressure. What volume will the gas occupy at 307° C and 500. mm pressure?

Group B

Use logarithms or a slide rule

⋆ 15. In an experiment 35.0 ml of hydrogen were collected in a eudiometer over mercury. The mercury level inside the eudiometer was 40. mm higher than that outside. The temperature was 25° C and the barometric pressure was 740.0 mm. Correct the volume of hydrogen to S.T.P.

⋆ 16. A gas collected over mercury in an inverted graduated cylinder occupies 60.0 ml. The mercury level inside the cylinder is 25 mm higher than that outside. Temperature: 20.° C; barometer reading: 715 mm. Correct the volume of gas to S.T.P.

⋆ 17. Hydrogen is collected by water displacement in a eudiometer. Gas volume, 25.0 ml; liquid levels inside and outside the eudiometer are the same; temperature, 17° C; barometer reading, 720.0 mm. Correct the volume to that of dry gas at S.T.P.

⋆ 18. Some nitrogen is collected over water in a gas-measuring tube. Gas volume, 45.0 ml; liquid levels inside and outside the gas-measuring tube are the same; temperature, 23° C; barometer reading, 732.0 mm. Correct the volume to that of dry gas at S.T.P.

⋆ 19. A volume of 50.0 ml of oxygen is collected over water. The water level inside the eudiometer is 65 mm higher than that outside. Temperature, 25° C; barometer reading, 727.0 mm. Correct the volume to that of dry gas at S.T.P.

⋆ 20. At 18° C and 745.0 mm pressure, 12.0 ml of hydrogen are collected over water. The liquid level inside the gas-measuring tube is 95 mm higher than that outside. Correct the volume to that of dry gas at S.T.P.

⋆ 21. The density of carbon dioxide at S.T.P. is 1.98 g/l. What is the weight of exactly one liter of the gas, if the pressure increases by 40. mm of mercury?

⋆ 22. The density of oxygen at S.T.P. is 1.43 g/l. Find the weight of exactly one liter of oxygen at a temperature of 39° C, if the pressure remains unchanged.

⋆**23.** The density of nitrogen is 1.26 g/l at S.T.P. Find the weight of exactly one liter of nitrogen at a temperature of 27° C and 90.0 cm of mercury pressure.

⋆**24.** A gas measures 400. ml at a temperature of 25° C, and under a pressure of 800. mm. To what temperature must the gas be cooled if its volume is to be reduced to 350. ml when the pressure falls to 740. mm?

SOME THINGS FOR YOU TO DO

1. Show the motion of molecules by adding a few drops of liquid bromine to a large flask. Stopper the flask. **CAUTION:** *Do not get any bromine on your fingers as it will burn them badly.*

2. Examine the barometer in your chemistry laboratory closely and note the refinements of construction to secure accurate readings. Do not change any of the adjustments on the instrument.

3. Consult recent issues of science news magazines to learn how closely scientists have been able to approach the absolute zero of temperature.

Chapter 10 · WATER

1. THE NATURE OF WATER

1. The abundance of water. Water is both our most abundant and our most useful liquid. The oceans, rivers, and lakes cover about three quarters of the surface of the earth. Besides this visible water, there are large amounts of underground water.

Water vapor is always present in the air, even over deserts. When it rains, part of this water vapor condenses to liquid water and falls to the ground.

Water is found in all living things and is absolutely essential for life. The body of a man who weighs 140 lb is composed of about 100 lb of water, which is the basic component of all body fluids. Fruits and vegetables contain as much as 90% to 95% water. Even meat is about 50% water.

2. The physical properties of water. Pure water is a transparent, odorless, tasteless, and almost colorless liquid. The faint blue or blue-green color of water is apparent only in deep layers.

Any odor or taste in water is due to impurities such as dissolved mineral matter, dissolved liquids, or even dissolved gases. The pronounced odor and taste of the water from some mineral springs is due to the presence of such substances in considerable quantity.

Water may exist as a gas, liquid, or solid. Liquid water changes to ice at 0° C, or 32° F, under standard pressure, 760 mm of mercury. As water solidifies, it gives off heat and expands one ninth in volume. Consequently, ice has a density of about 0.9 g/cm³. The density of ice increases slightly as ice is cooled below 0° C.

When water at 0° C is warmed, it contracts until its temperature reaches 4° C. Then water gradually expands as its temperature is raised further. *At its temperature of maximum density, 4° C, one milliliter of water has a mass of one gram.*

When the pressure on the surface of water is *one atmosphere* (760 mm of mercury), water boils at a temperature of 100° C, or 212° F. The steam that is formed by heating water at its boiling point occupies a much greater volume than that of the water from which it was formed. When one liter of water evaporates, the steam occupies about 1700 liters at normal atmospheric pressure.

When water is heated in a closed vessel so that the steam cannot escape, the boiling temperature of the water is raised above 100° C. Conversely, if the air and water vapor above the liquid in a closed vessel are partially removed by means of a vacuum pump, the water boils at a lower temperature than 100° C. Pressure cookers are popular for cooking food because the higher temperature of the water cooks the food in a shorter time, thus saving fuel. Vacuum evaporators are used to evaporate milk and to concentrate sugar solutions. Under reduced pressure the liquid boils away at a temperature low enough so that the sugar is not scorched.

3. **The structure and properties of water molecules.** Water molecules are composed of two atoms of hydrogen and one atom of oxygen, joined by polar

Fig. 10-1. Steam cannot escape from a pressure cooker until its pressure is about 15 lb/in² greater than atmospheric pressure. As a result, the temperature of the boiling water in the pressure cooker is higher than 100° C, and the food cooks faster. (Presto)

covalent bonds. Studies of the crystal structure of ice indicate that these atoms are not joined in a straight line. Rather, they form an angle as indicated by the electron-dot formula

$$H : \overset{\cdot\cdot}{\underset{\overset{|}{H}}{O}} :$$

VOCABULARY

Acid anhydride. An oxide of a nonmetal which unites with water to form a solution which contains an acid.

Analysis. A breaking apart to determine the composition, as of a chemical compound.

Anhydrous. Containing no water.

Basic anhydride. An oxide of a metal which unites with water to form a solution which contains a base.

Distillation. The process of evaporation followed by condensation of the vapors in a separate vessel.

Hydrate. A crystallized substance that contains water of hydration.

Hydrogen bond. A weak chemical bond between a hydrogen atom in one polar molecule and the negative atom in a second polar molecule.

Stable compound. A compound that does not decompose easily.

Synthesis. A combining of simple substances to make a more complex substance.

Unstable compound. A compound that decomposes easily.

Fig. 10-2. **Vacuum evaporators are used to concentrate the dilute sugar juice obtained from sugar cane. Under reduced pressure the water is evaporated from the sugar juice without scorching the sugar.** (Sugar Information)

Since oxygen is more strongly electronegative than hydrogen, the bonds are polar, the electronegativity difference indicating about 39% ionic character. Thus the electrons are not uniformly distributed about the molecule, but are on the average slightly clustered about the oxygen nucleus. This has the effect of giving the oxygen part of the molecule a partial negative charge, and leaves the hydrogen parts with a partial positive charge. Since the two hydrogen atoms are similarly partially charged, they tend to repel one another. This increases the size of the angle between the bonds in the molecule from the 90° we should expect from the electron-dot formula to about 105°. A water molecule may be more properly represented as

Since the polar covalent bonds in this molecule are unsymmetrically arranged, the molecule as a whole is polar.

The polarity of water molecules enables them to join together, or associate, into groups of molecules. A hydrogen atom of one water molecule may be weakly, but effectively, attracted to the oxygen of a second water molecule. Such a bond is called a **hydrogen bond.** A hydrogen of the second water molecule may be attracted to the oxygen of a third water molecule, and so on. While the number of molecules in a group decreases with an increase in temperature, the number usually ranges from eight to four in liquid water. The formation of molecular groups in water by hydrogen bonding causes water to be a liquid at room temperature while other substances with molecules of similar size and mass such as methane, CH_4, and ammonia, NH_3, are gases.

Ice consists of water molecules arranged in a definite hexagonal structure. They are held together by hydrogen bonds in a rather open hexagonal pattern (see Fig. 10-3). As heat is applied to ice, the increased energy of the atoms and molecules causes them to vibrate more vigorously. This stretches the hydrogen bonds, and the ice expands as it is heated.

When the melting point of ice is reached, the energy of the atoms and molecules is so great that the rigid open lattice structure of the ice crystals breaks down—the ice turns into water. Despite the fact that the hydrogen bonds in water at 0° C are longer than those in ice, they are more flexible and the groups of liquid molecules can crowd together more compactly than those in

DENSITY OF WATER

°C	g/ml	°C	g/ml
0	0.99987	10	0.99973
1	0.99993	20	0.99823
2	0.99997	30	0.99567
3	0.99999	40	0.99224
4	1.00000	50	0.98807
5	0.99999	60	0.98324
6	0.99997	70	0.97781
7	0.99993	80	0.97183
8	0.99988	90	0.96534
9	0.99981	100	0.95838

ice. As a result, H_2O molecules occupy less volume as water than they do as ice and ice is less dense than water.

As water is warmed from 0° C, two phenomena having opposite effects occur: *1.* the breaking down of some hydrogen bonds enables water molecules to crowd more closely together; and *2.* the increased energy of the water molecules causes them to overcome molecular attractions more effectively and spread apart. Up to 4° C, the first effect predominates and water increases in density. Above 4° C, while the first phenomenon continues to occur, the effect of the second is so much greater that the density of water decreases.

The presence of groups of molecules in water, which must absorb enough energy to be broken up into single molecules before water boils, makes the boiling point of water so high, and makes it necessary to use a large amount of heat to vaporize water at its normal boiling point.

4. Water is commonly used as a standard. It is easy to obtain water in *fairly pure* condition. For this reason it is used as a *scientific standard:*

1. *For defining the relationship between volume and mass in the metric system.* We have already mentioned that one milliliter of water at its tem-

perature of maximum density, 4° C, has a mass of one gram.

2. *For establishing a temperature scale and graduating thermometers.* The temperature at which water freezes is called 0° C or 32° F and fixes the *ice-point* on the thermometer scale. The boiling point of water under a pressure of 760 mm of mercury is called 100° C or 212° F and determines the *steam-point* on the thermometer scale.

3. *For measuring heat.* In defining the units used for measuring heat, water is used as a standard. For example, *the calorie is defined as the amount of heat that is needed to warm one gram of water one Centigrade degree. The* **British thermal unit,** *commonly abbreviated Btu, is the amount of heat needed to warm one pound of water one Fahrenheit degree.*

4. *For a standard of specific gravity.* Water is the standard for the specific gravity of solids and liquids. One cubic centimeter of iron has 7.6 times the mass of one cubic centimeter of water. Thus the *specific gravity* of iron is 7.6.

5. The chemical behavior of water.

1. *The stability of water.* Water is a very *stable compound;* that is, *a compound*

Fig. 10-3. **Model of the crystal structure of ice.** (Chemical Bond Approach)

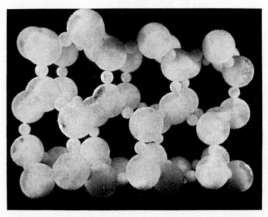

Fig. 10-4. **Water acts to promote some reactions, as shown when water is added to dry baking powder.**

which does not break up, or decompose, easily. Mercury(II) oxide, on the other hand, is a rather **unstable compound** because *it does not require much energy to decompose it into its elements.* Water is so stable that it does not decompose appreciably until its temperature reaches about 2700° C. The stability of water is evidence of the strength of the covalent bonds between the oxygen and hydrogen atoms.

2. *Behavior with metals.* In the study of hydrogen, we stated that such active metals as sodium and potassium react with cold water, setting free hydrogen and forming basic solutions.

$$2 \text{ Na} + 2 \text{ HOH} \rightarrow 2 \text{ NaOH} + \text{H}_2 \uparrow$$

Magnesium reacts with boiling water. When heated red hot, iron reacts with steam forming iron oxide and hydrogen. Aluminum and zinc also react with water at high temperatures.

3. *Behavior with metallic oxides.* The oxides of many metals are insoluble and water has little or no effect upon them, but water does react with the ionic oxides of the very active metals. The oxides of sodium, potassium, and calcium unite with water and form soluble hydroxides. Soluble hydroxides are compounds whose water solutions contain a *base.* Calcium hydroxide is formed when water is added to calcium oxide, CaO.

$$\text{CaO} + \text{H}_2\text{O} \rightarrow \text{Ca(OH)}_2$$

The compound calcium oxide, CaO, is known as an *anhydride.* The word anhydride means "without water." Since it forms a solution containing a base when water is added to it, calcium oxide is called a *basic anhydride.* We may define a **basic anhydride** as *the oxide of a metal which will unite with water to form a solution containing a base.*

4. *Behavior with oxides of nonmetals.* The oxides of such nonmetals as carbon, sulfur, and phosphorus are molecular compounds, containing polar bonds, which unite with water to form a solution containing an *acid.* For example, water unites with carbon dioxide to form carbonic acid, H_2CO_3.

$$\text{CO}_2 + \text{H}_2\text{O} \rightarrow \text{H}_2\text{CO}_3$$

Carbon dioxide is an anhydride, and since it forms a solution containing an acid with water, it is called an *acid anhydride.* In general, *the oxides of nonmetals unite with water to form solutions which contain an acid, and consequently are known as* **acid anhydrides.**

5. *Water of hydration.* Many positive ions, and a few negative ions, are surrounded by a definite number of water molecules in crystals formed by evaporating the water from their solutions. This water is called *water of hydration* or *water of crystallization. A crystallized substance that contains water of hydra-*

tion is a hydrate. For example, blue crystals of copper(II) sulfate consist of copper(II) ions, each surrounded by four water molecules, and sulfate ions, each with one water molecule. The formula of this substance is written as

$$CuSO_4 \cdot 5H_2O$$

The water molecules are totaled, and their loose attachment to the copper(II) and sulfate ions (shown empirically as $CuSO_4$) is indicated by the raised dot. If hydrates are heated to a temperature slightly above the boiling point of water, the water of hydration is driven off.

$$CuSO_4 \cdot 5 H_2O \rightarrow CuSO_4 + 5 H_2O$$

The substance which then remains is called an **anhydrous compound.** Anhydrous copper(II) sulfate, $CuSO_4$, is a white powder that may be prepared by heating the blue crystals gently in a test tube. The fact that water turns anhydrous copper(II) sulfate blue may be used as a *test for water.*

6. *Water promotes many chemical changes.* A good example of one of these changes is the reaction of baking powder, which is a mixture of dry chemicals. As long as baking powder is kept perfectly dry, no chemical action occurs. When water is added to the baking powder, the chemicals in the mixture react immediately, and bubbles of gas are liberated (see Fig. 10-4). Mixtures of many other dry substances do not react until water is added. The role of water in promoting chemical changes will be more fully explained in Unit 6.

6. **Water can be freed from mineral matter in solution.** Water can be freed from dissolved minerals by the process of *distillation.* An apparatus of the type shown in Fig. 10-5 is used in the laboratory to distill water, as well as other liquids. Water is added to the distilling flask and boiled to convert it into vapor. The vapor then passes through the inner of two concentric tubes which together are called the condenser. A stream of cold water flows continually through the outer tube of the condenser. Then the condensed water flows down the inner tube into a receiving vessel. *Distillation*

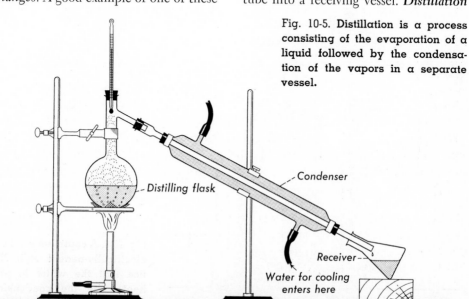

Fig. 10-5. **Distillation is a process consisting of the evaporation of a liquid followed by the condensation of the vapors in a separate vessel.**

Distilling flask

Condenser

Receiver

Water for cooling enters here

is a process of evaporation followed by condensation of the vapors in a separate vessel.

One type of continuous-action water still is shown in Fig. 10-6. The water which is used for condensation is somewhat preheated before it flows into the still. This increases the amount of distilled water which it is possible to obtain from a given amount of electric energy.

Certain synthetic resins are used to prepare water that is nearly free of dissolved matter. This method, called the *ion-exchange process*, will be discussed in Chapter 25. Distilled water, or water of equivalent purity obtained by the ion-exchange process, is used for filling storage batteries, for the preparation of medicines, and in certain chemical industries.

7. The composition of water by volume.

1. *By analysis, or "taking apart."* An apparatus of the type shown in Fig. 10-7

can be used to decompose water by the use of an electric current. The gases may be collected and tested to identify each one. If the tubes are graduated, the volume of each gas produced may be measured. In every case *when water is subjected to analysis, it yields two volumes of hydrogen to one volume of oxygen.*

2. *By synthesis, or "putting together."* The apparatus in Fig. 10-8 includes a eudiometer which is graduated so that the volume of any gas, or any mixture of gases, introduced into it may be measured. Two short platinum wires are sealed into the upper end of the tube so an electric spark can be used to ignite mixtures of gases inside the tube.

As shown in Fig. 10-8A, the tube is first filled with mercury. Suppose 20.0 ml of hydrogen and 20.0 ml of oxygen are introduced into the tube, as illustrated in Fig. 10-8B. Then when an electric spark is passed between the wires, the mixture ignites and forms water vapor. As the

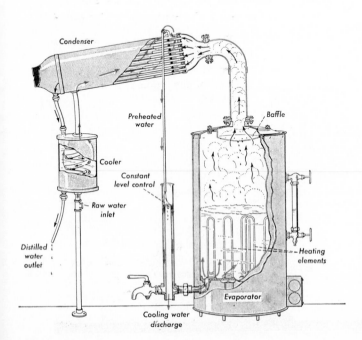

Fig. 10-6. **A continuous action, electrically-heated still. Notice that the water is preheated by the condensing vapor.**

water vapor condenses, mercury rises in the tube. But there will be 10.0 ml of gas remaining in the tube. If this gas is withdrawn and tested, it is found to be oxygen. Thus 20.0 ml of hydrogen united with 10.0 ml of oxygen, and left 10.0 ml of oxygen uncombined. Note that *the hydrogen and oxygen combined in the ratio of two volumes of hydrogen to one volume of oxygen.*

8. The composition of water by weight. In 1895, an American chemist, Dr. Edward W. Morley (1838–1923), determined the composition of water by weighing measured volumes of hydrogen, oxygen, and water which resulted from their union. It took him about

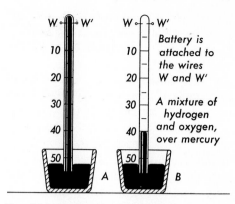

Fig. 10-8. **Eudiometer tubes like these are used to determine the composition of water by volume using the method of synthesis.**

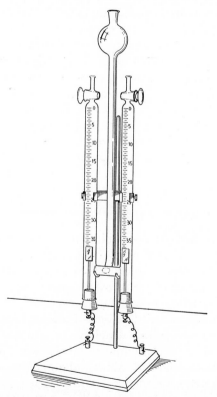

Fig. 10-7. **By using an apparatus of this type, water can be decomposed and the volumes of hydrogen and oxygen that are liberated can be measured.**

twelve years to perfect his apparatus, purify the gases, check temperatures and pressures, and devise various precautions to secure as accurate results as possible. As a result of his painstaking experiments, he concluded that *1.0000 part by weight of hydrogen unites with 7.9396 parts by weight of oxygen.* These quantities produce 8.9396 parts by weight of water. In elementary work these figures can be "rounded off"—*One part by weight of hydrogen unites with eight parts by weight of oxygen to form nine parts by weight of water.*

9. Deuterium oxide. While most water molecules are composed of hydrogen atoms with a mass number of 1 and oxygen atoms with a mass number of 16, there are other types of water molecules possible. This is because there are three isotopes of hydrogen with mass numbers of 1, 2, and 3, and three isotopes of oxygen with mass numbers of 16, 17, and 18. The possible combinations of these six isotopes give 18 types of water molecules. In water there is also a very small proportion of hydronium (H_3O^+) ions, hydroxide ions, and oxide ions which are formed from the various isotopes of hydrogen and oxygen. So actually water is a rather complex mixture of 33 kinds of molecules and ions.

While particles other than ordinary water molecules exist in only small traces in a water sample, one rare type of water molecule has been studied rather extensively. This is the *deuterium oxide* molecule, D_2O, in which the symbol D is used to represent an atom of the isotope of hydrogen with a mass number of 2. Professor G. N. Lewis (1875–1946), while doing research at the University of California, first separated deuterium oxide, sometimes called "heavy water," in 1932. Professor Hugh S. Taylor (1890–   ) and his co-workers at Princeton University subjected 2300 liters of water to electrolysis and finally succeeded in isolating 83 ml of deuterium oxide from this large volume of water. It is possible to separate D_2O from H_2O by electrolysis because D_2O molecules are not as readily decomposed by the passage of an electric current as are H_2O molecules. Thus the concentration of D_2O molecules increases as H_2O molecules are decomposed by electrolysis.

Deuterium oxide is about 10% denser than ordinary water. It boils at 101.42° C, freezes at 3.82° C, and has its maximum density at 11.6° C. Delicate tests have been devised for detecting deuterium oxide. It has been used as a "tracer" in research work in physiology. By tracing the course of deuterium oxide molecules through living organisms, new information has been obtained concerning certain life processes. Deuterium oxide usually has harmful effects on living things, particularly when present in high concentrations. The most important use of deuterium oxide is as a moderator in nuclear reactors (see Chapter 39).

2. HYDROGEN PEROXIDE

10. Preparation of hydrogen peroxide. Hydrogen peroxide, H_2O_2, is a second compound of hydrogen and oxygen. Water solutions containing up to 10% hydrogen peroxide may be prepared from a mixture of barium peroxide, BaO_2, and cold dilute sulfuric acid, H_2SO_4:

$$BaO_2 + H_2SO_4 \rightarrow BaSO_4 \downarrow + H_2O_2$$

The arrow pointing downward after the barium sulfate indicates that it forms a *precipitate*, or solid. The precipitate, barium sulfate, can be separated from the hydrogen peroxide by filtering.

An electrolytic method is used for commercial preparation of hydrogen peroxide. Sufficient sulfuric acid is added to water to make a solution of specific gravity 1.35 to 1.45. A direct current of electricity is then passed through the cold acid. At the positive terminal, persulfuric acid, $H_2S_2O_8$, is the principal product instead of oxygen as in the electrolysis of water. Persulfuric acid is not a stable compound but reacts with the water present to yield hydrogen peroxide and sulfuric acid:

$$H_2S_2O_8 + 2\ H_2O \rightarrow H_2O_2 + 2\ H_2SO_4$$

The hydrogen peroxide is then separated by distillation under reduced pressure.

Another commercial method of preparing hydrogen peroxide is assuming increased importance. In this method, hydrogen is used to reduce a complex carbon compound dissolved in benzene. The reduced compound in benzene is then mixed with water and air is blown through the mixture. The oxygen from the air oxidizes the carbon compound and hydrogen peroxide is formed. The hydrogen peroxide dissolves in the water, and this water solution of hydrogen peroxide is separated and concentrated by distillation. The oxidized carbon compound is again reduced with hydrogen, and the process repeated. This method uses only hydrogen and air for producing hydrogen peroxide.

11. The properties of hydrogen peroxide. Pure hydrogen peroxide is a colorless, syrupy liquid about 1.5 times as dense as water. It mixes with water in any proportion. A 3% solution of hydrogen peroxide is used as an antiseptic. In order to prevent the decomposition of the hydrogen peroxide, the solution is kept in dark bottles. A small quantity of acetanilide, added to the solution, acts as an *inhibitor* to prevent the decomposition of hydrogen peroxide into oxygen and water.

Hydrogen peroxide is an unstable compound which decomposes explosively at high temperatures. Traces of impurities in hydrogen peroxide solutions cause them to decompose. Hydrogen peroxide solutions of 3%, 30%, and 85% concentration are now marketed.

12. The uses of hydrogen peroxide. Hydrogen peroxide destroys the color of those organic compounds which can be converted to colorless oxides. It will destroy bacteria, too. Hydrogen peroxide is an important industrial bleaching agent for hair, wool, silk, ivory, and feathers. It is also used in 85% concentration as a source of oxygen for rockets.

13. The peroxide group. The peroxide group found in such compounds as barium peroxide, BaO_2, sodium peroxide, Na_2O_2, and hydrogen peroxide, H_2O_2, has the electron-dot configuration

$$:\overset{\displaystyle -}{\overset{..}{O}}:\overset{\displaystyle -}{\overset{..}{O}}:$$

In such compounds the two oxygen atoms are *linked together* by a nonpolar covalent bond. Metallic peroxides react

Fig. 10-9. **A tank in which wool fibers are bleached with a solution containing hydrogen peroxide before being blended and dyed for use in making carpets.**

with acids to form hydrogen peroxide. Peroxides must not be confused with dioxides, such as carbon dioxide, CO_2, sulfur dioxide, SO_2, or lead dioxide, PbO_2. In dioxides, the oxygen atoms are each bonded to the other kind of atom in the molecule, and not to each other. For instance, a possible electron-dot formula for carbon dioxide is

$$\overset{..}{O}::C::\overset{..}{\underset{..}{O}}$$

3. THE LAW OF MULTIPLE PROPORTIONS

14. The Law of Multiple Proportions. It was stated in Section 8 that hydrogen and oxygen unite in unvarying proportions, approximately 1 to 8, *by weight* to form water. This unvarying composition of water is an example of the Law of Definite Composition. It is true, also, that by indirect means it is possible to form another compound of hydrogen and oxygen, hydrogen peroxide. The composition of hydrogen peroxide is 1 part of hydrogen to 16 parts of oxygen by weight. Note that 8 compares with 16 just as 1 is to 2, a ratio of small whole numbers. It is not uncommon in chemistry for two elements to form more than one compound, as shown below.

H_2O　　1 g of H and　　　8 g of O

H_2O_2　　1 g of H and　　16 g of O

$FeCl_2$　56 g of Fe and　　71 g of Cl

$FeCl_3$　56 g of Fe and 106.5 g of Cl

From these data it is observed that:
1. the weight of the hydrogen in the first pair of compounds is fixed, or constant, and the weight of iron in the second pair of compounds is also constant; and 2. the weights of oxygen, 8 and 16, in the first case are in the simple ratio of 1 to 2, and the weights of chlorine, 71 and 106.5, in the second case are in the simple ratio of 2 to 3. It would be possible to give other examples, but in every case the *Law of Multiple Proportions* is found to be true: *When the same two elements unite to form two or more different compounds, if the amount of one element is constant, the weights of the other element in the series of compounds will be in the ratio of small whole numbers.*

This law was first proposed by John Dalton, as a direct consequence of his theory that matter exists in the form of atoms. He recognized the possibility that two kinds of atoms could combine in more than one way and in more than one proportion. But since only whole atoms could be involved in such combinations, the ratios of the weights of the second atom joining with fixed weights of the first atom would have to be in the ratio of small whole numbers. This ratio would be the same as the ratio of the actual numbers of atoms of

the second element joining with a fixed number of atoms of the first element.

Today it is recognized that the Law of Multiple Proportions arises from the fact that some elements show more than one valence or can combine in more than one way with another element. Iron can exist in compounds as iron(II) ions with a valence of $+2$ or iron(III) ions with a valence of $+3$. When these forms of iron combine with chloride ions, for example, there are two possible compounds, $FeCl_2$, iron(II) chloride, and $FeCl_3$, iron(III) chloride. The ratio of the numbers of atoms of chlorine combining with a single atom of iron is 2 to 3. And since the numbers of atoms which combine is proportional to the weights which combine, the ratio of the weights of chlorine combining with a fixed weight of iron in these two compounds is also 2 to 3.

When the electron-dot formula for water

$$H\!:\!\overset{\cdot\cdot}{\underset{\cdot\cdot}{O}}\!:$$
$$H$$

is compared with that for hydrogen peroxide,

$$H$$
$$:\!\overset{\cdot\cdot}{\underset{\cdot\cdot}{O}}\!:\!\overset{\cdot\cdot}{\underset{\cdot\cdot}{O}}\!:$$
$$H$$

it is obvious that there are two different ways in which these two kinds of atoms can combine. In water, 2 hydrogen atoms combine with only 1 oxygen atom. In hydrogen peroxide, 2 hydrogen atoms combine with 2 oxygen atoms. Since the numbers of atoms which combine is proportional to the weights which combine, the ratio of the weights of oxygen which combine with the same weight of hydrogen in these two compounds is 1 to 2, a ratio of small whole numbers.

SUMMARY

Water is our most abundant and most useful liquid. Pure water is transparent, odorless, tasteless, and almost colorless. Impurities may affect its odor and taste. Water freezes at 0° C and boils at 100° C under a pressure of 760 mm of mercury. Water molecules are polar molecules, and are joined by hydrogen bonds into groups of from eight to four in liquid water. Water is used: 1. as a standard for defining the relationship between volume and mass in the metric system; 2. for establishing a temperature scale and graduating thermometers; 3. for measuring heat; and 4. as a standard of specific gravity.

Water is a very stable compound. It reacts with active metals such as sodium, potassium, and calcium. Steam reacts with red-hot iron. The ionic oxides of very active metals are basic anhydrides, and the covalent oxides of nonmetals are acid anhydrides. Many crystals contain water of hydration which may be driven off by heat to form anhydrous compounds. Water promotes many chemical changes.

Distillation separates water from nonvolatile impurities, particularly dissolved minerals.

The composition of water can be determined by: 1. analysis; and 2. synthesis. By volume, water is composed of two volumes of hydrogen united with one volume of oxygen. By weight, water contains approximately one part hydrogen to eight parts oxygen.

Deuterium oxide is "heavy water." It is used in chemical and physiological research, and as a moderator in nuclear reactors.

Hydrogen peroxide is prepared: 1. from a mixture of barium peroxide and sulfuric acid in water; 2. by the electrolysis of sulfuric acid that has been diluted to a specific gravity of 1.35 to 1.45; or 3. by the use of hydrogen to reduce a complex carbon compound which has been dissolved in benzene. Hydrogen peroxide is an unstable compound that decomposes into water and oxygen. It is used to destroy bacteria and for bleaching. The peroxide group consists of two oxygen atoms linked together by a nonpolar covalent bond.

The Law of Multiple Proportions: When the same two elements unite to form two or more different compounds, if the amount of one element is constant, the weights of the other element in the series of compounds will be in the ratio of small whole numbers.

TEST YOURSELF ON THESE TERMS

acid anhydride
analysis
anhydrous
basic anhydride
British thermal unit
calorie
deuterium oxide
distillation
filtration

hydrate
hydrogen bond
ice point
inhibitor
Law of Multiple
   Proportions
meaning of ↓
mineral matter
peroxide group

precipitate
specific gravity
stable compound
steam point
synthesis
unstable compound
water as a scientific
   standard
water of hydration

QUESTIONS

Group A

1. Why is there always water vapor in the air, even over desert regions?
2. List six physical properties of water.
3. Under what conditions does one milliliter of water have a mass of one gram?
4. How does the volume of steam compare with the volume of water from which it was produced?
5. (a) What is a stable compound? Give an example. (b) What is an unstable compound? Give an example.
6. (a) List five metals which react with water. (b) Give the conditions under which they react.
7. (a) What is an anhydride? (b) Distingush between a basic anhydride and an acid anhydride. (c) What type of compound may be an acid anhydride? (d) What type of compound may be a basic anhydride?
8. What is the significance of the raised dot in $BaCl_2 \cdot 2\,H_2O$?
9. Give an example of a chemical change which is promoted by the presence of water.
10. What is the composition of water: (a) by volume? (b) by weight?
11. Give some uses for deuterium oxide.
12. What is a precipitate?
13. Why is acetanilide added to 3% solutions of hydrogen peroxide?
14. How is it possible for the same two elements to form more than one compound?

Group B

15. What effect does the pressure on a water surface have on the boiling temperature of the water?
16. Describe the structure of a water molecule and tell why it is a polar molecule.
17. (a) What is a hydrogen bond? (b) What effect does the presence of hydrogen bonds in water have on its boiling point?
18. What does the extreme stability of H_2O molecules indicate about the strength of the covalent bonds between the oxygen and hydrogen atoms?
19. How is deuterium oxide separated from ordinary water?
20. What chemical change does hydrogen peroxide produce in the dyes which it bleaches?
21. What conditions must be met for a series of compounds to illustrate the Law of Multiple Proportions?
22. Explain why ice occupies a greater volume than the water from which it is formed.
23. What particles are present in water beside ordinary H_2O molecules?
24. Explain why water has a point of maximum density at 4° C.
25. Distinguish between peroxides and dioxides.
26. Hydrogen peroxide decomposes according to the oxidation-reduction reaction $2\,H_2O_2 \rightarrow 2\,H_2O + O_2 \uparrow$. (a) What is the apparent valence of an atom of oxygen in the peroxide radical? (b) What is oxidized? (c) What is reduced?

PROBLEMS

Group A

1. A mixture of 50.0 ml of hydrogen and 30.0 ml of oxygen is ignited by an electric spark. What gas remains? What is its volume?
2. A mixture of 40.0 ml of oxygen and 120.0 ml of hydrogen is ignited. What gas remains and what is its volume?
3. What volume of hydrogen is needed for complete reaction with 37.5 ml of oxygen?
4. A mixture of equal volumes of oxygen and hydrogen has a volume of 100.0 ml. After the mixture is ignited, what gas remains, and what is its volume?

Group B

5. Water is 11.11% hydrogen and 88.89% oxygen. What masses of hydrogen and oxygen will be required to produced 50.00 g of water?
6. Hydrogen peroxide is 5.88% hydrogen and 94.12% oxygen. If one half of the oxygen is liberated when hydrogen peroxide is decomposed, what mass of hydrogen peroxide will be needed to produce 5.00 g of oxygen?

SOME THINGS FOR YOU TO DO

1. Prepare some anhydrous copper(II) sulfate by heating blue copper(II) sulfate crystals carefully. The open end of the test tube must be lower than the closed end to permit the water to run out. Examine the anhydrous copper(II) sulfate that results. Add a drop of water to a little of the powder to show how it can be used as a test to detect the presence of water.
2. Prepare a quantity of distilled water, using a Liebig condenser. Note any differences in taste and appearance of the distilled water when compared with tap water.
3. Show that hydrogen peroxide produces oxygen when it decomposes. Add a pinch of manganese dioxide to a test tube half full of hydrogen peroxide solution. Hold a glowing splint above the bubbling liquid.

CHECK YOUR PROGRESS IN CHEMISTRY

1. Describe the structure of a calcium atom, atomic number 20, mass number 40.
2. Distinguish between atomic weight and atomic mass.
3. (*a*) In which group of the Periodic Table is oxygen placed? (*b*) Where is hydrogen placed on the Periodic Table?
4. (*a*) What is the usual valence of hydrogen? (*b*) What is the valence of hydrogen in potassium hydride? (*c*) What is the usual valence of oxygen? (*d*) What is the valence of an oxygen atom in barium peroxide?
5. What type of bonding occurs in: (*a*) H_2O; (*b*) D_2O; (*c*) H_2O_2?

6. The English say Priestley, the French say Lavoisier, and the Swedish people say Scheele discovered oxygen. What part did each of these scientists play in the discovery?
7. Describe two commercial methods for producing oxygen.
8. What are two laboratory methods for producing hydrogen?
9. Draw electron-dot formulas for: (*a*) a molecule of oxygen; (*b*) a molecule of hydrogen.
10. When hydrogen is passed over heated iron oxide, iron and steam are produced. (*a*) Was the hydrogen oxidized or reduced? (*b*) Was the iron oxidized or reduced?
11. Draw a diagram of a laboratory burner, and use your diagram to explain its operation.
12. A wide-mouth bottle contains a colorless, odorless, and tasteless gas, which is either hydrogen or oxygen. What experiments would you conduct to establish the identity of the gas?
13. In what ways is water used as a scientific standard?
14. A gas has a volume of 45.0 ml when the barometer is 750. mm. If the temperature does not change, what will be the volume of the gas at standard pressure?
15. A volume of 100.0 liters of gas is measured at 25° C and 700. mm pressure. What volume will this gas occupy at −20.° C and 800. mm pressure?
★16. A quantity of hydrogen collected over water occupies 78.0 ml when the temperature is 23° C and the barometric pressure is 746 mm. The liquid level inside the gas-collecting bottle is the same as that outside. What volume will the dry hydrogen occupy at S.T.P.?

CHALLENGING YOUR KNOWLEDGE

1. What relationship is there between unpaired electrons in an oxygen molecule and the fact that liquid oxygen is slightly attracted by a magnet?
2. In the experiment of burning steel picture wire in pure oxygen, the end of the picture wire is sometimes dipped in powdered sulfur, and the sulfur ignited, before the wire is plunged into the oxygen. Why?
3. From a given amount of water, is it possible to prepare more hydrogen by electrolysis or by reaction with a metal such as sodium? Why?
4. Carbon dioxide is a gas which is about 1½ times as dense as air. What would happen if this gas surrounded the unglazed porcelain cup of the apparatus shown in Fig. 8-3?
5. Scientists have not yet reached Absolute zero, yet helium has been cooled below −273° C. Explain this seeming paradox.
6. What do scientists believe happens to molecular movement as a substance is cooled to Absolute zero?

Unit 4 · CHEMICAL CALCULATIONS

Chemical Composition
Equations and Energy of Reactions
Mass Relations in Chemical Reactions
Molecular Composition of Gases
Volume Relations in Chemical Reactions

Chapter 11 · CHEMICAL COMPOSITION

1. The significance of chemical formulas. We have learned to write formulas for compounds using our knowledge of the valence of the elements composing them. When it is known that a substance exists as simple molecules, its formula represents one molecule of the substance. Thus it is known as a *molecular formula.* In instances where the molecular structure is not known, or where it is known that the substance does not exist as simple molecules, the formula represents the simplest whole-number ratio of the atoms of the constituent elements. This is called an *empirical,* or simplest, *formula.*

Let us examine some chemical formulas to learn their full significance. The compound water has the molecular formula H_2O. This molecular formula represents *one molecule* of water. It shows that each molecule of water is made up of *two atoms of hydrogen* and *one atom of oxygen.* Since the atomic weight of hydrogen is 1.0 and the atomic weight of oxygen is 16.0, this molecular formula signifies that the *formula weight of water* is 18.0 [(1.0, the atomic

164

weight of hydrogen, $\times$ 2 atoms of hydrogen) + (16.0, the atomic weight of oxygen, $\times$ 1 atom of oxygen)].

The compound sodium chloride, table salt, has the empirical formula $NaCl$. It is a crystalline solid which has no simple molecular structure, being made up of an orderly arrangement of sodium and chloride ions. This empirical formula tells us the relative number of atoms of each element present in the compound sodium chloride. It shows that for each sodium atom there is one chlorine atom. Since the atomic weight of sodium is 23.0 and the atomic weight of chlorine is 35.5, this empirical formula signifies that the formula weight of sodium chloride is 58.5 (23.0 + 35.5).

The *formula weight* of any compound is *the sum of the atomic weights of all of the atoms present in the formula.*

2. Molecular weight. We have seen that a molecular formula represents 1 molecule of a substance. Since H_2O is a molecular formula and indicates 1 molecule of water, the formula weight, 18.0, is the relative weight of *one molecule* of water. *The formula weight of* *a molecular substance is its **molecular weight.***

In the strictest sense it is not correct to speak of the molecular weight of a nonmolecular substance, such as sodium chloride, which is represented by an empirical formula. The term *formula weight* is more generally applicable than the term *molecular weight* and therefore is preferred by chemists. However, both terms are widely used and, in elementary chemical calculations, the distinction is not significant.

3. The formula weight of a compound. If you wish to know the total weight of your chemistry class, you would add together the weights of all the individuals in the class. Similarly, if we wish to find the formula weight of any substance for which the formula is given, we must add together the atomic weights of all the atoms present, as represented by the formula. Let us use the formula of cane sugar, $C_{12}H_{22}O_{11}$, as an example.

Number of atoms	Atomic weight	Total weight
12 of C	12	$12 \times 12 = 144$
22 of H	1	$22 \times 1 = 22$
11 of O	16	$11 \times 16 = 176$
formula weight (molecular weight) = 342		

The formula for calcium hydroxide is $Ca(OH)_2$. The subscript $_2$ following the parentheses indicates that there are two hydroxide radicals, **OH**, with each calcium atom in calcium hydroxide.

Number of atoms	Atomic weight	Total weight
1 of Ca	40.	$1 \times 40. = 40.$
2 of O	16	$2 \times 16 = 32$
2 of H	1	$2 \times 1 = 2$
formula weight = 74		

VOCABULARY

Chemical formula. A shorthand notation using chemical symbols and numerical subscripts to represent the composition of substances.

Empirical formula. A chemical formula denoting the constituent elements of a substance and relative number of atoms of each.

Formula weight. The sum of the atomic weights of the atoms present in the chemical formula.

Gram-atomic weight (gram-atom). The mass of an element in grams equal to its atomic weight.

Gram-formula weight. The mass of a substance in grams equal to its formula weight.

Gram-molecular weight (gram-molecule). The mass of a molecular substance in grams equal to its molecular weight.

Mole. The gram-molecular weight of a molecular substance. Inpractice, extended to include gram-formula weights of nonmolecular substances and gram-atomic weights of elements represented as monatomic.

Molecular formula. A chemical formula denoting the constituent elements of a substance and number of atoms of each composing one molecule.

Molecular weight. The formula weight of a molecular substance.

It is usually easier in determining formula weights of substances containing such simple radical groups to consider the *combined atomic weights* of the radical group as we would the atomic weight of a single atom of any element present. Thus we may proceed as follows:

1 atom of Ca, at. wt. 40.   1 × 40. = 40.
2 OH radicals, combined
    at. wt. 17   2 × 17 = 34
    _____
            formula weight = 74

The atomic weights of the elements are relative weights based on an atom of carbon-12 having the assigned value of exactly 12. In the quantitative study of chemical reactions, the atomic weights and formula weights are exceedingly practical to use. They tell us the relative weights of elements or compounds that combine or react. We may convert these relative weights to any desired units. Thus formulas play a very important part in chemical calculations.

4. The percentage composition of a compound. Frequently it is important to know the composition of a compound in terms of the *mass percentage* of each constituent element. We may want to know the percentage of iron in the compound iron(III) oxide. Knowledge of the percentage of oxygen in potassium chlorate will enable us to determine the amount of this compound needed to furnish enough oxygen for a laboratory experiment.

The chemical formula of a compound enables us to determine directly its formula weight simply by adding the atomic weights of all the atoms present. The formula weight represents *all*, or *100%*, of the composition of the substance as indicated by the formula. The total atomic weight (atomic weight × number of atoms) of each element

present represents the *part* of the substance due to that element. The *fractional* part due to each element present is:

$$\frac{\text{total atomic weight of the element}}{\text{formula weight of the compound}}$$

The percentage of each element present in the compound is therefore a fractional part of 100 percent of the compound.

Bear in mind that atomic weights and formula weights are relative weights and are expressed by numbers without dimensions, that is, numbers without units of measure. This relationship is dimensionally correct when expressed as follows:

$$\frac{(\text{at. wt.} \times \text{No. atoms}) \text{ element}}{\text{formula wt. compound}} \times$$
$$100\% \text{ compound} = \% \text{ element}$$

Let us consider the compound iron(III) oxide mentioned earlier. The formula is Fe_2O_3. What is the percentage of each of the elements in this compound?

1. Formula weight of Fe_2O_3

total at. wt. of Fe = 2 × 56 = 112
total at. wt. of O = 3 × 16 = 48
_____
    formula weight of Fe_2O_3 = 160.

2. Percentage of Fe

$$\frac{\text{total at. wt. Fe}}{\text{formula wt. } Fe_2O_3} \times 100\% \, Fe_2O_3 = \% \, Fe$$

$$\frac{112 \, Fe}{160. \, Fe_2O_3} \times 100\% \, Fe_2O_3 = 70.0\% \, Fe$$

3. Percentage of O

$$\frac{\text{total at. wt. O}}{\text{formula wt. } Fe_2O_3} \times 100\% \, Fe_2O_3 = \% \, O$$

$$\frac{48 \, O}{160. \, Fe_2O_3} \times 100\% \, Fe_2O_3 = 30.0\% \, O$$

Of course, since there is no third element present, the percentage of oxygen is $100\% - 70.0\% = 30.0\%$.

Observe the dimensional character of the results of these simple computations. Many errors in the solutions to problems in chemistry can be avoided by consistently labeling each quantity properly and solving the expression for both the numerical value and the label of the result.

As a second example, let us use crystallized sodium carbonate. From its formula, $Na_2CO_3 \cdot 10 H_2O$, we see that 10 molecules of water have crystallized with sodium carbonate to form the hydrate. (The raised period indicates a bond to the water of hydration.) To find the percentage composition (to 3 significant figures) we proceed as before:

1. Formula weight $Na_2CO_3 \cdot 10 H_2O$

2 Na	$2 \times 23.0 =$	46.0
1 C	$1 \times 12.0 =$	12.0
3 O	$3 \times 16.0 =$	48.0
10 H$_2$O	$10 \times 18.0 =$	180.

formula weight $= 286$

2. Percentage of Na

$$\frac{46.0 \text{ Na}}{286 \text{ Na}_2\text{CO}_3 \cdot 10 \text{ H}_2\text{O}}$$

$\times 100\%$ Na$_2$CO$_3$ · 10 H$_2$O $= 16.1\%$ Na

3. Percentage of C

$$\frac{12.0 \text{ C}}{286 \text{ Na}_2\text{CO}_3 \cdot 10 \text{ H}_2\text{O}}$$

$\times 100\%$ Na$_2$CO$_3$ · 10 H$_2$O $= 4.2\%$ C

4. Percentage of O (in $CO_3^=$ group)

$$\frac{48.0 \text{ O}}{286 \text{ Na}_2\text{CO}_3 \cdot 10 \text{ H}_2\text{O}}$$

$\times 100\%$ Na$_2$CO$_3$ · 10 H$_2$O $= 16.8\%$ O

5. Percentage of H_2O

$$\frac{180. \text{ H}_2\text{O}}{286 \text{ Na}_2\text{CO}_3 \cdot 10 \text{ H}_2\text{O}}$$

$\times 100\%$ Na$_2$CO$_3$ · 10 H$_2$O $= 62.9\%$ H$_2$O

Approximate atomic weights usually have no more than two or three significant figures. Your accuracy cannot be improved by carrying out your computations beyond the accuracy limits of the data used. The sum of the mass percentages, therefore, may only approximate 100 percent. Such results do not detract from the validity of the chemistry involved but properly reflect the approximations employed in the computations.

5. The gram-atomic weight of an element. It has been estimated that if all the people on the earth were assigned the task of counting the molecules in a tablespoon of water and were required to count at the rate of one molecule each second, approximately 8×10^6 years would be required to complete the project. However impractical this may seem, we can realize that the number of molecules involved is so large that it staggers the imagination!

Fortunately, chemists are not ordinarily faced with the problem of weighing out a certain number of molecules of a compound or atoms of an element. They do frequently need to weigh out equal numbers of atoms or molecules of different substances. A knowledge of the atomic weights of the elements allows this to be done very simply.

Atomic weights are relative weights based on the assigned weight of carbon-12 as exactly 12. As the atomic weight of hydrogen is 1.0, the average weight of carbon atoms is 12 times the average weight of hydrogen atoms. It follows that 100 atoms of carbon weigh 12 times as much as 100 hydrogen atoms. Similarly, 1 million carbon atoms weigh 12 times as much as 1 million hydrogen atoms. Any given quantities of carbon and hydrogen which are in the ratio of 12:1 must have the same number of atoms.

Fig. 11-1. **The platform balance is used in the laboratory when accuracy to 0.1 gram is satisfactory.** (Ohaus Scale)

Let us consider the atomic weights of oxygen and sulfur, 16 and 32 respectively. Oxygen atoms are one half as heavy as sulfur atoms. Thus any given quantities of oxygen and sulfur which are in the ratio 1:2 (16:32) must have the same number of atoms. By similar reasoning using the atomic weights of other elements, we may recognize the following important generalization: *If the quantities of two elements are in the same ratio as their atomic weights, they contain the same number of atoms.*

Chemists measure quantities of substances in gram (mass) units and sometimes refer to their masses as their weights since they use "weighing" methods. However, it should be recognized that quantities measured in gram units are, in fact, mass quantities. It is evident that atomic weights are most useful when expressed in gram units. *The gram-atomic weight is that mass of an element in grams equal to its atomic weight.* The gram-atomic weight of an element is commonly referred to as a *gram-atom* of the element. Thus a gram-atom of oxygen is 16 g of oxygen, a gram-atom of sulfur is 32 g of sulfur, and a gram-atom of iron is 56 g of iron.

The most significant fact concerning the gram-atomic weights of elements is that *gram-atoms of all elements contain the same number of atoms.* This number of atoms is called the **Avogadro number,** the accepted modern value of which is 6.02483×10^{23} atoms per gram-atom of any element. This constant is quite useful and should be remembered to at least three significant figures: 6.02×10^{23}.

6. The mole concept. The formula weights of substances are simply the totals of atomic weights as denoted by the formulas. They too are relative weights having the same base as atomic weights, carbon-12 as 12. Atomic weights and formula weights are therefore fully comparable. The formula weight of a molecular substance is its molecular weight.

In a manner similar to that used in defining the gram-atomic weight of an element, we may define *the gram-molecular weight as the mass of a molecular substance in grams equal to its molecular weight.* The gram-molecular weight (1 *gram-molecule*) of H_2O is 18 grams of water. One gram-molecule of CO_2 is 44 grams of carbon dioxide. You will readily see that 18 g of water and 44 g of carbon dioxide must consist of the same number of molecules. *Gram-molecules of all molecular substances contain the same number of molecules.* This again is the Avogadro number, 6.02×10^{23} molecules per gram-molecule.

The gram-molecular weight is such a useful unit to chemists that it has been given a short name, the **mole.** The concept of the mole has been extended to include those substances which do not have molecules and are expressed by empirical formulas. Thus the **gram-formula weight** (the formula weight in grams) of sodium chloride, 58.5 g of sodium chloride, represents 1 mole of the salt. A gram-atom of an element commonly represented as monatomic constitutes 1 mole of the element. A gram-atom of zinc, 65 g of zinc, is 1 mole of that element. On the other hand, a mole of diatomic oxygen, O_2, is 32 g of oxygen. *The number of molecules in a mole of any molecular substance is the same as the number of atoms in a gram-atom of any element,* the Avogadro number.

Not only does the symbol of an element stand for one atom of that element, but it stands for 1 gram-atom as well. Similarly, the formula of a compound stands for 1 mole of that compound. As indicated in the preceding

paragraph, the symbol of an element commonly represented as monatomic and the formula of a diatomic elementary gas stand for 1 mole. The concept of the mole is a very useful tool for chemists and chemistry students.

7. Determining the empirical formula of a compound. When given the formula of a compound we may determine the percentage composition of the constituent elements. So if the percent of each element composing a compound is known, we may calculate the ratio of the atoms of the elements combined. The elements of a compound written in their smallest whole-number ratio constitute the empirical, or simplest, formula of the compound.

Fig. 11-2. **A diagram illustrating the mole-to-volume ratio of different substances.**

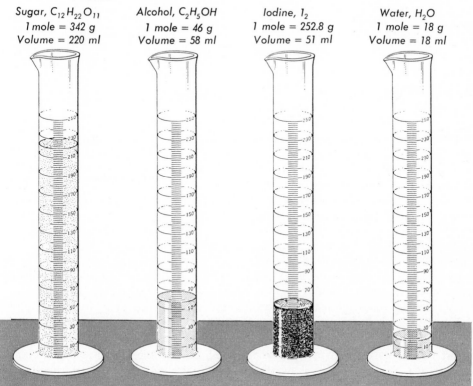

Sugar, $C_{12}H_{22}O_{11}$	Alcohol, C_2H_5OH	Iodine, I_2	Water, H_2O
1 mole = 342 g	1 mole = 46 g	1 mole = 252.8 g	1 mole = 18 g
Volume = 220 ml	Volume = 58 ml	Volume = 51 ml	Volume = 18 ml

This is the way in which most formulas are originally determined. A compound is analyzed to identify the elements present and determine their mass ratios or percentage composition. The empirical formula is then calculated from this information using the gram-atomic weight of each element to reduce the mass ratios to atom ratios.

Dr. Morley of Western Reserve University (see Chapter 10, Section 8) found that 1.0000 part by weight of hydrogen combined with 7.9396 parts by weight of oxygen to form 8.9396 parts by weight of water vapor. Every 8.9396 parts of water formed required 1.000 parts of hydrogen and 7.9396 parts of oxygen. Thus water consists of

$$\frac{1.0000 \text{ parts H}}{8.9396 \text{ parts water}}$$
$$\times \ 100\% \text{ water} = 11.186\% \text{ hydrogen}$$

and $\dfrac{7.9396 \text{ parts O}}{8.9396 \text{ parts water}}$
$$\times \ 100\% \text{ water} = 88.814\% \text{ oxygen}$$

The relative number of atoms of hydrogen and oxygen in water may be determined by comparing the mass percentages of the elements, or their actual masses by analysis, to their respective gram-atomic weights.

Number of gram-atoms of an element =

$$\frac{\text{mass of the element}}{\text{mass of 1 g-atom of the element}}$$

1. From percentage composition data. The simplest way to think of percentage composition is in terms of *parts per hundred*. Dr. Morley's experiments show that (rounding to 3 significant figures) 11.2% of water is hydrogen and 88.8% is oxygen, that is, 100.0 parts of water consist of 11.2 parts hydrogen and 88.8 parts oxygen. Similarly, they show that there are 11.2 g of hydrogen and 88.8 g

of oxygen per 100.0 g. of water. How many gram-atoms of hydrogen and oxygen are present in 100.0 g of water?

H: $\dfrac{11.2 \text{ g H}}{1 \text{ g/g-atom}} = 11.2$ g-atom H

O: $\dfrac{88.8 \text{ g O}}{16 \text{ g/g-atom}} = 5.56$ g-atom O

Remembering that 1 g-atom of one element has the same number of atoms as 1 g-atom of any other element (the Avogadro number), the relative number of atoms is

$$\text{H : O} = 11.2 : 5.56$$

2. From relative mass data. Since the table of approximate atomic weights is used we may round off the relative masses given to 1 part hydrogen and 8 parts oxygen in 9 parts of water. Accordingly, each 9-g quantity of water produced required 1 g of hydrogen and 8 g of oxygen. We can determine the number of g-atoms of hydrogen and oxygen in 9 g of water and reduce this to the relative number of atoms of each in water as before.

H: $\dfrac{1 \text{ g H}}{1 \text{ g/g-atom}} = 1$ g-atom H

O: $\dfrac{8 \text{ g O}}{16 \text{ g/g-atom}} = \frac{1}{2}$ g-atom O

The relative number of atoms is

$$\text{H : O} = 1 : \tfrac{1}{2}$$

From these calculations we may write the empirical formula of water as $H_{11.2}O_{5.56}$ or $HO_{1/2}$. Both formulas show the correct ratio of hydrogen atoms to oxygen atoms in the compound water. However, according to the Atomic Theory, only whole atoms combine chemically. We need to convert these atom ratios to their simplest whole-number values. This is accomplished by dividing each ratio by its lowest term.

$$\begin{array}{ccc} \text{H} & : & \text{O} \\ 5.56 \overline{\smash{\big)}\,11.2} & : & 5.56 \\ 2 & : & 1 \end{array}$$

and

$$\begin{array}{ccc} \text{H} & : & \text{O} \\ \frac{1}{2}\overline{\smash{\big)}\,1} & : & \frac{1}{2} \\ 2 & : & 1 \end{array}$$

The empirical formula of water is therefore H_2O.

Sometimes the operation just performed does not yield a simple whole-number ratio. In such instances the simplest whole-number ratio may be found by expressing the result as fractions and clearing. CAUTION: In some problems dividing by the lowest term may result in such ratios as 1:2.01 or 2.98 or 3.99. Remember that results obtained by using approximate atomic weights can be no more accurate than these values. You should not attempt to clear the fractions in such instances; simply round off to 2, 3, or 4 respectively. These operations are illustrated further in the sample problems which follow.

8. Finding the molecular formula. The analysis of a substance enables us to determine its empirical formula. This simplest formula may or may not be the molecular formula. We calculated the empirical formula of the gas, methane, and found it to be CH_4. Any multiple of CH_4, as C_2H_8, C_3H_{12}, or C_nN_{4n}, represents the same ratio of carbon and hydrogen atoms. How then may we know which is the correct molecular formula?

It is not possible to decide which is the true formula unless the molecular weight of the substance has been determined. Some substances lend themselves to known methods of determining molecular weights and some do not. These methods will be discussed in Chapters 14 and 19. If the molecular weight is known, it is a simple matter to decide which multiple of the empirical formula is the molecular formula.

Let us represent the correct multiple of the empirical formula by the sub-

SAMPLE PROBLEM

A compound is found by analysis to contain 75.0% carbon and 25.0% hydrogen. What is the empirical formula?

SOLUTION

Since the compound is 75.0% carbon, 75.0 parts per 100. or 75.0 g per 100.0 g is carbon. Similarly 25.0 g per 100.0 g of the compound is hydrogen. The number of gram-atoms of each in 100.0 g of the compound is determined by the following relation:

$$\text{No. of g-atoms of an element} = \frac{\text{mass of the element}}{\text{mass of 1 g-atom of the element}}$$

$$\text{C:} \quad \frac{75.0 \text{ g C}}{12 \text{ g/g-atom}} = 6.25 \text{ g-atom C}$$

$$\text{H:} \quad \frac{25.0 \text{ g H}}{1 \text{ g/g-atom}} = 25.0 \text{ g-atom H}$$

Relative number of atoms, $C : H = 6.25 : 25.0$

Smallest ratio of atoms $= \dfrac{6.25}{6.25} : \dfrac{25.0}{6.25} = 1 : 4$

Empirical formula $= CH_4$

SAMPLE PROBLEM

A compound contains carbon, 81.8%, and hydrogen, 18.2%. Find the empirical formula.

SOLUTION

Each 100.0-g quantity of the compound contains 81.8 g of carbon and 18.2 g of hydrogen as shown by the percentage composition.

$$\text{No. of g-atoms of an element} = \frac{\text{mass of the element}}{\text{mass of 1 g-atom of the element}}$$

C: $\quad \dfrac{81.8 \text{ g C}}{12 \text{ g/g-atom}} = 6.82$ g-atom C

H: $\quad \dfrac{18.2 \text{ g H}}{1 \text{ g/g-atom}} = 18.2$ g-atom H

Rel. No. atoms, $C : H = 6.82 : 18.2$

Smallest ratio of atoms $= \dfrac{6.82}{6.82} : \dfrac{18.2}{6.82} = 1 : 2.67$

Simplest whole number ratio $= 1 : 2.67 = 1 : 2\frac{2}{3} = 3 : 8$
Empirical formula $= C_3H_8$

SAMPLE PROBLEM

The reduction of 11.47 g of copper(II) oxide yields 9.16 g of copper. What is the empirical formula of the copper(II) oxide?

SOLUTION

Since copper(II) oxide is composed of copper and oxygen, the mass of oxygen removed in the reduction process must be

$$11.47 \text{ g} - 9.16 \text{ g} = 2.31 \text{ g oxygen}$$

$$\text{No. of g-atoms of an element} = \frac{\text{mass of the element}}{\text{mass of 1 g-atom of the element}}$$

Cu: $\quad \dfrac{9.16 \text{ g Cu}}{63.5 \text{ g/g-atom}} = 0.144$ g-atom Cu

O: $\quad \dfrac{2.31 \text{ g O}}{16 \text{ g/g-atom}} = 0.144$ g-atom O

Relative No. of atoms, $Cu : O = 0.144 : 0.144$
Smallest ratio of atoms $= 1 : 1$
Empirical formula $= CuO$

script $_x$. The molecular formula then becomes

(empirical formula)$_x$

which may be equated to the known molecular weight.

(empirical formula)$_x$ = molecular weight

In the case of methane the molecular weight is known to be 16. Our equation is

$$(CH_4)_x = 16$$
$$(12 + 4)_x = 16$$
$$x = 1$$
molecular formula = $(CH_4)_1$ or CH_4

Hence the empirical formula of methane is also the molecular formula. We have seen that this is true also in the case of water. For another example, see the Sample Problem which follows.

The analysis of starch reveals its empirical formula to be $C_6H_{10}O_5$. No precise method has been found for determining its molecular weight. Its molecular formula could be written $C_6H_{10}O_5$, $C_{60}H_{100}O_{50}$ or in any other form which is a multiple of the empirical formula.

Chemists write the formula for starch as $(C_6H_{10}O_5)_x$, but no one knows how to find the exact value of x.

Cellulose has the same empirical formula as starch, $C_6H_{10}O_5$. Chemists are certain, however, that its molecular structure involves some multiple different from that of starch. Its formula is commonly written $(C_6H_{10}O_5)_n$, where n for cellulose and the x for starch stand for different numbers, neither of which is known.

It is evident that the molecular formula of a molecular substance may be the simplest ratio of atoms indicated by the empirical formula, or it may be some whole-number multiple of the empirical formula. The empirical and molecular formulas of some other compounds are given in the following table.

Substance	Empirical formula	Molecular formula
Hydrogen peroxide	HO	H_2O_2
Benzene	CH	C_6H_6
Mercury(I) chloride	HgCl	Hg_2Cl_2
Glucose	CH_2O	$C_6H_{12}O_6$

SAMPLE PROBLEM

Hydrogen peroxide is found by analysis to consist of 5.9% hydrogen and 94.1% oxygen. Its molecular weight is determined to be 34. What is the correct formula?

SOLUTION

1. The empirical formula determined from the analysis by the method described in Section 7, is

HO

2. The molecular formula determined from the empirical formula and molecular weight is

$$(HO)_x = 34$$
$$(1 + 16)_x = 34$$
$$x = 2$$
molecular formula = $(HO)_2$ or H_2O_2

The empirical formula of a compound indicates what elements are present and the relative number of atoms of these elements. The molecular formula tells us the specific number of atoms of each element present per molecule of a molecular compound.

The formula weight is the sum of the atomic weights of all the atoms indicated by the formula. If it is a molecular formula, the formula weight is the same as the molecular weight. Atomic weights and formula weights expressed in grams are known as gram-atomic weights and gram-formula weights. Practical use of these units has resulted in the definition of the mole, a useful and important concept in chemistry.

The percentage composition of a compound may be determined if the formula is known. Conversely, the empirical formula may be determined if the composition of a compound is known.

The molecular formula can be written only if the molecular weight of the substance has been determined. It will always be a whole-number multiple of the empirical formula.

TEST YOURSELF ON THESE TERMS

atomic weight	gram-atom	mole
Avogadro number	gram-atomic weight	molecular formula
chemical formula	gram-formula weight	molecular weight
empirical formula	gram-molecular weight	percentage composition
formula weight	gram-molecule	simplest formula

PROBLEMS

Use table of approximate atomic weights inside front cover.

Group A

1. What is the formula weight of ammonia, NH_3?
2. Find the formula weight of sulfuric acid, H_2SO_4.
3. Dextrose, or grape sugar, has the formula $C_6H_{12}O_6$. Determine its formula weight.
4. Find the formula weight of ethyl alcohol, C_2H_5OH.
5. Calcium phosphate has the formula $Ca_3(PO_4)_2$. Determine the formula weight.
6. Crystallized magnesium sulfate, or Epsom salts, has the formula $MgSO_4 \cdot 7\,H_2O$. What is its formula weight?
7. Vinegar contains acetic acid, $HC_2H_3O_2$. Find the percentage composition of this compound.
8. All baking powders contain sodium hydrogen carbonate, $NaHCO_3$. Calculate its percentage composition.
9. What is the percentage composition of soap having the formula $C_{17}H_{35}COONa$?
10. Which of the following compounds contains the highest percentage of nitrogen: (*a*) $Ca(NO_3)_2$; (*b*) $CaCN_2$; or (*c*) $(NH_4)_2SO_4$?

11. A strip of pure copper weighing 6.356 g is heated in a stream of oxygen until it is completely converted to the black oxide. The mass of the oxide was found to be 7.956 g. What is the percentage composition of the copper(II) oxide?

12. How many kilograms of iron may be recovered from 1 metric ton (1000 kg) of Fe_3O_4?

13. Cinnabar, the ore from which mercury is extracted, has the formula HgS. Calculate the mass of mercury recovered from 1 kg of cinnabar.

14. Calculate the percentage of copper in each of the following minerals: cuprite, Cu_2O; malachite, $CuCO_3 \cdot Cu(OH)_2$; and cubanite, $CuFe_2S_4$.

15. Calculate the percentage of CaO in $CaCO_3$.

Group B

16. If 124.8 g of copper(II) sulfate crystals are heated to drive off the water of hydration, the loss of mass is 45 g. What is the percentage of water in hydrated copper(II) sulfate?

17. The anhydrous copper(II) sulfate produced in Problem 16 was found to contain copper, 31.8 g; sulfur, 16.0 g; and oxygen, 32.0 g. Determine the empirical formula of the hydrated copper(II) sulfate crystals.

18. One compound of platinum and chlorine is known to consist of 42.1% chlorine. Another consists of 26.7% chlorine. What are the two empirical formulas?

19. What is the empirical formula of silver fluoride which is found to contain 85% silver?

20. What is the percentage composition of the drug Chloromycetin, $C_{11}H_{12}N_2O_5Cl_2$.

21. Analysis: phosphorus, 43.67%; oxygen, 56.33%. What is the empirical formula?

22. Analysis: potassium, 24.58%; manganese, 34.81%; oxygen, 40.50%. What is the empirical formula?

23. Calculate the empirical formula for a compound having 37.70% sodium, 22.95% silicon, and 39.34% oxygen.

24. A compound has the following composition: sodium, 28.05%; carbon, 29.26%; hydrogen, 3.66%; oxygen, 39.02%. What is the empirical formula?

25. The anaylsis of a compound shows: nitrogen, 21.21%; hydrogen, 6.06%; sulfur, 24.24%; oxygen, 48.48%. Find the simplest formula.

26. What is the empirical formula of certain hydrated crystals having a composition of 56.14% $ZnSO_4$ and 43.86% water?

27. The analysis of a gas reveals its composition to be carbon, 92.3%; hydrogen, 7.7%. Its molecular weight is known to be 26. What is the molecular formula?

28. The percentages by weight of carbon in its two oxides are 42.8% and 27.3%. Use these data to illustrate the Law of Multiple Proportions.

Chapter 12 · EQUATIONS AND ENERGY OF REACTIONS

1. CHEMICAL EQUATIONS

1. Formula equations. The simplest way to illustrate chemical action is by the use of *word equations*. Such equations are useful because they enable us to state briefly what substances enter into chemical actions and what substances are produced. Word equations have *qualitative* significance.

Water is formed by the combustion of hydrogen in air. The word equation for this action is:

hydrogen + oxygen → water

We read, hydrogen *plus* oxygen *yields* water. Such an equation signifies that when hydrogen and oxygen react as indicated, water is the only product. Thus it briefly states an experimental fact. It does not tell us the circumstances under which the reaction occurs, or the quantities involved.

In our discussion of the Law of Conservation of Matter and Energy (Chapter 1, Section 11), we recognized a most useful generalization: *In ordinary chemical changes, the total mass of the re-*

176

acting substances is equal to the total mass of the products. This may be thought of in terms of the **Law of Conservation of Atoms.**

Suppose we replace the names of the *reactants*, hydrogen and oxygen, and the name of the *product*, water, with their respective formulas. The equation can now be rewritten as a *balanced formula equation* which conforms with the Law of Conservation of Atoms.

$$2 H_2 + O_2 \rightarrow 2 H_2O$$

This agreement is verified by comparing the total number of atoms of hydrogen and oxygen on the left side of the reaction sign ($\rightarrow$) to their respective totals on the right. Two molecules of hydrogen contain 4 atoms of hydrogen; 2 molecules of water also contain 4 hydrogen atoms. One molecule of oxygen contains 2 atoms of oxygen; 2 molecules of water also contain 2 oxygen atoms. Thus the chemical equation, just as any algebraic equation, *expresses an equality. Until it is balanced it cannot express an equality and is not a true equation.* The yield sign ($\rightarrow$) has the meaning of an equals sign ($=$), and in addition, indicates the direction in which the reaction proceeds.

Our formula equation now signifies much more than the word equation.

1. It tells us the relative proportions of the reactants, hydrogen and oxygen, and the product, water.
2. It tells us that 2 *molecules* of hydrogen react with 1 *molecule* of oxygen to form 2 *molecules* of water.
3. It tells us that 2 *molecular weights* of hydrogen react with 1 *molecular weight* of oxygen to form 2 *molecular weights* of water.

Atomic weights, and thus molecular weights, are relative masses and may be assigned any desired mass units. Therefore:

4. It tells us that 4 g (or 4 kg or 4 metric tons) of hydrogen react with 32 g (or 32 kg or 32 metric tons) of oxygen to form 36 g (or 36 kg or 36 metric tons) of water.

Most important of all:

5. *It tells us that 2 moles of hydrogen react with 1 mole of oxygen to form 2 moles of water.*

Finally, in any equation, the equality exists in both directions. If $x + y = z$, then $z = x + y$. So our chemical equation:

6. Tells us that 2 *moles* of water, if decomposed, would yield 2 *moles* of hydrogen and 1 *mole* of oxygen.

From the foregoing, it is evident that formula equations have *quantitative* significance. They represent facts concerning reactions which have been established by experiments or other means. However, they do not reveal either the ease with which reactions proceed or the conditions under which reactions occur.

It is possible to write an equation for a reaction which does not occur. For example, hydrogen and oxygen may be shown by an equation to yield hydrogen peroxide. Such an equation can be balanced to conform to the Law of Conservation of Atoms. However, it would be a false equation and therefore useless. It would be contrary to known facts, since hydrogen and oxygen do not combine directly to form hydrogen peroxide.

2. Factors in equation writing. A chemical equation has no value unless it is correct in every detail. Three factors must be considered in writing a balanced equation.

1. *The equation must represent the facts.* If we are to write the equation for a reaction, we must know the facts concerning the reaction. We must know all

VOCABULARY

Activation energy. Energy required initially to start a reaction.

Activity series. A table of metals or nonmetals arranged in order of descending activity.

Formula equation. A concise symbolized picture of a chemical change.

Free energy. The energy of a reaction which can be converted to useful work outside the reaction.

Heat of formation. The quantity of heat energy liberated or consumed when a compound is formed from its constituent elements.

Product. An element or compound resulting from a chemical action.

Reactant. An element or compound entering into a chemical action.

the reactants and all the products. The chemist relies upon analysis for facts and writes equations only for those reactions that are known to occur.

2. *The equation must include the symbols and formulas of all elements and compounds which are used as reactants or formed as products.* We must know these symbols and formulas and must be sure that they are correctly written. In most instances our knowledge of the valence of the elements and the valence method of writing correct formulas will enable us to satisfy this requirement without extensive experience with experiments or analyses.

3. *The Law of Conservation of Atoms must be satisfied.* There must be the same number of atoms of each kind on each side of the equation. A new atom cannot appear on the product side and none can disappear from the reactant side. This is the *balancing requirement.* It is met by adjusting the coefficients of the formulas of reactants and products to the smallest possible whole numbers which satisfy the Law of Conservation of Atoms.

3. Procedure in writing equations. Let us review some of the chemical reactions which we have studied and proceed to write the chemical equations which represent them. We must proceed in steps which satisfy the three factors in equation writing in their proper order. This order is as follows: *represent the facts; balance formulas of compounds as to valence* (formulas for elementary gases with diatomic molecules must be correctly written); and *balance the equation as to atoms.*

Hydrogen and oxygen may be prepared in the laboratory by the electrolysis of water. As the equation does not tell the rate or conditions under which the reaction proceeds we need not concern ourselves with these matters in writing the equation.

Step 1: What are the facts? The only reactant is water and the only products are hydrogen and oxygen. We may represent these facts by the word equation:

$$\text{water} \rightarrow \text{hydrogen} + \text{oxygen}$$

Now let us substitute the formulas for these substances as accurately as we know them to be.

$$H_2O \rightarrow H_2 + O_2 \text{ (not balanced)}$$

Step 2: Are the formulas correctly written? The covalence of hydrogen is 1 and of oxygen is 2, so the formula for water is correctly written as H_2O. Both hydrogen and oxygen exist in the free state as diatomic molecules, so the formulas of molecular hydrogen and molecular oxygen are correctly written as H_2 and O_2.

Step 3: Is the equation balanced as to atoms? Starting on the left we have 1 molecule of water consisting of 2 hydrogen atoms and 1 oxygen atom. On the right of the reaction sign $(\rightarrow)$ we have 1 molecule of hydrogen consisting of 2 atoms and 1 molecule of oxygen made up of 2 atoms. *But we had only 1 atom of oxygen on the left.* How may we adjust this difference? We cannot add a subscript $_2$ to the oxygen of the water formula for this would alter a formula which we have already established as correctly written. We can, however, increase the number of water molecules to two by placing the coefficient 2 ahead of the formula H_2O, making it 2 H_2O. Thus we have 2 molecules of water each with 1 oxygen giving us our necessary 2 atoms of oxygen on the left.

$$2 H_2O \rightarrow H_2 + O_2 \text{ (not balanced)}$$

Two molecules of water have a total of 4 atoms of hydrogen. We must now move to the right side of the equation and adjust the number of hydrogen atoms to 4. This may be done by placing the coëfficient 2 ahead of the hydrogen molecule, making it 2 H$_2$. We now have a total of 4 atoms of hydrogen on the right and our equation reads:

$$2 \text{ H}_2\text{O} \rightarrow 2 \text{ H}_2 \uparrow + \text{O}_2 \uparrow$$

We have achieved the same number of atoms of each element on both sides of the equation with the lowest whole-number ratio of coefficients possible. Thus the equation is balanced (the arrows pointing upward are used to indicate gaseous products).

In the burning of sulfur, oxygen combines with the sulfur to form sulfur dioxide gas. These are the facts, so we may write:

$$\text{sulfur} + \text{oxygen} \rightarrow \text{sulfur dioxide}$$
$$\text{S} + \text{O}_2 \rightarrow \text{SO}_2 \uparrow$$

Molecular oxygen is diatomic, O$_2$, and the valences of sulfur and oxygen in sulfur dioxide indicate that the formula, SO$_2$, is correctly written. All formulas are correctly written. The numbers of atoms of sulfur and oxygen are the same on both sides of the equation. No further adjustments are required; the equation is balanced.

Priestley produced oxygen by heating mercury(II) oxide. The facts are: heating mercury(II) oxide yields metallic mercury and oxygen gas.

$$\text{mercury(II) oxide} \rightarrow \text{mercury} + \text{oxygen}$$

Substituting the proper symbols and formulas, we write:

$$\text{HgO} \rightarrow \text{Hg} + \text{O}_2 \text{ (not balanced)}$$

Our valence check tells us that the formula of mercury(II) oxide is correctly written. The equation is not balanced with respect to oxygen. We can see that 2 molecules of HgO must decompose to yield the 2 atoms making up the diatomic molecule of oxygen. This will, however, produce 2 atoms of mercury. The balanced equation is:

$$2 \text{ HgO} \rightarrow 2 \text{ Hg} + \text{O}_2 \uparrow$$

We have recognized that zinc reacts with hydrochloric acid to produce hydrogen gas and zinc chloride. These facts may be represented by the word equation:

$$\text{zinc} + \text{hydrochloric acid} \rightarrow$$
$$\text{zinc chloride} + \text{hydrogen}$$

With proper consideration for valences we may write:

$$\text{Zn} + \text{HCl} \rightarrow \text{ZnCl}_2 + \text{H}_2 \text{ (not balanced)}$$

In balancing atoms we see that 2 molecules of HCl are required to furnish the 2 chlorine atoms of ZnCl$_2$ and the 2 hydrogen atoms of the diatomic hydrogen molecule. Thus our balanced equation is:

$$\text{Zn} + 2 \text{ HCl} \rightarrow \text{ZnCl}_2 + \text{H}_2 \uparrow$$

One of the most common mistakes that beginners make in balancing equations is that of destroying the valence balance of a formula in order to get the required number of atoms. Do not become discouraged at this time if equations offer considerable difficulty. The trouble lies not in the method of balancing but in the large number of facts that must be known. As you continue to make progress in class and gain experience in the laboratory, the equations that now seem difficult will prove to be simple.

Let us try an equation for a reaction encountered in a process of water purification. Aluminum sulfate and calcium hydroxide are added to water containing objectionable suspended matter.

These two substances react in water to produce two insoluble products, aluminum hydroxide and calcium sulfate. These facts may be represented by the word equation:

aluminum sulfate + calcium hydroxide →
  aluminum hydroxide + calcium sulfate

By valence balancing to assure correct formulas we may write:

$Al_2(SO_4)_3 + Ca(OH)_2 \rightarrow$
  $Al(OH)_3 + CaSO_4$ (not balanced)

We now begin at the left with $Al_2(SO_4)_3$ to balance for atoms. Two Al atoms are indicated. To provide 2 Al atoms on the right we place the coefficient 2 ahead of $Al(OH)_3$. Three SO_4 groups are indicated, so we place the coefficient 3 in front of $CaSO_4$. Our equation now reads:

$Al_2(SO_4)_3 + Ca(OH)_2 \rightarrow$
  $2 Al(OH)_3 + 3 CaSO_4$ (not balanced)

Fig. 12-1. **Most chemical reactions are of interest because of the products formed. This lightweight and easily fitted pipe is fabricated from plastics.** (Union Carbide)

Next we observe that there must be 3 Ca atoms on the left to equal the 3 Ca atoms now on the right. We place the coefficient 3 in front of $Ca(OH)_2$. This gives us 6 OH groups on the left and we observe that there are 6 OH groups on the right. We now have a balanced equation:

$Al_2(SO_4)_3 + 3 Ca(OH)_2 \rightarrow$
  $2 Al(OH)_3 \downarrow + 3 CaSO_4 \downarrow$

(The arrows pointing downward indicate those products which are insoluble and leave the reaction environment as precipitates.)

To be successful in writing chemical equations: 1. *you must know the symbols of the common elements;* 2. *you must know the usual valences of the common elements and radicals;* 3. *you must know the facts relating to the reaction for which an equation is to be written;* 4. *you must insure that all formulas are correctly written* prior to any attempt to balance atoms; and 5. *you must balance the equation as to atoms* of all elements present, so as to have the lowest ratio of whole-number coefficients possible.

4. General types of chemical reactions. There are various ways of classifying chemical reactions and no single scheme is entirely satisfactory. In elementary chemistry it is advantageous to learn to recognize reactions as falling into the main categories given below. Later on (in Unit 6) you will see other ways in which chemical reactions can be classified. The main types of reactions are:

1. *Composition reactions,* in which two or more substances combine to form a more complex substance. Composition reactions have the general form

$$A + X \rightarrow AX$$

Examples:
Iron and sulfur combine to form iron(II) sulfide.

$$Fe + S \rightarrow FeS$$

Water and sulfur trioxide combine to form hydrogen sulfate (sulfuric acid).

$$H_2O + SO_3 \rightarrow H_2SO_4$$

2. *Decomposition reactions,* the reverse of the first type, in which a complex substance breaks down to form two or more simpler substances. Decomposition reactions have the general form

$$AX \rightarrow A + X$$

Examples:
Water is decomposed yielding hydrogen and oxygen.

$$2\,H_2O \rightarrow 2\,H_2 \uparrow \ + O_2 \uparrow$$

Potassium chlorate is decomposed yielding potassium chloride and oxygen.

$$2\,KClO_3 \rightarrow 2\,KCl + 3\,O_2 \uparrow$$

3. *Replacement reactions,* in which one substance is displaced from its compound by another substance. Replacement reactions have the general form

$$A + BX \rightarrow AX + B$$
or
$$Y + BX \rightarrow BY + X$$

Examples:
Iron replaces copper from a solution of copper(II) sulfate yielding iron(II) sulfate and copper.

$$Fe + CuSO_4 \rightarrow FeSO_4 + Cu \downarrow$$

Chlorine replaces iodine from a solution of potassium iodide yielding potassium chloride and iodine.

$$Cl_2 + 2\,KI \rightarrow 2\,KCl + I_2$$

In each of the foregoing types of reactions some change in the sharing of electrons occurs or there is a transfer of electrons from one atom to another.
4. *Ionic reactions,* in which no transfer of electrons occurs but ions in solution combine to form a product that leaves the reaction environment. Ionic reactions may have the general form.

$$A^+(soln) + B^-(soln) \rightarrow AB$$

Example:
A solution of sodium chloride, containing sodium ions and chloride ions, added to a solution of silver nitrate, containing silver ions and nitrate ions, results in a reaction between the silver ions and chloride ions forming a white precipitate of silver chloride.

$$Ag^+ + Cl^- \rightarrow Ag^+Cl^- \downarrow$$

The sodium ions and nitrate ions remain uncombined in solution, but may be recovered as sodium nitrate by evaporating the water. For this reason, ionic reactions are sometimes called *exchange* reactions, the sodium ions and silver ions being regarded as having exchanged places.

When it is desirable to show what reagents are used to bring about ionic reactions, empirical or molecular equations may be written. The equations have the general form

$$AX + BY \rightarrow AY + BX$$

In this sense the ionic reaction just described may be written

$$NaCl + AgNO_3 \rightarrow NaNO_3 + AgCl \downarrow$$

In order for an ionic reaction to occur, a product must be formed that separates ions from the reaction environment (the solution) as a solid precipitate or an insoluble gas, or as a new molecular species. These reactions will be studied extensively in Unit 6.

**5. Six classes of decomposition re-
actions.** These reactions are promoted
by heat or electricity. The classes generally recognized are as follows:
1. *Metallic carbonates, when heated,
form metallic oxides and carbon dioxide.*
Calcium carbonate $CaCO_3$, on being
heated, will form calcium oxide, CaO.
Carbon dioxide, CO_2 is given off as a
gas.

$$CaCO_3 \xrightarrow{\Delta} CaO + CO_2 \uparrow$$

The Greek letter Δ (delta) may be used
to signify that heat energy is supplied
to the action.

Ammonium carbonate, $(NH_4)_2CO_3$,
because of the nonmetallic nature of the
ammonium radical, decomposes in a special manner. The equation for this reaction is:

$$(NH_4)_2CO_3 \xrightarrow{\Delta} 2 NH_3 + H_2O + CO_2$$

Ammonia, steam, and carbon dioxide are
produced.
2. *Many metallic hydroxides, when
heated, decompose into metallic oxides
and water.* If we heat calcium hydroxide,
$Ca(OH)_2$, strongly, steam is give off and
calcium oxide CaO, remains.

$$Ca(OH)_2 \rightarrow CaO + H_2O$$

Sodium hydroxide is a common exception to this rule.
3. *Metallic chlorates, when heated, decompose into metallic chlorides and oxygen.* This is the type of reaction used to
prepare oxygen from potassium chlorate.

$$2 KClO_3 \xrightarrow{\Delta} 2 KCl + 3 O_2 \uparrow$$

4. *Some acids, when heated, decompose
into nonmetallic oxides and water.* Acids
may be formed by the reaction of some
nonmetallic oxides, called acid anhydrides, and water. This reaction is the

reverse process. Several examples are:
Carbonic acid yields water and carbon
dioxide gas

$$H_2CO_3 \rightarrow H_2O + CO_2 \uparrow$$

Sulfurous acid yields water and sulfur
dioxide gas

$$H_2SO_3 \rightarrow H_2O + SO_2 \uparrow$$

The two reactions above take place quite
readily at room temperature. The following reaction occurs at elevated temperatures.

$$H_2SO_4 \xrightarrow{\Delta} H_2O + SO_3 \uparrow$$

5. *Some oxides, when heated, decompose.* Most oxides, are very stable compounds. There are only a few of them
which will decompose on heating. Two
of these oxides and the reactions for
their decomposition are:

$$2 HgO \xrightarrow{\Delta} 2 Hg + O_2 \uparrow$$
$$2 PbO_2 \xrightarrow{\Delta} 2 PbO + O_2 \uparrow$$

6. *Some decomposition reactions are
produced by electricity.* The following
are typical:

$$2 H_2O \xrightarrow{\text{(electricity)}} 2 H_2 + O_2 \uparrow$$
$$2 NaCl \xrightarrow{\text{(electricity)}} 2 Na + Cl_2 \uparrow$$

**6. Four classes of replacement re-
actions.** The quantities of energy involved in replacement reactions are generally less than for composition and decomposition reactions. The action is dependent on the relative activities of the
elements involved. We generally rely
on an *Activity Series* such as the one discussed in Section 12 of this chapter to
guide us in writing replacement equations. These reactions may be placed in
four general classes.
1. *Replacement of a metal in a compound by a more active metal.* A reac-

tion of this type is that of zinc and a solution of copper(II) sulfate, $CuSO_4$. Zinc is a more active metal than copper, thus it will replace copper from a solution of a copper compound.

$$Zn + CuSO_4 \rightarrow ZnSO_4 + Cu \downarrow$$

2. *Replacement of hydrogen in water by metals.* The very active metals, such as potassium, calcium, and sodium, react vigorously with water to replace half the hydrogen and form metallic hydroxides. The following reaction is typical.

$$Ca + 2 H_2O \rightarrow Ca(OH)_2 + H_2 \uparrow$$

More stable metals, such as magnesium, zinc, and iron, react at elevated temperatures with water (steam) to replace hydrogen. Because of the high temperature involved, oxides rather than hydroxides are formed. Metals less active than iron do not react appreciably with water.

3. *Replacement of hydrogen in acids by metals.* Many metals react with certain acids, such as hydrochloric acid and dilute sulfuric acid, to replace hydrogen and form the corresponding salt. We have used this method for the laboratory preparation of hydrogen by reacting sulfuric acid with zinc.

$$Zn + H_2SO_4 \rightarrow ZnSO_4 + H_2 \uparrow$$

4. *Replacement of halogens.* The halogens are four elements in Group VII of the Periodic Table having somewhat similar properties. They are fluorine, chlorine, bromine, and iodine. From their activity arrangement in the table in Section 12, fluorine is seen to be the most active; it replaces the other three halogens from their compounds. Chlorine replaces bromine and iodine from their compounds. Bromine replaces only iodine. An example of this type of re-

action is the addition of chlorine to potassium bromide solution.

$$Cl_2 + 2 KBr \rightarrow 2 KCl + Br_2$$

Chlorine replaces an iodide, forming the corresponding chloride.

$$Cl_2 + 2 NaI \rightarrow 2 NaCl + I_2$$

Bromine replaces an iodide, but not so vigorously as chlorine.

$$Br_2 + 2 KI \rightarrow 2KBr + I_2$$

7. Many reactions are reversible. Frequently the products of a chemical reaction can react to produce the original reactants. We learned in Chapter 8 that hydrogen could be used as a reducing agent to separate certain metals from their oxides. If dry hydrogen gas is passed over hot magnetic iron oxide, iron and steam are produced.

$$4 H_2 + Fe_3O_4 \rightarrow 3 Fe + 4 H_2O \uparrow$$

If the procedure is reversed and steam is passed over hot iron, magnetic iron oxide and hydrogen are formed.

$$3 Fe + 4 H_2O \rightarrow Fe_3O_4 + 4 H_2 \uparrow$$

Such reactions are said to be reversible and may be indicated by two reaction signs pointing in opposite directions ($\rightleftarrows$)

$$3 Fe + 4 H_2O \rightleftarrows Fe_3O_4 + 4 H_2$$

Conditions may be such as to allow both reactions to occur simultaneously. That is, if none of the products leaves the field of action, they may be able to react to form the original reactants. Under such circumstances, an *equilibrium* could develop between the two reactions after which the quantities of all the reactants would remain constant. The subject of equilibrium reactions will be discussed in Chapter 22.

2. ENERGY OF REACTIONS

8. Energy changes during chemical reactions. If a mixture of hydrogen and oxygen is ignited, water is produced and considerable heat energy is released. Under controlled conditions we would find the energy released during this reaction to be a characteristic amount which is directly proportional to the quantity of water produced. The source of the heat energy must be the reactants themselves since none was supplied externally other than to ignite the mixture. We may conclude that the water formed has *less* energy than did the reactants prior to the chemical action.

Conversely, if water is decomposed to produce hydrogen and oxygen, energy must be furnished in the form of electricity. Since energy is absorbed in this reverse reaction we may conclude that the products, hydrogen and oxygen, have *more* energy than did the reactant, water. We may write:

$$2 \, H_2 + O_2 \rightarrow 2 \, H_2O + energy$$

and

$$2 \, H_2O + energy \rightarrow 2 \, H_2 + O_2$$

or

$$2 \, H_2 + O_2 \rightleftarrows 2 \, H_2O + energy$$

Elementary hydrogen and oxygen exist as nonpolar diatomic molecules. Water molecules are covalent structures possessing polar characteristics because of the electronegativity difference between the constituent elements, hydrogen and oxygen.

When the single covalent bond of the hydrogen molecule is formed, both atoms release energy and the molecule has less energy (and is more stable) than the separate hydrogen atoms. Thus, energy is required to break this bond. Similarly, energy is required to break the single covalent bond of the oxygen mol-

ecule. However, a great deal of energy is released when the elements combine to form the two polar bonds of the water molecule, the net energy of the reaction appearing as heat. *The energy content of 1 mole of hydrogen gas + the energy content of $\frac{1}{2}$ mole of oxygen gas = the energy content of 1 mole of liquid water + 68.4 kilocalories.*

An energy change accompanies every chemical change. These energy changes may be in the form of heat, light, or electricity. Every substance has its own characteristic amount of energy by virtue of its structure and physical state. When chemical reactions occur, new substances are formed having characteristic amounts of energy greater or less than that of the reactants. If the energy of the products is less than that of the reactants, the excess energy is released. These are *exothermic reactions* and the energy of reaction is said to be *positive*. If the products possess more energy than the reactants, energy must be absorbed from an external source during the action. These are *endothermic reactions* and the energy of reaction is said to be *negative*. (Sometimes the opposite convention of signs for energy of reaction is encountered. Where it is desired to emphasize the fact that the product of an exothermic composition reaction has less *energy content* than did the reactants, the energy of reaction may be said to be negative.)

Fuels, whether for the furnace, automobile, or rocket, are energy-rich substances and the products of their combustion are energy-poor substances. In such instances the products of the chemical action may be of little concern compared to the kind and quantity of energy that is liberated.

The heat of reaction given out or absorbed when 1 mole of a compound is formed from its elements is called the **heat of formation** *of the compound.* Heats of formation are commonly expressed in kilocalories (kcal) per mole of the substance produced.

Most composition reactions are exothermic, yielding compounds with positive heats of formation. In Table 6 of the Appendix are listed the heats of formation of some common compounds. Note that most of the heats of formation are positive. Only a few compounds such as hydrogen iodide and carbon disulfide have negative heats of formation.

9. Stability and heat of formation. A compound with a high positive heat of formation is formed with the release of considerable energy. In order to decompose such a compound into its constituent elements the same amount of energy must be supplied to the reaction. *Such compounds are very stable.* The reactions forming them proceed spontaneously, once they start, and are usually vigorous. Carbon dioxide has a high heat of formation; +94.4 kcal per mole of the gas produced.

Compounds with low heats of formation are generally unstable. Hydrogen sulfide, H_2S, has a heat of formation of +5.3 kcal per mole. It is not very stable and decomposes when heated. Hydrogen iodide, HI, has a low negative heat of formation, −5.9 kcal per mole. It is a colorless gas which undergoes some decomposition when stored at room temperatures, so that violet iodine vapor may be seen throughout the container of the gas.

A compound with a high negative heat of formation is likely to be explosive. Such a compound is formed only by expending a great deal of energy. Mercury fulminate, $HgC_2N_2O_2$, has a heat of formation of −64.5 kcal per mole. It is used extensively as a det-

onator for explosives because of its instability.

It has been shown that the greater the difference in electronegativity of two elements, the greater is the strength of the bond between them when they combine chemically. It is not surprising, therefore, to observe a relationship between the separation of two elements on the electronegativity scale and the heat-of-formation measurements made when they react. In fact, observed heats of formation figure prominently in the calculations by which the electronegativity scale was formulated. Compounds formed between elements of Groups I and II and Groups VI and VII, which are far apart in electronegativity, are in general stable and have high heats of formation. Those formed between elements close together in electronegativity tend to be unstable and have low heats of formation.

10. The driving force of chemical reactions. Heats of formation give an indication of the stability of substances and aid in predicting reactions. However, the **driving force** of chemical action, *the force that makes reactions go,* involves other factors in addition to heats of formation. *The energy of a reaction which can be converted into useful work outside the reaction itself* is a measure of this driving force. It is called the **free energy change** of the reaction. The free energies of substances give more accurate indications of their stability, and their tendency to react and to form ions. The free energy is sometimes found to be approximately the same as the heat of formation. However, it frequently is higher or lower than the heat of formation.

11. Energy of activation. The heat of formation of liquid water from its elements at 18°C is quite high; +68.4

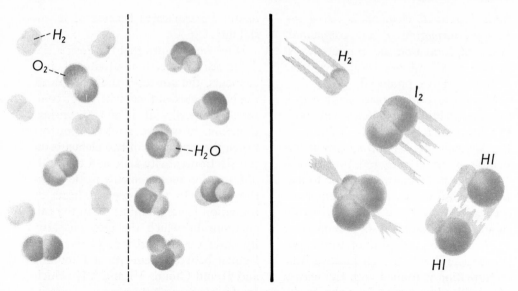

Fig. 12-2. Left, a mixture of hydrogen and oxygen molecules will form very stable water molecules when properly activated. Right, energy is required to break the bonds between atoms of diatomic molecules of hydrogen and iodine before hydrogen iodide molecules can be formed.

kcal per mole. The free energy change in this composition reaction is also quite high; +56.7 kcal per mole. Why then, do hydrogen and oxygen not combine spontaneously at ordinary temperatures?

Before hydrogen and oxygen atoms can combine to form water, their molecules must be broken up. The bonding forces of the atoms of the diatomic molecules, H_2 and O_2, must be counteracted. This requires an initial supply of energy from some external source. This additional energy is called the *activation energy* of the reactants. Once the formation of water molecules has started, the reaction energy released is more than sufficient to sustain the action. Thus a mixture of hydrogen and oxygen gases remains inert at room temperatures until the necessary activation energy is introduced by means of an electric spark or a flame. The composition equation written with electron-dot symbols shows the reaction.

$$2\ H{:}H + {:}\overset{\cdot\cdot}{O}{:}\overset{\cdot\cdot}{O}{:} \rightarrow 2\ H{:}\overset{\cdot\cdot}{\underset{H}{O}}{:}$$

The energy of activation may be supplied in certain reactions by the application of heat directly to the reactants. Activation energies may also be supplied by spark discharge, by light or X rays, or by bombardment with radioactive particles. Activation energy does not always involve separating the atoms of a diatomic molecule. It may also raise certain electrons to a higher energy level necessary for reaction.

12. The activity series of the elements. The quantities of energy involved in replacement reactions are generally less than those of composition or decomposition reactions. Compounds formed by replacement have higher positive heats of formation that the original compounds.

In general the ease with which the atoms of a metal lose electrons, as indicated by its ionization energy, determines the ease with which it forms compounds. In the replacement reaction

$$A + BX \rightarrow AX + B$$

metal **A** gives up electrons to **B** and replaces it, thus **A** is more active than **B**. If metal **B** were immersed in a solution of the compound **AX**, **B** could not replace **A**. Atoms of a more active metal lose electrons to positively charged ions of a less active metal under proper reaction conditions. Similarly, atoms of more active nonmetals acquire electrons from negatively charged ions of less active nonmetals.

From the study of numerous electrochemical reactions, chemists are able to devise an activity series of elements to help predict the course of replacement reactions. Some composition and decomposition reactions may likewise be predicted with the aid of an activity series. The series presented here lists separately the most important common elements in descending order of their metallic and nonmetallic activities.

Metals	Nonmetals
Lithium	Fluorine
Potassium	Chlorine
Calcium	Bromine
Sodium	Iodine
Magnesium	
Aluminum	
Zinc	
Chromium	
Iron	
Nickel	
Tin	
Lead	
Hydrogen	
Copper	
Mercury	
Silver	
Platinum	
Gold	

Fig. 12-3. **Some chemical reactions are of interest because of the energy released. The reaction between a high-energy fuel and an oxidizing agent provides the energy required to send the U. S. Navy's Polaris missile on its course after launching from a nuclear powered submarine.** (U. S. Navy)

The relative positions of the elements in the activity series enable us to apply some of the following generalizations to appropriate composition, decomposition, and replacement reactions.

1. Each element in the list displaces from a compound any of the elements below it; the larger the interval between elements in the series, the more vigorous the action.
2. All metals above hydrogen displace hydrogen from nonoxidizing acids.
3. Metals near the top of the series vigorously displace hydrogen from water. Magnesium displaces hydrogen from steam.
4. Metals above silver combine directly with oxygen; those near the top do so violently.
5. Metals below mercury may be forced to form oxides only indirectly.
6. Oxides of metals below mercury may be decomposed with mild heating.
7. Oxides of metals below chromium are easily reduced by heating with hydrogen.
8. Oxides of metals above iron resist reduction by heating with hydrogen.
9. Elements near the top of the series are never found free in nature.
10. Elements near the bottom of the series are often found free in nature.

SUMMARY

A chemical equation is a concise symbolized picture of a chemical reaction. Word equations have only qualitative significance. Formula equations have quantitative significance. An equation is useful only when it is correct in every respect.

Three factors must be satisfied in writing formula equations: 1. The equation must represent the facts; 2. The equation must include the symbols and formulas of all elements and compounds used as reactants and formed as products; and 3. The Law of Conservation of Atoms must always be satisfied.

In some chemical reactions a change occurs in the sharing of electrons or there is a transfer of electrons from one atom to another. In other reactions no electron transfer takes place, but ions in solution combine to form a product that leaves the reaction environment. Chemical reactions may be considered to fall into four main types: 1. Composition; 2. Decomposition; 3. Replacement; and 4. Ionic.

Energy changes accompany all chemical reactions. In exothermic reactions energy is released, and in endothermic reactions energy is absorbed. Heats of formation of substances give an indication of their stability. Reactions occur because of a driving force. This driving force is best defined by the free energy change of a reaction. Exothermic reactions sometimes require activation energy in order to start them.

An activity series of elements is useful in predicting whether specific replacement reactions will occur. The most active element in the series is found at the top and the least active at the bottom. The greater the interval between elements of the series in a reaction, the more vigorous will be the action.

TEST YOURSELF ON THESE TERMS

activation energy	endothermic	meaning of →
activity series	exothermic	meaning of ⇄
coefficient	formula equation	meaning of ↑
composition	free energy	meaning of ↓
decomposition	heat of formation	product
diatomic	ionic reaction	reactant

EQUATIONS

Group A

Write balanced formula equations for these reactions.

1. Carbon + oxygen → carbon dioxide.
2. Magnesium bromide + chlorine → magnesium chloride + bromine.
3. Zinc + hydrochloric acid (HCl) → zinc chloride + hydrogen ↑.
4. Hydrogen + nitrogen → ammonia (NH_3) ↑.
5. Sodium hydroxide + carbon dioxide → sodium carbonate + water.
6. Barium chloride + sodium sulfate → sodium chloride + barium sulfate ↓.
7. Zinc chloride + ammonium sulfide → zinc sulfide ↓ + ammonium chloride.
8. Ammonia + oxygen → nitric acid (HNO_3) + water.
9. Zinc + copper(II) sulfate →
10. Mercury(II) oxide $\xrightarrow{\Delta}$
11. Sodium + water →
12. Hydrogen + chlorine →
13. Copper + silver sulfate → copper(II) sulfate +
14. Potassium + water →
15. Sodium iodide + bromine →
16. Carbon + steam → carbon monoxide ↑ + hydrogen ↑.
17. Zinc + lead acetate → lead ↓ + zinc acetate.
18. Potassium chlorate $\xrightarrow{\Delta}$
19. Calcium carbonate $\xrightarrow{\Delta}$
20. Iron(III) oxide + carbon monoxide → iron + carbon dioxide.
21. Potassium hydroxide + chlorine → potassium chloride + potassium hypochlorite (KClO) + water.
22. Calcium oxide + diphosphorus pentoxide → calcium phosphate.
23. Calcium carbonate + hydrochloric acid → calcium chloride + water + carbon dioxide ↑.
24. Copper + sulfuric acid → copper(II) sulfate + water + sulfur dioxide ↑.
25. Calcium hydroxide + ammonium sulfate → calcium sulfate + ammonia ↑ + water.

Group B

Consult the Activity Series, Section 12, and the Tables of Solubilities and Heats of Formation in the Appendix, as necessary.

In each case: 1. write the balanced formula equation; 2. identify the type of reaction; and 3. tell why the reaction takes place.

26. Magnesium + oxygen →
27. Phosphorus + iodine → phosphorus tri-iodide.
28. Potassium iodide + chlorine →
29. Iron(III) chloride + ammonium sulfide →
30. Iron + sulfur → iron(II) sulfide.
31. Nickel chlorate $\xrightarrow{\Delta}$
32. Barium carbonate $\xrightarrow{\Delta}$
33. Silver nitrate + zinc chloride →
34. Mercury(II) hydroxide $\xrightarrow{\Delta}$
35. Ammonia + hydrogen sulfide → ammonium sulfide.
36. Zinc + sulfuric acid →
37. Iron + copper(II) nitrate → iron(II) nitrate +
38. Copper + silver nitrate → copper(II) nitrate +
39. Mercury(II) nitrate + ammonium sulfide →
40. Iron(III) hydroxide $\xrightarrow{\Delta}$
41. Phosphorus + oxygen →
42. Antimony + chlorine → antimony trichloride.
43. Sodium chlorate $\xrightarrow{\Delta}$
44. Barium chloride + magnesium sulfate →
45. Sodium bromide + chlorine →
46. Zinc chloride + phosphoric acid (H_3PO_4) →
47. Sodium sulfite + acetic acid ($HC_2H_3O_2$) → sodium acetate + sulfur dioxide ↑ + water.
48. Ammonium nitrate + potassium hydroxide → potassium nitrate + ammonia ↑ + water.
49. Silver sulfate + aluminum chloride →
50. Carbonic acid $\xrightarrow{\Delta}$

Chapter 13 · MASS RELATIONS IN CHEMICAL REACTIONS

1. Stoichiometric relations. The determination of empirical formulas of compounds always results from experimentation. Empirical formulas are derived from the relative numbers of gram-atoms of the elements composing compounds and, therefore, indicate the relative numbers of atoms present. Nothing can be inferred from the empirical formula about the nature of the association of the atoms, the make-up of the molecular structure, or whether the substance even exists in simple molecular units. Nevertheless, empirical formulas are very useful in calculations involving the combining and reacting relationships among chemical substances.

*The branch of chemistry which deals with the numerical relationships of elements and compounds and the mathe-*matical proportions of reactants and products in chemical transformations is known as stoichiometry (stoi-ki-yom-eh-tri). The determination of the percentage composition of compounds and of empirical formulas discussed in Chapter 11 are examples of stoichiometric relations.* An understanding of the mole concept together with some skill in writing and balancing chemical equations will enable you to solve stoichiometric problems involving the mass relations of reactants and products in chemical reactions. The introduction of the concept of mole volumes of gases in Chapter 14 will enable you to solve a great number of problems involving mass and volume relations of gaseous reactants and products by means of very simple computations.

VOCABULARY

Proportion. An equality between two ratios.
Stoichiometry. The branch of chemistry pertaining to the numerical relationships of chemical elements and compounds and the mathematical proportions of reactants and products in chemical transformations.

191

2. Mass relations of reactants and products. When carbon is burned in air, carbon dioxide is produced.

$$C + O_2 \rightarrow CO_2 \uparrow$$

We stated in Chapter 12 that the balanced equation signifies the mass proportions of the reactants and products, as well as the composition of each substance in terms of the kinds of elements and the relative number of each kind of atom present. *These mass proportions are most conveniently expressed in terms of moles of reactants and products.* Thus the equation signifies that 1 mole of carbon combines with 1 mole of oxygen to yield 1 mole of carbon dioxide. This may be indicated as follows:

$$
\begin{array}{ccc}
C & + \quad O_2 \quad \rightarrow & CO_2 \uparrow \\
1 \text{ mole} & 1 \text{ mole} & 1 \text{ mole} \\
= 12 \text{ g} & = 32 \text{ g} & = 12 \text{ g} + 32 \text{ g} \\
& & = 44 \text{ g}
\end{array}
$$

Because the equation shows the mass proportions of reacting substances and products, it is used when we wish to determine the mass of one substance that reacts with, or is produced from, a definite mass of another. This is one of the common problems chemists are called upon to solve.

3. Methods of solving mass-mass problems. Three general methods are employed in solving problems which involve mass relations of reactants and products. These are *the proportion method, the arithmetic method* and the *mole method.* Each method is explained in the following problem illustrations. Your instructor may prefer that you use a particular method regularly in your problem work. If not, it is suggested that you study each explanation carefully and use the method which seems most logical to you. The mole concept is quite important in advanced work in chemis-

try so, other considerations being equal, it is best to work with mole quantities wherever possible.

It is always desirable to make a preliminary mental estimate to determine the *order of magnitude* of the answer to a problem before undertaking the indicated computations. Thus you may avoid accepting an answer as correct which actually is quite absurd due to errors in computation or in operations with units.

4. Solution by proportion. Let us assume that we must determine how much calcium oxide will be produced by heating 50.0 g of calcium carbonate. Observe that the mass of the reactant is given and the mass of a product is required. From the data in the problem and the facts known concerning the reaction, we can proceed to *set up the problem.* This may be accomplished in three steps.

The *first step* is to write the balanced equation.

The *second step* is to show the problem specifications: what is given and what is required. To do this we write the quantity of calcium carbonate, 50.0 g, above the formula $CaCO_3$. Letting **X** represent the unknown quantity of calcium oxide produced, we write **X** above the formula CaO.

The *third step* is to show the mass proportions, established by the balanced equation, that are specifically involved in the problem. This is accomplished by writing under each substance involved in the problem the number of *moles* (gram-formula weights) indicated by the equation. By converting the number of moles of each substance to grams, we have the *equation weights* thus expressed in grams, or *gram-equation weights.* The problem is now set up ready to be solved.

2nd step   50.0 g   X

1st step $CaCO_3 \xrightarrow{\Delta} CaO + CO_2 \uparrow$

3rd step $\begin{cases} 1 \text{ mole} & 1 \text{ mole} \\ = 100. \text{ g} & = 56 \text{ g} \end{cases}$

The balanced equation indicates that 1 mole of $CaCO_3$, 100. g, yields 1 mole of CaO, 56 g. We may reason that any other mass of $CaCO_3$ used, and CaO produced, must be in the same ratio as that of the equation weights of $CaCO_3$ and CaO. This is an equality of ratios and is expressed by the *proportion:*

$$\frac{50.0 \text{ g } CaCO_3}{X} = \frac{100. \text{ g } CaCO_3}{56 \text{ g } CaO}$$

Solving:

$$X = \frac{50.0 \text{ g } CaCO_3 \times 56 \text{ g } CaO}{100. \text{ g } CaCO_3}$$

$$X = 28 \text{ g of } CaO$$

By estimating the order of magnitude of the answer from the quantities involved we see that 28 g of CaO is a reasonable answer. See the following Sample Problems.

SAMPLE PROBLEM

How many grams of potassium chlorate must be decomposed to yield 30.0 g of oxygen?

SOLUTION   (Proportion Method)

We set up the problem by *first*, writing the balanced equation; *second*, writing the specifications of the problem above the equation; and *third*, writing the number of moles of each specified substance under its formula and expressing its equation weight in grams. We will let X represent the quantity of potassium chlorate decomposed. (Recall that the at. wt. of oxygen is exactly 16 by definition and, unlike the at. wt. of other elements, is not limited in number of significant figures. Therefore we are not limited to 2 significant figures in this problem.)

$$\begin{array}{cc} X & 30.0 \text{ g} \\ 2 \text{ } KClO_3 & \rightarrow 2 \text{ } KCl + 3 \text{ } O_2 \uparrow \\ 2 \text{ moles} & 3 \text{ moles} \\ = 2[39 + 35.5 + 3(16)] \text{ g} & = 3(32) \text{ g} \\ = 245 \text{ g} & = 96 \text{ g} \end{array}$$

The ratio of $KClO_3$ decomposed to O_2 produced must equal the ratio of the equation weight of $KClO_3$ to the equation weight of O_2, so we may express the proportion:

$$\frac{X}{30.0 \text{ g } O_2} = \frac{245 \text{ g } KClO_3}{96 \text{ g } O_2}$$

Solving: $$X = \frac{30.0 \text{ g } O_2 \times 245 \text{ g } KClO_3}{96 \text{ g } O_2}$$

$$X = 76.6 \text{ g of } KClO_3$$

SAMPLE PROBLEM

In the decomposition of water by electrolysis: *a.* How many moles of water must be decomposed to yield 3.0 moles of hydrogen? *b.* How many moles of oxygen are produced?

SOLUTION   (Proportion Method)

a. The problem is set up as before except that we do not need to convert moles to gram-equation weights since the problem specifications are in moles rather than grams. Let X represent the quantity of water decomposed.

$$\begin{array}{ccccc} X & & 3.0 \text{ moles} & & Y \\ 2\,H_2O & \rightarrow & 2\,H_2 & + & O_2 \\ 2 \text{ moles} & & 2 \text{ moles} & & 1 \text{ mole} \end{array}$$

The proportion is:

$$\frac{X}{3.0 \text{ moles } H_2} = \frac{2 \text{ moles } H_2O}{2 \text{ moles } H_2}$$

$$X = \frac{3.0 \text{ moles } H_2 \times 2 \text{ moles } H_2O}{2 \text{ moles } H_2}$$

Solving: $X = 3.0 \text{ moles } H_2O$

b. Using the problem set-up of part *a,* we let Y represent the quantity of O_2 produced.

The proportion is:

$$\frac{3.0 \text{ moles } H_2}{Y} = \frac{2 \text{ moles } H_2}{1 \text{ mole } O_2}$$

$$Y = \frac{3.0 \text{ moles } H_2 \times 1 \text{ mole } O_2}{2 \text{ moles } H_2}$$

Solving: $Y = 1.5 \text{ moles } O_2$

Observe that   3 moles of $H_2O = 3(18)$ g $= 54$ g of H_2O
3 moles of $H_2 = 3(2)$ g $= 6$ g of H_2
1.5 moles of $O_2 = 1.5(32)$ g $= 48$ g of O_2
54 g of reactant $= 54$ g of products

5. Solution by arithmetic. In the arithmetic method we set up the problem in three steps as before: *1.* write the equation; *2.* write the problem specifications above the equation; and *3.* write the numbers of moles and the gram-equation weights below the equation. As an example, we will use the following problem set-up in which we wish to know the number of grams of calcium hydroxide produced from a reaction of 160 g of calcium oxide and water.

$$\begin{array}{ccc} 160 \text{ g} & & X \\ CaO & + H_2O \rightarrow & Ca(OH)_2 \\ 1 \text{ mole} & & 1 \text{ mole} \\ = 40. \text{ g} + 16 \text{ g} & & = 40. \text{ g} + 2(17.0) \text{ g} \\ = 56 \text{ g} & & = 74 \text{ g} \end{array}$$

The equation indicates that 1 mole of calcium oxide reacts with water to form 1 mole of calcium hydroxide. Thus, 56 g of CaO yield 74 g of $Ca(OH)_2$. We may reason that 1 g of CaO will yield $\frac{74}{56}$ g of $Ca(OH)_2$. So, 160 g of CaO will yield $160 \times \frac{74}{56}$ g of $Ca(OH)_2$. Solving:

$$X = 160 \text{ g } \cancel{CaO} \times \frac{74 \text{ g } Ca(OH)_2}{56 \text{ g } \cancel{CaO}}$$

$$X = 210 \text{ g of } Ca(OH)_2$$

By estimating the order of magnitude of the answer we see that 210 g is reasonable. See Sample Problem below.

6. Solution by moles. In chemistry, it is often convenient to consider quantities and quantity relationships in terms of moles. The same problem set-up may be used in the mole method as in the proportion and arithmetic methods. However, in solving by moles we are interested in converting the mass of a given substance into moles of that substance. In a manner similar to the arithmetic method we may determine the moles of the substance in question since our equation tells us the mole relationship between the reactants and products.

SAMPLE PROBLEM

In a demonstration of the replacement of hydrogen, 5.0 g of metallic sodium are permitted to react with water. *a.* How much sodium hydroxide can be recovered as a consequence of this action? *b.* How many moles of hydrogen are replaced from the water?

SOLUTION   (Arithmetic Method)

a. We set up the problem on the balanced equation as in earlier illustrations, letting X represent the quantity of NaOH recovered.

5.0 g		X		Y
2 Na	+ 2 H$_2$O →	2 NaOH	+	H$_2$
2 moles		2 moles		1 mole
= 2(23) g		= 2(23 + 17.0) g		= 2.0 g
= 46 g		= 80. g		

The equation indicates that 2 moles of Na produced 2 moles of NaOH,

or	46 g of Na yield 80. g of NaOH
then	1 g of Na would yield $\frac{80.}{46}$ g of NaOH
and	5.0 g of Na must give $5.0 \times \frac{80.}{46}$ g of NaOH

so

$$X = 5.0 \text{ g } \cancel{Na} \times \frac{80. \text{ g NaOH}}{46 \text{ g } \cancel{Na}}$$

$$X = 8.7 \text{ g NaOH}$$

b. Since the quantity of H$_2$ produced is to be expressed in moles, we may either convert the 5.0 g of Na to moles or find H$_2$ in grams and convert to moles. The latter plan follows more closely the solution of part *a* so we will let Y stand for the quantity of H$_2$ produced. Using the problem set-up for part *a:*

$$Y = 5.0 \text{ g Na} \times \frac{2.0 \text{ g H}_2}{46 \text{ g Na}}$$

$$Y = 0.22 \text{ g H}_2$$

Now   1 mole H_2 = 1 g-mol. wt. H_2 = 2.0 g

so $$Y = \frac{\text{wt. H}_2}{\text{wt. H}_2/\text{mole}} = \frac{0.22 \text{ g H}_2}{2.0 \text{ g H}_2/\text{mole}} = 0.11 \text{ mole H}_2$$

SAMPLE PROBLEM

What quantity of oxygen is required to oxidize 140 g of iron to iron(III) oxide?

SOLUTION   (Mole Method)

The problem set-up for this reaction is

$$
\begin{array}{ccc}
140 \text{ g} & \text{X} & \\
4 \text{ Fe} \quad + & 3 \text{ O}_2 & \rightarrow 2 \text{ Fe}_2\text{O}_3 \\
4 \text{ moles} & 3 \text{ moles} & \\
= 4(56) \text{ g} & = 3(32) \text{ g} & \\
= 224 \text{ g} & = 96 \text{ g} &
\end{array}
$$

1 mole Fe = 1 gram-atom Fe = 56 g
1 mole O_2 = 1 g-mol. wt. O_2 = 32 g

The number of moles in 140 g of Fe $= \dfrac{140 \text{ g}}{56 \text{ g/mole}} = 2.5$ moles

The equation shows that 1 mole of Fe combines with $\frac{3}{4}$ mole of O_2

so   2.5 moles of Fe combine with $2.5 \times \frac{3}{4}$ mole of O_2

or $$X = 2.5 \text{ moles Fe} \times \frac{3 \text{ moles O}_2}{4 \text{ moles Fe}}$$

$$X = 1.9 \text{ moles O}_2$$

Then $$X = 1.9 \text{ moles} \times \frac{32 \text{ g O}_2}{\text{mole}} = 61 \text{ g O}_2.$$

SUMMARY

Chemical arithmetic dealing with elements and compounds and the proportions of reactants and products in chemical reactions is called stoichiometry. Skill in writing and balancing equations and an understanding of the mole concept make possible the solution of a variety of chemical problems.

Problems involving mass relations of the reactants and products in chemical reactions are usually solved by one of three methods: the proportion method; arithmetic method; or mole method. Each method utilizes a balanced equation as the basis for the problem set-up. Whichever method is used, it is always desirable to make a preliminary mental estimate of the order of magnitude of the answer so as to avoid absurd results.

TEST YOURSELF ON THESE TERMS

arithmetic method	gram-formula weight	problem set-up
Avogadro number	gram-molecular weight	proportion
equation weight	gram-molecule	proportion method
gram-atom	mole	ratio
gram-atomic weight	mole method	stoichiometric relations
gram-equation weight	order of magnitude	stoichiometry

PROBLEMS

Group A

1. How many grams of oxygen can be prepared by the decomposition of 25.0 grams of mercury(II) oxide?
2. How many grams of oxygen can be prepared by the decomposition of 25.0 g of potassium chlorate?
3. How many grams of zinc are required for the replacement of 0.10 gram of hydrogen from sulfuric acid?
4. How many grams of sodium chloride are needed to complete the reaction with 10.0 grams of silver nitrate in water solution?
5. How many grams of silver chloride are precipitated in the reaction of Problem 4?
6. In a composition reaction between sulfur and oxygen, 80 grams of sulfur dioxide are formed. How many grams of sulfur were burned?
7. How many grams of hydrogen are required to completely reduce 25 grams of hot magnetic iron oxide?
8. What quantity of copper(II) oxide is formed by oxidizing 1 kilogram of copper?
9. What weight of anhydrous copper(II) sulfate may be obtained by heating 100. grams of $CuSO_4 \cdot 5\,H_2O$?
10. Suppose 10.0 grams of iron(II) sulfide are treated with enough hydrochloric acid to complete the reaction. How many grams of hydrogen sulfide gas could be collected?

Group B

11. An excess of sulfuric acid reacts with 150 g of barium peroxide. (*a*) How many moles of hydrogen peroxide are produced? (*b*) How many moles of barium sulfate are formed?
12. Approximately 130 g of zinc were dropped into a solution containing 100. g of HCl. After the replacement action had ceased, it was found that 41 g of zinc remained. How many moles of hydrogen were produced?
13. A mixture of 10.0 g of powdered iron and 10.0 g of sulfur is heated to its reaction temperature in an open crucible. (*a*) How many grams of iron(II) sulfide are formed? (*b*) The reactant in excess is oxidized. How much of its oxide is formed?

14. What mass of calcium hydroxide can be produced from 1 kg of lime-stone, calcium carbonate? (Decomposition of calcium carbonate by heating produces calcium oxide and carbon dioxide. Calcium hydroxide is formed by the composition reaction of calcium oxide and water.)

15. How many grams of air are required to complete the combustion of 93 g of phosphorus, assuming the air to be 23% oxygen?

16. How many metric tons of carbon dioxide may be produced from the combustion of a metric ton (1000 kg) of coke which is 90.% carbon?

17. What quantity of a 10% solution of H_2SO_4 is required in a replacement reaction with an excess of aluminum to produce 0.50 mole of aluminum sulfate?

18. A certain rocket uses butane, C_4H_{10}, as fuel. How much liquid oxygen should be carried for the complete combustion of each kilogram of butane to carbon dioxide and water vapor?

19. When 45 g of ethane gas, C_2H_6, are burned completely in air, carbon dioxide and water vapor are formed. (*a*) How many moles of carbon dioxide are produced? (*b*) How many moles of water are produced?

20. How many grams of sodium sulfate are produced in the reaction between 150 g of sulfuric acid and an excess of sodium chloride?

Chapter 14 · MOLECULAR COMPOSITION OF GASES

1. The Law of Combining Volumes of Gases. The Law of Definite Composition, formulated by Proust in 1799, served as a basis for Dalton's Atomic Theory. While Dalton investigated the masses of combining substances, his contemporary, the Swedish chemist Berzelius, was developing methods of chemical analysis. During this same period another contemporary of Dalton, the French chemist Joseph Louis Gay-Lussac (1778–1850), became interested in the combining volumes of gaseous substances.

Gay-Lussac investigated the composition reaction between hydrogen and oxygen. He noticed that 2 liters of hydrogen were required for each liter of oxygen consumed and that 2 liters of water vapor were formed.

hydrogen + oxygen → water vapor
2 vol.   1 vol.   2 vol.

He found that 1 liter of hydrogen combined with 1 liter of chlorine to form 2 liters of hydrogen chloride gas. Also 1 liter of hydrogen chloride combined with 1 liter of ammonia to produce a white powder with no residue of either gas remaining.

VOCABULARY

Gram-molecular volume. The volume, in liters, of 1 gram-molecular weight of a gas at S.T.P.; commonly referred to as the molar volume.

Molar volume. The volume, in liters, of 1 mole of a gas at S.T.P.; taken as 22.4 liters for ordinary gases; precisely 22.414 liters for the ideal gas.

Specific gravity. The ratio of the density of a substance to the density of a standard of reference. Solids and liquids are referred to water as a standard, gases are commonly referred to air as a standard.

Fig. 14-1. **Joseph Louis Gay-Lussac, a French chemist, is best known for his Law of Combining Volumes of Gases.** (Brown Brothers)

hydrogen + chlorine → hydrogen chloride
  1 vol.   1 vol.   2 vol.

hydrogen chloride	+ ammonia →	ammonium chloride
1 vol.	1 vol.	(a solid)

His friend, Berthollet, recognized a similar relationship in experiments with hydrogen and nitrogen. He found that 3 liters of hydrogen always combined with 1 liter of nitrogen to form 2 liters of ammonia.

hydrogen + nitrogen → ammonia
  3 vol.   1 vol.   2 vol.

In 1808 Gay-Lussac summarized the results of these experiments and set forth the principle which bears his name, *Gay-Lussac's Law of Combining Volumes of Gases: Under similar conditions, the volumes of reacting gases and of their gaseous products are expressed in ratios of small whole numbers.*

Proust had demonstrated the definite proportion of elements in a compound.

Dalton's Atomic Theory had explained this regularity in the composition of substances. However, Dalton pictured the atoms of two elements combining to form *a compound atom* of the product. He could not explain why one volume of hydrogen united with one volume of chlorine to form *two* volumes of hydrogen chloride gas. To do so would require that his atoms be subdivided. He had described the atoms of elements as "ultimate particles" and not capable of subdivision. Here was an inconsistency between Dalton's theory and Gay-Lussac's observations. Was there no explanation to resolve the difficulty?

2. Avogadro's Principle. Amadeo Avogadro (1776–1856) proposed a possible explanation for Gay-Lussac's simple ratios of combining gases in 1811. This *hypothesis* was to become one of the important laws of chemistry, although it was not until after his death that its implications were fully recognized.

Avogadro's hypothesis was that equal volumes of all gases, under the same conditions of temperature and pressure, contained the same number of molecules. He arrived at this plausible theory after studying the behavior of gases and immediately recognized its application to Gay-Lussac's volume ratios.

Avogadro reasoned that the molecules of all gases, as reactants and products, would be in the same ratio as their respective gas volumes. Thus the composition of water vapor could be represented as 2 molecules of hydrogen combining with 1 molecule of oxygen to produce 2 molecules of water vapor.

hydrogen + oxygen → water vapor
2 volumes   1 volume   2 volumes
2 molecules 1 molecule   2 molecules

Thus each molecule of oxygen must consist of at least two identical parts (*atoms*) which are equally divided between the two molecules of water vapor formed. Avogadro did not repudiate the atoms of Dalton. He merely postulated that they did not exist as independent ultimate particles but were grouped into molecules which were divisible by two. The simplest such molecule would, of course, contain two atoms.

Avogadro's reasoning applied equally well to the combining volumes in the composition of hydrogen chloride gas.

hydrogen + chlorine → hydrogen
                                              chloride
1 volume   1 volume   2 volumes
1 molecule   1 molecule   2 molecules

Each molecule of hydrogen must be divisible by two, with identical parts in each of the two molecules of hydrogen chloride. Likewise, each chlorine molecule must be divisible by two, with identical parts in each of the two molecules of hydrogen chloride.

By Avogadro's hypothesis, the simplest molecules of hydrogen, oxygen, and chlorine each contain two atoms. The simplest possible molecule of water contains two atoms of hydrogen and one atom of oxygen. The simplest molecule of hydrogen chloride contains one atom of hydrogen and one atom of chlorine.

The correctness of Avogadro's hypothesis is so widely recognized today that it has become known as *Avogadro's Principle*. It is supported by the Kinetic Theory of gases, and is employed extensively in the determination of molecular weights, atomic weights, and molecular formulas.

3. Molecules of active gaseous elements are diatomic. The application of Avogadro's Principle to Gay-Lussac's Law of Combining Volumes of Gases enables us to recognize the simplest possible makeup of elementary gas re-

actants. How may we determine whether this empirical structure is the correct one?

Chemists have analyzed hydrogen chloride gas and, with the aid of atomic weights, have determined the empirical formula to be HCl. By finding the molecular weight of the compound, HCl is established as the correct or molecular formula (see Chapter 11, Section 8). Thus a molecule of the compound contains *only* one atom of hydrogen and *only* one atom of chlorine. Since two molecules of HCl are formed from one molecule of hydrogen and one molecule of chlorine, each contains *only* two atoms. *Thus the hydrogen and chlorine molecules must be diatomic.* We may write the equation as follows:

$$H_2 + Cl_2 \rightarrow 2\ HCl$$

Similarly, the oxygen molecule may be proved to be diatomic since H_2O is

Fig. 14-2. **Amadeo Avogadro is best known for his molecular hypothesis concerning gases.** (Bettmann Archive)

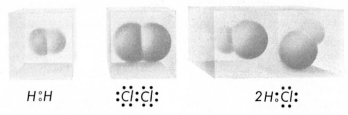

$H \overset{..}{\circ} H$:$\overset{..}{\underset{..}{C}}l$:$\overset{..}{\underset{..}{C}}l$: 2$H \overset{..}{\circ} \overset{..}{\underset{..}{C}}l$:

Fig. 14-3. As HCl is known to be the correct formula for hydrogen chloride gas, the molecules of hydrogen and chlorine are proved to be diatomic.

known to be the molecular formula of water vapor.

$$2 H_2 + O_2 \rightarrow 2 H_2O$$

Let us examine one additional gaseous reaction. Berthollet found that 3 *volumes* of hydrogen combined with *1 volume* of nitrogen to form 2 *volumes* of ammonia. By Avogadro's Principle we conclude that 3 *molecules* of hydrogen combine with *1 molecule* of nitrogen to form 2 *molecules* of ammonia. Analysis of ammonia reveals that it is composed of 82% nitrogen and 18% hydrogen. The atomic weights of nitrogen and hydrogen are 14 and 1.0 respectively. The molecular weight of ammonia is known to be 17.0. Therefore the molecular formula is:

N: $\dfrac{82 \text{ g N}}{14 \text{ g/g-atom}} = 5.9$ g-atom N

H: $\dfrac{18 \text{ g H}}{1.0 \text{ g/g-atom}} = 18$ g-atom H

N : H $= \dfrac{5.9}{5.9} : \dfrac{18}{5.9} = 1.0 : 3.0$

Empirical formula $= NH_3$
Molecular formula $= (NH_3)x$
and $\qquad (NH_3)x = 17$
thus $\qquad\qquad x = 1$
Molecular formula $= NH_3$

Two molecules of NH_3 produced must contain a total of 2 nitrogen atoms which must therefore compose the 1 molecule of nitrogen reactant. Again the

2 molecules of NH_3 produced must contain a total of 6 hydrogen atoms which therefore compose the 3 molecules of hydrogen reactant. We may summarize these relations as follows:

hydrogen	+	nitrogen	→	ammonia
3 volumes		1 volume		2 volumes
3 molecules		1 molecule		2 molecules
3 H_2	+	N_2	→	2 NH_3

Both nitrogen and hydrogen molecules are diatomic.

4. Molecules of the inert gases are monatomic. By using the methods described in the preceding sections, we are able to show that the molecules of all ordinary gaseous elements contain two atoms. Other methods have been used to show that the inert gaseous elements, such as helium and neon, have only one atom to each molecule. The rule does not apply to solids, and it may not even apply to the vapors of certain elements which are liquid or solid at room temperature. For example, at high temperatures the molecules of mercury and iodine are known to consist of only one atom each.

5. The density and specific gravity of gases. The *density* of a substance has been defined as its *mass per unit volume*. The mass of solids and liquids is expressed in *grams* and the volume in *cubic centimeters*. It is impractical, however, to express the densities of gases using the cubic-centimeter volume, since the mass in grams in every instance would be exceedingly small. The *liter* is a more suitable unit for gas-density measurements. In Chapter 9 it was shown that the volume of a gas is affected by both temperature and pressure changes. The *density* of a gas is therefore given in *grams-per-liter at S.T.P.*

It is frequently convenient to compare the density of a substance to that of a suitable standard. As this is a comparison of the masses of *equal* volumes of the two, it tells us how much more (or less) dense the one is than the standard of reference. The density of water is the standard of reference for solids and liquids; air is the most commonly used standard of reference for gases. *The ratio of the density of a substance to the density of the standard of reference is* called its *specific gravity.*

The density of oxygen is 1.43 grams per liter. Thus the mass of 1 liter of oxygen is 1.43 g at S.T.P. The density of air is 1.29 grams per liter; one liter of air has a mass of 1.29 g at S.T.P. The specific gravity of oxygen may be expressed:

$$\text{sp gr } O_2 = \frac{\text{density of } O_2}{\text{density of air}}$$

$$\text{sp gr } O_2 = \frac{1.43 \text{ g/l}}{1.29 \text{ g/l}} = 1.11$$

Observe that specific gravity is a dimensionless numerical ratio which tells us that oxygen is 1.11 times denser than air. Table 10, in the Appendix, lists the density and specific gravity of gases.

6. The molar volume of a gas. Oxygen is a diatomic gas. One mole contains the Avogadro number of molecules (6.02×10^{23}) and has a mass of 31.9988 g. One mole of diatomic hydrogen contains the same number of molecules and has a mass of 2.016 g. Helium is a monatomic gas. One mole of helium contains the Avogadro number of monatomic molecules and has a mass of 4.003 g. We have seen (Chapter 11, Section 6) that mole-quantities of all molecular substances contain the same number of molecules.

The volume occupied by 1 mole (1 g-mol. wt.) of a gas at S.T.P. is called its **molar volume,** *or its* **gram-molecular volume.** Since moles of gases have equal numbers of molecules, Avogadro's Principle tells us that they must occupy equal volumes under similar conditions of temperature and pressure. *The molar volumes of all gases are equal.* This has great practical significance in chemistry. Let us see how the molar volume of gases may be determined.

The densities of gases represent the masses of equal numbers of molecules

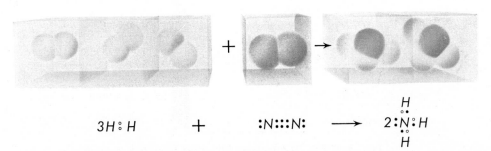

$$3H \,{}^{\circ}_{\circ}\, H \qquad + \qquad :N:::N: \qquad \longrightarrow \qquad 2:\overset{\displaystyle H}{\underset{\displaystyle H}{N}}:H$$

Fig. 14-4. **Application of Avogadro's Law to Gay-Lussac's Combining Volumes can show molecules of elementary gas reactants to be diatomic.**

measured under standard conditions of temperature and pressure. The differences in densities are due, therefore, to differences in the masses of the molecules of the different gases.

The density of hydrogen is 0.0899 g/l, measured at S.T.P. A mole of hydrogen, 1 g-mol wt., has a mass of 2.016 g. Now 0.0899 g of H_2 occupies 1 liter volume at S.T.P. What volume will 2.016 g of H_2 occupy under similar conditions? Obviously the molar volume will be as much greater than 1 liter as 2.016 g is greater than 0.0899 g. This proportionality may be expressed as follows:

$$\frac{\text{molar volume of } H_2}{1 \text{ liter}} = \frac{2.016 \text{ g}}{0.0899 \text{ g}}$$

Solving for molar volume:

$$\text{molar volume of } H_2 = \frac{2.016 \text{ g} \times 1 \text{ liter}}{0.0899 \text{ g}}$$

molar volume of H_2 = 22.4 liters

The density of oxygen is 1.43 g/l. A mole of oxygen has a mass of 31.9988 g. Following our reasoning in the case of hydrogen, we may compute the molar volume of O_2.

$$\frac{\text{molar volume of } O_2}{1 \text{ liter}} = \frac{32.0 \text{ g}}{1.43 \text{ g}}$$

$$\text{molar volume of } O_2 = \frac{32.0 \text{ g} \times 1 \text{ liter}}{1.43 \text{ g}}$$

molar volume of O_2 = 22.4 liters

Computations with other gases would yield similar results. However, it is clear from Avogadro's Principle that this is unnecessary. We may generalize the proportion used above to read as follows:

$$\text{density (D) of a gas} = \frac{1 \text{ mole of the gas}}{1 \text{ molar volume}}$$

or

$$D \text{ (of a gas)} = \frac{\text{g-mol. wt. (of the gas)}}{22.4 \text{ l}}$$

and

$$\text{g-mol. wt.} = D \times 22.4 \text{ l}$$

Thus we see that the *gram-molecular weight* of a gaseous substance is the mass, in grams, of 22.4 liters of the gas measured at S.T.P.; it is simply the density of the gas multiplied by the constant, 22.4 liters. Similarly, the density of a gas may be found by dividing its g-mol. wt. by the constant, 22.4 liters.

If the molecular formula of a gas is known, its density may be determined directly from the formula. Let us use sulfur dioxide, SO_2, as an example. The mass of a mole of SO_2 is 64 g. Thus

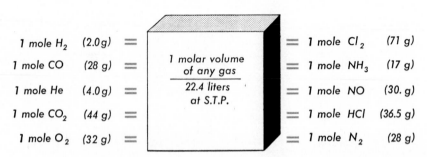

1 mole H_2	(2.0g)	=			=	1 mole Cl_2	(71 g)
1 mole CO	(28 g)	=	1 molar volume of any gas	=	1 mole NH_3	(17 g)
1 mole He	(4.0g)	=	22.4 liters at S.T.P.	=	1 mole NO	(30. g)
1 mole CO_2	(44 g)	=		=	1 mole HCl	(36.5 g)
1 mole O_2	(32 g)	=		=	1 mole N_2	(28 g)

Fig. 14-5. **At S.T.P., 22.4 liters of all gases have the same number of molecules, and the mass of each volume in grams is numerically equal to its molecular weight.**

$$D_{SO_2} = \frac{64 \text{ g}}{22.4 \text{ l}}$$

$$D_{SO_2} = 2.9 \text{ g/l}$$

★ **7. The molecular weight of gases determined experimentally.** Some substances do not exist as molecules under ordinary conditions. Other substances cannot be vaporized without undergoing decomposition. Of this latter group, those which are soluble in ordinary solvents may lend themselves to molecular-weight determinations by methods which will be discussed in Chapter 19. *The molecular weights of substances which are gaseous, or which may be vaporized without decomposition, may be determined by use of the molar-volume method.*

It would be impractical in the laboratory to weigh directly a molar volume (22.4 l) of a gas or vapor at standard conditions of temperature and pressure. Indeed, some substances, otherwise suitable for this method, are liquids or even solids under S.T.P. conditions. Consequently, any quantity of a gas or vapor which can be weighed to determine its mass precisely may be employed in the

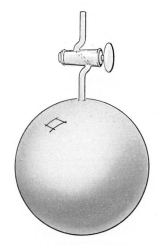

Fig. 14-6. **A type of glass bulb used in determining density of gases.**

molecular-weight determination. Its volume is measured under any suitable conditions of temperature and pressure. This volume may be converted to standard temperature and pressure, and then, by proportion, the mass of 22.4 liters may be calculated. The Sample Problem which follows illustrates how this experimental method is used to determine molecular weight.

★SAMPLE PROBLEM

A gas sample having a mass of 0.350 g was measured over water at 20.°C and 750. mm pressure. Its volume was 150. ml. What is its molecular weight?

SOLUTION

The partial pressure of the gas under consideration is the difference between the indicated pressure and the partial pressure due to water vapor, 750. mm − 17.5 mm, or (750. − 17.5) mm. As the temperature is lowered the volume will decrease in the ratio $\frac{273°\text{K}}{293°\text{K}}$. As the pressure is raised the volume will decrease in the ratio $\frac{(750. - 17.5) \text{ mm}}{760 \text{ mm}}$.

Therefore, the volume at S.T.P. is:

$$V_{\text{S.T.P.}} = 150.\ \text{ml} \times \frac{273°\text{K}}{293°\text{K}} \times \frac{(750. - 17.5)\ \text{mm}}{760\ \text{mm}}$$

$$V = 135\ \text{ml, or } 0.135\ l \text{ at S.T.P.}$$

When reduced to standard conditions, the density of the gas is proportional to 0.350 g per 0.135 liter.

Thus

$$\frac{0.350\ \text{g}}{0.135\ l} = \frac{\text{g-mol.wt.}}{22.4\ l}$$

Solving for g-mol.wt.:

$$\text{g-mol.wt.} = \frac{22.4\ l \times 0.350\ \text{g}}{0.135\ l}$$

$$\text{g-mol.wt.} = 58.1\ \text{g}$$
$$\text{mol.wt.} = 58.1$$

It follows naturally that the volume occupied by a known mass of a gas under any conditions of temperature and pressure can be calculated if the molecular formula of the gas is known. The molecular formula provides the mass of 1 mole of the gas which is known to occupy the molar volume, 22.4 liters, at S.T.P. By proportion, the volume of the known mass of the gas at S.T.P. can be determined. Then by application of the Gas Laws, the volume at any temperature and pressure can be computed. This is illustrated in the Sample Problem on the next page.

⋆ **8. Real gases and the ideal gas.** Precise experimental determinations of molar volumes of gases reveal that all gases deviate slightly from the perfect-gas characteristics assigned to them by the Gas Laws and Avogadro's Principle. This does not mean that the laws are only approximately true. Rather, it indicates that real gases do not behave as ideal gases over wide ranges of temperature and pressure.

Two factors contribute to the deviation of real gases from the perfect compliance of an ideal gas. Compression of a gas is *limited* by the fact that the molecules themselves occupy space and is *aided* by the fact that van der Waals (attractive) forces, however weak, do exist between the molecules.

Only when these two opposing forces within the gas exactly balance will it respond as an ideal gas. Such gases as ammonia and chlorine, which at ordinary temperatures are not far above their boiling (condensation) points, show rather marked deviations from 22.4 liters as the molar volume. Such gases as oxygen and nitrogen, having low boiling points, behave more nearly as ideal gases under ordinary conditions.

When expressed to five significant figures, the molar volume of an ideal gas is 22.414 liters. The molar volumes of ammonia and chlorine, measured under normal conditions, are 22.09 l and 22.06 l respectively; those of oxygen and nitrogen are 22.394 l and 22.404 l respectively. For most gases, deviations from ideal gas performance through ordinary ranges of temperature and pressure do not exceed 2 percent. This usually is within the limit of accuracy obtainable in laboratory experiments.

★SAMPLE PROBLEM

What is the volume of 10. g of carbon dioxide gas, CO_2, at 20.°C and 740 mm?

SOLUTION

The formula CO_2 indicates that the molecular weight is 44. Now 44 g (1 mole) of CO_2 occupy 22.4 *l* (1 molar volume) at S.T.P. The volume occupied by 10. g will be represented as **X**.

$$\frac{44 \text{ g}}{22.4 \text{ } l} = \frac{10. \text{ g}}{X}$$

Solving for **X**:

$$X = \frac{22.4 \text{ } l \times 10. \text{ g}}{44 \text{ g}}$$

$$X = 5.1 \text{ } l, \text{ at S.T.P.}$$

As the temperature rises the volume will increase in the ratio $\dfrac{293°K}{273°K}$.

As the pressure decreases the volume will increase in the ratio $\dfrac{760 \text{ mm}}{740 \text{ mm}}$.

Thus the volume at 20.°C and 740 mm is:

$$V_{20°, \text{ } 740 \text{ mm}} = 5.1 \text{ } l \times \frac{293°K}{273°K} \times \frac{760 \text{ mm}}{740 \text{ mm}}$$

$$V = 5.6 \text{ liters, at } 20.°C \text{ and } 740 \text{ mm}$$

SUMMARY

According to the Law of Gay-Lussac, the combining volumes of gases may be expressed in small whole numbers. If the product is a gas, its volume bears a simple whole-number relationship to the volumes of the reacting gases.

Avogadro suggested that equal volumes of gases, under similar conditions of temperature and pressure, contained the same number of molecules. He applied this hypothesis to explain Gay-Lussac's Law of Combining Volumes of Gases. The Avogadro Principle, together with the Law of Gay-Lussac and molecular-weight data, may be used to show that molecules of the active elementary gases are diatomic.

The density of gases is expressed in grams per liter measured at S.T.P. The specific gravity of a gas is the numerical ratio of its density to the density of a standard of reference, usually air. Specific gravity tells us whether a gas is heavier or lighter than an equal volume of air.

The volume occupied by 1 mole of a gas at S.T.P. is called the molar volume of the gas. Molar volumes of all gases are equal and are found experimentally to be 22.4 liters. This provides a simple experimental method for determining the molecular weights of gases, and of other molecular substances which can be vaporized without undergoing decomposition.

An ideal gas conforms exactly to the proportions of the Gas Laws and Avogadro's Principle. Real gases deviate slightly from the behavior of an ideal gas except where the responsible molecular forces just balance out.

TEST YOURSELF ON THESE TERMS

Avogadro's Principle	gram-molecular volume	molecular weight
density	ideal gas	monatomic molecule
diatomic molecule	molar volume	real gas
Gay-Lussac's Law	mole	specific gravity

PROBLEMS

Group A

1. Calculate the mass of one liter of hydrogen chloride gas, HCl, at S.T.P. to 3 significant figures.
2. What is the mass of one liter of hydrogen sulfide, H_2S, at S.T.P. calculated to 3 significant figures?
3. The mass of 1.00 l of gas at S.T.P. is 2.5 g. What is its molecular weight?
4. The mass of 1.00 l of nitrogen at S.T.P. is 1.25 g. (*a*) Calculate the molecular weight of nitrogen. (*b*) From this calculated molecular weight, determine the number of atoms in a molecule of nitrogen.
5. Hydrogen is the gas of lowest density. What is the mass of 300. ml of hydrogen at S.T.P.?
6. At standard conditions, 225 ml of sulfur dioxide gas have a mass of 0.6428 g. Calculate the molecular weight of sulfur dioxide.
7. What is the mass of 750. ml of CO_2 at S.T.P. to 3 significant figures?
8. If the mass of 250. ml of methane is 0.179 gram at S.T.P., what is the molecular weight of methane?
9. The compounds HBr, PH_3, and N_2O are all gaseous at room temperature. (*a*) Calculate their molecular weights to 2 significant figures. (*b*) What is the density of each?
10. Find the mass of 4.00 liters of each of the following to 3 significant figures: N_2, NH_3, and C_2H_2.

Group B

11. Calculate the specific gravity of carbon monoxide, CO, air standard, to 3 significant figures.
12. The specific gravity of argon, air standard, is 1.3796. What is the density of argon gas?
13. The specific gravity of a gas, air standard, is 2.695. What is the molecular weight of this gas?

14. Find the molecular weight of a gas whose specific gravity, air standard, is 1.554.

⋆**15.** A compound contains: nitrogen, 30.51%; oxygen, 69.49%. The density of the gas is 4.085 g/l (*a*) What is its empirical formula? (*b*) What is its molecular weight? (*c*) What is its correct formula?

⋆**16.** It is found that 1.00 *l* of a certain gas collected at a pressure of 720. mm of mercury, and at a temperature of 27° C weighs 1.30 g. Calculate its molecular weight.

⋆**17.** It is found that 1.00 *l* of nitrogen combines with 1.00 *l* of oxygen in an electric arc to form 2.00 *l* of a gas which, by analysis, contains 46.7% nitrogen and 53.3% oxygen. Its density is determined to be 1.34 g/*l*. (*a*) Find the empirical formula of the product. (*b*) What is the molecular formula? (*c*) Using the information of this problem, and the arguments of Avogadro, determine the number of atoms per molecule of nitrogen and oxygen.

⋆**18.** What volume will 2.0 g of CS_2 vapor occupy at 756 mm pressure and 50.° C?

⋆**19.** A 1.00 liter flask filled with a gas at S.T.P. is attached to a high vacuum pump and evacuated until the pressure is only 1.00×10^{-4} mm. Assuming no temperature change, how many molecules remain in the flask?

⋆**20.** A sample of a vapor having a mass of 0.865 g measured 174 ml at 100.° C and 745 mm. What is the molecular weight?

Chapter 15 · VOLUME RELATIONS IN CHEMICAL REACTIONS

1. Chemical problems involving gases. As illustrated in Chapter 13, the equation for a chemical reaction expresses quantities of reactants and products in *moles*. The numerical coefficients in the balanced equation tell us the number of moles of each substance.

Frequently a reactant or a product of a reaction is a gas. Indeed, all reactants and products may be gaseous in certain reactions. By applying Avogadro's Principle we recognize that single moles of all such gases have the same volume under similar conditions of temperature and pressure. At S.T.P. a mole of any gas occupies 1 molar volume, 22.4 liters. *Consequently, the relation in moles in the equation is also the relation of volumes of gases.*

It should be remembered that real gases deviate slightly from the behavior of an ideal gas. Calculations which involve the molar volume as 22.4 liters can give only approximately correct answers.

There are two general types of problems which involve chemical equations and the volumes of gases. These are:

volume-volume problems, in which a certain *volume of a gas* reactant or product is given and the *volume of another gas* reactant or product is required, and *mass-volume problems,* in which a certain *mass of a reactant or product* is given and the *volume of a gas* reactant or product is required, or vice versa.

2. Volume-volume problems. In this type of problem, the *volume* of one *gaseous substance* is given and we are asked to determine the *volume* of another *gaseous substance* involved in the chemical action. Since single moles of all gases at the same temperature and pressure occupy the same volume, in a correctly balanced equation the volumes of gases are proportional to the number of moles indicated by the numerical coefficients. To illustrate:

$$
\begin{array}{ccccc}
\text{(gas)} & & \text{(gas)} & & \text{(gas)} \\
2\,CO & + & O_2 & \rightarrow & 2\,CO_2 \\
\text{2 moles} & & \text{1 mole} & & \text{2 moles} \\
\text{2 vol.} & & \text{1 vol.} & & \text{2 vol.}
\end{array}
$$

The balanced equation signifies that 2 moles of CO react with 1 mole of O_2 to produce 2 moles of CO_2. From Avogadro's Principle, 2 volumes (liters, cubic feet, etc.) of carbon monoxide react with 1 volume (liter, cubic foot, etc.) of oxygen to produce 2 volumes (liters, cubic feet, etc.) of carbon dioxide, the temperature and pressure of all three gases being the same. Thus 10 liters of CO would require 5 liters of O_2 for combustion and would produce 10 liters of CO_2. The volume relationship is 2:1:2 under similar conditions of temperature and pressure.

Obviously, since the above reaction is exothermic, the resultant gas expands due to the rise in temperature. The volume relations apply only after the temperature of the gaseous product has been reduced to that of the reactants at the beginning of the reaction.

The conditions of temperature and pressure must be known in order to determine which substances exist as gases. Whenever the conditions are not stated they are assumed to be standard. Let us consider the combustion of methane.

(gas)	(gas)		(gas)		
CH_4	$+$	$2 O_2$	$\rightarrow$	CO_2	$+$	$2 H_2O$
1 mole		2 moles		1 mole		2 moles
1 vol.		2 vol.		1 vol.		

At temperatures under 100° C water is a liquid. Thus, if the volumes of the gaseous reactants are measured under ordinary conditions, water could not be included in the volume ratio. The reactants, methane and oxygen, and the product, carbon dioxide, are gases, and their volume relationship is seen to be 1:2:1.

Volume-volume problems are very simple to solve. The problem set-up is similar to that of mass-mass problems (see Chapter 13, Section 4), except that it is not necessary to use atomic weights to convert moles of the specified gases to their respective equation weights.

Once set up, most volume-volume problems may be solved by inspection. The following example shows how these problems are commonly solved.

Suppose we wish to know the volume of hydrogen which will combine with 4.0 liters of nitrogen to form ammonia gas. We set up the problem as follows:

$$\begin{array}{cccc} X & & 4.0\ l & \\ 3\ H_2 & + & N_2 & \rightarrow 2\ NH_3 \\ 3\ moles & & 1\ mole & \end{array}$$

The equation shows that H_2 and N_2 combine in the ratio of 3 moles to 1 mole. From Avogadro's Principle, these gases must combine in the ratio of 3 volumes to 1 volume. Thus, simply by inspection, it is evident that 4.0 liters of nitrogen require 12 liters of hydrogen for complete reaction. Since 2 moles of NH_3 is shown, it is equally plain that 8.0 liters of this gas are produced. This is, in reality, a solution by the proportion method:

$$\frac{X}{4.0\ l\ N_2} = \frac{3\ moles\ H_2}{1\ mole\ N_2}$$

Solving for X:

$$X = \frac{3\ moles\ H_2 \times 4.0\ l\ N_2}{1\ mole\ N_2}$$

$$X = 12\ liters\ of\ H_2$$

3. Mass-volume problems. In this type of problem, we are concerned with the relation between the *volume of gas* and the *mass* of another substance in a reaction. Either the mass of the substance is given and the volume of the gas is required, or the volume of the gas is given and the mass of the substance is required.

As an illustration let us determine the number of grams of calcium carbonate, $CaCO_3$, which must be decomposed to produce 4.00 liters of carbon

SAMPLE PROBLEM

Assuming air to be 21.0% oxygen by volume: a. How many liters of air must enter the carburetor to complete the combustion of 60.0 liters of octane vapor? b. How many liters of carbon dioxide are formed? (All gases are measured at the same temperature and pressure.)

SOLUTION

Octane has the formula C_8H_{18}, and its complete oxidation produces carbon dioxide and water. Since it is the oxygen of the air which combines with octane, we must determine first the amount of oxygen required. Let X be this volume, and Y the volume of CO_2 formed. The problem set-up is:

$$\begin{array}{ccccccc} \text{60.0 liters} & & \text{X} & & \text{Y} & & \\ 2\ C_8H_{18} & + & 25\ O_2 & \rightarrow & 16\ CO_2\uparrow & + & 18\ H_2O\uparrow \\ \text{2 moles} & & \text{25 moles} & & \text{16 moles} & & \end{array}$$

a. Solving by proportion:

$$\frac{\text{60.0 liters}}{X} = \frac{\text{2 moles}}{\text{25 moles}}$$

$$X = \frac{\text{60.0 liters} \times 25\ \text{moles}}{2\ \text{moles}}$$

$$X = 750.\ \text{liters of } O_2$$

Now 750. liters of O_2 is 21.0% of the air required.

So

$$\text{Air required} = \frac{\text{750. liters}}{0.210} = 3570\ \text{liters}$$

b. Solving as before:

$$\frac{\text{60.0 liters}}{Y} = \frac{\text{2 moles}}{\text{16 moles}}$$

$$Y = \frac{\text{60.0 liters} \times 16\ \text{moles}}{2\ \text{moles}}$$

$$Y = 480.\ \text{liters of } CO_2$$

Reminder: The volumes of air and CO_2 computed are those which would be measured at the temperature and pressure of the octane vapor prior to its combustion. Under such conditions, the water, formed as water vapor at the reaction temperature, would have condensed and could not enter the problem as a gas. The quantity of water can, of course, be computed in moles or grams using the method presented in Section 4.

dioxide, CO_2. The problem set-up is as follows:

$$X \qquad\qquad 4.00\ l$$
$$CaCO_3 \rightarrow CaO + \qquad CO_2$$
$$1\ mole \qquad\qquad 1\ mole$$
$$= 100.\ g \qquad\qquad = 22.4\ liters$$

Observe that the molar volume (22.4 liters) is substituted for the g-mol. wt. (44 g) of CO_2. This is possible since each mole of gas occupies 22.4 liters at S.T.P. (*and only at S.T.P.*). The problem may now be solved by any of the methods used previously in connection with mass-mass relations.

1. *Solution by proportion.* We reason that the ratio of the mass of $CaCO_3$ to the volume of CO_2 is equal to the *ratio* of the equation weight of $CaCO_3$ to the volume occupied by the equation weight of CO_2 (at S.T.P.).

$$\frac{X}{4.00\ l\ CO_2} = \frac{100.\ g\ CaCO_3}{22.4\ l\ CO_2}$$

$$X = \frac{100.\ g\ CaCO_3 \times 4.00\ l\ CO_2}{22.4\ l\ CO_2}$$

$$X = 17.9\ g\ of\ CaCO_3$$

2. *Solution by arithmetic.* We reason that 22.4 liters of CO_2 require 100. g of $CaCO_3$ (at S.T.P.) so

$$1\ liter\ requires\ \frac{100.}{22.4}\ g\ CaCO_3$$

Then,

$$4.00\ liters\ require\ 4.00 \times \frac{100.}{22.4}\ g = 17.9\ g$$

3. *Solution by moles.* We reason that 4.00 liters of CO_2 is $\frac{4.00}{22.4}$ mole of CO_2 (at S.T.P.).

Since 1 mole of CO_2 requires 1 mole of $CaCO_3$

Then $\frac{4.00}{22.4}$ mole requires $\frac{4.00}{22.4}$ mole of $CaCO_3$

Number of grams in $\frac{4.0}{22.4}$ mole of $CaCO_3$ is:

$$\frac{4.00}{22.4}\ mole \times \frac{100.\ g\ CaCO_3}{mole}$$
$$= 17.9\ g\ CaCO_3$$

4. Gases not measured at S.T.P. Gases are seldom measured under standard conditions of temperature and pressure. Only gas volumes under standard conditions can be placed in a proportion with the molar volume of 22.4 liters. Therefore, *gas reactants measured under conditions other than S.T.P. must first be corrected to S.T.P.* in accordance with the Gas Laws studied in Chapter 9 before proceeding with mass-volume calculations.

If the gas in question is a *product*, and its volume is to be measured under conditions other than S.T.P., *the volume at S.T.P. is first calculated from the chemical equation.* This volume at S.T.P. is then converted to the required conditions of temperature and pressure by proper application of the Gas Laws.

Volume-volume calculations do not require S.T.P. corrections since volumes of gases are related to moles rather than to mole volumes. Thus it is only necessary that measurements of gas volumes be carried out at a constant temperature and pressure in volume-volume problems.

★ **5. Gases collected over water.** The volume of a gaseous product in a mass-volume problem is calculated under S.T.P. conditions and must be corrected for any other specified conditions of temperature and pressure. If this gas is collected over water, the equilibrium vapor pressure of the water must be taken into account. At the specified temperature, the partial pressure of the gas is the difference between the measured pressure and the partial pressure of the water vapor.

Let us suppose that the volume of a gaseous product collected over water is to be determined at 29° C and 752 mm pressure by a mass-volume calculation. The volume at S.T.P. is computed from the chemical equation. The vapor pres-sure of water at 29° C is found in the tables to be 30. mm. Thus

$$V_{29°,\,752\,mm} =$$
$$V_{S.T.P.} \times \frac{302°\,K}{273°\,K} \times \frac{760\,mm}{(752\,-\,30.)\,mm}$$

See the following Sample Problems.

★SAMPLE PROBLEM

What volume of oxygen, collected over water at 20.° C and 750.0 mm pressure, can be obtained by the decomposition of 175 g of potassium chlorate?

SOLUTION

A mass is given and a gas volume is required. The volume of the gas at S.T.P. may first be found from the chemical equation. The problem set-up is as follows:

$$
\begin{array}{cc}
175\ g & X \\
2\ KClO_3 & \rightarrow\ 2\ KCl\ + \quad 3\ O_2\uparrow \\
2\ moles & 3\ moles \\
= 2[39 + 35.5 + 3(16)]\ g & = 3(22.4\ l) \\
= 245\ g & = 67.2\ l
\end{array}
$$

Solution by proportion:

$$\frac{175\ g\ KClO_3}{X} = \frac{245\ g\ KClO_3}{67.2\ l\ O_2}$$

Solving for X:

$$X = \frac{175\ g\ KClO_3 \times 67.2\ l\ O_2}{245\ g\ KClO_3} = 48.0\ l\ of\ O_2\ at\ S.T.P.$$

As the temperature is increased to 20.° C, the volume will increase in the ratio $\frac{293°\,K}{273°\,K}$. The vapor pressure of water at 20.° C is found to be 17.5 mm. As the pressure is decreased to 750.0 mm, the volume will increase in the ratio $\frac{760\,mm}{750.0\,-\,175.\,mm}$. Thus the volume of O_2 at 20.° C and 750.0 mm pressure is:

$$V_{20°,\,750\,mm} = 48.0\ l \times \frac{293°\,K}{273°\,K} \times \frac{760\,mm}{(750.0\,-\,17.5)\,mm}$$

$$V = 53.5\ l\ O_2\ at\ 20°\ C\ and\ 750.0\ mm$$

★6. **The gas constant.** Gases are seldom measured in the laboratory under standard conditions of temperature and pressure. They are commonly measured under conditions far removed from the standard and then calculated back to standard conditions using the familiar gas laws. The behavior of a real gas would be that of the ideal gas (which conforms strictly to the gas laws) only if its molecules had no volume and exerted no attraction for each other. The ideal gas behavior can be approximated by making measurements at reduced pressures and temperatures well above the liquefaction point.

From the Avogadro Principle, it follows that the volume of a mole is the same for all gases under similar conditions of temperature and pressure. Therefore, the volume of any gas is directly proportional to the number of moles (n) of the gas, if pressure and temperature are constant.

$$V \propto n \ (p \text{ and } T \text{ constant})$$

From Boyle's Law we know that the volume of a gas is inversely proportional to the pressure applied to it if the quantity of gas (moles of gas) and temperature are constant.

$$V \propto \frac{1}{p} \ (n \text{ and } T \text{ constant})$$

Similarly, from Charles' Law we know that the volume is directly proportional to the Kelvin temperature if the pressure and quantity of gas remain constant.

$$V \propto T \ (p \text{ and } n \text{ constant})$$

Thus, $\quad V \propto n \times \dfrac{1}{p} \times T$

By the insertion of a proportionality constant **R** of suitable dimensions, this proportion may be restated as an equation.

$$V = Rn \left(\frac{1}{p}\right) T$$

or $\qquad pV = nRT$

R is the proportionality constant known as the *gas constant* and, when the quantity of gas is expressed in moles, R has the same value for all gases. Conventionally the gas volume V is expressed in *liters*, the quantity n *in moles*, the temperature T in *Kelvin degrees*, and the pressure p in *atmospheres*. Of course, the standard pressure of 760 mm is *1 atmosphere* and so

$$\frac{\text{pressure in mm of Hg}}{760 \text{ mm of Hg/atm}} = \text{pressure in atm.}$$

With the convention of units stated, let us determine the dimensional units of the gas constant R from the ideal gas equation.

$$pV = nRT$$

Then, $\qquad R = \dfrac{pV}{nT}$

$$R = \frac{\text{atm} \times \text{liters}}{\text{moles} \times {}^\circ K}$$

Thus, R must have the dimensions *liter-atm per mole-°K.*

Careful measurements of the density of oxygen at low pressures yields the volume of 22.414 liters accepted as the precise molar volume of an ideal gas, that is, the volume occupied by 1 mole of ideal gas under conditions of 1 atm and 273.16 °K. Substituting in the ideal gas equation and solving the expression for R

$$R = \frac{pV}{nT} = \frac{1 \text{ atm} \times 22.414 \text{ l}}{1 \text{ mole} \times 273.16 \text{ °K}}$$

$$R = 0.082054 \text{ l-atm/mole-°K}$$

Suppose the properties of an unknown gas are being examined at a temperature of 28° C and 740. mm pressure and it is found that the mass of 1 liter is 4.62 g under these conditions. By an application of the gas constant R, 0.0821 l-atm/mole-°K, and the ideal gas equation, $pV = nRT$, the molecular weight of the gas can be determined directly since its use in the ideal gas equation enables moles per liter of the gas to be computed.

$$T = 273° + 28° = 301 \text{ °K}$$

$$p = \frac{740. \text{ mm}}{760 \text{ mm/atm}} = 0.974 \text{ atm}$$

$$pV = nRT$$

Solving for $\frac{n}{V}$, moles per liter:

$$\frac{n}{V} = \frac{p}{RT}$$

$$\frac{n}{V} = \frac{0.974 \text{ atm}}{\dfrac{0.0821 \text{ l-atm}}{\text{mole-°K}} \times 301 \text{ °K}}$$

$$\frac{n}{V} = \frac{0.974 \text{ mole}}{0.0821 \times 301 \times l}$$

$$\frac{n}{V} = 0.0395 \text{ mole/l}$$

This shows that the experimental mass of 1 liter of the gas, 4.62 g, constitutes 0.0395 mole.

Since 0.0395 mole has a mass of 4.62 g, the mass of 1 mole is

$$1 \text{ mole} \times \frac{4.62 \text{ g}}{0.0395 \text{ mole}} = 117 \text{ g}$$

Therefore, the molecular weight of the gas is 117.

SUMMARY

There are two general types of problems involving volume relations. One, in which volumes are given and volumes are required, refers only to gases. In the other, masses are given and volumes of gases are required, or vice versa. Both types of problems are based on an application of Avogadro's Principle.

When gas volumes are measured under conditions other than standard temperature and pressure, they must be adjusted to standard conditions before being placed in a proportion with the molar volume, 22.4 liters. Only gas volumes measured at standard conditions can be applied to the chemical equation. Calculations from a chemical equation yield gas volumes at standard temperature and pressure. If gas volumes at other temperatures and pressures are required, conversion to the required conditions is made by the proper application of the Gas Laws.

The gas laws can be developed into a useful form utilizing a gas constant which enables certain computations pertaining to gas measurements to be made with ease.

TEST YOURSELF ON THESE TERMS

gas constant	molar volume	volume ratio
gaseous product	partial pressure	volume-volume problem
gaseous reactant	proportion	mass-volume problem

PROBLEMS

In the absence of stated conditions of temperature and pressure, they are assumed to be S.T.P.

Group A

1. Carbon monoxide burns in oxygen to form carbon dioxide. (*a*) What volume of carbon dioxide is produced when 15 liters of carbon monoxide burn? (*b*) What volume of oxygen is required?
2. Acetylene gas, C_2H_2, burns in oxygen to form carbon dioxide and water vapor. (*a*) How many liters of oxygen are needed to burn 25.0 liters of acetylene? (*b*) How many liters of carbon dioxide are formed?
3. Ethane gas, C_2H_6, burns in air to produce carbon dioxide and water vapor. (*a*) How many liters of carbon dioxide are formed when 12 liters of ethane are burned? (*b*) How many moles of water are formed?
4. How many liters of air are required to furnish the oxygen to complete the reaction in Problem 3? (Assume the air to be 21% oxygen.)
5. How many grams of sodium are needed to liberate 4.0 liters of hydrogen from water?
6. What volumes of hydrogen and nitrogen are required to produce 20 liters of ammonia gas?
7. (*a*) How many liters of hydrogen are required to reduce 25.0 g of hot copper(II) oxide? (*b*) How many moles of water are formed?
8. When 130 g of zinc react with 150 g of HCl, how many liters of hydrogen are formed? (Note: first determine which reactant is in excess.)
9. (*a*) What volume of oxygen can be produced by the decomposition of 90.0 g of water? (*b*) What volume of hydrogen is produced in the same reaction?
10. If 400 ml of hydrogen and 400 ml of oxygen are mixed and ignited, (*a*) what volume of oxygen remains uncombined? (*b*) What volume of water vapor is formed if all gases are measured at 100° C?

Group B

11. (*a*) How many liters of sulfur dioxide gas at S.T.P. are formed when 50. g of sulfur burns? (*b*) What volume will this gas occupy at 25° C and 745 mm pressure?
12. What mass of magnesium reacting with hydrochloric acid will be required to produce 400. ml of hydrogen at 20.° C and 740. mm pressure?
★13. How many grams of oxygen are contained in 12.0 liters of the gas measured over water at 23° C and 745.0 mm pressure? (The vapor pressure of water at 23° C may be taken as 21 mm.)
★14. A replacement reaction between 5.0 g of aluminum and an excess of dilute sulfuric acid is used as a source of hydrogen gas. What volume of hydrogen is collected over water at 20.° C and 765 mm pressure?
15. What volume of dry air, measured at 29° C and 744 mm pressure, is required to complete the combustion of 1.00 mole of carbon disulfide, CS_2, to carbon dioxide, CO_2, and sulfur dioxide, SO_2?

16. What is the volume of the mixture of CO_2 and SO_2 produced in the reaction of Problem 15, if measured under the same conditions as the air used in the reaction?

17. Chlorine gas may be generated in the laboratory by a reaction between manganese dioxide and hydrogen chloride. The equation is:

$$MnO_2 + 4\,HCl \rightarrow MnCl_2 + 2\,H_2O + Cl_2 \uparrow$$

(a) What mass of MnO_2 is required to produce 1.00 liter of Cl_2 gas at S.T.P.? (b) What mass of HCl is required?

★ 18. In Problem 17, the HCl is available as a water solution which is 37.4% hydrogen chloride by weight, and the solution has a specific gravity (water standard) of 1.189. What volume of HCl solution (hydrochloric acid) must be furnished to the reaction?

★ 19. What quantity of chlorine gas would be contained in a 5.00 *l* flask at 20.° C and 600. mm pressure?

★ 20. What temperature must be maintained to insure that a 2.50 *l* flask containing 0.100 mole of a certain gas will show a continuous pressure of 745 mm?

★ 21. From the ideal gas equation, $pV = nRT$, and the density of a gas defined as the mass per unit volume, $D = m/V$, prove that the density of a gas at S.T.P. is directly proportional to its molecular weight.

★ 22. At 12.0° C and 740 mm, 1.07 *l* of a gas have a mass of 1.98 g. Calculate the molecular weight of the gas from the ideal gas equation.

CHECK YOUR PROGRESS IN CHEMISTRY

1. (a) Which term has more general application, *formula* weight or *molecular* weight? (b) What is the distinction between them?

2. Determine the formula weight for each of the following compounds: (a) H_2SO_4; (b) $NaOH$; (c) HgO; (d) $CuSO_4 \cdot 5H_2O$; (e) $HC_2H_3O_2$; (f) $MgBr_2$; (g) Al_2S_3; (h) $Ca(NO_3)_2$; (i) $Fe_2(Cr_2O_7)_3$; (j) $KMnO_4$.

3. A compound has the following composition: potassium 44.8%, sulfur 18.39%, oxygen 36.79%. Using atomic weights to 3 significant figures, determine its empirical formula.

4. A compound has the following composition: calcium 24.7%, hydrogen 1.2%, carbon 14.8%, oxygen 59.3%. What is the empirical formula of the compound?

5. An oxide of iron has the following composition: $Fe = 72.4\%$, $O = 27.6\%$. Using atomic weights to 3 significant figures, determine its empirical formula.

6. Write balanced equations for the following reactions: (a) composition reaction between hydrogen and oxygen; (b) decomposition of mercury(II) oxide; (c) oxidation of sulfur; (d) replacement reaction between zinc and hydrochloric acid; (e) reaction between silver nitrate and sodium chloride; (f) potassium chlorate heated strongly; (g) complete oxidation of phosphorus; (h) reaction between aluminum sulfate and calcium hydroxide; (i) metallic zinc and copper(II) sulfate solution; (j) reduction of copper(II) oxide with hydrogen.

7. What is the percentage composition of each of the following compounds: (*a*) SO_2; (*b*) $Ca(OH)_2$; (*c*) NaH_2PO_4; (*d*) $MgSO_4 \cdot 7 H_2O$?

8. Analysis of a compound reveals its composition to be 80.% carbon and 20.% hydrogen. Its molecular weight is 30. What is its molecular formula?

9. List the following elements in the order of their chemical activity: aluminum, calcium, copper, gold, hydrogen, iron, lead, potassium, silver, sodium, zinc.

10. How much ether, $(C_2H_5)_2O$, equals one mole?

11. What is the density of methane gas, CH_4, at S.T.P.?

12. What is the specific gravity (air standard) of the gas arsine, AsH_3?

13. How much copper will be produced when hydrogen is passed over 39.75 g of hot copper(II) oxide?

14. How many liters of hydrogen are required to reduce the copper(II) oxide of Problem 13?

15. An excess of copper is added to a solution containing 20.0 g of silver sulfate. How much silver is deposited?

16. What volume of hydrogen, measured at S.T.P., will be replaced by the action of 25 g of calcium metal and an excess of hydrochloric acid?

17. How many moles of calcium hydroxide are formed by the reaction between 60. g of calcium oxide and 20. g of water?

18. How many liters of ammonia can be prepared from 10.0 liters of nitrogen and 25.0 liters of hydrogen?

19. How many grams of charcoal, 90.0% carbon, must be burned to produce 100. liters of CO_2 measured at 20.° C and 747 mm pressure? (Use the at. wt. of C to 3 significant figures.)

★ 20. What volume of hydrogen, collected over water at 25° C and 755.0 mm pressure, can be obtained from 6.0 g of magnesium and an excess of sulfuric acid?

CHALLENGING YOUR KNOWLEDGE

1. The compound $C_3H_5(C_{17}H_{35}CO_2)_3$ forms CO_2 and H_2O when completely oxidized. Write the balanced equation.

2. Investigate the work of the Italian chemist, Stanislao Cannizzaro (1826–1910), in which he applied Avogadro's Principle to the determination of atomic weights. (Your instructor may be able to recommend a suitable college text or other source.) Prepare a brief report of Cannizzaro's logic for presentation to your class.

3. If 100 liters of a perfect gas at 0° C were subjected to 100 atmospheres of pressure (temperature remaining constant) the volume would be reduced to 1 liter. Hydrogen, however, would have a volume slightly greater than 1 liter, and nitrogen would have a volume slightly less than 1 liter. Can you explain these two different deviations of real gases from ideal-gas behavior?

4. Gasoline tank additives of questionable merit appear on the market from time to time. One such additive, in the form of white tablets, was analyzed by chemists. They found that the substance burned to produce

carbon dioxide and water vapor. Each gram of substance, when burned, yielded 3.44 g of CO_2 and 0.558 g of water. The density of its vapor was found to be 5.715 grams per liter. (*a*) What is the molecular formula? (*b*) What is the chemical name of the substance? (*c*) What is the most common use?

5. A tube contains 1.000 kilogram of hot copper(II) oxide. If 10.00 g of hydrogen are passed through the tube slowly and the water formed is expelled to the air, what remains in the tube and in what quantities? (Use accurate atomic weights in calculations.)

Unit 5 · CARBON AND ITS SIMPLE COMPOUNDS

Carbon
The Oxides of Carbon
Hydrocarbons

221

Chapter 16 · CARBON

1. Carbon is an abundant and important element. Carbon has been known from earliest times in the forms of charcoal and soot. In abundance, carbon ranks eleventh by weight among the elements in the earth's crust; but in importance, it ranks far higher than this. Carbon occurs in all living things. It is present in the tissues of our bodies and in the foods we eat. It is found in fuels, oils, wood, paper, textile fibers, and in all the plants and animals in the world. In addition, many thousands of carbon compounds have been made by synthesis in chemical laboratories. So important is the study of carbon compounds that it is a separate branch of chemistry called *organic chemistry*. Originally, organic chemistry was de-fined as the study of materials derived from living organisms, while inorganic chemistry was the study of materials derived from mineral sources. We have known for over a century that this is not a clear distinction. Many substances identical with those produced in plants and animals can be made also from mineral materials. As a result, *organic chemistry* today *includes the study of carbon compounds whether they are found in living organisms or not.*

In most substances containing carbon, the carbon is present in the *combined* form, usually associated with hydrogen, or with hydrogen and oxygen. However, in this chapter the solid element carbon will be described in its *free* or *uncombined* forms.

VOCABULARY

Destructive distillation. The process of decomposing materials by heating them in a closed vessel without access to either air or oxygen.

Organic chemistry. The study of carbon compounds, both natural and synthetic.

Refractory. Not readily melted; a substance which is not readily melted.

2. The structure and properties of carbon atoms. Carbon is the element with atomic number 6. It is located on the Periodic Table in the second period midway between the active metal lithium and the active nonmetal fluorine. Two of its six electrons are in the K shell, and are tightly bound to the nucleus. The remaining four L-shell electrons are the valence electrons. In order to attain a stable outer electronic shell, we might think that carbon atoms would either lose four electrons or gain four electrons; but carbon atoms usually do neither. They show a very strong tendency to share electrons and form covalent bonds. The four valence electrons make it possible for a carbon atom to form four covalent bonds. These covalent bonds are directed in space toward the four vertices of a regular tetrahedron if we assume the center of the atom is at the center of the tetrahedron (see Fig. 16-1).

★ The electron configuration of a carbon atom indicates that the valence electrons should be two 2s and two 2p electrons. However, when carbon atoms combine, it is believed that one of the 2s electrons acquires sufficient energy to occupy a 2p orbital. Thus the bonding electrons of a carbon atom are one 2s electron and three 2p electrons. A carbon atom therefore can form four covalent bonds with other carbon atoms or with atoms of other elements, especially the nonmetallic ones. Figure 16-2 represents a methane molecule, CH_4, in which a carbon atom is covalently bonded to four hydrogen atoms. Observe that the hydrogen atoms are symmetrically located as if at the vertices of a regular tetrahedron with the carbon atom at the center. The bond angles are equal, each being 109.5°. Since one of the valence electrons is a 2s electron and the other three are 2p electrons, it might be expected that one of the carbon-hydrogen bonds in methane would be different than the other three. This, however, is found experimentally not to be the case; all the bonds are equivalent. This can be explained by assuming resonance of the bonding carbon electrons between 2s and 2p orbitals, producing four hybrid bonds of equivalent nature.

The property of forming covalent bonds is so strong in carbon atoms that they not only join with other elements, but also link together with other carbon

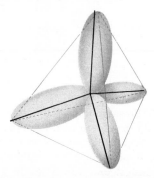

Fig. 16-1. **The four covalent bonds of a carbon atom are directed in space toward the four vertices of a regular tetrahedron if the center of the atom is at the center of the tetrahedron.**

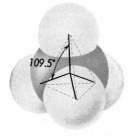

109.5°

Fig. 16-2. **In the methane molecule, CH_4, a carbon atom is covalently and symmetrically bonded to four hydrogen atoms. Similar molecules may be formed by bonding with other elements, such as chlorine and bromine.**

atoms in chains, rings, plates, and even in macromolecules, such as diamond. These varieties of ways in which carbon atoms can be linked account for the fact that there are several times as many carbon compounds as there are noncarbon compounds.

3. The allotropic forms of carbon. It has already been stated that oxygen can absorb energy and form ozone, a very active allotrope of oxygen. Several other elements exist in different allotropic forms, and carbon is such an element. It occurs in two allotropic forms, *diamond*, a beautiful crystalline form, and *graphite*, a grayish-black crystalline form.

When substances which contain combined carbon are heated, they produce black residues which are sometimes called *amorphous carbon* because they seem to have no definite crystalline shape. Examples of amorphous carbon are charcoal, coke, boneblack, and lampblack. X-ray photographs, however, reveal that the various forms of so-called amorphous carbon really consist of extremely tiny graphite crystals. Thus there are only two allotropic forms of carbon.

4. The occurrence of diamonds. At one time many famous diamonds were mined in India. Black diamonds are found in Brazil. Australia, too, produces diamonds, but the most famous mines in the world are located in South Africa. These mines produced the Cullinan diamond which weighed about one and one-third pounds, the largest ever found. A few diamonds are found occasionally in this country, particularly in the states of California, Georgia, and the Carolinas.

Natural diamonds from South Africa occur usually in the shafts of extinct volcanoes, where it is believed they were formed slowly under extreme heat and pressure.

5. The artificial preparation of diamonds. In 1954, scientists at the General Electric Company discovered how to make synthetic diamonds. They started with various carbon-containing compounds and subjected them to a temperature of 5000° F and a pressure of 400 tons per square inch. While small diamonds may be crystallized in a few minutes, larger ones, up to $\frac{1}{16}$ inch in length, require as much as 16 hours. These diamonds pass all the tests used to identify natural diamonds. They have the same structure as shown by X-ray photographs, they have the same hardness, and they burn in oxygen to form carbon dioxide.

6. The properties of diamond. Diamonds as they are mined do not have the shape or luster of cut stones. They must be cut and polished to give them that appearance. Diamond is one of the

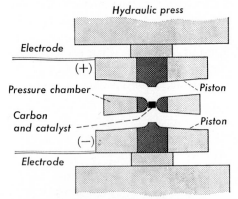

Fig. 16-3. **Pressure and temperature, combined with the action of a catalyst, result in the growth of diamond crystals within minutes. A pellet of pure graphite and a metal catalyst are placed inside a pressure chamber within a hydraulic press. Pistons, pushing into the top and bottom of the chamber, apply a pressure of 1,500,-000 pounds per square inch, while an electric current heats it to 4,400° F.**

hardest materials. It is the densest form of carbon; about 3.5 times as dense as water. This hardness and density can both be explained by its structure. Figure 16-4 shows that carbon atoms in diamond are covalently bonded in a strong, compact fashion, with internuclear distances of 1.54 Å. Note that each carbon atom is tetrahedrally oriented to its four nearest neighbors, giving a structure which is strong in all three dimensions. The rigidity of the structure gives diamond its hardness; the compactness gives it its density. A diamond is a macromolecule, which accounts for its extremely high melting point, above 3500° C. Since all the valence electrons are used in forming covalent bonds, none are free to migrate and diamond is a nonconductor of electricity.

Diamond is insoluble in ordinary reagents. Lavoisier burned a clear diamond in pure oxygen and obtained carbon dioxide as a product. This proved to him that diamond contains carbon. The English chemist Sir Humphry Davy (1778–1829) and other scientists repeated the experiment. They found that the mass of carbon dioxide produced by burning diamond in pure oxygen corresponds to the mass of carbon dioxide that should be produced if diamond were pure carbon.

7. Diamonds have many uses. The great hardness of diamonds makes them useful for several purposes. Circular saws with diamonds as teeth are used for cutting marble. A chip diamond is used by glass cutters. A diamond with a tiny hole drilled through it serves as a die for drawing the fine tungsten filament of electric lamps.

Black diamonds are not suitable for gems but are used for making diamond drills. A steel shoe, set at the end of a

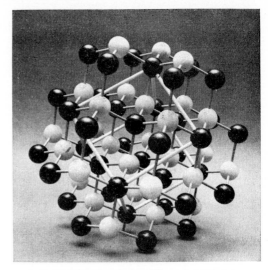

Fig. 16-4. **The crystal structure of diamond.** (Gabrielle)

steel pipe, is studded with black diamonds. As this drill is turned by a machine, it cuts through the hardest rock. Such drills are used in drilling oil wells and in digging tunnels through hard rock.

8. Electric furnaces produce high temperatures. Several types of electric furnaces are in use. One of the simplest forms consists of two carbon rods, which serve as electrodes. The rods are mounted in a block of **refractory material**, that is—a material which has a very *high melting point*. To start the furnace, the rods are brought together momentarily, and then separated slightly. The intense heat produced by the electric current vaporizes some of the carbon, forming carbon vapor. This vapor continues to conduct the electric current as an electric arc, producing a temperature of about 3500° C. Electric furnaces of this type are called **arc-type electric furnaces.** At the high temperature of such a furnace, some endothermic chemical reactions that cannot be brought about in any other way take place readily. Carbon disulfide, CS_2, and

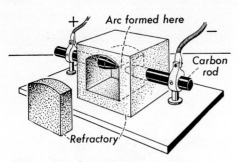

Fig. 16-5. **The electric arc, conducted from one carbon rod to the other by carbon vapor, produces a temperature of about 3500° C in an arc-type electric furnace.**

elementary phosphorus are produced in arc-type electric furnaces.

Another type of electric furnace has a central core of loose pieces of coke which is heated by the resistance it offers to the passage of an electric current. The central core is surrounded by a thick bed of material which prevents the heat from escaping easily. Accumulation of heat within the central mass results finally in a high temperature. Such furnaces are called *resistance furnaces.*

9. Occurrence and preparation of graphite. Natural graphite is a mineral found in several localities. New York and Pennsylvania supply some graphite, but Ceylon, Madagascar, and the Soviet Union are more important sources.

Artificial graphite is made in a resistance furnace by surrounding the central core with anthracite or coke. Iron(III) oxide is used as a catalyst. A temperature of 3000° C converts the anthracite to graphite.

10. The properties of graphite. Graphite is nearly as remarkable for its softness as diamond is for its hardness. It is easily crumbled and has a greasy feel. Graphite crystals are hexagonal in shape, with specific gravity of about 2.25. Although graphite is a nonmetal, it is a fairly good conductor of electricity.

The structure of graphite readily explains these observed properties. Figure 16-7 shows that the carbon atoms in graphite are arranged in layers of thin hexagonal plates. The distance between the centers of adjacent carbon atoms in a layer is 1.42 Å, less than the distance between adjacent carbon atoms in diamond. However, the distance between the centers of atoms in adjacent layers is 3.40 Å. Each carbon atom in a layer is bonded to only three other carbon atoms in that layer. Figure 16-7 shows the bonding within a layer as consisting of single and double covalent bonds between carbon atoms. The actual structure of a layer is a strong resonance hybrid structure produced by the movement of the fourth valence electron of

Fig. 16-6. **The carbon core offers resistance to the passage of an electric current and becomes heated by it. This type of resistance furnace is used for making graphite.**

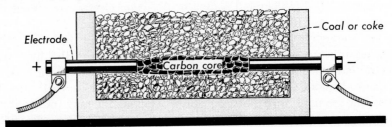

each carbon atom. The layers of carbon atoms are too far apart for the formation of covalent bonds between them. They are held together by weak attractive forces resulting from electronic motion within the layers. Thus each layer in graphite is a strongly-bonded macromolecule, accounting for its extremely high melting point, about 3500° C. The weak attraction between layers accounts for the softness of graphite and its greasy feel as one layer slides over another. On the average the carbon atoms in graphite are farther apart than they are in diamond, and so graphite has a lower specific gravity. The mobile electrons in a carbon atom layer make it an electrical conductor.

Like diamond, graphite does not dissolve in any ordinary reagent. It forms carbon dioxide when burned in oxygen.

11. Uses of graphite. Graphite is a very good lubricant, particularly when mixed with petroleum jelly to form a graphite grease. It may be used for lubricating machine parts that are subjected to temperatures too high for the usual oil lubricants.

Graphite has a very high melting point, about 3500° C. Hence, it is an excellent refractory. Mixed with a binder to hold the particles together, graphite can be made into crucibles which are used for melting steel and other metals. Graphite is also used for making the electrodes of electric furnaces. Powdered graphite is dusted over a wax impression of printer's type to make the surface a conductor of electricity. When immersed in a copper-plating bath, metallic copper is deposited on the graphite and takes the outline of the type. These plates are then nickel or chrome plated to insure longer wear. Books such as this one are printed from such plates, which are called electrotypes.

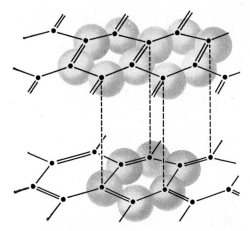

Fig. 16-7. The crystal structure of graphite. Two of the three possible layer resonance structures are shown. The third structure is a mirror image of the lower layer. The layers are held together by weak forces resulting from the movement of electrons within the layers.

Graphite leaves a gray streak or mark when it is drawn across a sheet of paper. In making "lead" pencils, graphite is powdered, mixed with clay, and then formed into sticks. The hardness of a pencil depends upon the relative amount of clay that is used.

Graphite is also used as a moderator in nuclear reactors (see Chapter 39).

12. Destructive distillation. When a complex material, such as wood or bituminous coal, is *heated in a closed retort or oven without access to air or oxygen, it decomposes into simpler substances.* This process is known as *destructive distillation.* Charcoal, coke, and boneblack are prepared by destructive distillation from wood, coal, and bones respectively. Lampblack is produced by burning gas or oil in a limited supply of air.

13. Charcoal. Destructive distillation of wood yields combustible gases, methanol (wood alcohol), acetic acid, and other volatile products. The solid residue is charcoal. Charcoal is prepared commercially by the destructive distillation of wood in iron retorts. The combustible gases given off provide supplementary fuel. The other volatile products are condensed and sold as by-products.

Charcoal is a porous, black, brittle solid that is odorless and tasteless. It is denser than water, but it often adsorbs enough gas to make it float on water. The ability to adsorb a large quantity of gas is the most remarkable physical property of charcoal. One cubic inch of freshly prepared willow charcoal adsorbs about 90 cubic inches of ammonia gas. Because of its ability to adsorb gases, charcoal is a good deodorizer. A layer of wood charcoal is often used between layers of sand and gravel in water purification for this purpose. Charcoal also removes the color from certain liquids. Gas masks for industrial or military use depend upon some form of carbon to adsorb the harmful gases from the air breathed by the wearer.

At ordinary temperatures, charcoal is inactive and insoluble in all ordinary re-

agents. It is a good reducing agent because it unites with oxygen at a high temperature. Charcoal is also a good fuel, but it is more expensive than other common fuels and is not widely used for this purpose.

14. Coke. When bituminous coal is heated in a hard-glass test tube, a flammable gas escapes, and a tarlike liquid condenses on the upper walls of the tube. If the heating is continued until all the volatile matter is driven off, coke is left as a residue.

Commercially, coke is prepared by the destructive distillation of bituminous coal in by-product coke ovens. The volatile products which are given off are separated into *coal gas*, which may be used as a fuel; *ammonia*, which is used in making fertilizers; and *coal tar*. The coal tar can be separated by distillation into many materials which are used to make drugs, dyes, and explosives. The black pitch that remains after distillation is used to surface roads.

About 50,000,000 tons of coke are produced each year in the United States. Coke is a gray solid that is harder and denser than charcoal. It burns with little

Fig. 16-8. **Charcoal is made by the destructive distillation of wood in large closed retorts. Liquid by-products collect in the storage tank. The combustible gases are used as fuel.**

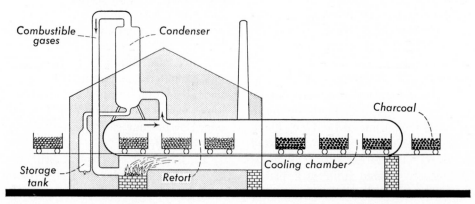

flame, has a high heat content, and is a valuable fuel.

Coke is an excellent reducing agent. It is widely used in the smelting of metals since many of the ores of iron, tin, copper, and zinc are oxides, or are converted into oxides. Millions of tons of coke are used each year to reduce these oxides to metals.

15. Boneblack. Animal charcoal, or *boneblack*, remains as a residue in the retort after the destructive distillation of bones. The by-products of the process include bone oil and pyridine, which are used for denaturing alcohol (making it unfit for human consumption). Boneblack usually contains calcium phosphate, as an impurity, but this can be removed by treating the boneblack with an acid.

Boneblack is used as an adsorbent to decolorize liquids. In sugar refineries, crude sugar solutions are decolorized by passing them through large tanks that are partially filled with boneblack. After passing through several such tanks in succession, the liquid is changed from a brown to a colorless solution. The color is adsorbed by the boneblack.

16. Lampblack. Finely divided particles of carbon, or soot, are set free when kerosene or light oil burns in an insufficient supply of air. The carbon is collected as a velvety black powder, called *lampblack*, on cool surfaces near the flame. Lampblack is used in making printer's ink, shoe polish, India ink, carbon paper, black varnish, and as a black pigment in paints.

17. Carbon black. *Carbon black* is made by burning natural gas in an insufficient supply of air. It is not so greasy or tarlike as lampblack. For many purposes it is more desirable than lampblack and is often substituted for it. Carbon black is especially useful as a

Fig. 16-9. **Coke is produced by the destructive distillation of bituminous coal in by-product coke ovens. Here the red-hot coke is being discharged from an oven into a waiting railroad car.** (American Iron and Steel)

Fig. 16-10. **Sugar solutions are decolorized by filtering through boneblack. The boneblack adsorbs the coloring matter and produces a water-white solution.**

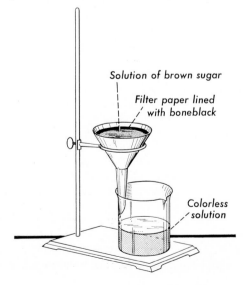

Solution of brown sugar

Filter paper lined with boneblack

Colorless solution

filler in the rubber mix for making auto-mobile tires. It helps to preserve the rubber and makes the tires wear much better.

18. Gas carbon and petroleum coke. Carbon scraped from the walls of the retorts in a coal gas plant is called *gas carbon*. A somewhat similar product, called *petroleum coke*, is scraped off the walls of the retorts in which petroleum has been distilled. Both gas carbon and petroleum coke are pressed into rods which are used as electrodes because they are fairly good conductors of electricity. Gas carbon rods are used for the positive electrodes of dry cells. Petroleum coke electrodes are used in the production of aluminum by electrolysis.

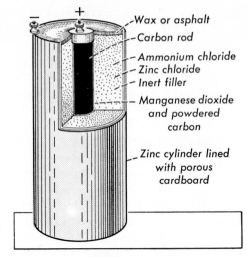

Fig. 16-11. **Sectional view of a dry cell. A carbon rod is used as the positive pole.**

SUMMARY

In the combined form, carbon occurs in all living things. Foods, fuels, paper, and textiles all contain carbon compounds. In addition, thousands of carbon compounds have been made by synthesis. Organic chemistry is the study of carbon compounds.

A carbon atom, with four valence electrons, forms covalent bonds with other elements, or with other carbon atoms. Carbon atoms may link together in chains, rings, plates, and in macromolecules like diamond. This accounts for the tremendous number of carbon compounds.

Uncombined or free carbon occurs in the allotropic forms known as graphite and diamond. Amorphous carbon includes charcoal, coke, bone-black, and lampblack. Amorphous carbon appears to have no definite shape but is really made up of microscopic crystals of graphite.

Diamond is one of the hardest substances known. Clear diamonds are used as gems, while specimens of dark color are used for diamond drills and saws. Graphite is a crumbly solid that is a conductor of electricity. It is used as a lubricant, in paints, as electrodes, and for making "lead" pencils.

In the arc-type electric furnace, carbon disulfide and elementary phosphorus are produced; the resistance-type is used for making graphite.

Charcoal is made by the destructive distillation of wood. Coke is a product of the destructive distillation of bituminous coal. Boneblack is obtained by the destructive distillation of bones.

At ordinary temperatures, all forms of carbon are inactive, but at higher temperatures they unite with oxygen to form carbon dioxide.

Carbon is a good adsorbent; thus it is suitable for use as a deodorizer, a decolorizer, and for use in gas masks. Because it is insoluble in ordinary reagents, it is useful in pigments, in paints and lacquers, and in printer's ink.

TEST YOURSELF ON THESE TERMS

allotropic forms	coke	lampblack
arc-type furnace	destructive distillation	organic chemistry
boneblack	diamond	petroleum coke
carbon black	gas carbon	refractory
charcoal	graphite	resistance furnace

QUESTIONS

Group A

1. Why does the study of carbon compounds constitute a separate branch of chemistry?
2. How can you show that sugar contains the element carbon?
3. What property of carbon atoms makes possible the large number of carbon compounds?
4. Why is amorphous carbon no longer classified as a third allotropic form of carbon?
5. Why are diamonds so useful for industrial purposes?
6. (*a*) What are the two types of electric furnaces? (*b*) How is the heat produced from the electricity in each furnace?
7. Give several reasons why graphite is suitable as a lubricant.
8. Why is the name "lead" pencil misleading? Suggest a better name.
9. (*a*) What is destructive distillation? (*b*) Is it really destructive? Explain.
10. Why is boneblack a relatively impure form of carbon?
11. Distinguish between lampblack and carbon black.
12. What use is made of petroleum coke?

Group B

13. Why does carbon form no ionic compounds?
14. How are artificial diamonds produced?
15. When coke is used as a reducing agent, what is oxidized?
16. Why is charcoal a good adsorbent?
17. What is the orientation in space of the valence bonds of a carbon atom?
18. What proof is there that a diamond is pure carbon?
19. How do printers make the "plates" from which books, such as this one, are printed?
20. Why will a form of carbon such as charcoal or coke remain after the destructive distillation of wood or bituminous coal?
21. Why is the specific gravity of graphite less than that of diamond?
22. Why is it so difficult to remove stains made by printer's ink?
23. Diamond is very hard and a nonconductor of electricity. Graphite is soft and is a conductor of electricity. Explain these properties in terms of the structure of diamond and graphite.
24. Powdered charcoal, copper(II) oxide, and manganese dioxide are all black substances. How could you identify each?

SOME THINGS FOR YOU TO DO

1. Examine a fine diamond with a magnifying glass. Note the shape of the different faces on the cut stone.
2. Hold a lump of natural graphite in the fingers and note the slippery feeling of the graphite. Rub it on a piece of paper and note the streak it leaves.
3. In a hood, add a drop of liquid bromine to an empty bottle, stopper it, and allow the bottle to fill with bromine vapor. CAUTION: *Bromine burns the flesh badly. Do not get any on your skin.* Now add a teaspoon of charcoal granules. What happens to the bromine vapor?
4. Prepare some carbon from sugar by the dehydrating action of concentrated sulfuric acid. Fill a tall beaker about one-third full of sugar. Add enough concentrated sulfuric acid to saturate the sugar. The action starts within a few minutes. Dispose of the residue as directed by your instructor since it will contain excess concentrated sulfuric acid.
5. Prepare a report on the production of synthetic diamonds.

Chapter 17 · THE OXIDES OF CARBON

1. CARBON DIOXIDE

1. Carbon dioxide is a common, widely distributed gas. Carbon dioxide comprises only about 0.04% of the atmosphere by volume, yet it is a very important component of air. The water of rivers, lakes, and oceans contains between twenty and thirty times as much dissolved carbon dioxide as is found in the atmosphere. The decay of organic matter on and below the surface of the ground produces carbon dioxide. Sometimes it accumulates in considerable amounts in low-lying areas such as bogs, swamps, and marshes; and in mines, caves, and caverns.

2. The discovery of carbon dioxide. Jan Baptista van Helmont (1577–1644),

a Belgian physician, is usually given credit for the discovery of carbon dioxide. About 1630 he recognized that a gas that would not support combustion was produced when wood burned. He also discovered that this same gas was produced when acids act on limestone and when fermentation takes place.

3. Preparation of carbon dioxide. *1. By burning carbonaceous material.* Carbon dioxide is one of the products of the complete combustion of any material which contains carbon. Carbon dioxide prepared in this way is mixed with other gases from the air. If these gases do not interfere with the uses for which the carbon dioxide has been prepared, this method is the cheapest and easiest of them all.

VOCABULARY

Enzyme. A catalyst produced by living cells.

Fermentation. A chemical change produced by the action of an enzyme.

Leavening agent. A substance which releases carbon dioxide in a dough or batter.

Sublime. To pass from the solid to the gaseous state without liquefying.

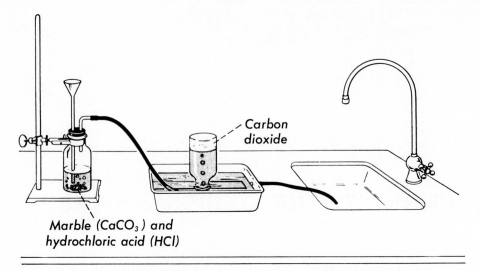

Fig. 17-1. **The laboratory preparation of carbon dioxide.**

2. *By heating a carbonate.* When calcium carbonate in the form of limestone, marble, or shells is heated strongly, calcium oxide and carbon dioxide are the products.

$$CaCO_3 \xrightarrow{\Delta} CaO + CO_2 \uparrow$$

Calcium oxide, known as *quicklime*, is used in large quantities for making plaster and mortar. The carbon dioxide is a by-product. It is piped from the kiln in which the limestone is heated and compressed into steel cylinders.

3. *By fermentation of molasses.* The enzyme *zymase*, produced by yeast, catalyzes the fermentation of the sugar, $C_6H_{12}O_6$, in molasses to produce ethanol (ethyl alcohol), C_2H_5OH, and carbon dioxide. While the process is complex, the over-all reaction is:

$$C_6H_{12}O_6 \rightarrow 2\ C_2H_5OH + 2\ CO_2 \uparrow$$

This is a method by which industrial alcohol is produced, and is an important source of carbon dioxide.

4. *By the action of an acid on a carbonate.* This is the usual laboratory method for preparing carbon dioxide. The gas-generating bottle in Fig. 17-1 contains a few pieces of marble, $CaCO_3$. If dilute hydrochloric acid is poured through the funnel tube, carbon dioxide is evolved rapidly. Calcium chloride, which remains in solution in the bottle, is also formed.

This reaction proceeds in two stages. *First,* the marble and hydrochloric acid undergo an exchange reaction, forming calcium chloride and carbonic acid:

$$CaCO_3 + 2\ HCl \rightarrow CaCl_2 + H_2CO_3$$

Second, carbonic acid is unstable and decomposes into carbon dioxide and water:

$$H_2CO_3 \rightarrow H_2O + CO_2 \uparrow$$

The equation which summarizes these two reactions is:

$$CaCO_3 + 2\ HCl \rightarrow CaCl_2 + H_2O + CO_2 \uparrow$$

Carbon dioxide may be collected by water displacement if it is generated rapidly. It may also be collected by displacement of air. In this case, the receiver must be kept *mouth upward* because the gas is more dense than air.

This is a general type reaction for an acid and carbonate. Almost any acid may be used instead of hydrochloric acid, even a weak one such as the acetic acid in vinegar. Almost any carbonate, too, may be used. The equation for the reaction between sodium carbonate and sulfuric acid is:

$$Na_2CO_3 + H_2SO_4 \rightarrow$$
$$Na_2SO_4 + H_2O + CO_2 \uparrow$$

5. By respiration and decay. This is a natural method of preparation of carbon dioxide. The foods we eat contain compounds of carbon. The oxygen we inhale in air is used in oxidizing our food, thus supplying us with heat and muscular energy. Carbon dioxide is one of the products of this oxidation which we exhale into the air. Both animals and plants give off carbon dioxide during respiration.

When plants and animals die, decay begins. Carbon dioxide is one of the products of complete decay of all vegetable and animal matter. This gas eventually finds its way into the surrounding air, or becomes dissolved in surface or underground streams.

4. The structure of the carbon dioxide molecule. Carbon dioxide molecules are linear with the two oxygen atoms symmetrically bonded to the carbon atom on opposite sides. See Fig. 17-2. Even though the carbon-oxygen bonds in the molecule are somewhat polar due to the small electronegativity difference between carbon and oxygen, the symmetry of the molecule causes it as a whole to be nonpolar.

From a consideration of the electron dot symbols for carbon and oxygen, we might assign the carbon dioxide molecule the electron dot formula

$$:\!\ddot{O}\!::\!C\!::\!\ddot{O}\!:$$

The carbon-oxygen bond distance predicted by this structure, however, is larger than that actually found in the carbon dioxide molecule, so that this structure is not an accurate representation. Carbon dioxide molecules are believed to be resonance hybrids of four electronic structures, each of which contributes about equally to the actual structure.

$$\left\{ \begin{array}{ll} :\!O\!::\!C\!::\!\ddot{O}\!:, & {}^-\!:\!\ddot{O}\!:\!C\!:::\!O\!:^+ \\ :\!\ddot{O}\!::\!C\!::\!O\!:, & {}^+\!:\!O\!:::\!C\!:\!\ddot{O}\!:^- \end{array} \right\}$$

Such a resonance hybrid does have the carbon-oxygen bond distance and energy actually observed for the carbon dioxide molecule.

5. The physical properties of carbon dioxide. Because of its simple nonpolar molecular structure, carbon dioxide is a gas at room temperature. It is colorless with a very faint pungent odor and a slightly pungent taste. The molecular weight of carbon dioxide is 44. Thus carbon dioxide has a density about 1.5 times that of air. The large, heavy molecules of carbon dioxide move more

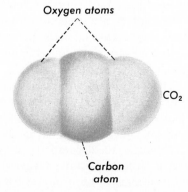

Fig. 17-2. **The carbon dioxide molecule is linear and consists of one carbon atom and two oxygen atoms.**

slowly than the smaller, lighter molecules of oxygen or hydrogen. Because of its higher density and slower rate of diffusion, carbon dioxide can be poured from one vessel to another. Figure 17-3 shows how pouring carbon dioxide down an incline extinguishes successive candles. Because of its high density and slow rate of diffusion, carbon dioxide sometimes collects at the bottom of caves, mines, or dry wells.

At room temperature, under a pressure of about 70 atmospheres, carbon dioxide molecules are pushed close enough together to attract each other and condense to a liquid. If this liquid is permitted to evaporate rapidly under atmospheric pressure, part of it changes into a gas, absorbing heat from the remainder, which is thus cooled until it solidifies in the form called *Dry Ice.*

Solid carbon dioxide has a high vapor pressure. This means that many molecules of carbon dioxide, even in the solid state, possess sufficient energy to escape from the surface of the solid into the air. The vapor pressure of solid carbon dioxide equals atmospheric pressure at −78.5° C. As a result, solid carbon dioxide under atmospheric pressure sublimes (changes directly into a gas) at this temperature. Liquid carbon dioxide does not exist at atmospheric pressure. At low temperatures, with pressures higher than 5 atmospheres, carbon dioxide may be liquefied.

6. **The chemical properties of carbon dioxide.** Carbon dioxide is a stable gas which neither burns nor supports combustion. Since burning magnesium is hot enough to decompose carbon dioxide, a piece of burning magnesium ribbon continues to burn in a bottle of the gas. The magnesium unites vigorously with the oxygen set free by the decomposition of the carbon dioxide.

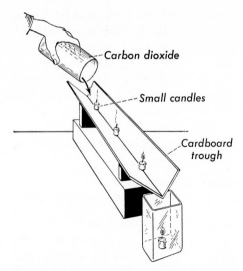

Fig. 17-3. **As the dense carbon dioxide flows down the inclined trough, the candles are extinguished, one after another.**

Carbon is produced, as shown by a coating of soot on the inside of the bottle.

$$2\ Mg + CO_2 \rightarrow 2\ MgO + C$$

Carbon dioxide dissolves readily in *cold water.* Some of the dissolved molecules also unite with the water forming carbonic acid, since carbon dioxide is the anhydride of carbonic acid. This weak acid exists only in water solution. It is easily decomposed by heat as represented by the following reversible equation:

$$H_2O + CO_2 \rightleftarrows H_2CO_3$$

When carbon dioxide is passed into a water solution of a hydroxide, it reacts with it to form a carbonate.

$$2\ NaOH + CO_2 \rightarrow Na_2CO_3 + H_2O$$

If the positive ion of the hydroxide forms an insoluble carbonate, this carbonate will be precipitated when carbon dioxide is bubbled through the hydroxide solution. Such a reaction, using limewater, a saturated solution of $Ca(OH)_2$, and precipitating white calcium carbonate, serves as a *test for carbon dioxide.*

$$Ca(OH)_2 + CO_2 \rightarrow CaCO_3 \downarrow + H_2O$$

Carbon dioxide is not considered to be poisonous, but a person will die in an atmosphere of carbon dioxide because of suffocation due to lack of oxygen.

7. **Carbon dioxide has many uses.** 1. *It is necessary for photosynthesis.* *Photosynthesis means "putting together by means of light."* It is the process by which green plants manufacture carbohydrate foods with the aid of sunlight. *Chlorophyll,* the green coloring matter in the leaves, acts as a catalyst. Carbon dioxide from the air and water from the soil are the raw materials. Glucose, a simple sugar, $C_6H_{12}O_6$, is one of the products formed. The following equation gives only the reactants and the final products of this synthesis.

$$6\ CO_2 + 6\ H_2O \rightarrow C_6H_{12}O_6 + 6\ O_2 \uparrow$$

The sugar may then be converted into starch and stored in various parts of the plant.

2. *Carbon dioxide is used in most fire extinguishers.* In the soda-acid type of fire extinguisher shown in Fig. 17-4, about 1.5 lb of sodium hydrogen carbonate (baking soda) is dissolved in water. The small, loosely-stoppered bottle contains sulfuric acid. When such an extinguisher is inverted, the acid spills and reacts with the sodium hydrogen carbonate solution.

$$2\ NaHCO_3 + H_2SO_4 \rightarrow$$
$$Na_2SO_4 + 2\ H_2O + 2\ CO_2 \uparrow$$

The pressure of the gas forces a stream of liquid a considerable distance. The carbon dioxide dissolved in the liquid is of some benefit in putting out the fire. However, water is the principal extinguishing agent.

The foam type of fire extinguisher is similar in construction to the soda-acid type. Sodium hydrogen carbonate is used to supply the carbon dioxide. A solution of aluminum sulfate, $Al_2(SO_4)_3$, which acts as an acid, is used to react with the sodium hydrogen carbonate and liberate the carbon dioxide. An extract of licorice, or some other sticky substance dissolved in the sodium hydrogen carbonate solution is used to prevent the escape of the gas by stabilizing the foam. The foam forms a blanket over the fire, shutting off the oxygen. Foam fire extinguishers are particularly effective for putting out oil and gasoline fires.

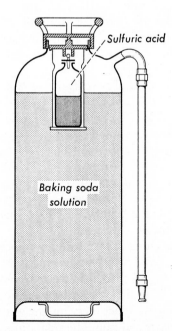

Fig. 17-4. **When a soda-acid fire extinguisher is inverted, the acid spills and reacts with the sodium hydrogen carbonate to liberate carbon dioxide.**

Fig. 17-5. **A liquid carbon dioxide fire extinguisher is effective in putting out oil fires.** (Walter Kidde)

Liquid carbon dioxide fire extinguishers are widely used and quite efficient. When the valve is opened, the flaring nozzle directs a stream of carbon dioxide "snow" against the flame. Such an extinguisher is effective against oil fires and may be used around electric switchboards.

3. Carbonated beverages contain carbon dioxide in solution. Soft drinks are charged by forcing carbon dioxide into the beverages under increased pressure. When the bottles are opened, the excess pressure is released and bubbles of carbon dioxide rapidly escape from the liquid. The carbonated beverage industry is the largest user of gaseous carbon dioxide.

4. Leavening agents produce carbon dioxide. Yeast is mixed with the flour and other ingredients in making dough for bread. The living yeast plants produce an enzyme which acts on the starches and sugars and causes fermentation. The equation for the fermentation of glucose is:

$$C_6H_{12}O_6 \rightarrow 2\ C_2H_5OH + 2\ CO_2 \uparrow$$

The bubbles of carbon dioxide which are formed become entangled in the plastic dough. They cause the dough to rise while they are being liberated. The alcohol, C_2H_5OH, produced by the fermentation, is vaporized and driven off during the baking process.

Baking powder differs from baking soda, sodium hydrogen carbonate, because it is always a dry mixture, not just one compound. It contains baking soda which supplies the carbon dioxide and some powder that forms an acid when water is added. The acid compound varies with the kind of baking powder used. Cornstarch is used in all baking powders to keep them dry until they are used.

5. Carbon dioxide is used as a refrigerant. Most of the carbon dioxide produced in the United States is in the form of solid carbon dioxide, Dry Ice. While Dry Ice costs more than ice for refrigeration, it is superior to ice in two respects: it leaves no liquid, but changes directly from a solid to a gas; also, because of its low temperature, one pound of Dry Ice produces a greater cooling effect than an equal weight of ice. It is useful for packing and shipping perishable fruits and vegetables, and ice cream. The temperature of Dry Ice is so low that is must never be handled with bare hands because serious frostbite may result.

8. Carbon dioxide in the air. Air usually contains between 0.03% and 0.04% carbon dioxide. However, the air in a crowded, poorly ventilated room will have more of this gas. Similarly, the air above tall chimneys in factory areas, where much fuel is consumed, will show a greater percentage of the gas.

All plants, animals, and man release carbon dioxide which is produced as a result of the oxidation of food. While the air inhaled by animals and man contains only traces, exhaled air may contain as much as 5% carbon dioxide. When we consider all the factors that add carbon dioxide to the air, it is remarkable that the atmosphere does not show wider variations in composition.

However, green plants remove carbon dioxide from the air and use it in the photosynthesis process. They return oxygen to the air as a by-product of this process. Thus green plants tend to maintain a balance and keep the percentage of atmospheric carbon dioxide nearly constant.

2. CARBON MONOXIDE

9. Carbon monoxide may contaminate the air we breathe. Air does not commonly contain carbon monoxide. But there are several ways by which this poisonous gas may get into the air which we breathe. If a coal fire is not properly banked and the furnace door is left open, carbon monoxide may escape. It then mixes with the air in living or sleeping rooms. An unvented gas space heater is also a potential source of

carbon monoxide in a home. Carbon monoxide is one of the components of some fuel gases. Leaking gas lines are dangerous because of the fire hazard as well as the poisonous nature of the gas. Carbon monoxide is present in the exhaust of internal combustion engines. Therefore, you should never leave the engine of an automobile running in a closed garage. Likewise, an automobile engine should not be kept running to provide heat to a car parked in cool weather with the windows closed. Because carbon monoxide has no odor and induces drowsiness before actual asphyxiation, it is very hazardous. The air in cities where automobile traffic is heavy may contain considerable amounts of this gas. The breathing of air containing as little as one part of carbon monoxide per thousand parts of air will produce nausea and headache in less than an hour. One part of carbon monoxide in one hundred parts of air may produce fatal results in ten minutes.

10. Preparation of carbon monoxide. *1. By reducing carbon dioxide.* When carbon burns completely, carbon dioxide is formed. If this gas comes into contact with white-hot carbon or coke, it is

Fig. 17-6. **Liquid carbon dioxide solidifies when allowed to expand suddenly inside this automatic press. The solid carbon dioxide is then compressed into 100-kg cakes and transferred to the conveyor line for sawing into conveniently sized pieces.** (Chemetron)

reduced to carbon monoxide. The equations are:

$$C + O_2 \rightarrow CO_2 \uparrow$$
$$CO_2 + C \rightarrow 2\ CO \uparrow$$

2. *By action of steam on hot coke.* It was noted in Chapter 8 that passing steam over red-hot coke produces a mixture of carbon monoxide and hydrogen called *water gas.* This is an industrial method of producing carbon monoxide for use as a fuel gas.

$$C + H_2O \rightarrow CO \uparrow + H_2 \uparrow$$

3. *By decomposing formic acid.* This is the usual laboratory method for preparing carbon monoxide. Formic acid has the formula, HCOOH. If it is allowed to trickle, a drop at a time, into hot, concentrated sulfuric acid, carbon monoxide is produced as each drop strikes the hot acid (see Fig. 17-7). Concentrated sulfuric acid is an excellent dehydrating agent. It removes a molecule of water from each molecule of the formic acid, leaving only carbon monoxide, CO.

$$HCOOH \rightarrow H_2O + CO \uparrow$$

CAUTION: When using this method, always be sure the connections are tight so that the carbon monoxide does not escape into the room.

11. Structure of the carbon monoxide molecule. Carbon monoxide molecules consist of one carbon atom and one oxygen atom covalently bonded. See Fig. 17-8. The distance between the nuclei is 1.13 A. The molecule is slightly polar, with *the carbon atom somewhat negative.* In order to account for these observed properties, the carbon monoxide molecule is believed, like carbon dioxide, to be a resonance hybrid of four structures:

$$\left\{ \begin{array}{ll} +:C:\ddot{O}:^-, & :C::\ddot{O}: \\ :C::O:, & -:C:::O:^+ \end{array} \right\}$$

Unlike carbon dioxide, however, these four structures do not contribute equally. The hybrid is estimated to be 10 percent $+:C:\ddot{O}:^-$, 20 percent each $:C::\ddot{O}:$ and $:C::O:$, and 50 percent $-:C:::O:^+$. Remember that while the electronegativity difference discussed in Chapter 6 would indicate that the oxygen in carbon monoxide would be negative, those data apply only to *single* bonds between elements. The structure of carbon monoxide is more complicated. The high proportional effect of the triple bonded structure, $-:C:::O:^+$, makes carbon monoxide molecules quite stable at ordinary temperatures, and gives the car-

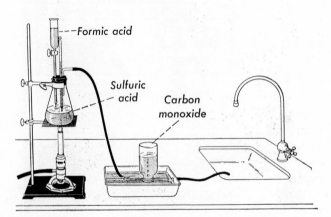

Fig. 17-7. **Carbon monoxide can be prepared in the laboratory by dehydrating formic acid with hot, concentrated sulfuric acid.**

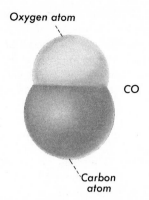

Oxygen atom

CO

Carbon atom

Fig. 17-8. The carbon monoxide molecule is a slightly polar molecule consisting of one carbon atom and one oxygen atom.

bon atom the slight negative charge in the polar molecule.

12. The physical properties of carbon monoxide. Carbon monoxide is a colorless, odorless, tasteless gas. It is very slightly less dense than air, is only slightly soluble in water, and is a rather difficult gas to liquefy. Carbon monoxide is not readily adsorbed by charcoal. Hence, an ordinary gas mask affords little protection against the gas. However, charcoal can be treated with certain oxides that oxidize carbon monoxide to carbon dioxide. Gas masks containing this treated charcoal will protect wearers against carbon monoxide.

13. The chemical properties of carbon monoxide. Carbon monoxide burns with a blue flame. You may have seen this blue flame above a coal fire just after a fresh supply of coal was added. Carbon monoxide is a very good reducing agent. It unites with oxygen so readily at high temperatures that it can take oxygen from most oxide ores.

14. The physiological action of carbon monoxide. This gas is poisonous because it unites very readily with *hemoglobin* (hee-moh-*gloh*-bin), the red sub-

stance in blood that serves as an oxygen carrier. If hemoglobin unites with carbon monoxide, it is not available for carrying oxygen. When sufficient carbon monoxide has been breathed, the person collapses because of oxygen starvation. The compound formed by carbon monoxide and hemoglobin is so stable that artificial respiration is not usually successful. Blood transfusions, which supply fresh hemoglobin, may help to revive victims of carbon monoxide poisoning. Autopsies performed on the bodies of those who have been killed by carbon monoxide reveal a peculiar red color in the blood of the victims. By this color, physicians can recognize the cause of death.

15. The uses of carbon monoxide. *1. As a reducing agent.* In the extraction of iron, copper, and some other metals from their oxides, carbon monoxide acts as a reducing agent.

$$Fe_2O_3 + 3\ CO \rightarrow 2\ Fe + 3\ CO_2 \uparrow$$

Our most useful heavy metals are obtained by such reactions.

2. As a fuel. Many fuel gases contain carbon monoxide mixed with other combustible gases. Manufactured gas, either coal gas or water gas, always contains carbon monoxide.

3. For synthesizing organic compounds. Methanol, CH_3OH, is made by synthesis from carbon monoxide and hydrogen. Under pressure, the two gases unite when a mixture of zinc oxide and copper is used as a catalyst.

$$CO + 2\ H_2 \rightarrow CH_3OH$$

Methanol is used in antifreeze for automobiles, and in the manufacture of formaldehyde. Carbon monoxide is also used in the synthesis of many other organic compounds.

SUMMARY

Carbon dioxide is present in the air, although only in small amounts, because it is a product of decay, of combustion, and of the respiration of living things. Carbon dioxide can be prepared by burning carbon or carbon compounds, by heating a carbonate, by fermentation of molasses, or by the action of an acid on a carbonate.

Carbon dioxide is a dense, colorless gas which is moderately soluble in water. Its water solution is carbonic acid. It is a stable gas that does not burn.

Carbon dioxide is used by plants during photosynthesis, in fire extinguishers, in carbonated beverages, as a leavening agent, and as Dry Ice in refrigeration.

Carbon monoxide can be prepared by the reduction of carbon dioxide, by the action of steam on hot coke, and by heating formic acid with concentrated sulfuric acid, which acts as a dehydrating agent. Carbon monoxide is a colorless, odorless, tasteless gas which is exceedingly poisonous. It burns with a blue flame.

The exhaust gases from internal combustion engines always contain some carbon monoxide. For this reason an automobile engine should never be left running in a closed garage. Carbon monoxide unites with the hemoglobin of the blood, causing death by oxygen starvation.

Carbon monoxide is used as a fuel, since it is one of the components of coal gas and water gas. It is used as a reducing agent in the extraction of iron, copper, and other metals from their ores. Large quantities of carbon monoxide are used for synthesizing organic compounds.

TEST YOURSELF ON THESE TERMS

decay	fermentation	resonance hybrid
Dry Ice	leavening agent	respiration
enzyme	photosynthesis	sublime

QUESTIONS

Group A

1. Why is carbon dioxide one of the important gases in the atmosphere when it occurs to only 0.04% by volume?
2. (*a*) What are the three commercial methods for preparing carbon dioxide? (*b*) What is the usual laboratory method? (*c*) Write balanced chemical equations for these methods of preparation.
3. What difficulties are experienced when collecting carbon dioxide: (*a*) by water displacement; (*b*) by air displacement?
4. How does a liquid carbon dioxide fire extinguisher put out fires?
5. What advantages does Dry Ice have over ice from water as a refrigerant?
6. What are the chemical properties of carbon dioxide?
7. What is the test for carbon dioxide?

8. (*a*) How is carbonic acid made? (*b*) Is it a strong acid?
9. Write a balanced equation for the reaction which occurs when a soda-acid fire extinguisher is discharged.
10. (*a*) What is the source of carbon dioxide in most leavening agents? (*b*) How is it released?
11. What are the sources of carbon monoxide which contaminate the atmosphere?
12. What is the function of sulfuric acid in the preparation of carbon monoxide from formic acid?
13. Why are both carbon dioxide and carbon monoxide gases at room temperature when water, with a lower molecular weight, is a liquid?
14. What are three uses of carbon monoxide?

Group B

15. Explain the part that the earth's surface waters play in regulating the carbon dioxide content of the atmosphere.
16. Why is carbon dioxide more dense than air?
17. What physical property of a solid determines whether it will sublime or melt when heated?
18. Does magnesium ribbon actually burn in carbon dioxide? Explain.
19. What is the function of an enzyme?
20. Distinguish between baking soda and baking powder.
21. Why does carbon dioxide diffuse more slowly than oxygen or hydrogen?
22. Can carbon monoxide be prepared by direct union of the elements?
23. Both carbon dioxide and carbon monoxide will produce asphyxiation. Do they act on the body in the same manner or differently? Explain.
24. When a bottle of limewater is left unstoppered, a white ring is formed on the inside of the bottle at the surface of the liquid. Explain its cause, and tell how it can be removed.
25. Explain why carbon dioxide molecules are nonpolar, while carbon monoxide molecules are polar.

PROBLEMS

Group A

1. How many grams of iron(III) oxide an be reduced by 50.0 g of carbon monoxide, according to the following equation:

$$Fe_2O_3 + 3\ CO \rightarrow 2\ Fe + 3\ CO_2 \uparrow$$

2. Calculate the number of grams of iron produced in Problem 1.
3. What will be the volume of carbon dioxide at S.T.P. which is liberated in the reaction of Problem 1?
4. How much sulfuric acid is required to react with 1.00 kg of baking soda in a soda-acid fire extinguisher, according to the following equation:

$$2\ NaHCO_3 + H_2SO_4 \rightarrow Na_2SO_4 + 2\ H_2O + 2\ CO_2 \uparrow$$

5. Calculate the volume of carbon dioxide at S.T.P. liberated during the discharge of the fire extinguisher of Problem 4.

Group B

6. How many grams of carbon monoxide can be obtained by the dehydration of 38 g of formic acid by sulfuric acid?

7. How many liters of carbon monoxide will be produced in Problem 6? The temperature is 27° C and the barometer reading is 750. mm.

8. What volume of carbon dioxide will be produced by the combustion of the carbon monoxide of Problem 7 if the product is restored to 27° C and 750. mm pressure?

9. It is desired to prepare 5.00 liters of dry carbon dioxide at 17° C and 740. mm pressure by the reaction between calcium carbonate and hydrochloric acid. How many grams of calcium carbonate will be required?

10. How many grams of HCl will be required for the reaction of Problem 9?

SOME THINGS FOR YOU TO DO

1. Fill a wide-mouth bottle with carbon dioxide and "pour" it over a candle flame. This shows two properties of carbon dioxide.

2. Siphon carbon dioxide gas from a large, elevated jug of the gas into a lower receiver. Use a rubber tube just as if you were siphoning water. When you estimate that the lower jar is full of carbon dioxide, prove it by pouring the gas over a candle flame.

3. Test a collection of minerals to find out which ones are carbonates. Add a drop of concentrated hydrochloric acid to each mineral. The carbonates will give off bubbles of carbon dioxide.

4. Make some baking powder from 5.0 g baking soda, 10.0 g cream of tartar, and 3.0 g cornstarch. Add a pinch of dried egg albumin and mix the powders thoroughly in a mortar. Test it to see if it "works" by adding water to some of the powder in a dry beaker. The egg albumin makes the bubbles more lasting. (For baking purposes, a more accurate mixture of the chemicals is necessary.)

5. Prepare a report on methods used to ventilate long vehicular tunnels such as the Lincoln Tunnel under the Hudson River at New York City.

6. Compare the labels on various brands of baking powder to determine their components. What similarities and what differences do you find?

Chapter 18 · HYDROCARBONS

1. **There are many carbon compounds.** The number of carbon compounds seems to be almost unlimited. More than 700,000 have been listed, and many new ones are being added each year. In this chapter we shall describe only a very few compounds which are basic to an understanding of organic chemistry. In Unit 15, other organic compounds important in everyday life will be discussed.

There are two reasons for the existence of so many carbon compounds.

1. Carbon atoms link together with covalent bonds. In Chapter 16, it was noted that carbon atoms readily form covalent bonds with other carbon atoms. This makes possible the existence of compounds in which as many as 70 carbon atoms are bonded together one after another to form a long chain. Some compounds are basically a long chain of carbon atoms, but have groups of other carbon atoms as side chains attached to the main chain. Other carbon compounds have carbon atoms linked together to form rings. Still others may consist of several such rings joined together. Not only are carbon atoms linked by single covalent bonds, but they are sometimes linked by double or triple covalent bonds.

VOCABULARY

Cracking. A process of breaking down complex organic molecules by the action of heat or a catalyst or both.

Homologous series. A series of similar compounds which conform to a general formula.

Hydrocarbon. A compound consisting of only the elements carbon and hydrogen.

Isomer. One of two or more compounds having the same molecular formula, but different structures.

Structural formula. A formula which indicates kind, number arrangement, and valence bonds of the atoms which compose a molecule.

2. *The same atoms may be arranged in several different ways.* One of the substances present in gasoline is an organic compound called *octane*. Its molecular formula is C_8H_{18}, so a molecule of octane consists of 8 carbon atoms and 18 hydrogen atoms. Using an electron-dot formula, and remembering that the valence of carbon is 4 while that of hydrogen is 1, the straight-chain structure for an octane molecule is written:

$$\begin{array}{c}
\text{H H H H H H H H} \\
\text{H:C:C:C:C:C:C:C:C:H} \\
\text{H H H H H H H H}
\end{array}$$

But there are other ways in which these same atoms can be arranged. For instance, here are three branched-chain formulas:

These are all arrangements of 8 carbon atoms and 18 hydrogen atoms in which each carbon atom shares four electrons and each hydrogen atom shares one electron. In addition to these four structures for octane, there are 14 others, making a total of 18 possible structures for octane. While they each have the same molecular formula, the different ar-

rangements of the atoms in the molecules gives each molecule slightly different properties. Thus each of these molecular arrangements represents a separate chemical compound. *These different compounds, all with the same molecular formula but with different structures, are called isomers.*

2. Structural formulas for organic compounds. The formula H_2SO_4 for sulfuric acid is satisfactory for most purposes in inorganic chemistry. But a molecular formula such as C_8H_{18} is not at all satisfactory in organic chemistry. We have already noted that there are 18 different isomers of this compound. In order to indicate clearly the particular isomer with which the organic chemist is dealing, he uses a **structural formula.** *Such a formula not only indicates what kinds of atoms and how many of each, but also indicates how they are arranged in the molecule.* Electron-dot formulas have been used to illustrate the isomers of octane. However, electron-dot formulas are tedious to draw for routine equation work, so the organic chemist frequently substitutes a dash (—) for the pair of shared electrons forming a covalent bond. Using the dash, he can represent the straight-chain structural formula for octane as:

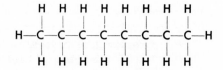

When structural formulas are written, there must be no dangling valence bonds. Each dash must represent an electron pair which forms the covalent bond linking two atoms.

3. Differences between organic and inorganic compounds. The basic laws of chemistry hold true equally for organic

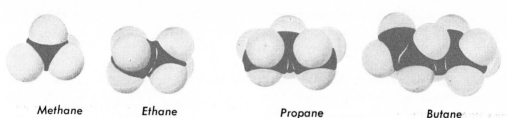

Methane   Ethane   Propane   Butane

Fig. 18-1. **Models of molecules of the first four members of the alkane series of hydrocarbons.**

chemistry as well as inorganic chemistry. The behavior of organic compounds, and the reactions between organic chemicals, however, show some differences from those of the inorganic compounds. Some of the important differences are as follows:

1. *Most organic compounds do not dissolve in water.* The majority of inorganic compounds do dissolve more or less readily in water. Organic compounds generally dissolve in such organic liquids as alcohol, chloroform, ether, carbon disulfide, or carbon tetrachloride.

2. *Organic compounds are decomposed by heat more easily than most inorganic compounds.* The decomposition (charring) of sugar when it is heated moderately is familiar. Such charring on heating is often a test for organic substances. But an inorganic compound, such as common salt (sodium chloride) can be vaporized at a red heat without decomposition.

3. *Organic reactions proceed at much slower rates.* Such reactions often require hours or even days for completion. Most inorganic reactions occur almost as soon as solutions of the reactants are brought together.

4. *Organic compounds exist as molecules consisting of atoms joined by covalent bonds.* Many inorganic compounds have ionic structures.

4. The several series of hydrocarbons. *Hydrocarbons,* as the name suggests, *are compounds composed of only two elements—hydrogen and carbon.* Any study of organic compounds must begin with a study of the hydrocarbons, because they have the basic structures from which other organic compounds are derived. There is a tremendous number of hydrocarbons, but they can be grouped into several different series of compounds based mainly on the bonding between carbon atoms.

1. The *alkanes* (al-*kaynes*), sometimes called the paraffin series, are straight-chain or branched-chain hydrocarbons in which the carbon atoms are connected by only single covalent bonds.

2. The *alkenes* (al-*keens*), sometimes called the olefin series, are straight- or branched-chain hydrocarbons in which two carbon atoms in the molecule are connected by a double covalent bond.

3. The *alkynes* (al-*kynes*), sometimes called the acetylene series, are straight- or branched-chain hydrocarbons in which two carbon atoms in the molecule are connected by a triple covalent bond.

4. The *alkadienes* (al-kah-*dy*-eens) are straight- or branched-chain hydrocarbons which have two double bonds between carbon atoms.

5. The *aromatic hydrocarbons* have resonating alternate single and double
covalent bonds in six-membered carbon rings.

5. The alkane series. This series is
sometimes called the *paraffin series.* The
word "paraffin" means little affinity. The
members of this series show little affinity
to react with other chemicals because
only single covalent bonds are present
in their molecules. Hydrocarbons in
which only single covalent bonds occur
are *saturated hydrocarbons.* Paraffin wax
is a mixture of hydrocarbons of this
series. The following table lists a few of
the members of the alkane series. Notice that the name of each member ends
in –*ane,* the same as the name of the
series, alk*ane.*

The structural formulas for the first
four members of the alkane series are:

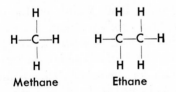

Methane   Ethane

ALKANE SERIES

Name	Formula	State at 20° C
Methane	CH_4	gas
Ethane	C_2H_6	gas
Propane	C_3H_8	gas
Butane	C_4H_{10}	gas
Pentane	C_5H_{12}	liquid
Hexane	C_6H_{14}	liquid
Heptane	C_7H_{16}	liquid
Octane	C_8H_{18}	liquid
Nonane	C_9H_{20}	liquid
Decane	$C_{10}H_{22}$	liquid
* * *		
Eicosane	$C_{20}H_{42}$	solid
* * *		
Hexacontane	$C_{60}H_{122}$	solid

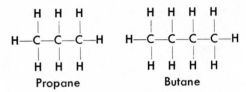

Propane   Butane

An examination of these formulas as
well as those in the table shows that one
member of the series differs from the
preceding one by the group.

These compounds are said to belong to
a *homologous series.* It is not necessary
to remember the formula of each member of a homologous series because a
general formula, such as C_nH_{2n+2} for the
alkanes can be derived. Suppose a member of this series has 30 carbon atoms
in its molecule. The number of hydrogen atoms is found by multiplying 30
by 2, then adding 2. The formula becomes $C_{30}H_{62}$.

**6. Methane is the first member of
the alkane series.** When organic compounds decay under water, methane is
formed. It occurs in coal mines, where
it is known by miners as *firedamp,* and
forms about 90% of natural gas. Methane gas bubbles come to the surface
when the mud at the bottom of stagnant
pools is stirred. Hence, another common
name for methane is *marsh gas.* Methane can be made in the laboratory by
heating soda lime (which contains sodium hydroxide) and sodium acetate.
The equation is:

$$NaC_2H_3O_2 + NaOH \rightarrow CH_4 \uparrow + Na_2CO_3$$

Commercially, methane is obtained from
natural gas.

Methane is a colorless, nearly odorless
gas which burns with a bluish flame. It

is used as a fuel in those places where natural gas is abundant.

$$CH_4 + 2 O_2 \rightarrow CO_2 \uparrow + 2 H_2O \uparrow$$

Methane reacts with such halogens as chlorine or bromine to form *substitution products*. An atom of a halogen is substituted for an atom of hydrogen. For example:

$$\underset{\underset{\displaystyle H}{|}}{\overset{\overset{\displaystyle H}{|}}{H-C-H}} + Br_2 \rightarrow \underset{\underset{\displaystyle H}{|}}{\overset{\overset{\displaystyle H}{|}}{H-C-Br}} + HBr$$

By supplying additional molecules of the halogen, an atom of halogen may be substituted for each of the atoms of hydrogen.

7. Ethane is the second member of the alkane series. Ethane, C_2H_6, occurs in natural gas and is produced in petroleum refining. It is a colorless gas which burns in air to form carbon dioxide and water. It undergoes substitution reactions with the halogens, yielding a variety of products. Ethane has a higher melting point and boiling point than methane, properties which would be expected because of its higher molecular weight.

8. Ethene (ethylene) is the first member of the alkene series. The alkenes are characterized by a double covalent bond between two carbon atoms. Consequently, the simplest alkene must have two carbon atoms. Its structural formula is:

$$\underset{\underset{\displaystyle H}{\diagup}\ \ \underset{\displaystyle H}{\diagdown}}{\overset{\overset{\displaystyle H}{\diagdown}\ \ \overset{\displaystyle H}{\diagup}}{C=C}}$$

and its name is ethene. The names of the alkenes are derived from the names of the alkanes with the same number of carbon atoms by merely substituting the suffix *–ene* for the suffix *–ane*. Since eth*ane* is the alk*ane* with two carbon atoms, the alk*ene* with two carbon atoms will be named *ethene*. However, this substance is also commonly called *ethylene*. The general formula for the alkenes is C_nH_{2n}.

Alkenes are made from petroleum by *cracking*. **Cracking is a process by which complex organic molecules are broken up into simpler molecules by the action of heat and usually a catalyst.** Ethene may be prepared in the laboratory by dehydrating ethyl alcohol. Hot concentrated sulfuric acid is used as the dehydrating agent.

$$C_2H_5OH \rightarrow C_2H_4 \uparrow + H_2O$$

An organic compound which has a double covalent bond between two carbon atoms is said to be *unsaturated*, because it is possible to add directly other atoms chemically to its molecule to form a new compound. For example, two bromine atoms may be added directly to ethene to form 1, 2-dibromoethane.

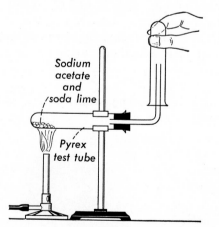

Sodium acetate and soda lime

Pyrex test tube

Fig. 18-2. A small quantity of methane can be prepared in the laboratory by heating a mixture of sodium acetate and soda lime.

$$CH_4 \quad + \quad Br_2 \quad \longrightarrow \quad CH_3Br \quad + \quad HBr$$

Fig. 18-3. Methane and bromine undergo a substitution reaction.

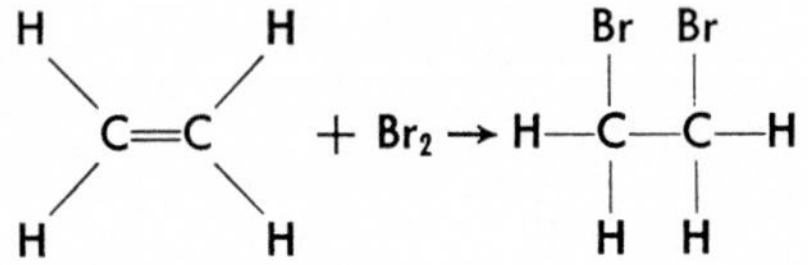

$$\begin{array}{c} H \\ \diagdown \\ \end{array} C = C \begin{array}{c} H \\ \diagup \\ H \end{array} + Br_2 \rightarrow H - \underset{\underset{H}{|}}{\overset{\overset{Br}{|}}{C}} - \underset{\underset{H}{|}}{\overset{\overset{Br}{|}}{C}} - H$$

It is impossible to add a single bromine atom to the ethene molecule, but two of them can be added. It seems obvious that as the double bond between the carbon atoms breaks, there is one valence bond available for each bromine atom.

The name of the product 1,2-dibromoethane is easily derived. The basic part of the name, *ethane*, is that of the alkane with 2 carbon atoms to which this molecule is structurally related. *Dibromo–* means 2 bromine atoms have been substituted for hydrogen atoms in ethane. *1,2–* means that one bromine atom is bonded to the first carbon atom and one bromine atom is bonded to the second carbon atom. An isomer, 1,1-dibromoethane has the structural formula

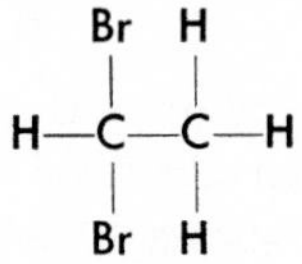

$$H - \underset{\underset{Br}{|}}{\overset{\overset{Br}{|}}{C}} - \underset{\underset{H}{|}}{\overset{\overset{H}{|}}{C}} - H$$

Ethene is a colorless gas that burns with a bright flame. Quantities of ethene are used for making ethyl alcohol. It is also used to make ethylene glycol, $C_2H_4(OH)_2$, a liquid which boils at a rather high temperature. Ethylene glycol is used as an antifreeze in automobile radiators. If present in the air in even minute quantities, ethene destroys chlorophyll. For that reason, it is used in yellowing bananas, oranges, lemons, and other citrus fruits. It is useful, too, for blanching celery. An ethene-oxygen mixture is sometimes used as an anesthetic.

Fig. 18-4. The two-carbon hydrocarbons, illustrating single, double, and triple covalent bonding between carbon atoms.

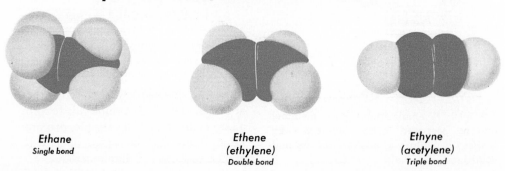

Ethane
Single bond

Ethene
(ethylene)
Double bond

Ethyne
(acetylene)
Triple bond

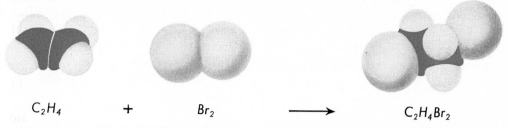

$$C_2H_4 \qquad + \qquad Br_2 \qquad \longrightarrow \qquad C_2H_4Br_2$$

Fig. 18-5. Ethene and bromine undergo an addition reaction.

9. **Ethyne (acetylene) is the first member of the alkyne series.** The alkynes are characterized by a triple covalent bond between two carbon atoms. The simplest alkyne must therefore have two carbon atoms and has the structural formula

$$H—C≡C—H$$

The names of the alk*ynes* are derived from the names of the alk*anes* with the same number of carbon atoms by substituting the suffix *–yne* for *–ane*. Hence the name of the simplest alkyne is *ethyne*, but this compound is more commonly known as *acetylene*. The general formula for the alkynes may be written as C_nH_{2n-2}.

Ethyne, a colorless gas, may be prepared by the action of water on calcium carbide,

$$CaC_2 + 2\ H_2O \rightarrow C_2H_2 \uparrow + Ca(OH)_2$$

or by cracking alkanes by passing them through an electric arc.

$$2\ CH_4 \rightarrow C_2H_2 \uparrow + 3\ H_2 \uparrow$$

Ethyne is more unsaturated than ethene because of the triple bond. It is possible chemically to add to an ethyne molecule two molecules of bromine to form 1,1,2,2,-tetrabromoethane.

$$H—C≡C—H + 2\ Br_2 \rightarrow H—\overset{\displaystyle Br}{\underset{\displaystyle Br}{C}}—\overset{\displaystyle Br}{\underset{\displaystyle Br}{C}}—H$$

Ethyne is extensively used in the synthesis of complex organic compounds in addition to its use in the oxyacetylene torch.

10. **Hydrocarbon bonding.** Hydrocarbon molecules contain carbon-hydrogen bonds and carbon-carbon bonds. Since the electronegativity difference between carbon and hydrogen is slight $(2.5 - 2.1$

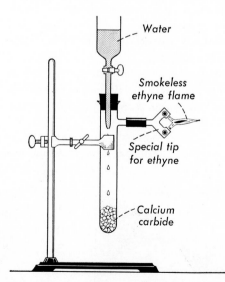

Fig. 18-6. A convenient method of preparing a small quantity of ethyne (acetylene) in the laboratory by the action of water on calcium carbide.

= 0.4) carbon-hydrogen bonds have about 4 percent ionic character and may be considered essentially nonpolar bonds. Carbon-carbon bonds, since they are between like atoms, are of course nonpolar bonds.

In the three two-carbon compounds already described, ethane, ethene, and ethyne, we observe that carbon atoms may be joined by single, double, and triple bonds. In Chapter 16, Section 2 we described the four valence bonds of a carbon atom as being directed in space toward the four vertices of a regular tetrahedron if the carbon kernel is in the center of the tetrahedron.

If two carbon atoms are joined by a single covalent bond, as in ethane, we may picture the two carbon-atom tetrahedra as sharing a common vertex. See Fig. 18-7 (left). It is possible for rotation to occur about this single bond. This rotation is somewhat restricted, however, by the interaction of the groups of carbon-hydrogen bonds at the ends of the molecule. The molecule possesses lowest energy when the carbon-hydrogen bonds at opposite ends of the molecule are staggered.

When two carbon atoms are joined by a double covalent bond, as in ethene, the two carbon-atom tetrahedra may be

assumed to be sharing a common edge. See Fig. 18-7 (center). Rotation about this bond is no longer possible, and the four single bonds which the two carbon atoms can form lie in the same plane. The internuclear distance is, as we would expect, shorter in ethene than in ethane. In ethane it is 1.53 Å, almost the same as that found in diamond, while in ethene, it is 1.33 Å.

In ethyne, the two carbon atoms are joined by a triple covalent bond. This may be pictured as two tetrahedra sharing a face, Fig. 18-7 (right). The two remaining single bonds are directed along the line of centers of the carbon nuclei, so an ethyne molecule will be linear. With triple bonding, the internuclear distance is still less. In ethyne this distance is 1.20 Å.

Because of the nonpolar or essentially nonpolar nature of the bonds in these hydrocarbons, as well as their structural symmetry, molecules of ethane, ethene, and ethyne are nonpolar.

11. Butadiene is an important alkadiene. Alkadienes have two double covalent bonds in each molecule. The *–ene* suffix indicates a double bond. The *–diene* suffix indicates two double bonds. The names of the alkadienes are derived in a manner similar to those of

Fig. 18-7. The tetrahedrally-directed valence bonds of carbon atoms may form single, double, and triple bonds.

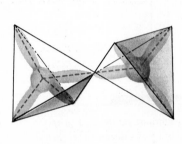 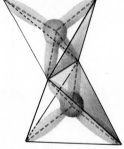 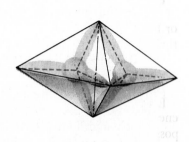

Single bond   *Double bond*   *Triple bond*

the other hydrocarbon series. Butadiene must, therefore, have four carbon atoms and contain two double bonds in its molecule. The structural formula of butadiene is

$$H \quad\quad H \;\; H \quad\quad H$$
$$\underset{H}{\overset{}{\diagdown}}C=C-C=C\underset{}{\overset{}{\diagup}}$$
$$\diagup \quad\quad\quad\quad\quad\quad \diagdown$$
$$H \quad\quad\quad\quad\quad\quad H$$

Actually this is 1,3-butadiene, since the double bonds follow the first and third carbon atoms, but 1,2-butadiene, its isomer, is so uncommon that 1,3-butadiene is commonly called simply butadiene.

Butadiene is prepared by cracking petroleum fractions containing butane. It is used extensively in the manufacture of GR–S rubber, the most common type of synthetic rubber.

12. The aromatic hydrocarbons. Benzene, the best-known aromatic hydrocarbon, has the molecular formula C_6H_6 and is represented by the structural formula

$$H \quad\quad\quad\quad\quad\quad\quad\quad H$$
$$| \quad\quad\quad\quad\quad\quad\quad\quad |$$
$$C \quad\quad\quad\quad\quad\quad\quad\quad C$$

H—C C—H   H—C C—H
H—C C—H ⟷ H—C C—H

$$C \quad\quad\quad\quad\quad\quad\quad\quad C$$
$$| \quad\quad\quad\quad\quad\quad\quad\quad |$$
$$H \quad\quad\quad\quad\quad\quad\quad\quad H$$

This formula shows that the bonds in benzene are not single bonds or double bonds, but each bond is a resonance hybrid bond. All the carbon-carbon bonds in the molecule are equivalent. As a result, benzene and other aromatic hydrocarbons do not show the property of unsaturation to the extent that the alkenes do.

Because of the complexity of writing the single and double bonds when drawing the structural formula of benzene, the benzene ring is usually abbreviated in this manner:

Benzene is prepared commercially by the distillation of coal tar. It is a flammable liquid that is used as a solvent, and as a starting point in the manufacture of other chemicals, principally dyes, drugs and explosives. Benzene has a strong, yet fairly pleasant aromatic odor. It is less dense than water and only very slightly soluble in water. Benzene is poisonous and should be used only where there is adequate ventilation since the vapors are harmful to breathe and are very flammable.

More complex hydrocarbons related to benzene have side chains leading off from the ring, as is the case with toluene. Toluene, or methyl benzene, is obtained from coal tar or petroleum.

The xylenes or dimethylbenzenes, $C_6H_4(CH_3)_2$, are a mixture of three liquid isomers. The xylenes are used as starting materials for the production of certain synthetic fibers and films.

Naphthalene, $C_{10}H_8$, is a coal tar product which crystallizes in white shining scales. It is the largest single constituent of coal tar, sometimes occurring in quantities as high as 6%. The naphthalene molecule has a structure corresponding to two benzene rings joined together as shown at the top of the left column on page 254.

Naphthalene may be used, either as flakes or balls, to kill the larvae of clothes moths that attack woolen garments. If used in sufficient amount in a sealed closet or tightly closed chest, the vapors of naphthalene are quite effective for this purpose. Naphthalene is also used as a raw material for the manufacture of some resins and dyes.

Anthracene, $C_{14}H_{10}$, has a structure like three benzene rings joined together.

Like naphthalene, it forms a whole series of hydrocarbons that differ from the compounds related to benzene in that there is more than one ring. Anthra-

cene, like naphthalene, is obtained commercially from coal tar. It is used in the production of alizarin, a well-known red dye, and other synthetic dyes which have largely replaced naturally-occurring plant dyes.

Turpentine, $C_{10}H_{16}$, is an unsaturated hydrocarbon with a complex ring structure. It is obtained from the resin (a thick gummy sap) of the longleaf pine tree. The resin flows slowly from diagonal gashes cut through the bark into the wood of the tree. Turpentine is distilled from the resin. It is used in large quantities as a thinner for paints and enamels, as well as in the manufacture of certain types of varnishes. It makes paints and varnishes spread more easily and also causes them to penetrate the wood better. In some paints and varnishes, a volatile petroleum product is used instead of turpentine.

Asphalt consists chiefly of a mixture of hydrocarbons of complex structure.

Fig. 18-8. Molecular models of common aromatic hydrocarbons.

Benzene

Naphthalene

Toluene

Anthracene

It was the first organic engineering material to be used by man and has been used as an adhesive and waterproofing material from the beginning of civilization. Large deposits of natural asphalt occur in Texas, Oklahoma, Utah, and California. The world's largest deposits are in western Canada. Natural asphalt is also found on the island of Trinidad, in Venezuela, Iran, and other oil-rich regions. Petroleum pitch is an artificial asphalt which is often substituted for natural asphalt. Asphalt is used for paving streets and in the manufacture of certain types of roofing shingles, flooring materials, adhesive compounds, and rope sizing. Asphalt is important for its waterproofing properties.

SUMMARY

The number of carbon compounds seems to be almost unlimited. The great number of carbon compounds is due: *1.* to the ability of carbon atoms to join other carbon atoms forming chains or rings; and *2.* to the existence of isomers. Isomers have the same molecular formula, but a different arrangement of the atoms in the molecule. Structural formulas indicate what atoms are present and also how they are linked together in the molecule.

Organic compounds are, for the most part, not soluble in water, and many of them are decomposed by heat. Organic compounds exist as molecules consisting of atoms joined by covalent bonds, while many inorganic compounds have ionic structures. Organic reactions proceed at much slower rates than inorganic reactions.

Hydrocarbons are compounds of carbon and hydrogen. Methane is the first in a long series of saturated hydrocarbons known as the alkanes. Methane is obtained from natural gas. The alkanes show little tendency to react with other chemicals. Ethene is the simplest of the alkenes, the hydrocarbons with a double covalent bond between two carbon atoms. Ethene is an unsaturated hydrocarbon which is made from petroleum by cracking. Cracking is a process by which complex organic molecules are broken up into simpler molecules by the action of heat and usually a catalyst. Ethyne is the first member of the alkyne series, the series characterized by a triple covalent bond between two carbon atoms. Butadiene is an important alkadiene used in the manufacture of one type of synthetic rubber. Benzene is a ring compound. It is obtained commercially by distilling coal tar. Naphthalene has a structure corresponding to two benzene rings joined together. It is also a coal tar product, and is used as a moth preventive. Anthracene has a structure like three benzene rings joined together. It is used in the preparation of certain dyestuffs.

TEST YOURSELF ON THESE TERMS

acetylene series	aromatic hydrocarbon	paraffin series
alkadiene	homologous series	saturated
alkane	hydrocarbon	structural formula
alkene	isomer	substitution product
alkyne	olefin series	unsaturated

QUESTIONS

Group A

1. Give two reasons for the existence of so many carbon compounds.
2. What does a dash $(-)$ represent in a structural formula?
3. What information do you obtain from a properly written structural formula?
4. (*a*) How is methane produced in nature? (*b*) In the laboratory?
5. How are alkenes produced from petroleum?
6. What are two uses for ethyne?
7. What do the terms *saturated* and *unsaturated* mean when applied to hydrocarbons?
8. Why must calcuim carbide be sold in air-tight metal cans?
9. How are naphthalene and anthracene related structurally to benzene?
10. Name the five main series of hydrocarbons and describe the bonding in each.

Group B

11. Give four important differences between organic and inorganic compounds.
12. What are the general formulas for: (*a*) the alkane series; (*b*) the alkene series; (*c*) the alkyne series?
13. A hydrocarbon contains 6 carbon atoms. Give its empirical formula if it is: (*a*) an alkane; (*b*) an alkene; (*c*) an alkyne.
14. Draw structural formulas for the three isomers of pentane.
15. Beyond the first four members of the alkane series, how are the hydrocarbons of this series named?
16. Write a balanced formula equation for the complete combustion of: (*a*) methane; (*b*) ethene; (*c*) ethyne; (*d*) butadiene.
17. (*a*) What is resonance? (*b*) Using structural formulas explain the resonance in the benzene molecule. (*c*) Is a double bond in a benzene molecule the same as a double bond in an ethene molecule?
18. Draw a structural formula for 2,2-dichloropropane.
19. Why would you expect organic compounds with their covalent bonds to be less stable to heat than inorganic compounds with ionic bonds?
20. (*a*) Is it geometrically possible for the four hydrogen atoms attached to the end carbon atoms in the 1,3-butadiene molecule to lie in the same plane? (*b*) If carbon-hydrogen bonds on adjacent singly-bonded carbon atoms tend to repel each other, would it be likely that all six hydrogen atoms lie in the same plane? (*c*) If they do, what is their relation to the plane of the carbon atoms?

SOME THINGS FOR YOU TO DO

1. Take six paper clips and link them together, first in a straight chain, and then in a shorter chain with branch side chains. See how many different ways you can link the paper clips together, simulating the linkages of carbon atoms in the five different isomers of hexane.

Do

2. Collect some marsh gas, which is principally methane, from the decaying vegetation along the shore of a pond, stream or lake. Fill a bottle under water, hold it inverted and insert a funnel in the neck of the bottle to direct bubbles of gas up into the water-filled bottle. Use a stick to stir up some dead leaves at the bottom of the pond, and catch the bubbles of gas, as they rise, in the bottle. When you have a bottle full of the gas, test its combustibility with a match. Bring a full bottle of the marsh gas to class and demonstrate its combustibility.

CHECK YOUR PROGRESS IN CHEMISTRY

1. What type of bonding occurs in the oxides of carbon and in the hydrocarbons?
2. What is the significance of a balanced formula equation?
3. Define: (*a*) molecular weight; (*b*) formula weight; (*c*) gram-molecular weight; (*d*) gram-formula weight; (*e*) gram-atomic weight; (*f*) mole.
4. What two scientific laws are sometimes included with Boyle's Law and and Charles' Law as the Gas Laws?
5. How do you identify: (*a*) mass-mass problems; (*b*) mass-volume problems; (*c*) volume-volume problems?
6. (*a*) Why do carbon atoms join together in chains and rings? (*b*) Do any other elements of Group IV of the Periodic Table behave in similar fashion?
7. How does the crystal structure of graphite explain the desirability of this material as a lubricant?
8. What industrial uses are there for diamonds?
9. (*a*) What type of composition reaction is carried out in an electric furnace? (*b*) Name several compounds produced by this type of reaction.
10. (*a*) List the forms of amorphous carbon. (*b*) What is the source of each? (*c*) By what process is each prepared?
11. Why does carbon dioxide sometimes collect in low-lying regions, at the bottom of mine shafts, or in dry wells?
12. A lime kiln produces 5600. kilograms of quicklime, CaO, daily by heating limestone, $CaCO_3$. What volume of carbon dioxide is also produced each day?
13. From the formulas CO_2 and CO, calculate the mass of 1.0 liter of carbon dioxide and carbon monoxide respectively.
14. You are given four wide-mouth bottles each containing a colorless gas. If one bottle contains oxygen, another hydrogen, a third carbon dioxide, and a fourth carbon monoxide, what tests will enable you to distinguish them?
15. Describe the structure of a carbon dioxide molecule.
16. Calculate the molecular weight of propane.
17. What is the mass of 1.0 liter of ethene at S.T.P.?
18. When burned completely, decane, $C_{10}H_{22}$, forms carbon dioxide and water vapor. Write the chemical equation.
19. Draw structural formulas for three isomers of trichloropentane.
20. Give examples of organic and inorganic compounds which illustrate the four main differences between these two types of compounds.

CHALLENGING YOUR KNOWLEDGE

1. A volume of 40.0 ml of dry carbon dioxide is collected over mercury at 20.° C and 740. mm barometric pressure. The mercury level in the eudiometer is 20. mm above that outside. What weight of calcium carbonate was required to generate this gas?

2. The element which appears in the greatest number of compounds is hydrogen. The element forming the second greatest number of compounds is carbon. Why are there more hydrogen compounds than carbon compounds?

3. Why are so many organic compounds insoluble in water but readily soluble in a liquid like benzene?

4. Draw structural formulas for each of the 18 isomers of octane.

5. What will be the mass of 1.0 liter of butane vapor at S.T.P.?

6. How do you account for the fact that the water from certain mineral springs is carbonated in nature?

7. Draw (*a*) the three possible structural formulas for naphthalene; (*b*) the four possible structural formulas for anthracene.

8. For the compound propadiene (*a*) draw the structural formula; (*b*) write the electron-dot formula; (*c*) using tetrahedral carbon atoms, draw the molecule showing the orientation of the valence bonds; (*d*) from your drawing decide whether all the hydrogen atoms lie in the same plane or not.

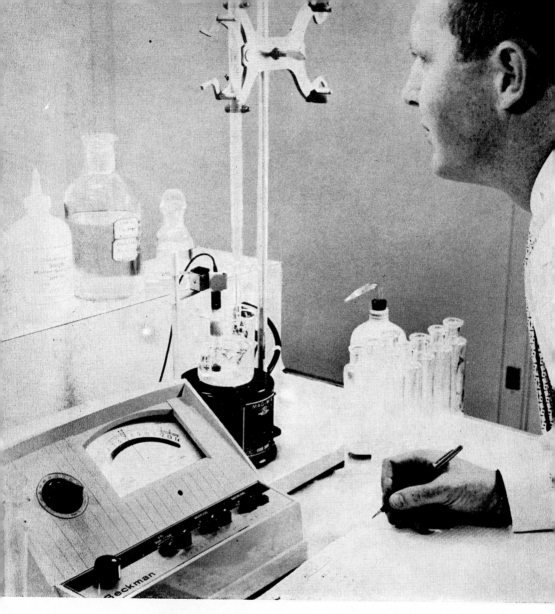

Unit 6 · IONIZATION

259

Chapter 19 · SOLUTION AND CRYSTALLIZATION

1. PROPERTIES OF SOLUTIONS

1. The nature of solutions. If a lump of sugar is dropped into a beaker of water, it disappears gradually. The sugar is said to dissolve in the water. Careful examination of the water with a microscope does not reveal the dissolved sugar. More sugar may be added and it, too, will dissolve. But if this process of adding sugar is continued, ultimately a point is reached where the sugar no longer dissolves.

By tasting the liquid, we can tell that the sugar is present in the water. The molecules of sugar have become mixed with the molecules of water so that the same degree of sweetness is detected in all parts of the water. It is evident that a mixture of molecules of sugar and water known as a *solution* has been prepared.

In general terms, *a solution is a homogeneous mixture of two or more substances, the composition of which may be varied within definite limits. The dissolving medium is called the solvent.*
260

The *substance dissolved* is called the *solute.* The simplest solution consists of molecules of a single solute diffused throughout a single solvent.

Not all substances form true solutions in water. If clay is mixed with water, for example, very little actually dissolves. The particles of clay are huge when compared to molecules, and a turbid, heterogeneous mixture, called a *suspension*, results. Because the components of the mixture have different densities, they readily separate into two distinct phases. It is possible, however, for particles which are very small, but larger than molecules, to be kept permanently suspended by the bombardment of the water molecules. Such mixtures may appear to be homogeneous, but careful examination shows that they are not true solutions. Mixtures of this type are called *colloidal suspensions* and are discussed extensively in Unit 10.

It was stated in Chapter 6, Section 5, that electrovalent solids do not exist as molecules. Each has a crystal lattice composed of ions bound together by electrostatic forces. Such substances, which form water solutions that conduct electricity, are called *electrolytes*. In general, covalent substances form molecular solutions with water which do not conduct electricity. Such substances are called *nonelectrolytes*. Acids are exceptions. When they are undissolved they are molecular, but their solutions conduct electricity. Thus, acids are electrolytes. Solutions of electrolytes have physical properties which are different from solutions of nonelectrolytes. They will be considered in detail in Chapters 20 and 21. The remainder of our present discussion of the properties of solutions will deal with solutions of nonelectrolytes.

2. Types of solutions. Matter may exist in three states: solid, liquid, and gas. Therefore, we may expect to have nine different types of solutions. These are given in the accompanying table.

All mixtures of gases are solutions since they consist of homogeneous mix-

TYPES OF SOLUTIONS

Solute	Solvent	Example
Gas	Gas	Air
Gas	Liquid	Soda water
Gas	Solid	Hydrogen in palladium
Liquid	Gas	Water vapor in air
Liquid	Liquid	Alcohol in water
Liquid	Solid	Mercury in copper
Solid	Gas	Sulfur vapor in air
Solid	Liquid	Sugar in water
Solid	Solid	Copper in nickel

tures of molecules. Solutions of solids in liquids are by far the most common. Since water is a liquid at ordinary temperatures, we may think of water vapor in air as a liquid-in-gas solution. Solutions of gases in solids are rare. The *adsorption* of hydrogen by palladium and platinum approaches the nature of a solution.

In general, substances of similar composition such as silver and gold, or

VOCABULARY

Deliquescence (del-i-*kwes*-ens). The property of certain substances to take up water from the air to form a solution.

Effervescence (ef-er-*ves*-ens). The rapid escape of a gas from a liquid in which it is dissolved.

Efflorescence (ef-lo-*res*-ens). The property of hydrated crystals to lose water of hydration when exposed to the air.

Gram-equivalent weight. The mass of a reactant in grams which contains, replaces, or reacts with (either directly or indirectly) 1 gram-atom of hydrogen.

Hygroscopic (hy-gro-*skop*-ik). Absorbing and retaining moisture from the atmosphere.

Immiscible (i-*mis*-i-b'l). Not capable of being mixed.

Miscible (*mis*-i-b'l). Capable of being mixed.

Solubility. The amount of solute dissolved in a given amount of solvent at equilibrium, under specified conditions.

Solute. The dissolved substance in a solution.

Solution. A homogeneous mixture of two or more substances, the composition of which may be varied within definite limits.

Solvent. The dissolving medium in a solution.

Fig. 19-1. **The photographer uses a variety of carefully prepared solutions in the darkroom.** (Eastman Kodak)

alcohol and water, are apt to form solutions. *When two liquids are mutually soluble in each other, they are said to be* **miscible.** Ethanol and water are miscible in all proportions. Similarly, ether and ethanol are completely miscible. Ether and water, on the other hand, are practically **immiscible.** Chemists frequently dry the inside surface of freshly washed glassware by rinsing first with distilled water, then with ethanol, and finally with ether. The ether has a high vapor pressure and quickly evaporates, leaving a dry glass surface.

3. Solution equilibrium. We may think of the solution process as being *reversible.* Suppose we again consider the lump of sugar dropped into a beaker of water. The sugar molecules which break away from the crystals and enter the water have completely random motions. Some of these molecules which break away may come in contact with the undissolved sugar. Here they are attracted by the sugar molecules in the crystal and become a part of the crystal structure once more. Thus, the solution

process includes both the act of dissolving and the act of crystallizing.

At first, since there are no sugar molecules in solution, the solution process occurs in the direction of dissolving. Molecules leave the crystal structure and diffuse throughout the water. As the **solution concentration** or *number of sugar molecules per unit volume of solution* increases, the reverse process begins. The rate at which the sugar crystals rebuild increases as the concentration of the sugar solution increases. Eventually, if undissolved sugar remains, sugar crystals rebuild as fast as they dissolve. The concentration of the solution reaches the maximum possible under existing conditions and the solution is said to be *saturated.* An *equilibrium* is reached between undissolved sugar and sugar dissolved in water. **Solution equilibrium is the physical state in which the opposing processes of dissolving and**

Fig. 19-2. **Pharmacists are often required to prepare solutions in filling a physician's prescriptions.** (American Cyanamid)

crystallizing of a solute occur at equal rates. A **saturated solution** is one in which the dissolved and undissolved solutes are in equilibrium.

If more water is added to the sugar solution, it is no longer saturated, because the concentration of solute molecules has been decreased. Now more sugar dissolves to restore the same *equilibrium concentration* of solute molecules. Solution equilibrium thus acts to limit the quantity of a solute which can dissolve in a given quantity of solvent. The **solubility** of a solute is defined as the amount of that solute dissolved in a given amount of a certain solvent at equilibrium, under specified conditions.

4. **The influence of pressure on solubility.** Ordinary changes in pressure affect the solubility of solids and liquids so slightly that they may be neglected altogether. Of course, the "solubility" of one gas in another is independent of pressure. All mixtures of gases are homogeneous and obey the Gas Laws in the same manner as individual gases. The solubility of gases in liquids and solids, on the other hand, is appreciably affected by changes in pressure.

Carbonated beverages *fizz* or *effervesce* when poured into an open glass tumbler. At the bottling plant carbon dioxide gas is forced into solution in the flavored water under a pressure of from 5 to 10 atmospheres. While under such pressure the gas-in-liquid solution is sealed in bottles. When the cap is removed, the pressure is reduced to 1 atmosphere and much of the carbon dioxide escapes from solution as gas bubbles. *This rapid evolution of a gas from a liquid in which it is dissolved* is known as *effervescence.*

Solutions of gases in liquids reach equilibrium in about the same way that

Fig. 19-3. **A saturated solution contains the equilibrium concentration of solute, under existing conditions.** (Gabrielle)

solids in liquids do. The attractive forces between gas molecules are negligible on the average and their motions are relatively great. If a gas is in contact with the surface of a liquid, gas molecules may easily enter the liquid surface. As the concentration of dissolved gas molecules increases, some begin to escape from the liquid and re-enter the gaseous phase above the liquid. An equilibrium is eventually reached between the rates at which gas molecules are dissolving and escaping from solution. After an equilibrium is attained between the gas in solution and its atmosphere above the liquid, there is no increase in the concentration of the gaseous solute. Thus the solubility of the gas is limited to its equilibrium concentration in the liquid, under existing conditions.

If the pressure of the gas above the liquid is increased, the equilibrium is disturbed and more gas dissolves. This action, of course, increases the concentration of the dissolved gas. This, in turn, causes gas molecules to escape from the liquid surface at a faster rate. A new equilibrium with a higher concentration of solute is established at the higher pressure. Thus the solubility of the gas in the liquid is increased. *The solubility of gases in liquids is directly proportional to the pressure of the gas above the liquid.* This is **Henry's Law,** proposed by William Henry, an English chemist (1775–1836).

Gases that react chemically with their liquid solvents are generally more soluble than those which do not form compounds with the solvent molecules. Oxygen, hydrogen, and nitrogen are only slightly soluble in water. Ammonia, carbon dioxide, and sulfur dioxide are more soluble, probably due to the formation of unstable compounds with the water solvent. Such gases deviate from Henry's Law.

If different gases are mixed in a confined space, each gas exerts the same pressure it would if it alone occupied the space. The pressure of the mixture is the *total* of the individual, or *partial*, pressures of the gases composing the mixture. This is known as **Dalton's Law of Partial Pressures** and may be stated more formally as follows: *the total pressure exerted by a mixture of gases is equal to the sum of the partial pressures of the various gases comprising the mixture.* The partial pressure of each gas in the mixture is proportional to the number of molecules of that gas, at a definite temperature and for a constant volume.

If a mixture of gases is in contact with a liquid, the solubility of each gas is proportional to its partial pressure. If we may assume that the gases present in the mixture do not react in any way when in solution, each will dissolve to the same extent it would if the other gases were not present.

Air is about 20 percent oxygen and when air is bubbled through water, only about 20 percent as much oxygen dissolves as would dissolve if pure oxygen were used, at the same pressure. Oxygen remains dissolved in the water only because it is in equilibrium with the oxygen in the air above the water. If the oxygen were removed from the atmosphere above the surface of the water, all of the dissolved oxygen would eventually escape from the water. This fact has great significance when we consider the abundance of life that exists in water.

5. The influence of temperature on solubility.
1. Gases in liquids. A glass of water drawn from the hot water tap often appears milky because tiny bubbles of air are suspended throughout the water. Part of the air which was dissolved in the cold water has been driven out of solution as the water was heated.

Raising the temperature of a solution increases the speed of its molecules. Molecules of dissolved gas leave the solvent

Fig. 19-4. **A comparison of the amounts of three common solutes that can be dissolved in 100. g of water at 60.° C.**

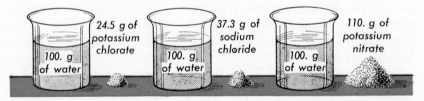

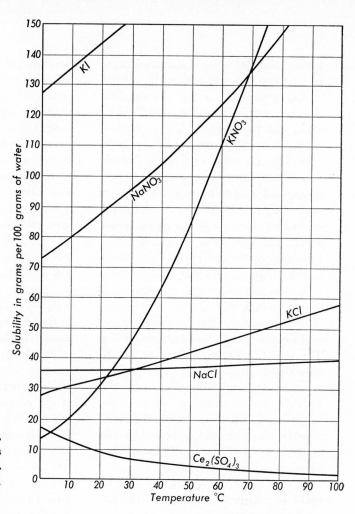

Fig. 19-5. **Solubility curves.** The solubility of a solute is expressed in grams per 100. grams of solvent, at a stated temperature.

at a faster rate than gas molecules enter the solvent. This lowers the equilibrium concentration of the solute. The solubility of a gas decreases as the temperature of the solvent is increased. Table 11 of the Appendix shows that the solubility of gases varies with the kind of gas, and that it decreases as the temperature of the gas is increased.

2. *Solids in liquids.* An excess of sugar added to water results in an equilibrium between the sugar solute and the undissolved crystals characteristic of a saturated solution.

If the solution is warmed, the solid sugar dissolves as the temperature of the solution rises. It is evident that the sol-ubility of the sugar in water has increased with the rise in temperature.

Cooling the solution causes solid sugar to separate, indicating that the solubility diminishes as the temperature falls. No more than the equilibrium concentration of solute may normally remain in solution. Thus with the lowering of the temperature, the equilibrium is shifted and sugar crystals separate from solution faster than solid crystals dissolve.

It is possible, however, to cool a hot saturated solution very carefully so that the excess solute does not separate. Such a solution is said to be *supersaturated*. There is a strong tendency, in a supersaturated solution, to reestablish normal equilibrium. By a slight disturbance, or by seeding the solution with a small crystal, the excess solute will separate and the equilibrium concentration of solute will be established.

Increasing the temperature usually increases the solubility of solids in liquids. Sometimes, however, the reverse effect is observed. A certain rise in temperature may result in a large increase in solubility in one case, a slight increase in another, and a decrease in still another. For example, the solubility of potassium nitrate in 100. g of water changes from 13 g to nearly 140 g with a temperature change from 0.° C to 70.° C. Under similar circumstances the solubility of sodium chloride increases only about 2 g. The solubility of cerium sulfate, on the other hand, decreases nearly 14 g. Typical solubility curves are shown in Fig. 19-5. If the solubility curve for cane sugar in water were included, the graph would have to be extended considerably. At 0.° C, 179 g of sugar dissolves in 100. g of water. This increases to 487 g at 100.° C. The solubility of solids depends upon the nature of the solid, the solvent used, and the temperature.

When a solid dissolves in a liquid we may think of the solid as having changed in physical state to a liquid. In such a change, heat is absorbed. Thus we should expect the temperature of the solution to be lowered as the solid dissolves, and the solubility of the solid to increase as temperature is raised. Deviations from this normal pattern may indicate that some kind of chemical activity occurs between solute and solvent.

Similar reasoning may be applied to solutions of liquids in liquids. As no change in physical state occurs when such solutions are prepared, we might reasonably expect little change in temperature. Where large changes in temperature are observed, as in the case of sulfuric acid in water, some type of chemical activity between solute and solvent is suggested. When water is the solvent this chemical activity may be a form of *hydration*. The process of hydration will be studied in Chapter 20.

6. Increasing the rate of solution. The rate at which a solid dissolves in a liquid depends on the nature of the solid and that of the liquid. In general, the more nearly the solute and solvent are alike in structure the more rapidly will solution occur. However, we may increase the rate of solution of a solid in a liquid in three ways.

1. By stirring. The diffusion of solute molecules throughout the solvent occurs rather slowly. By stirring or shaking the mixture we aid in the dispersion of the solute particles and bring fresh portions of the solvent in contact with the undissolved solid.

2. By powdering the solid. Solution action occurs only at the surface of the solid. By grinding the solid into a fine powder we greatly increase the surface area. Hence, finely powdered solids will dissolve much more rapidly than large lumps or crystals of the same substance.

3. By heating the solvent. The rate of solution rises with temperature. If we apply heat to a solvent the molecular activity increases and the solution action is speeded. At the same time, with most solids, the solubility of the substance is increased.

7. Solutions may be dilute or concentrated. The more solute that is dissolved in a solvent, the more *concentrated* the solution becomes. Conversely, the more solvent that is added, the more *dilute* the solution becomes. In the first instance *the concentration of solute particles was increased.* In the second, *the concentration of solute was decreased.*

We may increase the concentration of solutions by adding solute or by removing solvent by evaporation.

The terms *dilute* and *concentrated* are qualitative and are useful in a general sense. However, they lack the definiteness, or quantitative significance, which chemists require in describing the precise concentration of solutions.

8. Methods of expressing concentrations. We may express the concentration of solutions quantitatively in terms of the *mass of solute and the volume of solution*. One method expresses the mass of solute in *moles*. Another gives the solute in *gram-equivalent weights*. *The gram-equivalent weight of a substance is usually defined as the mass in grams which contains, replaces, or reacts with (either directly or indirectly) 1 gram-atom of hydrogen.*

An atom of hydrogen, as a reactant, may release or acquire one electron. A gram-atom of hydrogen, the Avogadro number of hydrogen atoms, exchanges the Avogadro number of electrons in a reaction with another substance. Thus, the gram-equivalent weight of a reactant may be thought of very conveniently as *the mass of the substance that acquires or furnishes the Avogadro number of electrons.*

The gram-equivalent weight of an element is found ordinarily by dividing its gram-atomic weight by its valence. In order to know the gram-equivalent weight of an oxidizing or reducing agent it is necessary to know the specific reaction in which the reactant takes part.

1. Molarity. The **molarity** *of a solution is an expression of the number of moles of solute per liter of solution. A molar* (1-M) *solution is one containing 1 mole of solute per liter of solution.* Solutions of the same molarity have the same concentration of solute molecules. Equal volumes have the same number of molecules of solute.

You will recall that the meaning of the mole has been extended to include the gram-formula weight of substances represented by empirical formulas. Thus a molar solution may contain 1 gram-molecular weight of a molecular solute per liter of solution, or 1 gram-formula weight of a nonmolecular solute per liter of solution. Sometimes the terms *formality* and *formal solution* are used when it is desired to distinguish the latter type of solute.

2. Normality. The **normality** *of a solution is an expression of the number of gram-equivalent weights of solute per liter of solution. A normal* (1-N) *solution is one containing 1 gram-equivalent weight of solute per liter of solution.* Equal volumes of solutions of the same normality are exact chemical equivalents.

The advantage of having solution concentrations expressed in molarity or normality is that any desired mass of solute may be taken in the form of its solution simply by measuring out a certain volume. The disadvantage is that the mass or volume of solvent present is not known precisely.

Another way of expressing the concentration of solutions quantitatively is to give the mass of solute and the mass of solvent.

3. Molality. The **molality** *of a solution is an expression of the number of moles of solute per kilogram of solvent. A molal* (1-m) *solution is one containing 1 mole of solute per kilogram of solvent.* Molality is preferred over molarity when portions are to be weighed.

In addition to the methods listed, the concentrations of solutions are sometimes expressed in *percentages*. A 10% sugar-water solution consists of 1 g of sugar for every 9 g of water. Also, *grams of solute per 100. g of solvent* is a method frequently used.

9. Solvents are selective. It was stated in Section 6 that, in general, the more nearly solutes and solvents are alike structurally the more rapidly will solution occur. It is also true, in a very general sense, that the *possibility* of solvent action is increased by a similarity in the composition and structure of substances. Chemists believe that the distribution of electronic forces helps to explain why solvents are selective; that is, why they will dissolve some substances readily, and others not at all.

In Chapter 10 the water molecule was described as a polar structure with a distinct negative region (the oxygen atom) and a distinct positive region (the hydrogen atoms). The water molecule is frequently referred to as the *water dipole.* When a molecule contains polar covalent bonds which are *unsymmetrically distributed,* the molecule has dipole characteristics (a negative region and a positive region) and is said to be polar.

The carbon tetrachloride molecule, CCl_4, contains four polar covalent bonds. However, since these are *symmetrically* distributed, due to the regular tetrahedral structure, the molecule is nonpolar. Gasoline-type hydrocarbons, while very unsymmetrical in bond distribution, are practically nonpolar. Neither hydrogen nor carbon has a strong tendency to attract electrons and their electronegativity difference is small.

If we apply the rough rule that *like dissolves like* to these typical solvents we would expect water to dissolve polar-type substances and carbon tetrachloride to dissolve nonpolar-type substances. Polar solute molecules and charged ions of crystals are held together by strong attractive forces. They are more likely to be attracted away from the solid structure by polar water molecules than by nonpolar solvents. Thus many ionic crystalline salts and molecular solids like table salt and sugar are readily dissolved by water. Many organic compounds, such as oils and greases, which are insoluble in water, are readily dissolved by nonpolar carbon tetrachloride.

Ethyl alcohol, C_2H_5OH, is typical of a group of solvents which dissolve both polar and nonpolar substances.

$$H-\overset{\overset{\displaystyle H}{|}}{C}-\overset{\overset{\displaystyle H}{|}}{\underset{\underset{\displaystyle H}{|}}{C}}-O-H$$

Fig. 19-6. **Molecular diagrams of three common solvents. Differences in molecular structure may help to explain why they are selective.**

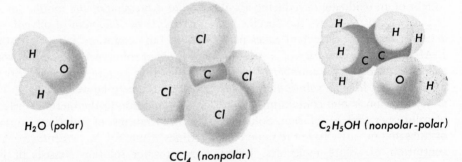

H₂O (polar)   CCl₄ (nonpolar)   C₂H₅OH (nonpolar-polar)

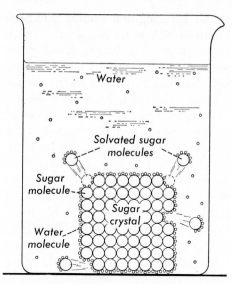

Fig. 19-7. **A possible mechanism of the solution process.**

There are five essentially nonpolar carbon-hydrogen bonds and one carbon-carbon bond which is completely nonpolar. The carbon-oxygen bond and the hydrogen-oxygen bond are polar. The presence of distinct polar and nonpolar regions may account for the fact that alcohol is a good solvent for some polar and some nonpolar substances.

10. Solvation. The actual manner in which substances enter into solution is not fully understood by chemists. However, some of the facets of the solution process that are fairly well understood may be examined by referring again to a sugar crystal placed in a beaker of water.

The crystal of sugar is composed of a regular lattice structure of sugar molecules held together by the attractive forces acting between the molecules themselves, called van der Waals attractions. Energy is required to remove a sugar molecule from the crystal in order for it to go into solution. Similarly, there is some attraction between the water

molecules and energy is required to overcome these molecular attractive forces to make room for the sugar molecule among them.

An attractive force also exists between unlike molecules, its magnitude depending on the nature of the molecules themselves. Water molecules are attracted to the surface molecules of the sugar crystal and energy is released. Thus, both energy-acquiring and energy-yielding activities occur in the solution process. If the net result is exothermic, the temperature of the solution is raised. If the net result is endothermic, as in the case of the sugar-water solution, the temperature of the solution is lowered.

We may think of solution occurring because of the attraction between solute and solvent. The movements of solvent molecules are random and as they cluster about the surface molecules of the solute crystal enough energy may be released to enable them to carry off solute molecules. This process, arising from the attraction between unlike molecules of solute and solvent, is known as *solvation*. Where water is the solvent, the solvation process is known more specifically as *hydration*. The solute molecule which leaves the crystal associated with its cluster of solvent molecules is said to be *solvated*. Where water molecules compose the solvent cluster, the solute molecule is said to be *hydrated*.

11. Hydrogen bonds affect the properties of solvents. An electronegative atom is one which has a great tendency to attract electrons. Hydrogen forms distinctly polar covalent bonds with such highly electronegative elements as fluorine, oxygen, chlorine, and nitrogen. The hydrogen end of such a bond is unique in that it consists of an exposed proton. In all other elements, except hydrogen, which tend to lose electrons, the atom kernel has an electronic shell that tends to repel the highly electronegative regions of other particles. The hydrogen end of a polar bond, however, attracts the relatively negative atoms of other molecules with enough force to be recognized as a loose chemical bond known as the hydrogen bond. By far the most common hydrogen bonds involve oxygen, although those with fluorine are generally stronger.

Such properties of water as the abnormally high boiling and melting points may be attributed in part to the presence of hydrogen bonds between molecules. The formation of hydrogen bonds between solvent and solute increases the solubility of the solute. Hydrogen bond formation between water and ethyl alcohol may partially explain their complete miscibility.

12. Freezing and boiling points of solutions. Salt water freezes at a much lower temperature than fresh water. Sea water is a dilute solution of common salt, NaCl, and other minerals. When a dilute solution is cooled enough for freezing to occur, the crystals produced are those of the *pure solvent*, not of the solution itself. In general, *solutes lower the freezing point of the solvent in which they are dissolved.* We make use of this fact when we add alcohol or ethylene glycol to the water of an automobile radiator during the winter months.

François Raoult (rah-oo) (1830–1901), a French chemist, found that a molal (1-m) solution of alcohol in water has a freezing point of −1.86° C. Later investigations revealed that 1-molal solutions of all nonelectrolytes in water

Fig. 19-8. Ice crystals are formed by molecules of water joined by hydrogen bonds. Here the space between molecules is exaggerated to show how each hydrogen in each molecule is joined to an oxygen in a neighboring molecule. See also Fig. 10-3, page 151.

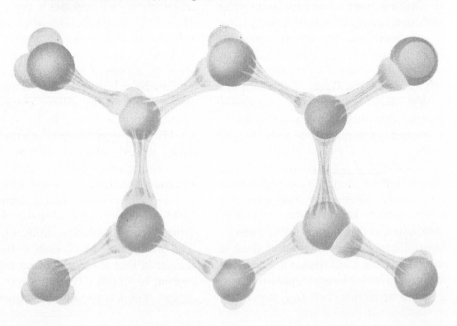

freeze at this same temperature. The difference between this temperature and the normal freezing point of water, 0° C, is 1.86 C°; this temperature interval is called the *molal freezing point depression of water.*

Experiments with different molalites proved that *the lowering of the freezing point is proportional to the molecular concentration of the solute.* Solvents other than water have their own characteristic molal-freezing point depressions.

The boiling point of a solution is higher than that of the pure solvent, provided the solute is not a volatile substance. Experiments have shown that, in dilute solutions of nonvolatile nonelectrolytes, *the elevation of the boiling point is proportional to the molecular concentration of the solute.* Molal solutions of nonelectrolytes in water raise the boiling point 0.52 C°. That is, the solution boils at 100.52° C at 760 mm pressure. Thus *0.52 C° (100.52° C − 100° C) is the molal boiling-point elevation of water.*

The freezing points and boiling points of solutions of electrolytes are altered in an abnormal manner. Such solutes are not molecular and do not conform to the generalization about molecular substances just described.

* **13. Molecular weights of solutes.** In Chapter 14, Section 7, Avogadro's Principle was applied to determine the molecular weights of gases and volatile liquids by the molar-volume method. Now we shall see how molecular weights can be determined for those substances which cannot be vaporized without decomposition, *but which are soluble in water or some other common solvent.* Of course such solutes must form molecular solutions and must not react with the solvent.

In the previous section it was stated that the freezing-point depression and the boiling-point elevation depend on the relative number of solute molecules mixed with a definite number of solvent molecules, rather than upon the nature of the solute. Molal solutions of all nonelectrolytes in water freeze at −1.86° C and, if the solute is nonvolatile, boil at 100.52° C at standard pressure. Knowing this we have a method of determining the molecular weights of such substances. The freezing point depression is more frequently used in determining molecular weights.

Suppose a known mass of nonelectrolyte is dissolved in a known mass of water and the freezing point of this solution is determined experimentally. Knowing the concentration of the solution and its freezing-point depression, we may readily calculate the mass of this solute which must be dissolved in a kilogram of water to give the molal-freezing point depression, which for water is 1.86 C°.

$$\frac{\text{g solute/kg } H_2O}{\text{depression, C}°} = \frac{1 \text{ mole solute/kg } H_2O}{1.86 \text{ C}°}$$

Solving for 1 mole solute:

$$\frac{1 \text{ mole solute} \times \text{depr. C}°}{\text{kg } H_2O} =$$
$$\frac{\text{g solute} \times 1.86 \text{ C}°}{\text{kg } H_2O}$$

$$1 \text{ mole solute} = \frac{\text{g solute} \times 1.86 \text{ C}°}{\text{depression, C}°}$$

Suppose 5.00 g of a substance dissolved in 100.0 g of water lowers the freezing point of the water 0.370 C°. *Remember that the mass of solute dissolved in 1 kg of water, which lowers the freezing point 1.86 C°, is a mole of the solute and is numerically equal to the molecular weight.* Then 50.0 g of this solute dissolved in 1 kg of water will lower the freezing point 0.370 C°. From the above expression, on substituting the problem data,

$$1 \text{ mole solute} = 50.0 \text{ g} \times \frac{1.86 \text{ C}°}{0.370 \text{ C}°}$$

$$1 \text{ mole solute} = 250. \text{ g}$$

Therefore,

mol. wt. solute = 250.

Molecular weights may be calculated from the boiling-point elevation in the same manner, remembering that the molal boiling-point elevation of water is 0.52 C°. Solvents other than water may be used in molecular weight determinations for substances not soluble in water. Each has its own characteristic molal freezing-point depression and molal boiling-point elevation which would be used instead of those for water.

2. CRYSTALLIZATION

14. The nature of crystals. Substances generally separate from solutions as crystalline solids. In fact, most substances exist as solids in some characteristic crystalline form. A *crystal is a homogeneous portion of a substance bounded by plane surfaces making definite angles with each other, giving a regular geometric form.*

The arrangement of particles composing a crystal is determined by a mathematical analysis of photographs of the diffraction patterns produced when the crystal is illuminated by X rays. The pattern of points which describe the arrangement of particles in a crystal structure is known as the *crystal lattice*. The smallest portion of the crystal lattice which determines the pattern of the lattice structure is called the *unit cell*. The

Fig. 19-9. The kind of symmetry found throughout a crystalline substance is determined by the type of unit cell which generates the lattice structure.

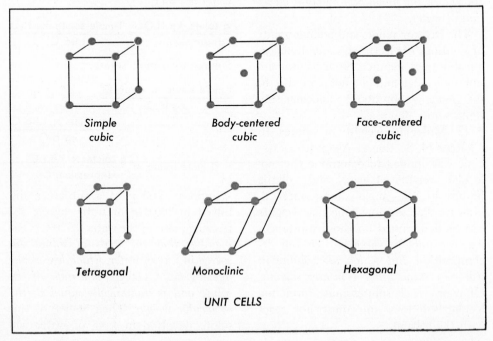

Simple cubic

Body-centered cubic

Face-centered cubic

Tetragonal

Monoclinic

Hexagonal

UNIT CELLS

unit cell defines the kind of symmetry to be found throughout a crystalline substance. The different kinds of unit cells are shown in Figure 19–9.

The classification of crystals by shape, a part of the science of *crystallography*, helps chemists to identify crystals. Any crystal can be placed in one of six crystalline systems.

1. *Isometric (or cubic)*, in which the 3 axes are at right angles as in a cube.

2. *Tetragonal*, in which the 3 axes are at right angles, but only two, the lateral axes, are equal.

3. *Triclinic*, in which there are 3 unequal axes and oblique intersections.

4. *Hexagonal*, in which 3 equilateral angles intersect at angles of 60° and with a vertical axis of variable length at right angles.

5. *Orthorhombic*, in which there are 3 unequal axes at right angles.

6. *Monoclinic*, in which there are 3 unequal axes, with one oblique intersection.

Crystals of common salt, NaCl, are isometric (cubic). This can be seen by sprinkling a little table salt on a black surface and examining with a magnifying lens. Alum crystals are also isometric, being formed as *octahedrons*. Copper(II) sulfate pentahydrate forms blue crystals that are of the triclinic system.

Crystals of salts are commonly formed by the evaporation of their solutions, or by the cooling of their hot saturated solutions. Crystals are also formed when some substances change from the liquid to the solid state and when others change from the gaseous to the solid state. Most of us are familiar with snowflake crystals which are formed when water vapor changes to the solid state. The hydrogen bond helps to determine the shape of ice crystals which are formed when water freezes. Molten sugar, sulfur, and iron form crystals in a similar manner when they change from the liquid to the solid state. In some cases crystals grow from the solid state.

15. Binding forces in crystals. The regularity of crystal structures is their most fascinating feature. All crystalline structure is the result of the universal tendency in nature for the symmetrical distribution of force. Where the opportunity occurs, ions or atoms or molecules arrange themselves in positions of least energy. The more opportunity there is for these particles to orient themselves during the formation of crystals, the more symmetrical and regular they will be. Thus, crystals that form slowly will be more nearly perfect.

The classification of crystals into the six crystalline systems is based on considerations of symmetry. It is frequently more useful to classify crystals according to the types of lattice structure, that is, whether the particles that compose the crystal lattice are *ionic, covalent, metallic,* or *molecular*. Of these, the ionic and molecular crystals represent the two extremes, the others being intermediate types.

1. *Ionic crystals.* The crystal lattice consists of an array of positive and negative ions arranged in a characteristic pattern with such regularity that no molecular units are evident within the crystal. The binding forces are the strong electrostatic bonds of positive and negative charges. Consequently, ionic crystals are hard and brittle, have rather high melting points, and are good insulators. Generally speaking, compounds consisting of Group I and Group II metals combined with the Group VI and Group VII nonmetals and the nonmetallic radicals form crystals of this type.

2. *Covalent crystals.* The crystal lattice

Fig. 19-10. **A garnet crystal, left, and a quartz crystal, above, show how crystalline structure follows a characteristic pattern.** (American Museum of Natural History)

consists of an array of atoms that share electrons with their neighboring atoms. The binding forces are strong covalent bonds which extend in fixed directions. The resulting crystals are giant, compact, interlocking structures called macromolecules. They are very hard and brittle, have rather high melting points, and are nonconductors. Diamond, silicon carbide (carborundum), silicon dioxide (quartz) and oxides of transition metals are of this type.

3. *Metallic crystals.* The crystal lattice consists of positive ions permeated by a cloud of valence electrons commonly referred to as the *electron gas.* The binding force is the attraction between the positive ions of the metal and the electron cloud. The valence electrons may be considered to have been donated by the atoms of the metal and to belong to the crystal as a whole. These electrons are free to migrate throughout the crystal lattice giving rise to the high electric conductivity associated with metals. The hardness characteristics and melting points of metallic crystals vary over wide ranges for different metals. Sodium, iron, tungsten, copper, and silver are typical examples of metallic crystals that have good electric conductivity but

quite different characteristics such as hardness and melting point.

4. *Molecular crystals.* The crystal lattice consists of symmetrical aggregates of discrete molecules. The binding force is the relative weak van de Waals force between the molecules. The covalent chemical bonds which bind the atoms within the molecules are much stronger than the forces which form the crystal lattice. Thus, molecular crystals have low melting points, are relatively soft, volatile, and good insulators. Iodine, carbon dioxide, water, and hydrogen form crystals of this type.

16. **The importance of crystals.** Chemists have learned a great deal about the structure of matter from the study of crystals. The extraordinary strength of single crystals of certain pure metals is attracting great interest and techniques for growing large metallic crystals are being investigated by many scientists. (See Fig. 35-12.)

Natural minerals can be identified by studying the shape of the crystals they form. Several natural crystals, such as the diamond, are valuable as gems. Certain types of crystals are used to aid broadcasting stations maintain stable signal frequencies. Germanium crystals and silicon crystals are important in transistor and other semi-conductor applications.

17. Chemists purify chemicals by crystallization. Suppose we wish to purify some impure potassium nitrate. The potassium nitrate may be dissolved in distilled water and the concentration of the solution increased by evaporation. After the saturation point is reached, crystals of potassium nitrate of a rather high degree of purity begin to separate from the solution as it is allowed to cool. By filtering out these crystals and dissolving them again in water, the process can be repeated to produce crystals of still higher purity. Such crystals are said to be *recrystallized*. Crystallization and recrystallization are much used by chemists to obtain pure chemicals.

Fig. 19-11. Reagent chemicals must meet rigid standards of purity. (Mallinckrodt Chemical Works)

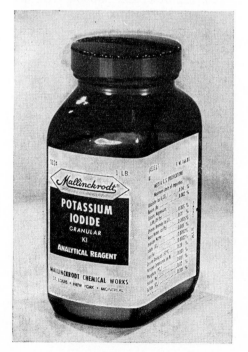

The saturated solution which is left after a "crop" of crystals has formed is known as the "mother liquor." By evaporating the mother liquor still more, a second, or even a third, crop of crystals may be obtained. Each successive crop, however, will be less pure than the crop before it.

If a solution is cooled rapidly or stirred while crystallization is taking place, smaller crystals are formed. Such small crystals are generally purer than large crystals formed by slow evaporation. This is because large crystals are more likely to have some of the mother liquor incorporated in them. Crystals that contain water held mechanically *decrepitate*, or crackle, when heated. Steam forms within the crystal, and its expansion causes the crystal to burst open. Lead nitrate crystals scattered over the bottom of an Erlenmeyer flask show decrepitation quite strikingly when the flask is heated gently.

Sometimes it is possible to separate two different chemicals dissolved in the same solution by means of *fractional crystallization*. When the solvent is evaporated, the less soluble chemical crystallizes first, and may be removed by filtration.

18. Standards of purity. Examination of the labels on the containers of chemicals in the laboratory stock room reveals several different terms used to indicate grades of purity. Some, marked "technical," are comparatively cheap because they are not highly refined. Yet they are not supposed to contain impurities which would interfere with the commercial uses for which they are intended. Chemicals of higher purity may be marked "purified," "N.F." "U.S.P.," "C.P.," or "reagent." The terms N.F. and U.S.P. mean the chemicals or drugs are pure enough to meet the specifications listed in the National Formulary and the United States Pharmacopoeia, respectively. The United States Pharmacopoeia is the official publication used by pharmacists as a guide in compounding medicines. The letters C.P. stand for *"chemically pure"* and designate a grade which is usually much higher in quality than U.S.P. or N.F. The letters A.C.S. are often seen on labels of highest grade chemicals, used as *analytical reagents* in chemical laboratories. These chemicals meet the specifications of the *American Chemical Society* Committee on Analytical Reagents. It is not possible, of course, for manufacturing chemists to attain absolute purity in their products.

19. Water of hydration. In Chapter 10 it is stated that some crystals unite chemically with water when they crystallize from a water solution. Such crystals are known as *hydrates*. The water

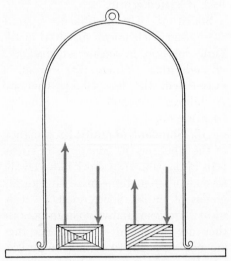

Fig. 19-12. Hydrated crystals of different substances have different aqueous vapor pressures (arrows up). In an atmosphere of normal aqueous pressure (arrows down) the crystal on the left will effloresce. The one on the right will not. In dry air both will effloresce.

they contain is called *water of hydration* or *water of crystallization*. Common examples are: $CuSO_4 \cdot 5\,H_2O$; $ZnSO_4 \cdot 7\,H_2O$; $CoCl_2 \cdot 6\,H_2O$; and $Na_2CO_3 \cdot 10\,H_2O$. Alum is the *double* salt $K_2SO_4 \cdot Al_2(SO_4)_3 \cdot 24\,H_2O$.

Each hydrate holds a definite proportion of water which is necessary for the formation of the crystal structure. Water of hydration must not be confused with the mechanically held water mentioned in Section 17. The water of hydration may be driven off by applying heat, producing the *anhydrous* form of the substance. The anhydrous form of the blue copper(II) sulfate crystals is a white powder.

Many compounds form hydrates when they crystallize. Some have two or more hydrated forms which are stable over different temperature ranges. Many other compounds form crystals which do not require water of hydration. Examples are: $NaCl$, KNO_3, and $KClO_3$.

20. Efflorescence. Suppose we place ten grams of sodium sulfate crystals, $Na_2SO_4 \cdot 10\,H_2O$, on a watch glass and counterpoise it on a balance. In a few minutes the crystals begin to show a loss of mass. By the end of the laboratory period the loss in mass may amount to a gram or more.

Some hydrated crystals hold water of hydration very loosely. Water is given off from them when they are exposed to relatively dry air. The crystals lose their glassy luster and become powdery. *This loss of water when such crystals are exposed to the air is called efflorescence.* Efflorescence occurs much more rapidly in a warm, dry atmosphere than in one that is cool and moist. Hydrates which effloresce have higher vapor pressures than that of the water vapor in the air about them. Sodium carbonate decahydrate, $Na_2CO_3 \cdot 10\,H_2O$, has a

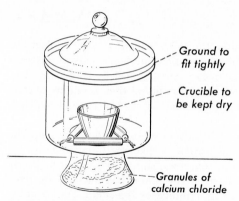

Ground to fit tightly

Crucible to be kept dry

Granules of calcium chloride

Fig. 19-13. A deliquescent substance, such as anhydrous calcium chloride, silica gel, or activated alumina, is used to maintain a dry atmosphere in a laboratory desiccator.

on a balance. After the calcium chloride has been exposed to the air for half an hour, we find that it shows a decided gain in mass. The granules have become moist, or perhaps have even formed a solution with water from the air. *Deliquescence is the property of certain substances to take up water from the air to form a solution.* Such substances are very soluble in water and their crystals have aqueous vapor pressures that are low compared to the normal range of partial pressures of water vapor in the air.

Many materials such as silk, wool, hair, and tobacco take up water vapor from the air. The water molecules may be held in pores and imperfections of the solid. All such materials, along with deliquescent substances, are classed as *hygroscopic.* Common table salt is hygroscopic only because it contains a small amount of magnesium chloride, a very deliquescent substance. The presence of this impurity causes table salt to "cake" and clog the holes of a salt shaker.

high aqueous vapor pressure and when exposed to the atmosphere, it effloresces forming the monohydrate, $Na_2CO_3 \cdot H_2O$. Thus a pound of freshly packaged "washing soda" may weigh considerably less when purchased.

21. Deliquescence. Let us place a few grams of calcium chloride granules on a watch glass and counterpoise them

Fig. 19-14. Calcium chloride removes water vapor from the air to control the dust on an unpaved road. (Solvay Process Division)

A solution is made up of two parts; the solute which is dissolved, and the solvent in which the solute is dissolved. Solutions are homogeneous mixtures of particles no larger than molecular size. Solutes may be classed as electrolytes or nonelectrolytes depending on the ability of their solutions to conduct electricity. The properties of the solutions of electrolytes and nonelectrolytes are quite different.

We may have solutions of gases, or liquids, or solids in other gases, liquids, and solids. Substances of similar composition are likely to form solutions.

Solution equilibrium places a limit on the quantity of solute which can dissolve in a given quantity of solvent. Equilibrium is influenced by temperature. The solubility of a solute is determined by the equilibrium concentration of solute particles.

The solubility of a gas in a liquid is influenced by pressure in accordance with Henry's Law. Gases which react with their liquid solvent are more soluble than those which do not. The solubility of a gas decreases as the temperature is raised. Solids are generally more soluble at higher temperatures. We may hasten the formation of a solution in several ways.

The concentration of a solution may be described qualitatively as either dilute or concentrated. Concentration is described precisely by stating the molarity, normality, or molality of the solution.

Molecular solutes lower the freezing point of their solvents characteristic amounts. If nonvolatile, they raise the boiling point characteristic amounts also. Each solvent has a specific molal-freezing point depression and molal-boiling point elevation. These properties are used to determine molecular weights of soluble substances which cannot be easily vaporized.

Solids usually separate from solution as crystals. Crystals assume characteristic forms and are classified according to their lattice structure as ionic, molecular, covalent, or metallic.

Specific amounts of water are essential to the formation of crystals of some substances. Some hydrated crystals lose water of hydration when exposed to air and are said to effloresce. Substances which remove water from the air to form solutions are said to be deliquescent.

TEST YOURSELF ON THESE TERMS

anhydrous	equilibrium concentration	monoclinic
concentrated	gram-equivalent weight	mother liquor
C.P.	Henry's Law	normality
crystals	hydrate	saturated
Dalton's Law	hydration	solubility
decrepitate	hydrogen bond	soluble
deliquescence	hygroscopic	solute
dilute	immiscible	solution equilibrium
dissolve	isometric	solvation
effervescence	miscible	solvent
efflorescence	molality	supersaturated
electronegative	molarity	U.S.P.

Group A

1. List, by name, five common solvents.
2. Why are the terms *dilute* and *concentrated* not entirely satisfactory as applied to solutions?
3. (*a*) Name the nine different types of solutions possible. (*b*) Which type is the most common?
4. Why does carbonated water effervesce when it is drawn from the soda fountain?
5. What action limits the amount of a solute which can dissolve in a given quantity of solvent under fixed conditions?
6. Explain the difference between *dissolve* and *melt*.
7. What is the influence of pressure on the solubility of: (*a*) a gas in a liquid; and (*b*) a solid in a liquid?
8. What is the influence of temperature on the solubility of: (*a*) a gas in a liquid; and (*b*) a solid in a liquid?
9. (*a*) What is the difference between *miscible* and *immiscible*? (*b*) Give an example of each.
10. What method of expressing the concentration of a solution would be used if the solute is given: (*a*) in moles per liter of solution; (*b*) in moles per kilogram of solvent; and (*c*) in gram-equivalent weights per liter of solution?
11. What is the distinguishing characteristic of *polar* molecules?
12. Alcohol is a nonelectrolyte and is soluble in water, yet a molal solution of alcohol in water does not give the molal-boiling elevation of water. Explain.
13. (*a*) Explain why anhydrous calcium chloride may be used to keep the air in a basement dry. (*b*) Suggest a suitable method of accomplishing this.
14. What do the letters "A.C.S." on a bottle of iron(II) sulfate mean?

Group B

15. Explain the expression *saturated solution* in terms of solution equilibrium.
16. (*a*) What determines the amount of oxygen which remains dissolved in water which is at constant temperature and in contact with the atmosphere? (*b*) Explain what would happen if the oxygen were removed from the air above the water.
17. Suppose you wished to make a concentrated solution of copper(II) sulfate in water. How would you hasten the solution process?
18. The carbon tetrachloride molecule contains four polar covalent bonds yet the molecule as a whole is nonpolar. Explain.
19. How may we explain the fact that alcohol is a good solvent for both water and ether?
20. Why do caps sometimes blow off the tops of ginger ale bottles when they are exposed to direct sunlight for some time?

21. Why is cold water more appropriate than hot water for making a saturated solution of calcium hydroxide?
22. Tobacco growers prefer to handle dried tobacco leaves during damp weather. Explain.
23. A package of washing soda ($Na_2CO_3 \cdot 10\ H_2O$) labeled "one pound" was found to weigh only 14 ounces. Was the packer necessarily dishonest? Explain.
24. A bottle of alum crystals was erroneously labeled "sodium chloride." How could the error be detected at once by an alert chemistry student?
25. From which substance, sodium nitrate or sodium chloride, could potassium nitrate be more easily separated by fractional crystallization? Explain.
26. How are the solubility curves like those in Fig. 19-5 constructed?
27. How can you account for the fact that metallic solids are good conductors of electricity and ionic solids are not?
28. Camphor crystals are soft and volatile. Explain.

PROBLEMS

★ 1. A solution consists of 60.0 g of cane sugar, $C_{12}H_{22}O_{11}$, in 150.0 g of water. What is the freezing point of the water?
★ 2. What is the boiling point of the solution described in Problem 1?
★ 3. The analysis of a compound shows: carbon, 32.0%; hydrogen, 4.0%; oxygen, 64.0%. Fifteen grams of the compound added to 1000. g of water lowered the freezing point of the water 0.186 C°. (*a*) Find the empirical formula. (*b*) What is the molecular weight of the compound? (*c*) What is the molecular formula?
★ 4. A compound contains: carbon, 40.00%; hydrogen, 6.67%; oxygen, 53.33%. Nine grams of the compound dissolved in 500. g of water raised the boiling point of the water 0.052 C°. (*a*) Find the empirical formula. (*b*) Find the molecular weight. (*c*) What is the molecular formula?
★ 5. The analysis of a compound shows: carbon, 30.4%; hydrogen, 1.69%; bromine, 68%. The substance is soluble in benzene and 10.0 g of it lower the freezing point of 100. g of benzene 2.17 C°. The normal freezing point of benzene is 5.48° C, and the molal freezing-point depression is 5.12 C°. (*a*) Find the empirical formula of the compound. (*b*) Determine the molecular weight. (*c*) What is the molecular formula?

SOME THINGS FOR YOU TO DO

1. Prepare a supersaturated solution of "hypo" by dissolving 50 g of sodium thiosulfate in 10 ml of water with the aid of heat. Allow the solution to cool undisturbed. Add a tiny crystal of hypo and watch the crystals form.
2. Test the solubility of gum camphor or iodine crystals in both water and alcohol. Which is the better solvent?
3. See how large and nearly perfect a crystal of alum you can get to "grow" from a saturated solution. Select a well-formed, single crystal to start. Wipe the crystal each day with a soft cloth to prevent the growth of secondary crystals. The solution must be stored in a place of nearly uniform temperature.

Chapter 20 · THE THEORY OF IONIZATION

1. Some solutions conduct electricity. In Chapter 19, Section 1, it was stated that solutions of electrovalent and covalent compounds may have different properties, due to differences in the chemical nature of electrovalent and covalent solutes. Electrovalent compounds are ionic, and their water solutions conduct electricity.

The conductivity of a solution may be tested qualitatively by the use of the apparatus shown in Fig. 20-1. An incandescent lamp is connected in series with a switch and a pair of platinum electrodes which can be dipped into the test solution. A battery, or other source, having a voltage rating similar to that of the lamp serves as the source of current. If the liquid under test is a *conductor of electricity*, the lamp filament glows when the switch is closed.

If pure water is used in the beaker, the filament does not glow. Thus pure water is (for all practical purposes) a *nonconductor*. Water solutions of such covalent substances as sugar, alcohol,

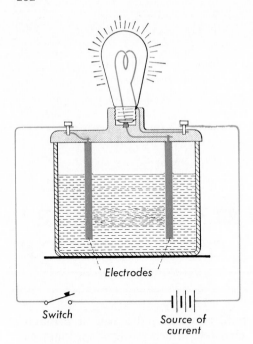

Fig. 20-1. **Solutions that conduct electricity will enable the lamp to glow when the switch is closed.**

and glycerin do not conduct electricity; these solutes are *nonelectrolytes*.

Solutions of electrovalent substances, such as sodium chloride, copper(II) sulfate, and potassium nitrate, are *conductors*. These solutes are *electrolytes*. Hydrogen chloride is an example of a covalent compound which in water solution, conducts an electric current. Such substances are also called electrolytes.

2. Electrolytes lower the freezing point more than nonelectrolytes. One mole of a *nonelectrolyte* dissolved in 1 kg of water lowers the freezing point of the water 1.86 C°. Molal solutions of *electrolytes* have a somewhat greater influence on the freezing point. For example, 1 mole of sodium chloride dissolved in 1 kg of water lowers the freezing point *nearly twice* as much as 1 mole of sugar, and 1 mole of potassium

sulfate in 1 kg of water lowers the freezing point *nearly three times* as much as 1 mole of sugar. In general, *electrolytes in water solutions lower the freezing point nearly 2, or 3, or more times as much as nonelectrolytes in water solutions of the same molality.*

3. Electrolytes raise the boiling point more than nonelectrolytes. One mole of sugar dissolved in 1 kg of water raises the boiling point of the water 0.52 C°. Molal solutions of electrolytes have a greater effect on the boiling point of the solvent than do nonelectrolytes. Sodium chloride solutions have boiling point elevations *almost twice* those of sugar solutions of equal molality. A 1-m solution of potassium sulfate shows *almost three times* the rise in boiling point as a 1-m solution of sugar. In general, *electrolytes in water solutions raise the boiling point nearly 2, or 3, or more times as much as nonelectrolytes in water solutions of the same molality.*

4. The behavior of electrolytes explained. Michael Faraday, an English chemist and physicist (1791–1867), first used the terms *electrolyte* and *nonelectrolyte* in his experiments on the conductivity of solutions. He concluded that conducting solutions contained particles which carried electricity from one electrode to the other. Faraday called these particles *ions* and assumed that they were produced from molecules by the electric potential difference between the electrodes. As other properties of electrolytic solutions were revealed, it became apparent that they contained ions regardless of the presence of the charged electrodes.

In 1887 the Swedish chemist Svante Arrhenius (1859–1927) published a report of his study of the behavior of solutions of electrolytes, known as the *Theory of Ionization.* Arrhenius believed that ions were produced by the *ioniza-tion* of molecules of electrolytes in water solution. He considered the ions to be electrically charged. When molecules ionized, they produced both positive ions and negative ions. The solution as a whole contained equal numbers of positive and negative charges. He considered the ionization to be complete only in very dilute solutions. In more concentrated solutions the ions were in equilibrium with *un-ionized* molecules of the solute.

For many years these assumptions formed the basis of the theory of solutions. Recently, however, some of the concepts of Arrhenius have been modified or replaced by new and different concepts concerning the structure of crystals and of the water molecule.

It is a great tribute to Arrhenius that his original theory of ionization served so long as the sole guide for the studies of the properties of solutions. You must remember that present-day knowledge of the crystalline structure of electrovalent compounds was not available to him when, at the age of 28, he published his thesis on ionization.

5. The modern theory of ionization. In the modern theory of ionization the solvent plays an important part in the solution process. Water is by far the most important solvent. The nature of the polar water molecule, discussed extensively in Chapters 10 and 19, is of great importance in understanding the solution process. According to present-day concepts, the theory of ionization assumes:

1. *That electrolytes in solution exist in the form of ions.*
2. *That an ion is an atom or a group of atoms which carries an electric charge.*
3. *That the water solution of an elec-trolyte contains an equal number of positive and negative charges.*

6. The structure of electrovalent compounds. Electrovalent compounds result from the actual transfer of electrons from one kind of atom to another. Consequently, electrovalent compounds are not made up of neutral atoms; they consist of atoms which have lost or gained electrons. Those atoms which *gained* electrons in forming the compound have a *negative* charge. Those which *lost* electrons carry a *positive* charge. Such atoms or groups of atoms which carry an electric charge are called *ions*. In forming an ion, an atom loses electric neutrality and gains chemical stability.

Ions have quite different properties from the atoms from which they were produced. This is reasonable because of the difference in structure and electric characteristics resulting from the formation of ions. A neutral sodium

Fig. 20-2. **Svante August Arrhenius, a Swedish chemist, first proposed the theory of ionization for which he was awarded the Nobel Prize in 1903.** (Brown Brothers)

atom with a single 3s electron revolving in its M shell is different from a sodium ion. The sodium ion does not have the 3s electron and thus has one excess positive charge of electricity and an octet in the L shell. We must remember that chemical properties are determined chiefly by the outer electron arrangement of an atom or an ion. If the outer electronic structure is different, the properties will be different. The loss of the M-shell electron gives sodium the stable electronic configuration of neon. *The charge of an ion is the same as its valence.* In fact, the charge on the ion is what determines its valence.

Electrovalent compounds usually exist in the form of crystals made up in a very orderly fashion as described in Chapter 19. For example, the cubic structure of crystalline sodium chloride is shown in Fig. 20–3. By X-ray analysis, the crystals are known to be composed of ions. Other electrovalent compounds crystallize in different patterns, each built up in a manner which depends on the relative size and valence of the ions.

7. The hydration of ions. Suppose a few crystals of salt are dropped into a beaker of water. The water dipoles immediately exert an attractive force on the ions forming the surfaces of the crystals. The negative oxygen end of several water dipoles exerts an attractive force on a positive sodium ion. Likewise, the positive hydrogen end of other water dipoles exerts an attractive force on a negative chloride ion. This weakens the bond by which the sodium and chloride ions are held together in the crystal lattice and they are torn away to diffuse throughout the solution, loosely bonded to these solvent molecules. Other sodium and chloride ions are similarly attracted by solvent molecules and diffuse in the solution. In this way the salt crystal is gradually dissolved and the ions spread throughout the solution. *The separation of ions from the crystals of electrovalent compounds during the solution process is called* **dissociation.** We may represent the dissociation of sodium chloride crystals by use of an ionic equation:

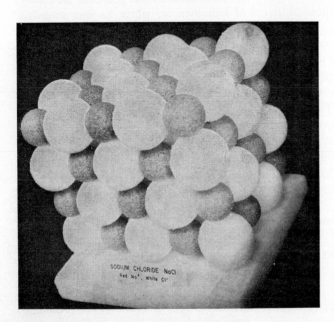

SODIUM CHLORIDE NaCl
Red Na⁺, White Cl⁻

Fig. 20-3. Model of a portion of a cubic sodium chloride crystal. The lattice structure is composed of sodium ions and chloride ions. Each ion has six neighbors of opposite charge, the arrangement being repeated in each direction to the edge of the crystal. (H. Bassow, Fieldston School)

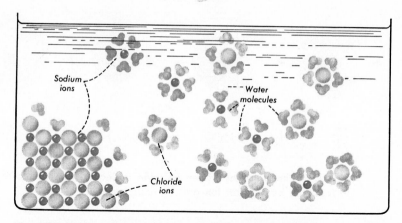

Fig. 20-4. When sodium chloride crystals are dissolved in water, the polar water molecules exert attracting forces which weaken the ionic bonds. The process of solution occurs as the ions of sodium and chloride become hydrated.

$$Na^+Cl^- \rightarrow Na^+ + Cl^-$$

Sodium chloride is said to *dissociate* when it is dissolved in water.

The number of water dipoles which attach themselves to the ions of the crystal depends largely upon the size and charge of the ion. *This attachment of water molecules to ions of the solute is called* **hydration.** The ions are said to be *hydrated.* The degree of hydration of these ions is somewhat indefinite, water molecules being interchanged continuously from ion to ion and between ions and solvent. In certain cases the water dipoles are not involved in reforming the crystal structure during the evaporation of the solvent. This is true of sodium chloride whose crystals do not contain water of hydration. On the other hand, a characteristic number of water molecules is retained by ions in forming the crystal lattice of a salt in the hydrated form.

We can see that extensive hydration of the solute ions ties up a substantial portion of the solvent molecules. This reduces the number of *free* water mol-

ecules in the spaces separating hydrated ions of opposite charge. Attraction between ions becomes stronger and the crystal begins to form again. A practical limit of solubility is reached as the tendency for hydrated ions to reform the crystal lattice reaches an *equilibrium* with the tendency of ions to be hydrated.

$$Na^+Cl^- \rightleftarrows Na^+ + Cl^-$$

Ionic compounds can act as electrolytes in another way. Since they consist of ions, any effect which reduces sufficiently the mutual attraction between the ions enables them to conduct electricity. We have seen how water does this. Heating produces the same effect. If an electrovalent compound is heated until it melts, or *fuses,* the ions become mobile and conduct an electric current through the molten material. Some solids, silver nitrate and potassium chlorate for example, melt at fairly low temperatures. The electric conductivity of such fused salts can be quite easily demonstrated in the laboratory. Ionic compounds such as sodium chloride must be

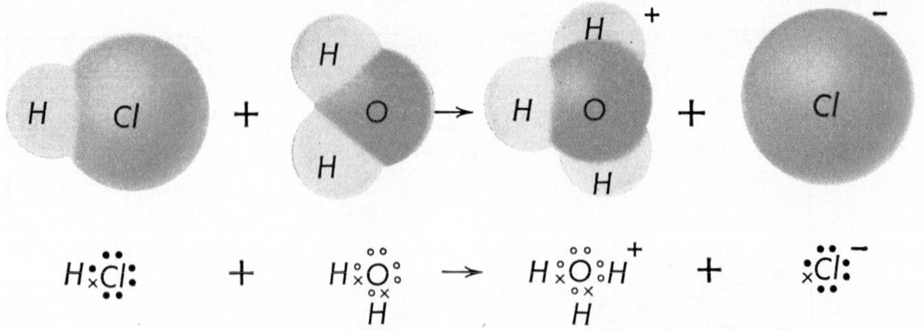

Fig. 20-5. The polar hydrogen chloride molecule ionizes in water solution to form the hydronium ion and the chloride ion.

heated to a high temperature before they melt, but when melted, will conduct electricity.

8. Some covalent compounds ionize. Covalent bonds are formed by the sharing of electrons by two atoms, the shared electrons revolving about both atoms joined by the covalent bond. If one of the atoms is highly electronegative, the valence electrons may be thought of as spending more time revolving about this atom. In this way, one end of the covalent molecule tends to be more negative and the other end more positive. This type of molecule is said to be a polar molecule. How strongly polar it is depends on the electronegativity difference between the two atoms forming the covalent linkage.

The covalent bond is generally weaker than the electrovalent bond. When polar covalent molecules are dissolved in water, the water dipoles weaken the bonds and the molecules are pulled apart. *Thus the portions of the polar solute molecule become hydrated as ions.* Since the ions *did not exist* in the undissolved solute, but were formed by the action of the solvent, the process is called *ionization.*

Hydrogen chloride, in the liquid state, does not conduct electricity. The hydrogen and chlorine atoms are connected by a covalent bond, but the more highly electronegative chlorine attracts the electrons forming the covalent bond. Consequently, the chlorine end of the molecule tends to be negative, while the hydrogen end tends to be positive. They are polar molecules.

Hydrogen chloride dissolved in water does, however, conduct an electric current because it is ionized in water solution.

Arrhenius believed that the process of ionization involved simply the ionization of the solute molecule on entering the solution. Thus in the case of hydrogen chloride:

$$HCl \rightarrow H^+ + Cl^-$$

Today, chemists recognize that single hydrogen ions, actually protons, do not exist *free* in a water solution. They do, however, show a strong tendency to become hydrated. Thus the solvent plays a definite part in the separation of protons from the solute molecules, as shown in the equation:

$$HCl + H_2O \rightarrow H_3O^+ + Cl^-$$

The H_3O^+ ion is a hydrated proton $(H^+ \cdot H_2O)$ *and is known as the hydronium ion.* Because of the ionization, a solution of hydrogen chloride in water has decidedly different properties from hydrogen chloride gas and as a consequence, the solution is given the name *hydrochloric acid*.

Aluminum chloride, Al_2Cl_6 (usually represented by the empirical formula $AlCl_3$), is a nonconductor in the liquid state. In water solution, however, it is a good conductor. It must, therefore, ionize during the solution process. We may represent the ionization as in the case of hydrogen chloride:

$$Al_2Cl_6 + 12\ H_2O \rightarrow$$
$$2\ Al(H_2O)_6{}^{+++} + 6Cl^-$$

or more simply using the empirical formula:

$$AlCl_3 + 6\ H_2O \rightarrow Al(H_2O)_6{}^{+++} + 3\ Cl^-$$

Other hydrated aluminum ions are probably formed at the same time.

9. Some electrolytes are strong, others are weak. The strength of an electrolyte is determined by the number of its ions in solution. Electrovalent compounds are ionic as crystalline solids. Their solutions are therefore completely ionized. Hydrogen chloride has such a strong tendency to ionize in water solution that, even at ordinary dilutions, it is considered to be completely ionized. Such substances are said to be *strong electrolytes*. Their water solutions conduct electricity exceedingly well.

A water solution of acetic acid, $HC_2H_3O_2$, is a poor conductor. The fact that the solution conducts at all tells us that some ionization has occurred. This may be shown according to the reversible reaction:

$$HC_2H_3O_2 + H_2O \rightleftarrows H_3O^+ + C_2H_3O_2{}^-$$

We must assume that the ion concentration is low. Acetic acid molecules show only a slight tendency to hydrate as ions. Such substances are said to be *weak electrolytes*. Solutions of weak electrolytes are largely molecular.

We must be sure not to confuse the terms strong and weak with the terms dilute and concentrated. *Strong and weak* refer to the *degree of ionization. Dilute and concentrated* refer to the *amount of solute dissolved in a solvent.*

10. Water ionizes slightly. Water is a polar covalent compound. Probably because of the influence of these polar molecules on each other, water ionizes to the extent of about two molecules in a billion. These few ions, however, are very important in chemistry as will be shown in Chapter 22. Such slight ionization may be neglected when dealing with substances such as hydrogen chloride which ionize completely, but must be taken into consideration when dealing with very weak electrolytes.

Fig. 20-6. The formation of a hydrogen bond between two water dipoles may be an intermediate step in the ionization of water.

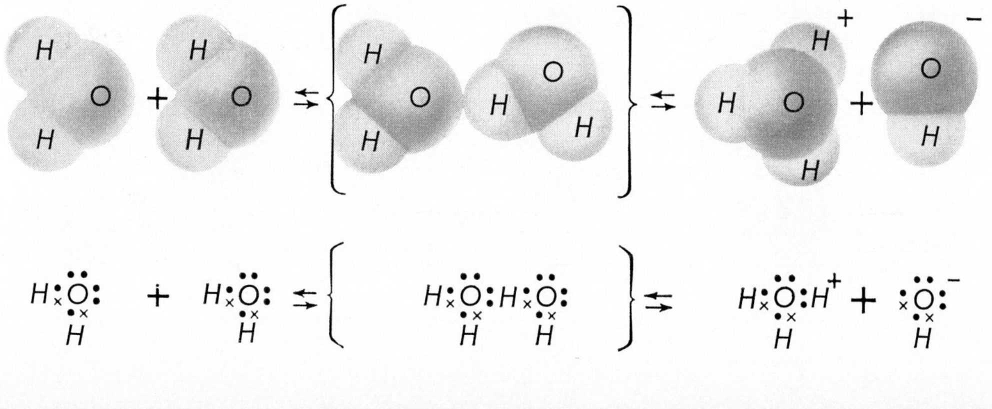

The ionization of water probably begins with the formation of a hydrogen bond between two water molecules. Under just the right conditions this bond may be stronger than the normal covalent bond of the molecule. The result of such a chance situation would be the formation of a hydrated proton and a hydroxide ion according to the reversible reaction:

$$H_2O + H_2O \rightleftarrows H_3O^+ + OH^-$$

Chemically the *hydronium ion*, H_3O^+, acts just like a hydrogen ion. In any reaction involving the hydronium ion the water of hydration is always left behind. Thus whenever the hydrogen ion, H^+, is indicated in connection with its water solution, *it is understood that this ion can exist only in the hydrated form, H_3O^+.*

11. Some substances do not ionize. We have seen that some substances do not conduct an electric current either as a pure substance, or in water solution. Many covalent compounds do not show the polar nature that characterizes the hydrogen chloride molecule. The attractive force of each of the atoms for the electrons forming the covalent bond may be about the same. The valence electrons are thus almost equally shared, and little separation of electric charge occurs. Such molecules with *symmetrical electronic fields* are not acted on by water dipoles to produce ions. Consequently, such substances are nonelectrolytes.

Carbon tetrachloride is a covalent compound with four polar bonds symmetrically distributed. The structure as a whole is nonpolar, and it is a nonelectrolyte. Furthermore, it is not acted on by water molecules because of the dissimilar nature of their electronic fields.

12. Electrolytes affect the freezing and boiling points abnormally. Molal solutions have a definite solute particle-to-solvent molecule ratio. The lowering of the freezing point of a solvent by a solute is directly proportional to the number of particles of solute present. The same reasoning applies to the elevation of the boiling point of a solvent by a solute. How, then, do we explain why one mole of hydrogen chloride dissolved in 1 kg of water lowers the freezing point more than one mole of sugar does? The abnormal lowering is caused by the separation of each molecule of hydrogen chloride which ionizes into two particles. Suppose that in a concentrated solution, 90 out of every 100

Fig. 20-7. **Five sugar molecules produce only five particles in solution. Five hydrogen chloride molecules, on the other hand, produce ten particles when dissolved in water.**

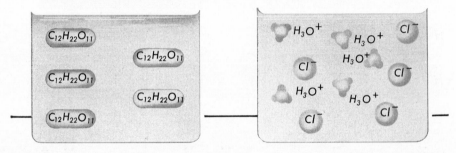

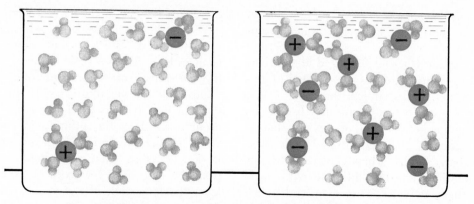

Fig. 20-8. The ions in the dilute solution on the left are far apart and act independently. The activity of the ions in the solution on the right is somewhat restricted because of the concentration. Thus the apparent number of ions present may be less than the actual number.

molecules ionize. Then, for every 100 molecules in solution, there are formed 190 particles (180 ions and 10 un-ionized molecules). Such a solution would therefore have its freezing point lowered 1.9 (190 ÷ 100) times as much as that of the solution of a solute which does not ionize. Suppose 100% of the hydrogen chloride molecules were ionized, as in a more dilute solution. We would then expect the lowering of the freezing point to be double that caused by the solute in a solution of a nonelectrolyte having the same molality.

The following equation shows the complete ionization of sulfuric acid in dilute solutions.

$$H_2SO_4 + 2\,H_2O \rightarrow 2\,H_3O^+ + SO_4^=$$

Every molecule of sulfuric acid which ionizes forms *three ions*. Two are hydronium ions which have one positive charge each; one is a sulfate ion with two negative charges. A solution of sulfuric acid of a given molality should, therefore, lower the freezing point of its solvent *three times* as much as a solution of a nonelectrolyte of the same molality. Careful experiments show this supposition to be true for very dilute solutions, in which the apparent degree of ionization reaches 100%. Under these circumstances the ionization theory is in accord with the facts. Of course, the reason for the different rise in the boiling point caused by electrolytes in solution is that ionization increases the number of particles present in the solution.

13. The degree of ionization can be measured. The larger the number of ions in a given volume of a solution the better a conductor of electricity it will be. It is possible to measure the degree of ionization by measuring the electric conductivity.

It is also possible to find the degree of ionization by measuring the lowering of the freezing point by an ionized solute in a measured amount of solvent. If a molal solution of an electrolyte of the type of sodium chloride freezes at −3.72° C [0° − (2 × 1.86 C°)], we may assume that the solute is 100% ionized.

Actual measurements, however, give

only an *apparent degree of ionization.* We have seen that electrovalent compounds, by the very nature of their structure, must be 100% ionized in solution. Experimental results give a degree of ionization somewhat less than 100%. We may explain this discrepancy by the attraction between ions of opposite charge, especially in concentrated solutions. Charged ions, when close together in solution, tend to interfere with each other's activities. They may tend to act as a group rather than as individual hydrated ions. In this way the *apparent* number of ions may be less than the actual number. The freezing and boiling points will be influenced accordingly. By diluting such a solution we may reduce the influence of the ions on each other and increase the apparent degree of ionization.

Water solutions of various concentrations of sodium chloride, for example, are observed to give the molal freezing-point lowerings shown below.

Concentration of NaCl in water solution	Freezing-point lowering/mole NaCl, in C°
0.10 m	3.48
0.010 m	3.60
0.0010 m	3.66
0.00010 m	3.72

14. Ionization explains electrolysis. Electrolysis is an important method of producing chemical reactions. We have seen one example of electrolysis in the preparation of oxygen and hydrogen by decomposing water. Now an explanation of the chemical action during this electrolysis is possible. Since water ionizes only slightly, additional ions must be supplied in order for an adequate electric current to be conducted between the electrodes. These may come from an ionic compound such as sodium hydroxide. However, sulfuric acid is most commonly used to supply the necessary ions.

When the electrodes are connected to a source of direct current, certain changes take place on their surfaces. In the electrolysis of water containing a dilute solution of sulfuric acid, three types of ions are present. There are *hydronium ions* from the sulfuric acid, and also a few hydronium ions from the ionization of water. There are *sulfate ions* from the acid, and a few *hydroxide ions* from the ionization of water. The hydronium ions carry a single positive charge and are attracted to the negative electrode, called the **cathode.** (Ions attracted to the cathode of an electrolytic cell are commonly referred to as *cations.*) At the cathode, each hydronium ion is discharged by gaining an electron, e^-, and forms a hydrogen atom. Two atoms combine to form a hydrogen molecule, and groups of these molecules bubble from the solution as hydrogen gas.

$$2\ H_3O^+ + 2\ e^- \rightarrow 2\ H_2O + H_2^0 \uparrow$$

The reaction at the positive electrode, called the *anode,* is not as simple. There are two types of negative ions in the solution, hydroxide ions and sulfate ions. Both of these are attracted to the anode. (Ions attracted to the anode of an electrolytic cell are commonly referred to as *anions.*) There are a great many more sulfate ions than hydroxide ions. Even so, the hydroxide ions give up electrons to the anode more easily than the sulfate ions; they are the ions discharged. Four hydroxide ions are required to produce a molecule of oxygen.

$$4\ OH^- - 4\ e^- \rightarrow 2\ H_2O + O_2^0 \uparrow$$

Observe that *twice* as many electrons are involved in liberating a molecule of oxygen as are needed to liberate a molecule of hydrogen. Consequently, twice as many hydrogen molecules are liberated as oxygen molecules. The relative volumes of the two gases liberated are *two and one—two volumes of hydrogen and one of oxygen.*

$$4\ H_3O^+ + 4\ OH^- \xrightarrow[\text{of 4 e}^-]{\text{transfer}}$$
$$2\ H_2\uparrow + O_2\uparrow + 6\ H_2O$$

If ions other than those of sulfuric acid are used to conduct the current between the electrodes, the same electrode reactions take place in most cases, *providing very dilute solutions are used.* Under this condition, hydronium ions take electrons more readily than many other positive ions. Therefore, they are liberated at the cathode in preference to those positive ions. Even if dilute solutions of sodium hydroxide or sodium chloride are used, hydrogen is liberated directly from the water. No metallic sodium is ever liberated from such solutions. Hydroxide ions in dilute solutions of electrolytes give up electrons more readily than many other negative ions. Therefore, in accordance with the reaction described above, oxygen is liberated at the anode in preference to these negative ions, which remain in the solution.

Fig. 20-9. **The electrolysis of water.**

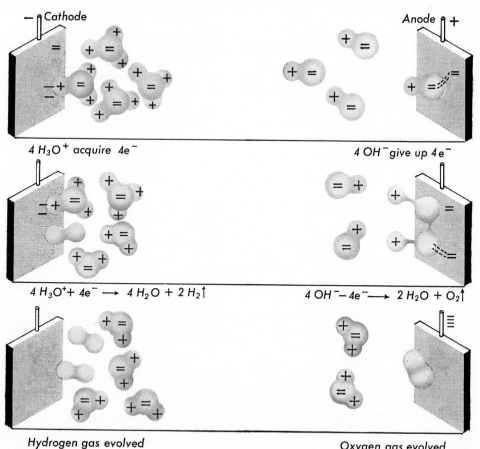

$4\ H_3O^+$ acquire $4\ e^-$ $4\ OH^-$ give up $4\ e^-$

$4\ H_3O^+ + 4\ e^- \longrightarrow 4\ H_2O + 2\ H_2\uparrow$ $4\ OH^- - 4\ e^- \longrightarrow 2\ H_2O + O_2\uparrow$

Hydrogen gas evolved   *Oxygen gas evolved*

SUMMARY

Substances whose water solutions conduct electricity are called electrolytes. Those whose water solutions do not conduct electricity are nonelectrolytes.

Water molecules are polar covalent molecules. The electrons are unevenly distributed, causing the oxygen end of the molecule to be more negative, and the hydrogen end more positive.

Electrovalent compounds are composed of ions. Water dipoles exert an attracting force on these ions, weakening their bonds. The ions enter the solution as hydrated particles—that is, loosely bonded to water dipoles. The degree of hydration of ions in water solution is somewhat indefinite. Solubility is limited by the tendency of hydrated ions to reform the crystal lattice as the number of free water molecules separating the ions diminishes.

Polar covalent molecules may ionize in water solution as hydrated ions. Strong electrolytes ionize practically completely, weak electrolytes only slightly. Water ionizes very slightly, forming hydronium ions and hydroxide ions. Hydrogen ions are never free in water solutions but are hydrated in the form of hydronium ions.

Electrolytes affect the freezing and boiling points of solvents to a greater extent than do nonelectrolytes. They have more particles per volume of solution.

The apparent degree of ionization may be measured by electric conductivity, or by freezing point depression or boiling point elevation. The apparent degree of ionization increases with increased dilution of an electrolyte. Electrovalent compounds are actually 100% ionized in solution.

In the electrolysis of water, hydronium ions are discharged at the negative electrode; hydrogen gas is given up. Hydroxide ions are discharged at the positive electrode; oxygen gas is given up. The function of the dilute acid added to the water is to increase its conductivity.

TEST YOURSELF ON THESE TERMS

anode	electrolysis	nonelectrolyte
cathode	electrovalent structure	polar molecule
covalent structure	hydrated ion	strong electrolyte
degree of ionization	hydronium ion	theory of ionization
dipole	ion	valence
dissociation	ionization	weak electrolyte

QUESTIONS

Group A

1. What is the distinction between an electrolyte and nonelectrolyte?
2. What effect does the addition of electrolytes have on the boiling points and freezing points of solvents such as water?
3. What theory helps to explain the behavior of electrolytes?
4. What are the important assumptions of this theory?
5. What is an ion?

Group B

6. Write the equation for the ionization of water.
7. Explain why the water molecule is a polar molecule.
8. Why is it not possible to have a molecule of an electrovalent compound?
9. What is the nature of the crystal structure of an electrovalent compound?
10. How does an atom differ from an ion?
11. How may we account for the stability of an ion?
12. (*a*) How do water molecules cause an electrovalent compound to dissociate? (*b*) How may the process be reversed?
13. Why is the dissociation of electrovalent compounds 100%?
14. Melted potassium chloride conducts an electric current. Explain.
15. (*a*) Explain how the action of water on a polar compound like hydrogen chloride produces ionization. (*b*) Write the equation for the ionization of hydrogen chloride in water solution showing the part played by the water.
16. What is the distinction between dissociation and ionization?
17. Describe the solution equilibrium in a saturated solution of sodium nitrate containing an excess of the crystals.
18. (*a*) What are symmetrical covalent molecules? (*b*) Why don't they ionize?
19. Explain the abnormal freezing point lowering and boiling point elevation of solvents produced by electrolytes in terms of the theory of ionization.
20. (*a*) Write an equation for the dissociation of calcium chloride. (*b*) What will be the freezing point of a 1-molal solution of calcium chloride in water?
21. What are two ways of measuring the apparent degree of ionization?
22. Why does the measurement of the apparent degree of ionization not coincide with the theory that electrovalent compounds are 100% dissociated in solution?
23. How does a concentrated solution of a weak electrolyte differ from a dilute solution of a strong electrolyte?
24. (*a*) Write equations for the electrode reactions during the electrolysis of water. (*b*) Why must two volumes of hydrogen be liberated for each volume of oxygen?

SOME THINGS FOR YOU TO DO

1. Locate a copy of the JOURNAL OF THE AMERICAN CHEMICAL SOCIETY, Vol. 34, page 353 (April 1912) and read the address of Svante Arrhenius before the Chicago Section of the American Chemical Society. Try the technical branch of your public library or the technical library of a nearby chemical industry or university.
2. Ask your instructor for permission to arrange an apparatus similar to Fig. 20-1 and test the conductivity of different solutions he may suggest. Keep a record of your results and report your findings to your class.

Chapter 21 · ACIDS, BASES, AND SALTS

1. ACIDS

1. Acids are an important class of substances. Compounds whose water solutions contain ions are traditionally classed as *acids*, *bases*, or *salts*. Even in ancient times acids were recognized as a separate class of chemicals. Today we encounter them, directly or indirectly, in practically all of our normal activities.

Nearly all fruits contain acids and so do many common foods. In lemons, oranges, and grapefruit, it is citric acid. In apples, it is malic acid. The souring of milk produces lactic acid. Butter which has become rancid contains butyric acid. The fermentation of hard cider forms the acetic acid of vinegar. These, because of their origin and nature, are called *organic* acids. Chemists prepare large quantities of important industrial acids synthetically. Some are made by composition reactions directly from the elements. They are often manufactured from minerals and are known as *inorganic* acids, or more commonly as *mineral* acids. These substances are referred to as the *traditional acids* al-

though the modern concept of acids presented in Section 4 broadens this category to include many substances not considered to be acids in the traditional sense.

2. Important industrial acids. If a manufacturing chemist were asked to name the most important acid, he would probably say *sulfuric acid*. This is a very versatile mineral acid. It has been said that the consumption of sulfuric acid is an index to the state of civilization and prosperity of a country. If a dye chemist, or one engaged in making explosives, were asked, he would tell you that *nitric acid* is important. A third important industrial acid is *hydrochloric acid*. It is used for cleaning metals before they are plated. It composes about 0.4 percent of the human gastric juice and aids in the preparation of food for digestion. We shall study each of these mineral acids in detail.

1. Sulfuric acid. This acid, which has the formula H_2SO_4, is a dense, oily liquid with a high boiling point. *Concentrated sulfuric acid* is approximately 36 normal (36 N) and contains 95%–98%

sulfuric acid, the balance being water. Its specific gravity is 1.84. Ordinary *dilute sulfuric acid* is made by adding 1 part of concentrated sulfuric acid into 6 parts of water. Other dilutions are sometimes used.

CAUTION: *The acid may be added to water slowly with stirring, but water must never be added to concentrated sulfuric acid. This causes a very violent reaction which produces steam, and spatters the concentrated acid.*

2. *Nitric acid.* This acid is a volatile liquid which has the formula HNO_3. The 100% nitric acid is too unstable for marketing, but the *concentrated nitric acid* of commerce is fairly stable. It contains 68% nitric acid dissolved in water and is approximately 16 normal (16 N). Its specific gravity is 1.42. Such a solution of pure nitric acid is colorless. It may turn brown on standing, however, due to slight decomposition. Nitric acid may be mixed with water in any proportion. Ordinary *dilute nitric acid* is usually made by adding 1 part of nitric acid to 5 parts of water. It contains about 10% nitric acid.

3. *Hydrochloric acid.* Hydrogen chloride, HCl, is a gas which is extremely soluble in water, forming a colorless solution known as hydrochloric acid. *Concentrated hydrochloric acid* contains in water solution about 38% hydrogen chloride and is approximately 12 normal (12N). Its specific gravity is nearly 1.20. Ordinary dilute hydrochloric acid is made by adding 1 part of concentrated hydrochloric acid to 4 parts of water. Such a solution contains from 6% to 8% hydrogen chloride. Hydrochloric acid may be diluted to any concentration desired.

3. The nature of acids. Arrhenius first gave the clue to the chemical nature of acids in his *Theory of Ionization.* He concluded that all acids ionize in water solutions to form hydrogen ions.

The three acids we have just described are essentially covalent and have one element in common, *hydrogen.* Sulfuric

VOCABULARY

Acid. A substance which gives up protons to another substance.

Acid anhydride. A compound derived from an acid by the removal of water from the acid.

Amphiprotic. Capable of acting either as an acid or as a base.

Base. A substance which acquires protons from another substance.

Indicator. A substance which changes color on the passage from acidity to alkalinity, or the reverse.

Neutralization. The reaction between hydronium ions and hydroxide ions to form water.

pH. Hydronium ion index; the common logarithm of the reciprocal of the hydronium-ion concentration.

Salt. A compound composed of positive ions of a metal or radical and negative ions produced when certain acids transfer protons to a base.

Standard solution. One that contains a definite concentration of solute which is known precisely.

Fig. 21-1. Sulfuric acid is widely used to remove scale from iron and steel products. In this photograph a rubber-lined tank contains the acid. The descaling process is known in the steel industry as "pickling" and the tank of sulfuric acid is called the "pickling bath." (B. F. Goodrich Industrial Products)

and nitric acids in pure form are exceedingly poor conductors, being only very slightly ionized. Liquid hydrogen chloride, as has been stated already, is considered to be a nonconductor of electricity. In water solution, however, each of these substances becomes strongly ionized due to the hydrating action of the water dipoles. We may represent their ionization in water solutions by the following equations:

$$H_2SO_4 + 2 H_2O \rightarrow 2 H_3O^+ + SO_4^=$$
$$HNO_3 + H_2O \rightarrow H_3O^+ + NO_3^-$$
$$HCl + H_2O \rightarrow H_3O^+ + Cl^-$$

The hydronium ion, H_3O^+, is common to all of these solutions. It is apparent that the acidic properties they have in common must be the properties of this ion.

Acids which ionize completely, or nearly so, in water solution provide a high concentration of hydronium ions, and are called *strong* acids. Sulfuric, nitric, and hydrochloric acids are strong mineral acids. Acids which furnish few hydronium ions in water solution, such as acetic and carbonic acids, are known as *weak* acids. They are only slightly ionized in water, even in solutions that are quite dilute.

4. Modern definition of acids. The hydronium ion is in reality a hydrated proton. In water solution it is in the hydrated form $H^+ \cdot H_2O$ or H_3O^+, protons combined with polar water molecules. *We may consider that protons (hydrogen ions) will not be released by such molecules as HCl unless there are molecules or ions present which can accept them.* This explains why hydrogen chloride, dissolved in a nonpolar solvent such as toluene, remains a nonconductor.

Hydrogen chloride dissolved in ammonia reacts in the same way it does in water.

$$HCl + H_2O \rightarrow H_3O^+ + Cl^-$$
$$HCl + NH_3 \rightarrow NH_4^+ + Cl^-$$

The manner in which the reaction occurs may be seen by using electron-dot formulas.

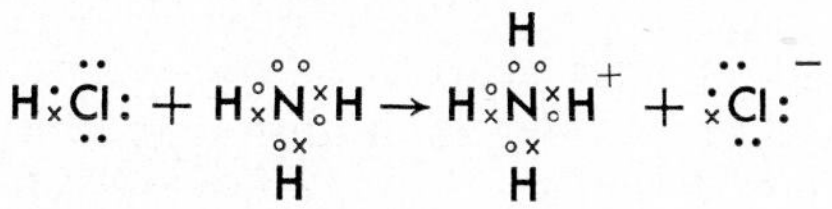

$$H{\overset{\times}{\underset{\times}{\cdot}}}Cl{:} + H{\overset{\circ}{\underset{\times}{N}}}{\overset{\circ}{\underset{\times}{H}}} \rightarrow H{\overset{\circ}{\underset{\times}{N}}}{\overset{\circ}{\underset{\times}{H}}}^+ + {:}Cl{:}^-$$

The proton is transferred directly to the ammonia structure forming the *ammonium ion.* The proton is given up by the hydrogen chloride molecule, which is said to be a *proton donor.* In the modern concept advanced by J. N. Brönsted, a Danish chemist, *an acid is simply a*

proton donor—a substance which gives up protons to another substance. Thus hydrogen chloride is an acid, according to Brönsted's theory, even though it doesn't contain hydrogen ions when pure.

According to this general definition, water is an acid when ammonia is dissolved in it. Some water molecules donate protons to ammonia molecules according to the following reversible reaction:

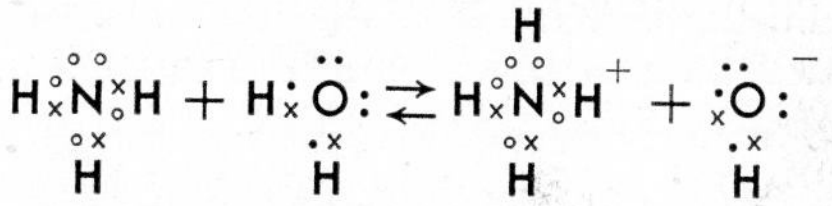

$$H{\overset{\circ}{\underset{\times}{N}}}{\overset{\circ}{\underset{\times}{H}}} + H{\overset{\cdot\cdot}{\underset{\cdot}{O}}}{:} \rightleftarrows H{\overset{\circ}{\underset{\times}{N}}}{\overset{\circ}{\underset{\times}{H}}}^+ + {:}{\overset{\cdot\cdot}{\underset{\times}{O}}}{:}^-$$

$$NH_3 + H_2O \rightleftarrows NH_4^+ + OH^-$$

Furthermore, in water solutions of the strong mineral acids described in Section 3, the hydronium ion, H_3O^+, becomes the acid since it is the actual proton donor in reactions involving the solutions.

This modern definition of acids is very broad, being concerned with the behavior of substances as a source of protons for combination with the molecules or ions of other substances. It is

Fig. 21-2. When hydrogen chloride is dissolved in ammonia, a proton is donated by the polar HCl molecule to the NH$_3$ molecule to form the ammonium ion, NH$_4$$^+$, and the chloride ion, Cl$^-$. In this reaction hydrogen chloride acts as the acid and ammonia acts as the base.

$$H{\overset{\cdot\cdot}{\underset{\cdot\cdot}{\times}}}Cl{:} \quad + \quad H{\overset{\circ}{\underset{\times}{N}}}{\overset{\circ}{\underset{\times}{H}}} \quad \rightarrow \quad H{\overset{\circ}{\underset{\times}{N}}}{\overset{\circ}{\underset{\times}{H}}}^+ \quad + \quad {:}Cl{:}^-$$

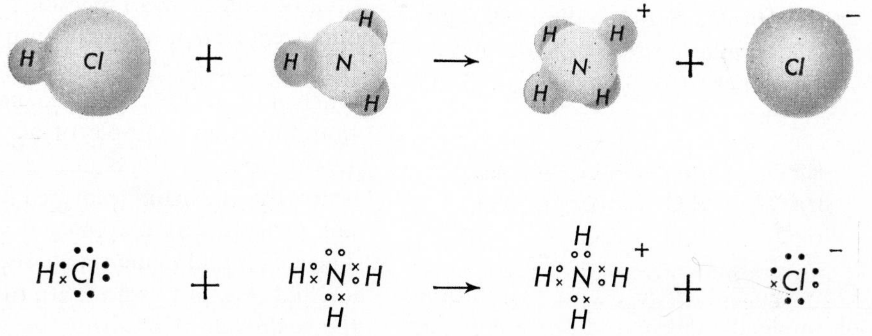

not concerned with the production of ions at all. It is very useful in advanced chemistry as well as in elementary chemistry. Definitions do not alter the facts of chemistry; they are useful if they help one organize the facts of chemistry. In our discussions, this broad concept of acids will be used extensively.

5. Properties of traditional acids. Most traditional acids are quite soluble in water. Other physical properties differ so widely that it is not possible to mention many general similarities. However, they have many chemical properties in common.

1. Acids contain ionizable hydrogen in covalent combination with a nonmetallic element or radical. The strength of an acid depends upon the degree of ionization in water solution, not upon the *amount* of hydrogen in the molecule. Sulfuric acid ionizes in two stages, depending on the amount of dilution, according to the following ionic equations:

$$H_2SO_4 + H_2O \rightarrow H_3O^+ + HSO_4^-$$
$$HSO_4^- + H_2O \rightarrow H_3O^+ + SO_4^=$$

The first stage is completed in fairly concentrated solutions. In this form sulfuric acid may produce *acid salts*, in which the HSO_4^- ion is present. Sodium *hydrogen* sulfate, $NaHSO_4$, is an example. The second stage is completed in rather dilute solutions. Here the $SO_4^=$ ion is present. Under such conditions *normal salts* are formed. Sodium sulfate, Na_2SO_4, is an example.

The rather weak phosphoric acid ionizes in three stages.

$$H_3PO_4 + H_2O \rightarrow H_3O^+ + H_2PO_4^-$$
$$H_2PO_4^- + H_2O \rightarrow H_3O^+ + HPO_4^=$$
$$HPO_4^= + H_2O \rightarrow H_3O^+ + PO_4^\equiv$$

Only the first stage occurs in solutions of moderate concentrations producing

the *dihydrogen phosphate ion,* $H_2PO_4^-$. In more dilute solutions the *monohydrogen phosphate ion,* $HPO_4^=$, is formed. In very dilute solutions appreciable concentrations of the normal *phosphate ion,* $PO_4^\equiv$, may be formed.

2. Acids furnish protons when they react with bases. Their many common properties depend on this characteristic behavior. Acids which furnish only one proton per molecule are called *monoprotic acids.* Examples are HCl, HNO_3, and $HC_2H_3O_2$. Sulfuric acid H_2SO_4, is *diprotic,* giving two protons per molecule. Phosphoric acid, H_3PO_4, is *triprotic.*

3. Acids have a sour taste. Lemons, grapefruit, and limes are sour. These contain weak acids in solution. A solid acid tastes sour as it dissolves in the saliva forming a water solution. Most laboratory acids are very corrosive and powerful poisons. You should never use the *taste test* for an acid in the laboratory.

4. Acids affect indicators. If a drop of an acid solution is placed on a test strip of blue *litmus,* the *blue* color changes to *red.* Litmus is a dye extracted from certain lichens. Some other substances may be used as indicators. *Phenolphthalein* is colorless in the presence of acids. *Methyl orange,* another indicator, turns red in acid solutions.

5. Acids neutralize hydroxides. If solutions of an acid and a metallic hydroxide are mixed in equivalent quantities, each exactly cancels the properties of the other. This process is called *neutralization* and is an example of an ionic reaction. The products are a salt and water, the salt being recovered in crystalline form by the evaporation of water. The acid is said to neutralize the hydroxide, but it is just as accurate to say that the hydroxide neutralizes the acid.

When one mole of sodium hydroxide is treated with one mole of hydrochloric acid the following equation may be written:

$$HCl + NaOH \rightarrow NaCl + H_2O$$

Since both reactants and the salt product are in completely ionized form, the ionic equation is more appropriate.

$$H_3O^+ + Cl^- + Na^+ + OH^- \rightarrow$$
$$Na^+ + Cl^- + 2 H_2O$$

Observe that sodium ions and chloride ions remain in solution and actually play no part in the reaction. By writing the simplest ionic equation, these *spectator* ions are eliminated and only those which actually participate in the primary action are shown.

$$H_3O^+ + OH^- \rightarrow 2 H_2O$$

This shows that the neutralization reaction is entirely between the hydronium ion and the hydroxide ion of the soluble metallic hydroxide. In all neutralizations of very soluble hydroxides by strong acids the reaction is the same. The nonmetallic ions of the acid and the metallic ions of the hydroxide undergo no chemical change. We may prefer to write the complete equation because it shows what salt could be recovered by evaporation of the water solvent.

6. *Acids react with many metals.* They set free hydrogen and form a salt. The equation for the action of sulfuric acid on zinc is typical:

$$Zn + H_2SO_4 \rightarrow ZnSO_4 + H_2 \uparrow$$

Written ionically, the equation is:

$$Zn + 2 H_3O^+ + SO_4^= \rightarrow$$
$$Zn^{++} + SO_4^= + H_2 \uparrow + 2 H_2O$$

or simply

$$Zn + 2 H_3O^+ \rightarrow Zn^{++} + H_2 \uparrow + 2 H_2O$$

The salt separates as crystals of $ZnSO_4$ on evaporation of the water. Remember that in solution, such *salts* are simply a dispersion of hydrated ions.

7. *Acids react with oxides of metals.* They form salts and water. As an example, consider copper(II) oxide and sulfuric acid. The equation follows:

$$CuO + H_2SO_4 \rightarrow CuSO_4 + H_2O$$

Ionically:

$$CuO + 2 H_3O^+ + SO_4^= \rightarrow$$
$$Cu^{++} + SO_4^= + 3 H_2O$$

8. *Acids react with carbonates.* They liberate carbon dioxide and produce a salt and water.

$$CaCO_3 + 2 HCl \rightarrow$$
$$CaCl_2 + H_2O + CO_2 \uparrow$$

Ionically:

$$Ca^{++}CO_3^= + 2 H_3O^+ + 2 Cl^- \rightarrow$$
$$Ca^{++} + 2 Cl^- + 3 H_2O + CO_2 \uparrow$$

6. Naming the traditional acids. Some acids are *binary* compounds, containing only *two* elements; others are *ternary* compounds, containing *three* elements.

1. *Binary acids.* Hydrogen chloride in water solution is called *hydrochloric* acid. The prefix *hydro–* shows it is a binary acid. The root *–chlor–* is derived from the element chlorine. Binary acids always have the ending *–ic*. A water solution of HBr is called *hydro-brom-ic* acid. A water solution of hydrogen sulfide, H_2S, is known as *hydro-sulfur-ic* acid.

2. *Ternary acids.* The formulas and names of the various oxygen acids of chlorine may be used to illustrate the general method of naming acids which contain hydrogen, oxygen, and a third element.

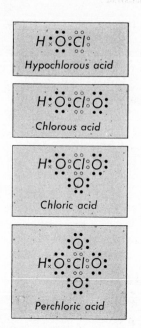

Fig. 21-3. Electron-dot formulas of the four oxy-acids of chlorine.

$HClO_4$................per-*chlor-ic* acid
$HClO_3$.................*chlor-ic* acid
$HClO_2$................*chlor-ous* acid
$HClO$.............*hypo-chlor-ous* acid

In all of these acids chlorine is the central element. For this reason the root *chlor–* is used in each case. $HClO_3$ is named *chlor-ic acid*. No prefix is used. The acid of chlorine which contains *more* oxygen than chloric acid is called *per-chlor-ic* acid. The chlorine acid containing *one less* oxygen atom per molecule than chloric acid is called *chlor-ous* acid. The acid of chlorine which contains *still less* oxygen than chlorous acid has the prefix *hypo–*, the root *–chlor–*, and the suffix *–ous*.

To use these rules for naming acids it is necessary to know the formula for one ternary oxygen acid in any series. Chloric acid is $HClO_3$, nitric acid is HNO_3, bromic acid is $HBrO_3$, sulfuric acid is H_2SO_4, and phosphoric acid is H_3PO_4.

7. Acid anhydrides. The oxides of nonmetallic elements that react with water form acids. When carbon dioxide dissolves in water a reversible reaction occurs.

$$CO_2 + H_2O \rightleftarrows H_2CO_3$$

Carbonic acid decomposes into water and carbon dioxide. Because the acid has in reality been *dehydrated*, carbon dioxide is called the *acid anhydride* of carbonic acid. *Oxides that react with water to form acids, or that are formed by the removal of water from acids, are known as acid anhydrides.*

There are several acids which do not contain oxygen. The reaction between an acid anhydride and water cannot be considered a general method of preparing acids. However, it is an important method of preparing some oxygen-containing acids.

Sulfur dioxide is the acid anhydride of sulfurous acid.

$$SO_2 + H_2O \rightleftarrows H_2SO_3$$

Sulfur trioxide is the acid anhydride of sulfuric acid.

$$SO_3 + H_2O \rightleftarrows H_2SO_4$$

These anhydrides are important in the manufacture of sulfuric acid. Sulfuric acid, because it is cheap and has a high boiling point, is used in the production of several other acids. Hydrochloric acid is an example, although important quantities of hydrochloric acid are now being produced by direct composition from the elements hydrogen and chlorine.

Nitric acid can also be produced by the reaction of sulfuric acid with a nitrate. This process is not generally used commercially because it is more expensive than other processes.

2. BASES

8. The nature of bases. There are several substances found in almost every home that have long been called bases. Household ammonia, an ammonia-water solution, is a common cleaning agent. Lye is a commercial grade of sodium hydroxide, NaOH, used for cleaning clogged sink drains. Limewater is a solution of calcium hydroxide, $Ca(OH)_2$. Milk of magnesia, a suspension of magnesium hydroxide, $Mg(OH)_2$, in water, is used as an antacid, a laxative, and an antidote for strong acids.

Arrhenius considered a base to be any soluble hydroxide which destroyed the properties of an acid when their solutions were mixed. We know, of course, that the only reaction occurring in the neutralization is between hydronium ions and hydroxide ions. The nonmetal of the acid and the metal of the hydroxide remain in solution as hydrated ions.

Bases are now defined as substances which acquire protons from another substance. The hydroxide ion is the most common base. It reacts with the hydronium ion to form water. The soluble metallic hydroxides which yield hydroxide ions when dissolved in water, together with ammonia water, are still frequently referred to as bases. However, *it is the hydroxide ion which reacts as the base in the neutralization process.* Ammonia-water solutions are traditionally referred to as ammonium hydroxide. However, ammonium hydroxide as an actual molecule probably does not exist in these solutions except through the possibility of the formation of hydrogen bonds between some NH_4^+ ions and OH^- ions. These solutions are more appropriately called ammonia-water solutions, or simply NH_3-Aq (aqua-ammonia). The most common basic solutions used in the laboratory, those of NaOH, KOH, $Ca(OH)_2$, and NH_3-Aq, are said to be *alkaline* in their behavior.

In the modern concept of Brönsted, an acid is simply a proton donor. Accordingly, *a base is a proton acceptor.* Since the OH^- ion is not the only particle that combines with protons, our general use of the term base includes other substances which accept protons.

We have stated that hydrogen chloride ionizes in water solution as a result of the hydrating action of the solvent dipoles.

$$HCl + H_2O \rightarrow H_3O^+ + Cl^-$$

Here the water molecule is the base, accepting protons to form the hydronium ion H_3O^+. In the neutralization reaction between HCl and NaOH described earlier, the H_3O^+ ion may be considered to be the acid, since it, and not the HCl molecule, is the proton donor. The OH^- ion is, of course, the proton acceptor or base.

When HCl is dissolved in liquid ammonia, the NH_3 molecule acts as the base.

$$HCl + NH_3 \rightarrow NH_4^+ + Cl^-$$

When NH_3 is dissolved in water, protons are donated by the water which, therefore, acts as an acid. Ammonia accepts protons and, therefore, is the base. A low concentration of NH_4^+ ions and OH^- ions is produced in the reversible action.

$$NH_3 + H_2O \rightleftarrows NH_4^+ + OH^-$$

This general concept of acids and bases is quite broad, but is very useful in more advanced studies of nonaqueous solutions. In elementary chemistry, the bases we deal with most frequently are the soluble metallic hydroxides and their water solutions containing the basic hydroxide ion.

9. The characteristics of hydroxides.
1. Hydroxides of the active metals furnish OH⁻ ions in solution. Sodium and potassium hydroxides are very soluble in water. They are electrovalent (ionic) compounds and so are completely ionized in water solution. Their solutions are *strongly basic* due to the high concentration of OH^- ions.

$$Na^+OH^- \rightarrow Na^+ + OH^-$$
$$K^+OH^- \rightarrow K^+ + OH^-$$

Calcium, strontium, and barium hydroxides are not very soluble in water. However, they too are ionic compounds. Their water solutions are completely ionized and, because of their low solubility, are *moderately basic.*

$$Ca^{++}(OH^-)_2 \rightarrow Ca^{++} + 2\ OH^-$$
$$Sr^{++}(OH^-)_2 \rightarrow Sr^{++} + 2\ OH^-$$
$$Ba^{++}(OH^-)_2 \rightarrow Ba^{++} + 2\ OH^-$$

We can see that the strength of the base depends on the concentration of OH^- ions in solution and not on the number of hydroxide ions per formula weight of the compound.

Ammonia-water solutions are *weakly basic* due to a low concentration of OH^- ions. Ammonia, NH_3, is not a strong base and so does not acquire very many protons from water molecules when in solution. Relatively few NH_4^+ ions and OH^- ions are formed.

2. Soluble hydroxides have a bitter taste. Possibly you have tasted lime-water and know that it is bitter. Soapsuds also taste bitter because of the presence of hydroxide ions. The *taste test* should never be used in the laboratory. Strongly basic solutions are very *caustic.* The accompanying metallic ions are sometimes poisonous.

3. Solutions of hydroxides feel slippery. The very soluble hydroxides, such as sodium hydroxide, attack the skin and are capable of producing severe caustic burns. Their solutions have a soapy, slippery feeling when rubbed between the thumb and fingers.

4. Soluble hydroxides affect indicators. The basic OH^- ions in solutions of the soluble hydroxides cause *litmus* to turn from *red* to *blue.* This is just the opposite color change to that caused by H_3O^+ ions of acid solutions. In a basic solution, *phenolphthalein* turns *red*, and *methyl orange* is *yellow.* The insoluble hydroxides, on the other hand, seldom produce enough OH^- ions to cause these changes; they do not affect indicators.

5. Hydroxides neutralize acids. The neutralization of HNO_3 by KOH may be represented by the equation:

$$KOH + HNO_3 \rightarrow KNO_3 + H_2O$$

Of course, ionic KOH is dissociated in water solution and exists as hydrated K^+ ions and OH^- ions.

$$K^+OH^- \rightarrow K^+ + OH^-$$

In water solution, the covalent HNO_3 is ionized and exists as hydrated protons and nitrate ions.

$$HNO_3 + H_2O \rightarrow H_3O^+ + NO_3^-$$

The complete ionic equation for this neutralization reaction may be written:

$$H_3O^+ + NO_3^- + K^+ + OH^- \rightarrow$$
$$K^+ + NO_3^- + 2\ H_2O$$

Removing the spectator ions, those which undergo no change during the reaction, we have:

$$H_3O^+ + OH^- \rightarrow 2\ H_2O$$

This is the only action that takes place in the neutralization reaction. The hydrated K^+ and NO_3^- ions are joined in the form of ionic crystals of the salt, KNO_3, only upon removal of water by evaporation.

6. *Hydroxides react with the oxides of nonmetals.* They form salts and water. As an example, the equation for the reaction of carbon dioxide and sodium hydroxide is

$$CO_2 + 2\,NaOH \rightarrow Na_2CO_3 + H_2O$$

7. *Certain hydroxides may have either acidic or basic properties.* Hydroxide substances which are weakly basic in the presence of acids may also behave as acids in the presence of strong bases. Zinc hydroxide, $Zn(OH)_2$, reacts with hydrochloric acid to produce zinc chloride and water.

$$Zn(OH)_2 + 2\,HCl \rightarrow ZnCl_2 + 2\,H_2O$$

In the presence of a solution of sodium hydroxide it acts as an acid forming the *zincate* ion, $ZnO_2^=$.

$$Zn(OH)_2 + 2\,NaOH \rightarrow Na_2ZnO_2 + 2\,H_2O$$

We may more readily understand this behavior of $Zn(OH)_2$ if we rewrite its formula as H_2ZnO_2. Thus,

$$H_2ZnO_2 + 2\,NaOH \rightarrow Na_2ZnO_2 + 2\,H_2O$$

Such substances which may have either acidic or basic properties under certain conditions are said to be **amphiprotic.** The hydroxides of aluminum, chromium, tin, and lead are also *amphiprotic.*

In the modern concept of acids and bases, water is an amphiprotic substance. When a water molecule accepts a proton from hydrogen chloride it acts as a base. On the other hand, when a water molecule donates a proton to ammonia it acts as an acid. Indeed, in the slight ionization of water, one water molecule donates a proton to another water mol-

ecule. Thus, some of the water molecules behave as an acid while others behave as a base.

10. **Naming hydroxides.** The method of naming the hydroxides is very simple. The name of the metallic ion is merely followed by the term *hydroxide.* For example, $Zn(OH)_2$ is called *zinc hydroxide.* $Bi(OH)_3$ is called *bismuth hydroxide.*

If two hydroxides are formed by a metal, appropriate Roman numerals are used to denote the lower and higher valence of the metal respectively. Thus $Fe(OH)_2$ is called *iron(II) hydroxide* and $Fe(OH)_3$ is called *iron(III) hydroxide.*

11. **Basic anhydrides.** In Chapter 8, Section 3, it was stated that the active metals react with water to produce hydrogen gas and the corresponding hydroxide. These metallic hydroxides are ionic in structure and exist in solution as hydrated metallic and hydroxide ions.

The denser metals form hydroxides which are practically insoluble in water. These are produced more conveniently by indirect methods using a salt and a soluble hydroxide. See Fig. 21-4.

$$Fe^{+++} + 3\,Cl^- + 3\,Na^+ + 3\,OH^- \rightarrow$$
$$Fe(OH)_3 \downarrow + 3\,Na^+ + 3\,Cl^-$$

As the reaction involves only the Fe^{+++} and OH^- ions, we may write the simpler net equation:

$$Fe^{+++} + 3\,OH^- \rightarrow Fe(OH)_3 \downarrow$$

Such precipitates vary somewhat in composition, depending on the conditions under which they are formed. The actual composition is that of a *hydrated oxide.* In the case above the precipitate is more correctly represented as

$$Fe_2O_3 \cdot (H_2O)_n,$$

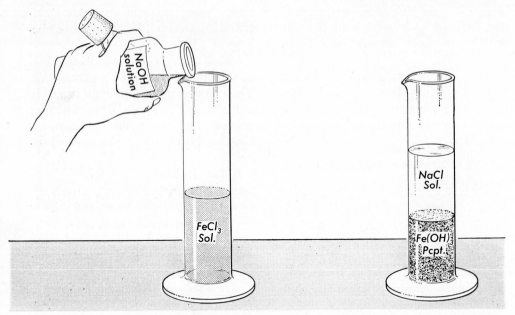

Fig. 21-4. **The hydroxides of heavy metals are practically insoluble.**

where n is some small integer which varies with conditions. It is a matter of convenience in equation writing to represent such precipitates as hydroxides. Aluminum, chrominum, tin, and lead also form hydrated oxides.

The oxides of active metals react with water to produce the corresponding hydroxides. If the hydroxide is soluble in water, the solution is basic due to the presence of OH^- ions. Oxides of sodium, potassium, calcium, strontium, and barium react vigorously with water. You may have seen a plasterer *slaking* quicklime, CaO, by adding water to it. He was forming *slaked lime*, $Ca(OH)_2$.

$$CaO + H_2O \rightarrow Ca(OH)_2$$

*Oxides which react with water to produce solutions containing the basic OH^- ions are called **basic anhydrides.*** The oxides of the active metals are *basic anhydrides.* They are electrovalent compounds which, as solids, have ionic crystalline structures. In contrast, acid anhydrides are oxides of nonmetals. They are covalent compounds which, in the solid state, have molecular crystalline structures.

3. STANDARD SOLUTIONS

★ **12. The pH of a solution.** The concentration of H_3O^+ ions in a solution may be expressed as *gram-ions of hydronium ion* per liter. (Gram-ion is to the ion what gram-atom is to the atom: the "ionic weight" expressed in grams.) A more convenient way, however, is to indicate the concentration indirectly by a numerical scale called the *pH scale.* This scale is sometimes known as the *hydronium-ion index.* Numerically, the pH of a solution is the common logarithm of the number of liters of solution that contains 1 gram-ion of hydronium ions, 19 g of H_3O^+ ions.

The number of liters of solution required to furnish 1 gram-ion of H_3O^+ is equal to the *reciprocal* of the H_3O^+ ion concentration given in gram-ions of H_3O^+ per liter. This is expressed by chemists as

$$\frac{1}{[H_3O^+]}$$

where $[H_3O^+]$ means hydronium ion concentration in *gram-ions (moles) per liter.* Thus, *the pH of a solution is defined as the common logarithm of the reciprocal of the hydronium ion concentration* and is expressed by the equation:

$$pH = \log \frac{1}{[H_3O^+]}$$

Pure water is slightly ionized. Chemists have found that it contains 0.0000001 gram-ion of H_3O^+ per liter. The pH of water is therefore:

$$pH = \log \frac{1}{0.0000001}$$

$$pH = \log \frac{1}{10^{-7}}$$

$$pH = \log 10^7$$

$$pH = 7$$

The common logarithm of a number is the power to which 10 must be raised to give the number. Thus 0.0000001 is 10^{-7} and its reciprocal is 10,000,000, or 10^7. The logarithm of 10^7 is 7.

We know that the H_3O^+ and OH^- ion concentrations in pure water are equal. Water is therefore *neutral. All solutions in which the H_3O^+ and OH^- ion concentrations are equal are called* **neutral solutions.** The product of the two ionic concentrations is a *constant;* for pure water at room temperature it is $10^{-7} \times 10^{-7} = 10^{-14}$. Thus, in any solution, if the concentration of one ion *decreases,* the concentration of the other

Fig. 21-5. **Approximate pH values over a wide range may be determined by the use of special indicators.** (Micro Essential Laboratory)

must *increase.* The total range of pH values is from 0 to 14. All neutral solutions have a pH of 7.

If the H_3O^+ ion concentration is *greater* than that in pure water, the number of liters required to provide 1 gram-ion of H_3O^+ ions is *smaller.* Consequently, the pH is a *smaller* number than 7. Such a solution is *acidic.* Conversely, if the H_3O^+ ion concentration is *less than* that in pure water, the pH is a *larger* number than 7. Such a solution is *basic.*

Special indicators, such as Hydrion paper, show varying shades of color which correspond to the whole range of pH values. To measure the *acidity* or *alkalinity* (basicity) of a solution, a drop of the solution is placed on the paper and the color is compared to the Hydrion color chart furnished with the test papers.

The color plates (pages 310–311) show the colors obtained when using solutions of different pH values to which Gramercy Universal Indicator has been added. Gramercy Universal Indicator is a mixture of solutions of dyes that can be

APPROXIMATE pH OF SOME COMMON SUBSTANCES

0.1-N HCl	1.1
0.1-N H_2SO_4	1.2
gastric juice	2.0
lemons	2.3
vinegar	2.8
0.1-N $HC_2H_3O_2$	2.9
soft drinks	3.0
apples	3.1
grapefruit	3.1
oranges	3.5
cherries	3.6
tomatoes	4.2
bananas	4.6
bread	5.5
potatoes	5.8
rainwater	6.2
milk	6.5
pure water	7.0
eggs	7.8
0.1-N $NaHCO_3$	8.4
seawater	8.5
milk of magnesia	10.5
0.1-N NH_3	11.1
0.1-N Na_2CO_3	11.6
0.1-N NaOH	13.0

used to measure the pH of a solution. To 10 ml of solution, 1 ml of the indicator solution is added. By comparing the color produced with those of an indicator color chart, a rather accurate determination of the pH is obtained.

★ **13. Standard solution.** Many chemical reactions occur in solution. It was stated in Chapter 13 that just so much of one substance would react with a given quantity of another substance. If the concentration of one solution is known, it is sometimes a simple matter to determine the concentration of another solution by reacting the two solutes.

In Chapter 19, Section 8, the methods of expressing the concentration of solutions quantitatively were given as *molality, molarity (formality),* and *normality;* there being certain advantages to each. A **standard solution** is one that *contains a definite concentration of solute which is known precisely.* This concentration may be stated in terms of molality, molarity, or normality.

★ **14. Standard solutions of known molality.** We can prepare a *molal* (1-m) solution of a substance by weighing out precisely *one mole* of the substance and then dissolving it in exactly *1 kilogram* of solvent. A *half-molal* (0.5-m) solution contains *one half mole* of solute per kilogram of solvent. A *two-molal* (2-m) solution has *two moles* of solute in 1 kilogram of solvent. Of course, 0.5 mole of solute dissolved in 0.5 kg of solvent, or 0.25 mole of solute in 0.25 kg of solvent gives a 1-m solution.

Molal solutions are important to the chemist because (for a given solvent) *two solutions of equal molality have the same ratio of solute to solvent molecules.* Molality is preferred when portions are to be weighed. This type of solution is essential in molecular weight determinations.

★ **15. Standard solutions of known molarity.** A *molar* (1-M) solution contains *1 mole* of solute per *liter* of solution. The gram-formula weight of sodium chloride, NaCl, is 58.5 g. This quantity of NaCl dissolved in enough water to make exactly 1 liter of solution gives a 1-M solution. Half this quantity of NaCl in 1 liter of solution gives a 0.5-M solution, and twice this quantity of NaCl per liter of solution gives a 2-M solution.

A volumetric flask similar to the one shown in Fig. 21-6 is commonly used in preparing solutions of known molarity. A measured quantity of solute is dissolved in a portion of solvent in the flask and then additional solvent is added to fill the flask to the mark on the neck.

Thus, the quantity of solute and the volume of solution are known and the concentration can be expressed in terms of its molarity.

As another example, the molecular weight of H_2SO_4 is 98. To make 1 liter of a 1-M solution of H_2SO_4 requires 98 g of the solute. A 0.5-M solution needs only one half of 98 g, or 49 g, of H_2SO_4 per liter of solution. Observe that molar solutions are based on the *volume of solution*. Molal solutions are based on the *mass of solvent. Equal volumes of molecular solutions of equal molarity have the same number of molecules.* Molarity is preferred when volumes of solution are to be measured.

★ **16. Standard for gram-equivalent weights.** Hydrogen is commonly used as the standard for equivalent relationships among reactants and their products. The

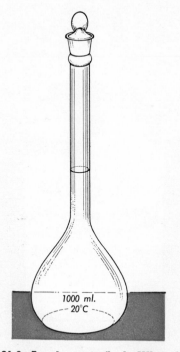

Fig. 21-6. A volumetric flask. When filled to the mark at 20 ° C, it contains precisely one liter.

gram-equivalent weight of a substance was defined in Chapter 19, Section 8 in terms of its mass which contains, combines with, or replaces, 1 gram-atom of hydrogen. The gram-equivalent weight of an element is *ordinarily* determined by dividing its gram-atomic weight by its valence.

The gram-equivalent weight of oxygen is 8 g (16 g ÷ 2). Eight grams of oxygen combines with 1 gram of hydrogen. Sodium has a gram-equivalent weight of 23 g (23 g ÷ 1). Twenty-three grams of sodium will replace 1 g of hydrogen, and will combine with 8 g of oxygen. Thus 23 g of Na, 8 g of O_2, and 1 g of H_2 are *chemical equivalents.*

The gram-equivalent weight of a compound is *ordinarily* determined by dividing its molecular (formula) weight by its total positive (or negative) valence. A mole of H_2SO_4 is 98 g and the total valence (positive or negative) is 2. One gram-equivalent weight of sulfuric acid is 49 g, one-half mole. One mole of $Ca_3(PO_4)_2$ is 310 g. The total valence is 6. One gram-equivalent weight of $Ca_3(PO_4)_2$ is 51.7 g, one-sixth mole.

Gram-equivalent weights are very convenient to use in acid-base neutralizations since these reactions require equal numbers of hydronium and hydroxide ions. One g-ion (1 mole) of hydronium ions, 19 g of H_3O^+, combines with 1 g-ion (1 mole) of hydroxide ions, 17 g of OH^-, to form 2 moles of water, 36 g of H_2O in a neutralization reaction. Thus, *1 gram-equivalent weight of any acid furnishes 1 mole of protons and 1 gram-equivalent weight of any basic substance accepts 1 mole of protons.*

Special consideration must be given to oxidizing and reducing agents. For such reactants it is helpful to consider the gram-equivalent weight in terms of the mass of the substance that acquires or furnishes the Avogadro number of electrons in a specific reaction. Oxidation-reduction reactions will be considered in Chapter 23.

⋆ **17. Standard solutions of known normality.** A *normal* (1-N) *solution* contains 1 *gram-equivalent weight* of solute per *liter* of solution. A mole of the monoprotic acid HCl has a mass of 36.5 g and can furnish 1 mole of hydrogen as protons. Thus, 1 mole of HCl in 1 liter of solution provides 1 mole of protons to form 1 mole (1 g-ion) of H_3O^+ and has a 1-N concentration. Suppose we require a solution of HCl which furnishes 0.1 g-ion of H_3O^+ per liter, a 0.1-N HCl solution. It is evident that 3.65 g of HCl must be used diluted to 1 liter volume. *However, this is 3.65 g of anhydrous hydrogen chloride in one liter of solution,* not 3.65 g of the concentrated hydrochloric acid on hand in the laboratory. How may we determine the volume of concentrated hydrochloric acid which will contain 3.65 g of hydrogen chloride? This may be found very simply from the *assay* information printed on the manufacturer's label on the bottle of concentrated hydrochloric acid. See Fig. 21-7.

Suppose the concentrated HCl is 37.23% HCl by weight and has a specific gravity of 1.19. One ml of the solution has a mass of 1.19 g of which 37.23% is HCl. One ml then contains

$$0.3723 \times 1.19 \text{ g} = 0.443 \text{ g of HCl}$$

and the volume of solution needed to provide 3.65 g of HCl is

$$3.65 \text{ g} \div 0.443 \text{ g/ml} = 8.24 \text{ ml con. HCl}$$

We have already seen that 1 mole of H_2SO_4 contains 2 gram-equivalents. A 1-N solution contains 49 g (98 g ÷ 2) of H_2SO_4 per liter of solution. A 5-N solution contains 245 g (49 g × 5) of H_2SO_4

per liter, and 0.01-N H_2SO_4 contains 0.49 g (49 g ÷ 100) H_2SO_4 per liter of solution. Concentrated sulfuric acid is usually 95%–98% H_2SO_4 and has a specific gravity of about 1.84.

Crystalline salts containing water of hydration must be given special consideration in making up standard solutions. For example, crystalline copper(II) sulfate has the empirical formula

$$CuSO_4 \cdot 5 H_2O$$

A 1-M $CuSO_4$ solution would contain 159.5 g of $CuSO_4$ per liter of solution. However, the formula weight of this

Fig. 21-7. **The manufacturer's label on a reagent bottle carries information that is important to the chemist.** (Baker Chemical Works)

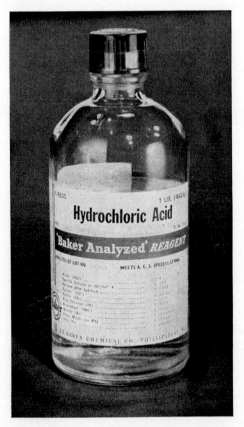

Hydrochloric Acid

'Baker Analyzed' *REAGENT*

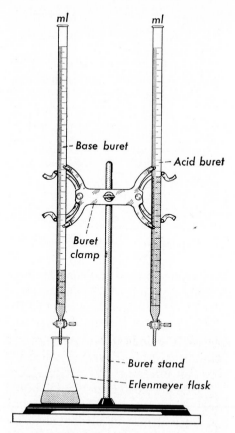

ml   ml

Base buret

Acid buret

Buret
clamp

Buret stand

Erlenmeyer flask

Fig. 21-8. Burets are used to measure standard solutions accurately.

★ **18. Standard solutions and titration.** In a neutralization reaction the basic OH^- ion acquires a proton from the H_3O^+ ion to form 2 molecules of water. Thus, 1 g-ion of H_3O^+ ions (19 g) and 1 g-ion of hydroxide ions (17 g) are chemically equivalent. For neutralization to occur H_3O^+ ions and OH^- ions must be available in equal numbers.

Suppose we wish to know the concentration of acetic acid in a sample of vinegar. We may *titrate* the vinegar against a sodium hydroxide solution of known normality, using a pair of burets as shown in Fig. 21-8. The standard solution is added to a measured volume of the vinegar until the two solutions are mixed in equivalent quantities. This is shown by the color change of a suitable indicator in the vinegar.

Assume that the standard solution was 0.10-N NaOH and 50. ml were required to neutralize 10. ml of the vinegar. Since it takes 5.0 times as much sodium hydroxide solution as acid, it is obvious that the acid solution is 5.0 times as concentrated as the basic solution. Therefore, the vinegar is 0.50 N due to the amount of acetic acid present. A 1.0-N solution of acetic acid, $HC_2H_3O_2$, contains 60. g of solute per liter. Then the 0.50-N solution contains 30. g of $HC_2H_3O_2$ per liter. A liter of vinegar has a mass of approximately 1000 g. The sample of vinegar is, therefore, 3% acetic acid.

This method of determining the concentration of a solution is called *titration*. The *end-point* of the titration is reached when the quantities of acid and hydroxide (H_3O^+ ions and OH^- ions) are chemically equivalent. Ideally, the indicator color change should occur at a pH of 7. Actually, it may be desirable to use an indicator which changes color at a higher or lower pH.

hydrate is 249.5; crystalline copper(II) sulfate is 64% $CuSO_4$. This fact must be recognized when weighing out moles or gram-equivalents of such crystalline hydrates.

If a mole of a solute contains 1 g-eq. wt., the molarity and normality of the solution *are the same*. Thus a 1-M HCl solution is also a 1-N solution. If a mole of solute has 2 g-eq. wt., a 1-M solution is 2 N. A 1-M H_2SO_4 solution is therefore 2 N. Similarly a 1-M H_3PO_4 solution is 3 N. *The advantage of normality is that solutions of equal normality are chemically equivalent, volume for volume.*

★ **19. Indicators in titration.** Chemists have a wide choice of indicators for use in titrations. They are able to choose one which changes color over the right pH range for any particular reaction. Let us see why it is not always suitable to have our indicator change color at a pH of 7.

Solutions of soluble hydroxides and acids mixed in chemically equivalent quantities may not be exactly neutral. They will be neutral only if both solutes are ionized to the same degree. The purpose of the indicator is to show that the end-point has been reached—that is, when equivalent quantities of the two solutes are together. The accompanying table shows the color changes of several common indicators used in acid-hydroxide titrations. Note how the variation of transition intervals of different indicators would enable a chemist to choose the best indicator for a given reaction.

The combinations of acidic and basic solutions involved in titration, which have end-points occurring in different pH ranges, are as follows:

1. *Strong acid—strong hydroxide:* pH is about 7. Litmus may be a suitable indicator.

2. *Strong acid—weak hydroxide:* pH is less than 7. Methyl orange may be a suitable indicator.

3. *Weak acid—strong hydroxide:* pH is greater than 7. Phenolphthalein may be a suitable indicator.

4. *Weak acid—weak hydroxide:* pH may be either greater than or less than 7, depending on which solution is stronger. None of the indicators works very well.

★ **20. pH measurements.** Indicators used to detect the end-points in neutralization reactions are organic compounds possessing weak acidic or basic characteristics. When added to a solution in suitable form and concentration, an indicator imparts a characteristic color to the solution. If the pH of the solution is changed, as in titration, the color of the indicator changes over a definite range of pH values, called the *transition interval.*

The difference in color of an indicator at pH values above and below its transition interval may be attributed to the fact that the un-ionized indicator molecule possesses a color different from that of the indicator ions. The ratio of the indicator-ion concentration to that of

TABLE OF INDICATOR COLORS

INDICATOR		COLOR		TRANSITION INTERVAL
	Acid	Transition	Alkaline	(pH)
Methyl violet	yellow	aqua	violet	0.2– 2.0
Methyl yellow	red	orange	yellow	2.9– 4.0
Bromphenol blue	yellow	green	blue	3.0– 3.6
Methyl orange	red	orange	yellow	3.1– 4.4
Methyl red	red	buff	yellow	4.4– 6.0
Litmus	red	pink	blue	5.5– 8.0
Bromthymol blue	yellow	green	blue	6.0– 7.6
Phenol red	yellow	orange	red	6.8– 8.4
Phenolphthalein	colorless	pink	red	8.3–10.0
Thymolphthalein	colorless	pale	blue	9.3–10.5
Alizarine yellow	yellow	green	violet	10.1–12.1

APPROXIMATE pH OF SOLUTIONS USING GRAMERCY UNIVERSAL INDICATOR

ZnCl₂

pH=5.5 ▼

0   5   10

NaCl

pH=7.0 ▼

0   5   10

K₂CO₃

pH=9.5 ▼

0   5   10

(NH₄)₂SO₄

pH=6.0 ▼

0   5   10

KNO₃

pH=7.0 ▼

0   5   10

NaHCO₃

pH=8.0 ▼

0   5   10

BORAX BEAD TESTS FOR CERTAIN METALS

Mn

Cu

Co

Cr

Ni

Fe

(All beads formed in the oxidizing flame)

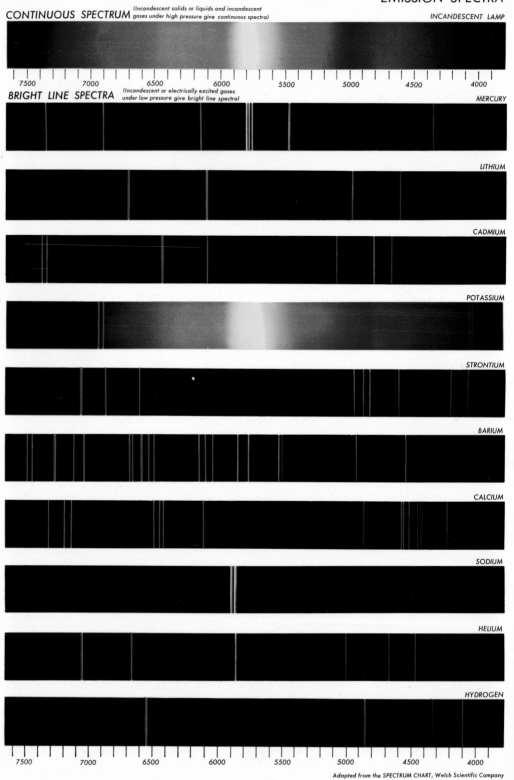

EMISSION SPECTRA

CONTINUOUS SPECTRUM (Incandescent solids or liquids and incandescent gases under high pressure give continuous spectra)

INCANDESCENT LAMP

7500 7000 6500 6000 5500 5000 4500 4000

BRIGHT LINE SPECTRA (Incandescent or electrically excited gases under low pressure give bright line spectra)

MERCURY

LITHIUM

CADMIUM

POTASSIUM

STRONTIUM

BARIUM

CALCIUM

SODIUM

HELIUM

HYDROGEN

7500 7000 6500 6000 5500 5000 4500 4000

Adapted from the SPECTRUM CHART, Welch Scientific Company

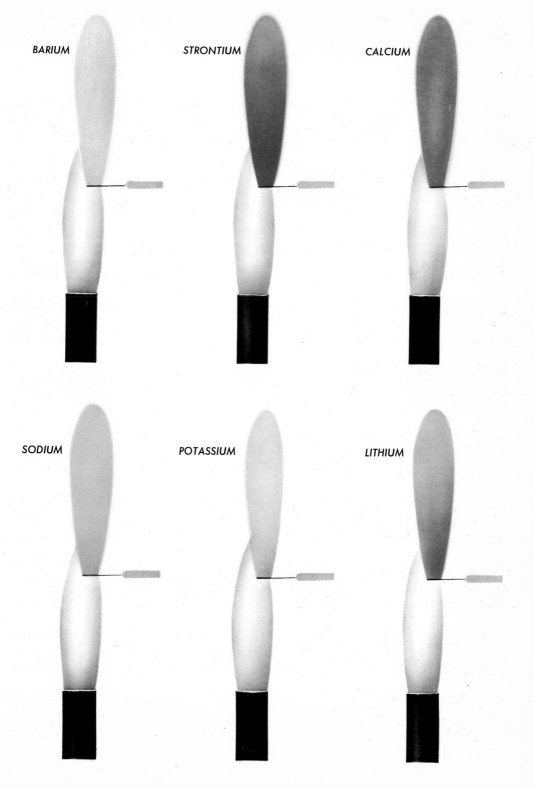

BARIUM

STRONTIUM

CALCIUM

SODIUM

POTASSIUM

LITHIUM

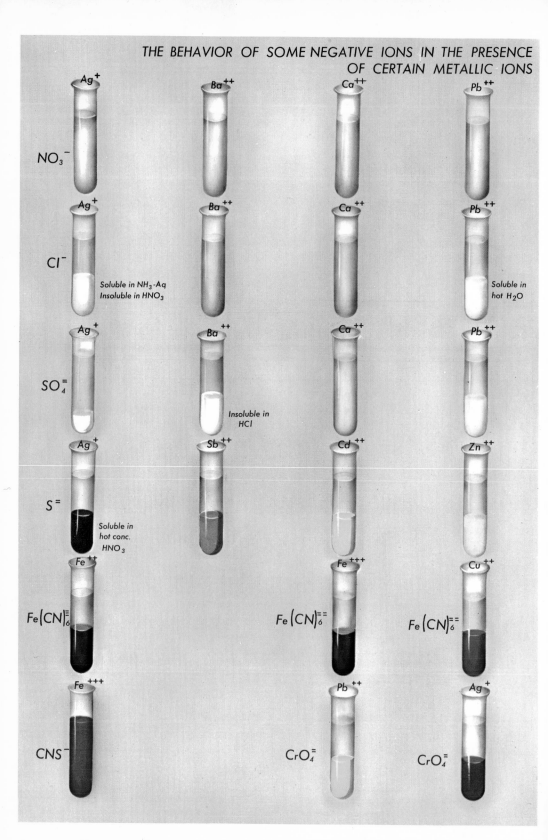

THE BEHAVIOR OF SOME NEGATIVE IONS IN THE PRESENCE
OF CERTAIN METALLIC IONS

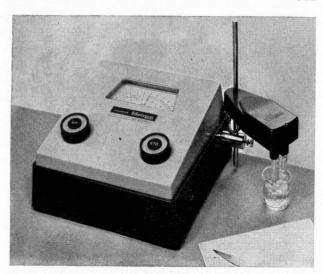

Fig. 21-9. **A modern laboratory pH meter.** (Coleman Instruments)

indicator molecules is a function of the pH of the solution. Therefore, the indicator color is dependent on the pH and changes as a function of the pH of the solution.

If an indicator added to different solutions assumes the same *transition color*, the solutions may be considered to have the same pH. This is the basis for the common *colorimetric* determination of pH. A measured volume of a suitable indicator is added to each solution whose pH is to be determined. The color is then compared with that of the same indicator in solutions of known pH. Using careful colorimetric techniques, the pH of a solution can be estimated to the nearest 0.1 pH unit.

While the use of indicators for determining end-points in titrations and the pH of solutions involves simple and common techniques in chemistry, it is by no means the only way these procedures may be performed. Modern instruments employing electrometric techniques enable the chemist to make rapid titrations and pH determinations with higher precision than is possible using the various colorimetric methods.

Electrometric instruments are divided into two groups, *potentiometric* and *conductometric*. The theory of operation of the two groups is entirely different and quite complicated. Very briefly, the potentiometric method is similar to common indicator methods in that a change of the electric potential of a special electrode is a function of the pH of the solution. A large change in potential at the end-point of a titration, for example, is equivalent to a color change of an indicator. Modern *glass-electrode* pH meters are now available which cover the entire pH range, are very convenient to use, and give more accurate readings than are obtainable by colorimetric means.

Conductometric methods rely on the fact that ions present in an electrolytic solution contribute to the electric conductivity of the solution. If ions of one electrolyte unite with ions of another to form a slightly ionized or slightly soluble product, the conductivity of the solution will undergo an appreciable change. Conductometric instruments are designed to detect this change in electric conductivity.

4. SALTS

21. The nature of salts. Common table salt, NaCl, is only one of a large class of compounds which the chemist calls by the name *salt*.

An acid in water solution ionizes forming H_3O^+ ions and negatively charged nonmetallic ions. A soluble metallic hydroxide is an ionic solid which, when dissolved in water, dissociates releasing OH^- ions and positively charged metallic ions. The hydronium and hydroxide ions are almost entirely removed in neutralization, as they form water which is only very slightly ionized. The negative ions of the acid and the positive ions of the hydroxide have no part in the neutralization reaction; they are simply spectator ions. For example:

$$HCl + H_2O \rightarrow H_3O^+ + Cl^-$$
$$K^+OH^- \rightarrow K^+ + OH^-$$
$$H_3O^+ + Cl^- + K^+ + OH^- \rightarrow$$
$$K^+ + Cl^- + 2\,H_2O$$

Or simply,

$$H_3O^+ + OH^- \rightarrow 2\,H_2O$$

After the water is evaporated, the oppositely charged ions are no longer isolated from each other by water dipoles. They form a characteristic ionic crystalline structure and separate from solution as a salt. *A compound, composed of positive ions of a metal or radical and negative ions produced when certain acids transfer protons to a base, is called a salt.* All true salts, by this definition, are electrovalent substances. They are strong electrolytes and are completely ionized in water solution.

22. Salts have varied properties. The properties of the hundreds of salts known to chemists differ widely. It is, therefore, almost impossible to list any general properties at all. We have observed that some salts combine with water to form crystals containing water of hydration.

Probably the most important property of a salt is its solubility. In Table 7 of the Appendix, a rather complete list of salts is provided together with their solubility characteristics. However, a few general solubility rules that are worth remembering are given below.

23. Salt-producing reactions. There are several ways in which salts are formed, but not all of them are applicable to the formation of every salt.

1. Direct union of the elements. Sodium may be burned in chlorine to produce the salt, sodium chloride.

$$2\,Na + Cl_2 \rightarrow 2\,NaCl$$

SOLUBILITY OF SALTS

1. Common sodium, potassium, and ammonium compounds are soluble in water.

2. Common nitrates, acetates, and chlorates are soluble.

3. Common chlorides are soluble except silver, mercury(I), and lead. (Lead(II) chloride is soluble in hot water.)

4. Common sulfates are soluble except calcium, barium, strontium, and lead.

5. Common carbonates, phosphates, and silicates are insoluble except sodium, potassium, and ammonium.

6. Common sulfides are insoluble except calcium, barium, strontium, magnesium, sodium, potassium, and ammonium.

2. *Salts are formed by the replacement of the hydrogen of an acid by a metal.* Zinc reacts with hydrochloric acid to form zinc chloride and hydrogen.

$$Zn + 2\ HCl \rightarrow ZnCl_2 + H_2 \uparrow$$

3. *The oxide of a metal may react with an acid to form a salt.* Sodium oxide, Na_2O, can be treated with hydrochloric acid to form sodium chloride and water.

$$Na_2O + 2\ HCl \rightarrow 2\ NaCl + H_2O$$

4. *The oxide of a nonmetal may react with a soluble hydroxide to form a salt.* Carbon dioxide, in reacting with limewater, $Ca(OH)_2$, forms calcium carbonate and water.

$$CO_2 + Ca(OH)_2 \rightarrow CaCO_3 \downarrow + H_2O$$

5. *Acids neutralize soluble hydroxides and form salts.* Sodium hydroxide and hydrochloric acid are mixed in chemically equivalent quantities. The solvent is evaporated and sodium chloride remains. Many different salts can be prepared by neutralization.

$$NaOH + HCl \rightarrow NaCl + H_2O$$

6. *Two salts may be prepared at one time by ionic reactions.* A solution of sodium sulfate, Na_2SO_4, added to a solution of barium chloride, $BaCl_2$, reacts according to the following equation:

$$Ba^{++} + 2\ Cl^- + 2\ Na^+ + SO_4^= \rightarrow$$
$$2\ Na^+ + 2\ Cl^- + Ba^{++}SO_4^= \downarrow$$

It is not usually possible to separate two salts unless one of them is insoluble. In this case barium sulfate is only very slightly soluble. It readily precipitates and can be filtered from the solution. The water may then be evaporated to obtain the other, which of course would not be in pure form since the $BaSO_4$ precipitated from its saturated solution.

7. *Salts may be formed by the action of an acid on a carbonate.* If we add some hydrochloric acid, HCl, to a solution of sodium carbonate, Na_2CO_3, the following reaction occurs:

$$2\ HCl + Na_2CO_3 \rightarrow$$
$$2\ NaCl + H_2O + CO_2 \uparrow$$

Carbon dioxide bubbles out of the mixture as a gas. The sodium chloride may be recovered by evaporation.

24. Naming salts. Salts are generally named by combining the names of the ions of which they are composed. For example, the name of $Ba(NO_3)_2$ is barium nitrate. Conventionally the more metallic ion, in this case the barium ion Ba^{++}, is named first. The name of the negative ion, in this case the nitrate ion NO_3^-, follows.

Over the years many inconsistencies have been encountered among the names of salts which have been carried

SALT NOMENCLATURE

Formula	Stock Name
Binary salts	
$CuCl$	copper(I) chloride
$CuCl_2$	copper(II) chloride
FeO	iron(II) oxide
Fe_2O_3	iron(III) oxide
Fe_3O_4	iron(II, III) oxide
$MnCl_2$	manganese(II) chloride
$MnCl_4$	manganese(IV) chloride
Ternary salts	
$Fe_3(PO_4)_2$	iron(II) phosphate
$Hg(NO_3)_2$	mercury(II) nitrate
Cu_2SO_4	copper(I) sulfate
$CuSO_4$	copper(II) sulfate
Mixed salts	
$KCaPO_4$	potassium calcium phosphate
$NaHCO_3$	sodium hydrogen carbonate

COMMON ACIDS

Formula	Name of Acid	Name of Negative Ion of Salt
HF	hydrofluoric	fluoride
HBr	hydrobromic	bromide
HI	hydriodic	iodide
HCl	hydrochloric	chloride
HClO	hypochlorous	hypochlorite
$HClO_2$	chlorous	chlorite
$HClO_3$	chloric	chlorate
$HClO_4$	perchloric	perchlorate
H_2S	hydrosulfuric	sulfide
H_2SO_3	sulfurous	sulfite
H_2SO_4	sulfuric	sulfate
HNO_2	nitrous	nitrite
HNO_3	nitric	nitrate
H_2CO_3	carbonic	carbonate
H_3PO_3	phosphorous	phosphite
H_3PO_4	phosphoric	phosphate

into our present nomenclature in spite of the fact that they do not provide for a simple translation from name to formula or from formula to name. In 1940 the International Union of Pure and Applied Chemistry recommended a comprehensive system for naming inorganic compounds, known as the *Stock system*, which provides the uniformity and simplicity needed to improve our system of chemical nomenclature.

The general methods for naming compounds were given in Chapter 6, Section 17. The part of the Stock system that applies to the naming of salts containing metals with variable valences is used throughout this text. Several examples of Stock nomenclature for binary, ternary, and mixed salts are given in the table on page 313. Observe that the more electropositive cation is named first in mixed salts.

The names of negative ions take the same root and prefix as the acid in which they occur. But the ending *–ic* is changed to *–ate*, and the ending *–ous* is changed to *–ite*. Salts derived from binary acids take the ending *–ide*. The accompanying table shows the formulas for many common acids. It also gives the names of the acids, and the names of the negative ions of the salts which are produced by the reactions of these acids.

SUMMARY

In the modern sense, an acid is a proton donor. Hydrogen ions are protons and in water solution are always hydrated in the form H_3O^+. Acids are covalent molecular substances which ionize in water solution. Strong acids ionize completely in dilute solutions. Weak acids ionize incompletely. Diprotic acids ionize in two stages. Triprotic acids ionize in three stages. The last stage may make only slight progress even in very dilute solutions.

Acids have many common characteristics which may be due to the formation of H_3O^+ ions in their water solutions. Nonmetallic oxides that combine with water to form acids, or that are formed by the removal of water from acids, are called acid anhydrides.

Bases are substances which combine with the hydronium ions from acids. In the modern sense they are proton acceptors. The hydroxide ion is the most common base. Hydroxide ions are present in water solutions of soluble metallic hydroxides. The hydroxides of the active metals are ionic substances. Those which are very soluble in water form solutions which are strongly basic. Those which are moderately soluble form solutions which are moderately basic. Ammonia dissolves in water, taking some protons from the water molecules to form a low concentration of NH_4^+ and OH^- ions. Ammonia-water solutions are weakly basic. The common characteristics of soluble hydroxides are attributed to the properties of the hydroxide ion. Oxides which react with water to produce solutions containing the basic OH^- ions are called basic anhydrides. The oxides of the active metals are basic anhydrides.

A convenient way of indicating the concentration of hydronium ions in a solution is to use the pH scale. The pH range extends from 0 to 14. Numerically, the pH is the logarithm of the number of liters of a solution that contains 1 gram-ion of H_3O^+ ions. The pH of pure water is 7. This is also the pH of any neutral solution. A pH less than 7 indicates an acid, greater than 7, an alkaline solution. Indicators are used to show the pH of a solution, and also to show the end-point of neutralization reactions or titrations.

Standard solutions are solutions of precisely known concentrations. Concentration is expressed in molality, molarity, or normality. Solutions of equal molality for a given solvent have the same ratio between the number of solute and solvent molecules. Molecular solutions of equal molarity have the same number of molecules, volume for volume. Solutions of equal normality are chemically equivalent, volume for volume.

Salts are compounds formed by any positive ion except hydrogen combined with any negative ion except hydroxide ions. Salts are ionic substances which are completely dissociated in water solution.

TEST YOURSELF ON THESE TERMS

acid	glass electrode	normal solution
acid anhydride	gram-equivalent weight	pH
acid salt	gram-ion	pH meter
amphiprotic	hydrated oxide	proton acceptor
base	hydronium ion	proton donor
basic anhydride	indicator	salt
binary	molal solution	standard solution
buret	molar solution	ternary
common logarithm	monoprotic acid	titration
diprotic acid	neutralization	transition interval
end-point	normal salt	triprotic acid

Group A

1. Name the three most important industrial acids and tell why each is important.
2. What ion is responsible for the acidic properties of acid solutions?
3. Why is an acid thought of as a proton donor?
4. (*a*) What is an acid anhydride? (*b*) A basic anhydride? (*c*) Give an example of each.
5. (*a*) State the rules for naming binary acids. (*b*) For naming ternary acids.
6. Why may a base be defined as a proton acceptor?
7. Write the net ionic equation of the neutralization reaction.
8. Aluminum hydroxide has basic properties in the presence of a strong acid, and acidic properties in the presence of a solution which is strongly basic. (*a*) Write the formula of aluminum hydroxide so as to show its basic properties. (*b*) Rewrite the formula to show its acidic properties. (*c*) What term is used to describe such substances?
9. What is the nature of true salts?
10. How are salts named?
11. What method would you use to prepare a small quantity of calcium sulfate quickly and safely in the laboratory? Justify the method used and write the equation.
12. Would barium sulfate be a suitable source of the sulfate ion for an ionic reaction with another salt? Explain.

Group B

13. Explain why a water solution of hydrogen chloride has acidic properties but pure hydrogen chloride does not, in the usual sense.
14. Hydrogen chloride, HCl, has 1 gram-atom of hydrogen per mole and hydrogen carbonate, H_2CO_3, has 2 gram-atoms of hydrogen per mole. Yet hydrochloric acid is described as a *strong* acid and carbonic acid as a *weak* acid. Explain.
15. (*a*) How can you justify calling hydrogen chloride an acid when it is dissolved in ammonia? (*b*) Write the equation.
16. (*a*) Explain the manner in which water may be considered to be an acid. (*b*) Write an equation which illustrates this behavior using electron-dot formulas.
17. (*a*) How would you test the soil in your lawn or garden to find out whether it is acidic or basic? (*b*) If you find it to be acidic, what can be added to it to remedy the condition?
18. (*a*) What basic solution would you use for cleaning a greasy sink? Explain. (*b*) For removing grease spots from clothing? Explain.
19. What basic solutions would you use for neutralizing acid stains on clothing? Explain.
20. Test your saliva with litmus paper. (*a*) Is the saliva acidic or alkaline? (*b*) Do you think that a tooth paste is likely to be acidic or basic? Test some of them.

21. Which of the following salts are soluble, and which are insoluble in water: NaCl, CaCO$_3$, BaSO$_4$, (NH$_4$)$_2$S, Al(C$_2$H$_3$O$_2$)$_3$, Ag$_2$SO$_4$, Pb(NO$_3$)$_2$, Hg$_2$Cl$_2$, Mg$_3$(PO$_4$)$_2$, CuS?

22. In a neutralization reaction between hydrochloric acid and potassium hydroxide, the K$^+$ ion and the Cl$^-$ ion are called *spectator ions*. (*a*) Explain. (*b*) How could the potassium chloride be recovered?

★ 23. What indicator would you use to show the end-point of the neutralization reaction described in Question 22? Justify your selection.

★ 24. (*a*) Explain the meaning of pH. (*b*) What is the range of the pH scale?

★ 25. How many moles of sodium hydroxide are needed to neutralize: (*a*) 1 mole of hydrochloric acid; (*b*) 1 mole of sulfuric acid; and (*c*) 1 mole of phosphoric acid? (*d*) Write the equation for each reaction.

26. What mass of calcium hydroxide is required to make up 1.0 liter of 0.010-N solution?

★ 27. (*a*) What volume of water contains a mole of H$_3$O$^+$ ions? (*b*) How many gram-ions of hydronium ions is this? (*c*) How many grams of H$_3$O$^+$ ion? (*d*) What is the mole-concentration of OH$^-$ ion in this volume of water? (*e*) How many gram-ions of hydroxide ions is this? (*f*) How many grams of OH$^-$ ion?

★ 28. What is the normality of (*a*) a 0.004-M solution of phosphoric acid? (*b*) a 0.15-M solution of potassium hydroxide? (*c*) a 2-M solution of sulfuric acid?

PROBLEMS

Group A

1. How many grams of sodium hydroxide are required to neutralize 54.75 g of hydrogen chloride in water solution?

2. We may prepare nitric acid in the laboratory by reacting sodium nitrate with sulfuric acid. Sodium hydrogen sulfate is also formed. (*a*) How many grams of sulfuric acid are required to produce 50.0 g of nitric acid? (*b*) How many grams of sodium hydrogen sulfate are formed?

3. How many liters of carbon dioxide can be collected at 20.° C and 745 mm pressure from a reaction between 25 g of calcium carbonate and an excess of hydrochloric acid?

★ 4. What quantity of potassium nitrate would you add to 500. g of water to prepare a 0.25-m solution?

★ 5. How many grams of sugar, C$_{12}$H$_{22}$O$_{11}$, are contained in 50.0 ml of an 0.800-M solution?

Group B

6. How many solute molecules are contained in each milliliter of a 0.1-M solution?

★ 7. What is the molality of a solution that contains 2.0 g of sodium chloride in 100.0 g of water?

★ 8. (*a*) What is the pH of a 0.01-M solution of HCl, assuming complete ionization? (*b*) What is the OH$^-$ ion concentration of a 0.01-M solution of sodium hydroxide? (*c*) What is the pH of this solution?

★ 9. How many milliliters of a 0.150-N solution of a metallic hydroxide are required to neutralize 30.0 ml of a 0.500-N solution of an acid?

★10. A chemistry student finds that it takes 34 ml of a 0.50-N acid solution to neutralize 10. ml of a sample of household ammonia. What is the normality of the ammonia-water solution?

★11. The stockroom supply of concentrated sulfuric acid is 98% H_2SO_4 by weight and has a specific gravity of 1.84. (*a*) How many milliliters are needed to make 1.0 liter of 1.0-N H_2SO_4 solution? (*b*) To make 100. ml of 0.20-N solution?

★12. An excess of zinc reacts with 400. ml of hydrochloric acid and 2.55 liters of H_2 gas are collected over water at 20.° C and 745.0 mm. What was the normality of the acid? (Vapor pressure of water at 20.° C is 17.5 mm.)

SOME THINGS FOR YOU TO DO

1. Take home some test strips of both red and blue litmus paper and Hydrion paper. Test as many different things as you can and make a list as follows: acidic, basic, neutral.

2. Using Hydrion paper, determine the approximate pH of those substances.

3. Test samples of a blood-red beet and a purple cabbage to see how each one is affected by a strong acid. How is each affected by a strong hydroxide solution?

Chapter 22 · CHEMICAL EQUILIBRIUM

★ 1. Reversible reactions may reach equilibrium. Many chemical reactions are reversible—that is, the products may re-form the original reactants under suitable conditions. We have seen that mercury(II) oxide decomposes when heated strongly.

$$2 \text{ HgO} \rightarrow 2 \text{ Hg} + \text{O}_2 \uparrow$$

However, mercury and oxygen combine to form mercury(II) oxide when heated gently.

$$2 \text{ Hg} + \text{O}_2 \rightarrow 2 \text{ HgO}$$

Suppose mercury(II) oxide is heated in a closed container from which neither the mercury nor the oxygen can escape. It is possible, once the decomposition is under way, for the mercury and oxygen that have been liberated to recombine forming mercury(II) oxide again. Thus both reactions proceed at the same time. Under just the right conditions, the speed of the composition reaction may become equal to the speed of the decomposition reaction. Mercury and oxygen combine to form mercury(II) oxide just as fast as mercury(II) oxide decom-

poses to form mercury and oxygen. We should then expect the amount of mercury(II) oxide, mercury, and oxygen to remain constant as long as these conditions persist. A state of *equilibrium* has been reached between the two chemical actions. *Both reactions continue but the net change is zero.* The equilibrium may be shown in the following manner:

$$2 \text{ HgO} \rightleftharpoons 2 \text{ Hg} + \text{O}_2$$

Chemical equilibrium is a state of balance in which the speeds of opposing reactions are exactly equal.

★ 2. Equilibrium is a dynamic state. We have already discussed examples of opposing processes, such as evaporation and condensation, occurring simultaneously at the same speed. The evaporation of a liquid in a closed vessel and the condensation of its saturated vapor proceed at equal rates. The equilibrium vapor pressure established is characteristic of the liquid at the prevailing temperature.

If an excess of sugar is placed in water, sugar molecules go into solution and some of these in turn separate to rejoin

319

the crystals. At saturation, molecules of sugar are separating from solution at the same rate that other crystal molecules are going into solution. These are examples of *physical equilibria.* The opposing physical processes occur at exactly the same speed. Equilibrium is a *dynamic* state in which two opposing processes continue to take place at the same time and at the same speed.

Electrovalent compounds, such as sodium chloride, are completely ionized in water solution. When an excess of sodium chloride is placed in water, a saturated solution eventually results. Equilibrium occurs as the rate of association of ions re-forming the crystal equals the rate of dissociation of ions from the crystal. This is shown in the following ionic equation.

$$Na^+Cl^- \rightleftarrows Na^+ + Cl^-$$

Polar compounds, such as acetic acid, are quite soluble in water. Molecules of acetic acid in water solution ionize forming H_3O^+ and $C_2H_3O_2^-$ ions. However, pairs of these ions tend to rejoin, forming acetic acid molecules in the so-

lution. This tendency is so great that equilibrium is quickly established between un-ionized molecules in solution and their hydrated ions, even in fairly dilute solutions. This is an example of *ionic equilibrium.* The ionic equilibrium of acetic acid in water solution may be represented by the following equation:

$$HC_2H_3O_2 + H_2O \rightleftarrows H_3O^+ + C_2H_3O_2^-$$

Most chemical reactions reach a state of equilibrium unless prevented by the removal or escape of at least one of the substances involved. In some changes the forward reaction is nearly completed before the speed of the reverse reaction becomes high enough to establish equilibrium. *Here the products of the forward reaction* ($\rightarrow$) *are favored.* In other changes the forward reaction is barely under way when equilibrium is established. *In such cases the products of the reverse reaction* ($\leftarrow$), *the original reactants, are favored.* In still others, both the forward and reverse reactions occur to nearly the same extent before chemical equilibrium is established. *Neither reaction is favored; considerable concen-*

VOCABULARY

Buffer. A substance which, when added to a solution, causes a resistance to any change in pH.

Buffered solution. A solution containing a relatively high concentration of a buffer salt which tends to maintain a constant pH.

Equilibrium. A dynamic state in which two opposing processes take place at the same time and at the same rate.

Equilibrium constant. The product of the concentrations of the substances produced at equilibrium divided by the product of the concentrations of reactants, each concentration raised to that power which is the coefficient of the substance in the chemical equation.

Hydrolysis. The reaction of a salt with water to form a solution which is acidic or basic.

Ionization constant. The equilibrium constant of a reversible reaction by which ions are produced from molecules.

trations of both reactants and products are present at equilibrium.

Chemical reactions are employed ordinarily to convert available reactants into more desirable products. Naturally, chemists strive to produce as much of these products as possible from the reactants used. Chemical equilibrium may seriously limit the possibilities of a seemingly useful reaction. It is important that we recognize the conditions that influence the *speed* of a reaction in our study of chemical equilibrium.

★ **3. Factors affecting the speed of reaction.** Reaction speeds range all the way from those which are practically instantaneous to those which may take months, or even years, to complete. *The speed of reaction is measured by the amount of reactants converted to products in a unit of time.* In order for reactions (other than simple decompositions) to occur at all, particles (atoms, molecules, and ions) must come in contact, and this contact must result in interaction. Thus the speed of such reactions depends on *the collision frequency of the reacting substances* and *the collision efficiency.*

Any change in conditions that affects either the frequency of collisions or the collision efficiency will influence the reaction speed. Let us consider several factors affecting the speed of reaction.

1. Nature of the reactants. Hydrogen may combine vigorously with chlorine under certain conditions. Under the same conditions it may react only feebly with nitrogen. Sodium and oxygen combine much more rapidly than iron and oxygen under similar circumstances. Platinum and oxygen do not combine directly. Atoms, ions, and molecules are the particles of substances that react and their tendencies to react depend on their structures.

2. Amount of surface. A lump of coal burns slowly when kindled in air. The rate of burning can be increased by breaking the lump into smaller pieces exposing new surfaces. If the lump is powdered, suspended in the air, and ignited, it burns explosively.

Chemical action involving a *liquid* or *solid* takes place at the exposed surfaces. Increasing the amount of surface exposed hastens the action, other conditions being the same. *Gases* and *dissolved* particles do not have surfaces in the sense just described.

3. Use of catalysts. The speed of many reactions is increased by the use of catalytic agents. Some reactions are slowed by the presence of certain catalysts (inhibitors). A catalytic agent that is effective in one reaction may have no influence in another. Many important industrial processes would not be economically feasible without the use of catalytic action.

Chemists believe that catalytic agents influence the speed of reactions in one of two general ways. First, the catalyst may form an intermediate compound with one reactant. This compound, in turn, may react more vigorously with the second reactant to form the product and release the catalyst. Such agents are called *carrier catalysts.* Manganese dioxide is thought to behave in this manner when it is mixed with potassium chlorate in the laboratory preparation of oxygen. Second, other catalytic agents may simply provide a surface on which certain gas reactants condense. Reactions are speeded by the more efficient contact between the molecules of the reactants. Such agents are called *contact catalysts.* They are usually metals in the form of thin foil, wire gauze, or fine powder. Finely divided nickel is used as a catalyst in the hydrogenation of vegetable oils to form many kinds of shortening.

4. *Effect of temperature.* We have already recognized that a rise in temperature speeds a chemical reaction. On the average, reaction speeds are roughly doubled by a temperature increase of 10 C°. This large increase in speed of reaction can be accounted for partially by the increase in collision frequency of the reactants. However, particles of reactants which collide must also react if the chemical change is to move along. At higher temperatures more particles possess enough energy to react when collisions occur. They have the necessary *activation energy* (see Chapter 12, Section 11). A rise in temperature results in an increase in *collision efficiency* as well as *collision frequency*.

5. *Effect of concentration.* If a small lump of charcoal is heated in air until combustion begins and then lowered into a bottle of pure oxygen, the reaction proceeds at a much faster rate. A substance which oxidizes in air reacts much more vigorously in pure oxygen. The partial pressure of oxygen in air is approximately one fifth of the total pressure. In pure oxygen, at the same pressure as the air, we should expect to have five times the *concentration* of oxygen molecules. If other conditions are constant, speed of reaction is proportional to the concentration of oxygen.

The concentration of gases increases with pressure according to Boyle's Law. It is not possible to change, to any appreciable extent, the concentration of pure solids and pure liquids since they are practically incompressible. The concentration of gases and substances in

Fig. 22-1. Carbon burns faster in oxygen than in air because of the higher concentration of oxygen molecules.

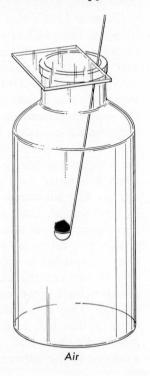

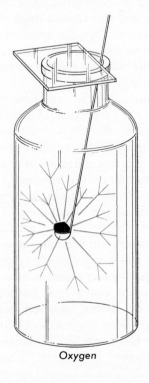

Air   Oxygen

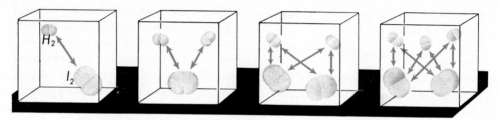

Fig. 22-2. **Under constant conditions, the collision frequency increases with the concentration of each reactant.**

solution can be changed. The speed of the carbon combustion was proportional to the concentration of oxygen *only*, since the carbon was a solid.

Now we shall consider the reaction between two gases. Hydrogen combines with iodine vapor in a reversible reaction to form the gas, hydrogen iodide.

$$H_2 + I_2 \rightleftarrows 2 HI$$

Suppose some hydrogen gas and iodine vapor are brought together in a closed vessel. *Under constant conditions*, the composition reaction proceeds at a rate proportional to the frequency of effective collisions between the two kinds of molecules. Thus *the speed of the reaction is proportional to the concentrations of both hydrogen and iodine.*

If the concentration of hydrogen in the vessel is doubled, the chances of a collision between hydrogen and iodine molecules is doubled; the reaction speed is therefore *doubled*.

If the concentration of iodine is also doubled, the chances of a collision are *four times as great*. Of course, other conditions which affect the speed of the reaction must remain the same.

★ **4. The Law of Mass Action.** In 1867 two Norwegian scientists, Guldberg and Waage, stated the general principle known as the **Law of Mass Action.** This law in its modern form is as follows: *The speed of a reaction is proportional*

to the product of the concentrations of the reacting substances. Concentration is expressed in *moles of gas per liter of volume* or *moles of solute per liter of solution.* How does the Law of Mass Action apply to the reaction between hydrogen and iodine vapor?

Let S_1 be the speed of the forward ($\rightarrow$) reaction forming hydrogen iodide. $[H_2]$ and $[I_2]$ represent the molecular concentrations of hydrogen and iodine in moles per liter. Then

$$S_1 \propto [H_2] \times [I_2]$$

where $\propto$ is a proportionality sign and is read *"is proportional to."* If the concentrations of both hydrogen and iodine vapor are *1 mole per liter*, at a fixed temperature the speed of the reaction is a certain constant value called the *velocity constant:*

$$S_1 = k_1$$

where k_1 is the velocity constant for the forward reaction. For *any* concentration of hydrogen and iodine, the reaction speed is expressed as follows:

$$S_1 = k_1 \times [H_2] \times [I_2]$$

If $[H_2]$ is *2 moles per liter* and $[I_2]$ is *1 mole per liter*, the equation becomes

$$S_1 = k_1 \times 2 \times 1 = 2 k_1$$

The speed of the reaction is *twice* the value for 1 mole per liter concentrations of both reactants. If now $[I_2]$ is also increased to *2 moles per liter*:

$$S_1 = k_1 \times 2 \times 2 = 4 k_1$$

The speed of the reaction is *four times* the value for 1 mole per liter concentrations of both reactants. Similarly, if $[H_2]$ is *3 moles per liter* and $[I_2]$ is *2 moles per liter*:

$$S_1 = k_1 \times 3 \times 2 = 6 k_1$$

The speed of the reaction is *six times* the value for 1 mole per liter concentrations of both reactants.

At the fixed temperature of the forward reaction, hydrogen iodide molecules decompose. Let this reaction speed in the reverse ($\leftarrow$) direction be S_2 for the formation of hydrogen and iodine. However, two molecules of HI must decompose to form a molecule of H_2 and a molecule of I_2. Thus the speed of the reverse reaction *is proportional to the molecular concentration of HI squared.*

$$S_2 \propto [HI] \times [HI]$$

and

$$S_2 \propto [HI]^2$$

or

$$S_2 = k_2 \times [HI]^2$$

where k_2 is the velocity constant for the decomposition of HI at the fixed temperature.

★ **5. The equilibrium constant is important to chemists.** Many chemical reactions seem to be feasible and might be expected to yield useful products. However, after they are started, they *appear* to slow down and finally stop without having run to completion. Such reactions are reversible and, under just the right conditions, reach a *state of equilibrium*. Both forward and reverse processes occur at the same rate and the concentration of products and reactants remains constant.

Chemists must understand chemical equilibria in order to determine the conditions under which such reactions will yield satisfactory results. Knowledge of equilibrium enables them to predict whether certain reactions are practical. They are then able to improve the yields of desired products formed by reversible reactions.

Suppose that two substances, A and B, react to form products C and D, and that C and D, in turn, react to produce A and B. Under certain conditions equilibrium occurs in this reversible reaction. This *hypothetical* equilibrium reaction may be shown by the equation:

$$A + B \rightleftarrows C + D$$

Initially, the concentration of C and D is zero and that of A and B is maximum. In accordance with the Law of Mass Action the speed of the forward reaction *decreases* as A and B are used up. During the same time the speed of the reverse reaction increases, from its initial value of zero, as C and D are formed. As equilibrium is established, these two reaction rates become equal. The individual concentrations of A, B, C, and D undergo no further change as long as the same reaction conditions prevail. *At equilibrium, the ratio of the product* $[C] \times [D]$ *to the product* $[A] \times [B]$ *has a definite numerical value.* It is known as the **equilibrium constant** of the reaction and is designated by the letter K. Thus

$$\frac{[C] \times [D]}{[A] \times [B]} = K$$

Notice that the concentrations of substances on the right side of the chemical equation are given in the numerator. The concentrations of those on the left side of the chemical equation are in the denominator. Equilibrium concentrations are given in *moles per liter*. The constant, K, is independent of the initial concentrations but is dependent on the fixed temperature of the system.

The value of K for a given equilibrium reaction is important to the chemist because it shows him the extent to which the reactants are converted into the products of the reaction. If K is equal to 1, the products of the concentrations in the numerator and denominator have the same value. If the value of K is very small, the forward reaction occurs only very slightly before equilibrium is established. A large value of K indicates an equilibrium in which the original reactants are largely converted to products. If the values of K are known for different reaction temperatures, the chemist may select the most favorable conditions for a desired reaction. The numerical value of K for a particular equilibrium system is obtained by analyzing the equilibrium mixture and determining the concentrations of all substances present.

An equilibrium reaction may involve more than one molecule of a substance in the chemical equation. For example, in the reaction

$$3A + B \rightleftarrows 2C + 3D$$

the equilibrium constant is:

$$\frac{[C]^2[D]^3}{[A]^3[B]} = K$$

*In the general form, the **equilibrium constant** is the product of the concentrations of the substances produced at equilibrium divided by the product of the concentrations of the reacting substances, each concentration raised to that power which is the coefficient of the substance in the chemical equation.*

In Section 4, the chemical equation

for the hydrogen-iodine-hydrogen iodide equilibrium was written as follows:

$$H_2 + I_2 \rightleftarrows 2\,HI$$

The speeds of the forward and reverse reactions are respectively:

$$S_1 = k_1[H_2][I_2]$$
$$S_2 = k_2[HI]^2$$

At equilibrium

$$S_1 = S_2$$

and

$$k_1[H_2][I_2] = k_2[HI]^2$$

or

$$\frac{k_1}{k_2} = \frac{[HI]^2}{[H_2][I_2]}$$

then

$$K = \frac{k_1}{k_2} = \frac{[HI]^2}{[H_2][I_2]}$$

★ **6. Factors that disturb equilibrium.** In systems that have attained chemical equilibrium, opposing reactions occur at equal speeds. Any change which alters the speed of either reaction *disturbs the equilibrium*. By displacing an equilibrium in the proper direction, chemists are often able to increase production of important industrial chemicals.

In 1888 the French chemist Henri Louis Le Chatelier (luh-*shah*-te-lyay) (1850–1936) published an important principle which is the basis for much of our knowledge of equilibrium. The *principle of Le Chatelier* may be stated as follows: *If a system at equilibrium is subjected to a stress, the equilibrium will be displaced in such direction as to relieve the stress.* This is a general law of chemistry that applies to all kinds of dynamic equilibria, physical and ionic, as well as chemical. In applying Le Chatelier's principle to chemical equilibrium, we shall consider three important factors (stresses).

1. *Change in concentration.* According to the Law of Mass Action, the speed of a reaction increases with an increase in the concentration of either reactant. Consider the hypothetical reaction:

$$A + B \rightleftharpoons C + D$$

An increase in the concentration of A will displace the equilibrium to the *right.* Both A and B will be used up faster and more of C and D will be formed. The equilibrium will be re-established with a lower concentration of B. *The effect has been to shift the equilibrium in such direction as to reduce the stress caused by the increase in concentration.* Similarly, an increase in the concentration of B will drive the reaction to the *right.* An increase in either C or D will displace the equilibrium to the *left.* A *decrease* in the concentration of either C or D will have the same effect as an *increase* in the concentration of A or B; to displace the equilibrium to the *right. Changes in concentration have no effect on the value of the equilibrium constant.* All concentrations will be re-adjusted, when equilibrium is re-established, to give the same numerical ratio for the equilibrium constant.

2. *Change in pressure.* A change in pressure can only affect equilibrium systems in which *gases* are involved. According to the principle of Le Chatelier, *if the pressure on an equilibrium system is increased, the reaction is driven in the direction which relieves the pressure.*

The Haber process for the synthesis of ammonia from its elements offers an excellent illustration of the influence of pressure on an equilibrium system.

$$N_2 + 3\,H_2 \rightleftharpoons 2\,NH_3$$

The equation indicates that 4 molecules of the reactant gases form 2 molecules of ammonia gas. If the equilibrium mixture of these three gases is subjected to an increase in pressure, the concentration of ammonia will be increased. The concentration of hydrogen and nitrogen will be decreased. *The equilibrium shifts in the direction which produces fewer molecules, consequently a lower pressure.* It is evident that *high* pressure is desirable in this industrial process (see Fig. 22-3).

Consider the reaction of the following equation.

$$CaCO_3 \rightleftharpoons CaO + CO_2 \uparrow$$

Carbon dioxide is the only gas in the equilibrium mixture. The products therefore are favored by a *low* pressure.

In the reaction,

$$CO + H_2O \text{ (vapor)} \rightleftharpoons CO_2 + H_2$$

there are equal numbers of molecules of gaseous reactants and gaseous products. Pressure could not be relieved by a shift in equilibrium. Thus, pressure has *no effect* on this equilibrium reaction.

Obviously an increase in pressure on confined gases amounts to an increase in the concentration of these gases. Thus, *changes in pressure do not affect the value of the equilibrium constant.*

3. *Change in temperature.* Chemical reactions are either exothermic or endothermic. Reversible reactions are exothermic in one direction and endothermic in the other. The effect of changing the temperature of an equilibrium mixture depends on which of the opposing reactions is endothermic.

The *addition* of heat, according to Le Chatelier's principle, will shift the equilibrium so that heat is absorbed. This favors the *endothermic* reaction. Conversely, the *removal* of heat favors the *exothermic* reaction. A rise in temperature increases the speed of any reaction. In an equilibrium, the speeds of the opposing reactions are raised *unequally*. Thus, *the value of the equilibrium constant, for a given system, is affected by the operating temperature.*

The synthesis of ammonia is exothermic.

$$N_2 + 3 H_2 \rightleftarrows 2 NH_3 + 24 \text{ kcal}$$

Therefore, a high temperature is not desirable as it favors the decomposition of ammonia, the endothermic reaction. However, at ordinary temperatures, the forward reaction is too slow to be feasible. Fortunately, it may be accelerated by the use of a suitable catalyst so that, at moderate temperatures and very high pressures, satisfactory yields of ammonia are realized.

★ **7. Some reactions run to completion.** Many reactions are reversible under suitable conditions and a state of equilibrium may be established unless at least one of the products escapes or is removed. An equilibrium reaction may be driven in the preferred direction by applying the principle of Le Chatelier.

Some reactions appear to go to completion in the forward direction. No one has found a method of recombining potassium chloride and oxygen directly when potassium chlorate decomposes. Sugar may be caused to decompose into carbon and water by the application of heat. Yet no conditions favorable for the recombination of these products are known.

Many compounds are formed by the interaction of ions in solutions. If solutions of two electrolytes are mixed, two pairs of ions are possible. These pairings may or may not occur. If dilute solutions of sodium chloride and potassium bromide are mixed, no reaction occurs. The resulting solution merely contains a mixture of Na^+, K^+, Cl^-, and Br^- ions. Association of ions occurs only if enough water is evaporated to cause crystals to separate. The yield would be a mixture of NaCl, KCl, NaBr, and KBr.

In some combinations of ions, reactions do occur. *Such reactions may run to completion in the sense that the ions are almost completely removed from solution.* They are sometimes referred to as *end reactions.* Chemists can pre-

Fig. 22-3. Pressure increases the yield of ammonia since the equilibrium shifts in the direction which produces fewer molecules.

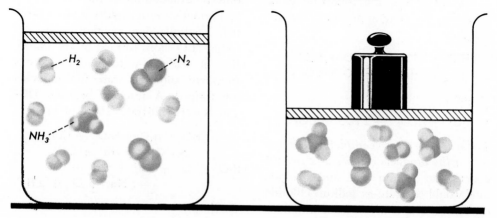

dict that certain ion reactions will run to completion. The extent to which the reacting ions are removed from solution depends on *the solubility of the compound formed* and *the degree of ionization, if it is soluble.* Thus a product which *escapes as a gas, is precipitated as a solid,* or *is only slightly ionized,* effectively removes the reacting ions from solution. We shall consider a specific example of each type of end reaction.

1. *Formation of a gas.* Unstable substances formed as products of ionic reactions decompose spontaneously. An example is carbonic acid which yields a gas as a decomposition product.

$$H_2CO_3 \rightarrow H_2O + CO_2 \uparrow$$

Carbonic acid is produced in the reaction between sodium hydrogen carbonate and hydrochloric acid as shown by the following equation written empirically.

$$NaHCO_3 + HCl \rightarrow NaCl + H_2CO_3$$

Since the water solution of HCl contains H_3O^+ and Cl^- ions, a closer examination of the reaction mechanism suggests that the HCO_3^- ion acts as a base and acquires a proton from the H_3O^+ acid. Certainly Na^+ and Cl^- ions are merely spectators in the water environment. Thus, the following equations may be more appropriate for this reaction.

$$H_3O^+ + HCO_3^- \rightarrow H_2O + H_2CO_3$$
$$H_2CO_3 \rightarrow H_2O + CO_2 \uparrow$$

or, more simply:

$$H_3O^+ + HCO_3^- \rightarrow 2 H_2O + CO_2 \uparrow$$

The reaction runs to completion because one of the products escapes as a gas. Of course, the sodium ions and chloride ions would separate as sodium chloride crystals on evaporation of the water.

The reaction between iron(II) sulfide and hydrochloric acid written empirically illustrates this action more simply.

$$FeS + 2 HCl \rightarrow FeCl_2 + H_2S \uparrow$$

The hydrogen sulfide formed is only moderately soluble and is given off as a gas, the iron(II) chloride being formed on evaporation of water.

2. *Formation of a precipitate.* When solutions of sodium chloride and silver nitrate are mixed, a white precipitate of silver chloride immediately forms.

$$Na^+ + Cl^- + Ag^+ + NO_3^- \rightarrow$$
$$Na^+ + NO_3^- + Ag^+Cl^- \downarrow$$

If gram-equivalents of the two solutes are used, only sodium ions and nitrate ions remain in solution in quantity. The silver ions and chloride ions combine to form insoluble silver chloride. *The reaction runs to completion because an insoluble product is formed.*

The only reaction that occurs is between the silver ions and chloride ions and by omitting the spectator ions Na^+ and NO_3^- from the equation, it may be rewritten in its simplest form

$$Ag^+ + Cl^- \rightarrow Ag^+Cl^- \downarrow$$

Crystalline sodium nitrate is recovered only by evaporation of the water.

3. *Formation af a slightly ionized product.* Neutralization reactions occur between H_3O^+ ions formed by the ionization of acids in water and OH^- ions from basic solutions, water molecules being formed. A reaction between HCl and NaOH illustrates these processes.

$$HCl + H_2O \rightarrow H_3O^+ + Cl^-$$
$$Na^+OH^- \rightarrow Na^+ + OH^-$$
$$H_3O^+ + Cl^- + Na^+ + OH^- \rightarrow$$
$$Na^+ + Cl^- + 2 H_2O$$

Or simply

$$H_3O^+ + OH^- \rightarrow 2\,H_2O$$

Water is only very slightly ionized and exists essentially as covalent molecules. Thus hydronium ions and hydroxide ions are effectively removed from the solution. *The reaction runs to completion because the product is very slightly ionized.* In the reaction between hydrochloric acid and sodium hydroxide, the sodium chloride crystallizes on evaporation of the water.

★ **8. The common ion effect.** Suppose hydrogen chloride gas is bubbled into a saturated solution of sodium chloride. As the hydrogen chloride dissolves, sodium chloride separates as a precipitate. This is an application of the *Law of Mass Action,* the chloride ion being *common* to both solutes. The concentration of chloride ions is increased, that of the sodium ions is not. As sodium chloride crystals separate, the concentration of sodium ions in the solution is lowered. Thus an increase in the concentration of chloride ions has the effect of decreasing the concentration of sodium ions in the solution. *This is known as the common ion effect.*

Of course, equilibrium will finally be established between the rate of dissociation of sodium chloride crystals and the rate of association of sodium and chloride ions.

$$Na^+Cl^- \rightleftarrows Na^+ + Cl^-$$

Further additions of hydrogen chloride will disturb this equilibrium and drive the reaction to the *left.* By *forcing* the reaction to the left, more sodium chloride is caused to separate. This further reduces the concentration of the sodium ions in solution.

The common ion effect is also observed when *one* of the ions of a weak electrolyte is added in excess to a solution. Acetic acid is such an electrolyte. A 0.1-M $HC_2H_3O_2$ solution is about 1.3% ionized. The ionic equilibrium may be shown by the equation:

$$HC_2H_3O_2 + H_2O \rightleftarrows H_3O^+ + C_2H_3O_2^-$$

Sodium acetate is an ionic salt and is completely dissociated in water solution. Small additions of sodium acetate to a solution containing acetic acid will greatly increase the concentration of the acetate ion. The equilibrium will shift in the direction which uses acetate ions faster. More molecules of acetic acid are formed and the concentration of hydronium ions is reduced. In general, *the addition of a salt with an ion common to the solution of a weak electrolyte reduces the ionization of the electrolyte.* A 0.1-N $HC_2H_3O_2$ solution has a pH of 2.9. A solution containing 0.1-N concentrations of both acetic acid and sodium acetate has a pH of 4.6.

Approximately 1.3% of the solute molecules in a 0.1-M acetic acid solution are ionized at room temperature and 98.7% of the $HC_2H_3O_2$ molecules remains un-ionized. Thus, the water solution contains three species of particles which are in equilibrium with one another; $HC_2H_3O_2$ molecules, H_3O^+ ions, and $C_2H_3O_2^-$ ions.

At equilibrium, the speed of the forward reaction in which $HC_2H_3O_2$ molecules ionize with H_2O to form H_3O^+ and $C_2H_3O_2^-$ ions is equal to the speed of the reverse reaction in which H_3O^+ and $C_2H_3O_2^-$ ions react to form H_2O and $HC_2H_3O_2$ molecules. The equilibrium constant for this system expresses the equilibrium ratio of ions to molecules and is called the ionization constant K_i.

From the equilibrium equation, it is evident that:

$$K_i' = \frac{[H_3O^+][C_2H_3O_2^-]}{[HC_2H_3O_2][H_2O]}$$

Because H_2O molecules are in such great excess at the 0.1-M concentration of $HC_2H_3O_2$ molecules, we may consider, without appreciable error, that the mole concentration of water H_2O remains a constant. Thus,

$$K_i'[H_2O] = \frac{[H_3O^+][C_2H_3O_2^-]}{[HC_2H_3O_2]} = K_i$$

To determine the numerical value of the ionization constant K_i for acetic acid at a specified temperature, the equilibrium concentration of H_3O^+ ions, $C_2H_3O_2^-$ ions, and $HC_2H_3O_2$ molecules must be known at this temperature. Since 1 molecule of $HC_2H_3O_2$ ionizes in water to give 1 H_3O^+ ion and 1 $C_2H_3O_2^-$ ion, these concentrations can be found experimentally by measuring the pH of the solution.

Suppose that a precise electrometric experiment shows the pH of a 0.1000-M solution of acetic acid to be 2.876 at 25° C. The numerical value of K_i for $HC_2H_3O_2$ at 25° C may be determined as follows.

$$[H_3O^+] = [C_2H_3O_2^-] = 10^{-2.876} \text{ mole/}l$$

Antilog $(-2.876) =$
  antilog $(0.124 - 3) = 1.33 \times 10^{-3}$

$$[H_3O^+] = [C_2H_3O_2^-] = 1.33 \times 10^{-3}$$

$[HC_2H_3O_2] =$
  $0.1000 - 0.00133 = 0.0987$

$$K_i = \frac{[H_3O^+][C_2H_3O_2^-]}{[HC_2H_3O_2]}$$

$$K_i = \frac{(1.33 \times 10^{-3})^2}{9.87 \times 10^{-2}}$$

$$K_i = 1.79 \times 10^{-5}$$

A rise in temperature will cause the equilibrium to shift according to Le Chatelier's principle and K_i will have a new value for each temperature. An increase in the concentration of $C_2H_3O_2^-$ ions, as by the addition of $NaC_2H_3O_2$, disturbs the equilibrium causing a decrease in $[H_3O^+]$ and an increase in $[HC_2H_3O_2]$. Eventually the equilibrium is reestablished with the same value of K_i, but with a higher concentration of un-ionized acetic acid molecules and a lower concentration of H_3O^+ ions, thus a higher pH.

The pH of a weakly acidic or alkaline solution tends to remain practically constant, regardless of the addition of other ions, if the proper salts are present. The concentration of hydronium ions will not vary appreciably in a solution of acetic acid containing a high concentration of sodium acetate. Similarly, the hydroxide-ion concentration in an ammonia-water solution will remain almost constant if the solution contains a high concentration of ammonium chloride. Salts used in this way are called *buffer salts*. The solutions are said to be *buffered* against changes in pH due to the addition or removal of small quantities of acids or alkalies.

Buffer action has many important applications in chemistry and physiology. The human blood is buffered so as to maintain a pH of about 7.3. Slight variations in pH are essential for the stimulation of certain physiological functions. However, pronounced changes would lead to serious disturbances of normal body functions, or even death.

⋆ 9. The ionization constant of water. Pure water is a very poor conductor of electricity; it is therefore very slightly ionized. According to the modern concept of acids and bases, some water molecules donate protons, acting as an acid. Other water molecules which accept these protons act as a base.

$$H_2O + H_2O \rightleftarrows H_3O^+ + OH^-$$

The degree of ionization is slight and equilibrium is quickly established with a very low concentration of H_3O^+ and OH^- ions.

Conductivity experiments with very pure water at room temperature show that 1 g-ion of H_3O^+ ions and 1 g-ion of OH^- ions are present in 10^7 liters. Thus $[H_3O^+]$ and $[OH^-]$ are each 10^{-7} g-ion (mole) per liter. The expression for the equilibrium constant is

$$K = \frac{[H_3O^+][OH^-]}{[H_2O]^2}$$

A liter of water contains

$$\frac{1000. \text{ g}}{18.0 \text{ g/mole}} = 55.5 \text{ moles}$$

and this concentration of water molecules remains substantially the same in all dilute solutions.

Thus, both $[H_2O]^2$ and K in the above equilibrium expression are constants and their product is the constant K_w, *the ionization constant for water*, which is equal to the product of the molar concentrations of the H_3O^+ and OH^- ions.

$$K_w = K[H_2O]^2 = [H_3O^+][OH^-]$$

At 25° C,

$$K_w = [H_3O^+][OH^-] =$$
$$10^{-7} \times 10^{-7} = 10^{-14}$$

The product (K_w) *of the molar concentrations of* H_3O^+ *and* OH^- *has this constant value not only in pure water, but in all water solutions at 25° C.* Thus an acid solution with a pH of 4 has a $[H_3O^+]$ of 10^{-4} gram-ion (mole) per liter and a $[OH^-]$ of 10^{-10} gram-ion per liter. An alkaline solution with a pH of 8 has a $[H_3O^+]$ of 10^{-8} gram-ion per liter and a $[OH^-]$ of 10^{-6} gram-ion per liter.

★ **10. Hydrolysis of salts.** In general, when normal salts are dissolved in water, we expect the solutions to remain neutral. Many salts, such as NaCl and KNO_3, behave in this way. They are formed from *strong* acids and *strong* hydroxides. Solutions of these salts have a pH of 7. When other salts are dissolved in water, solutions may be produced that are not neutral, but may be either acidic or alkaline. Such salts are said to *hydrolyze* in water solution. *Hydrolysis is the action of a salt with water to form a solution which is acidic or basic.*

Suppose we dissolve some sodium carbonate in water and, by testing it with litmus paper, find that it turns red litmus *blue*. The solution contains an excess of OH^- ions and is basic. The modern concept of acids and bases is useful in explaining this phenomenon.

The sodium ion shows little tendency to combine with the hydroxide ion in solution. The carbonate ion, $CO_3^=$, is a base which accepts a proton from the water to form the slightly ionized bicarbonate ion, HCO_3^-, according to the following equation:

$$CO_3^= + H_2O \rightleftarrows HCO_3^- + OH^-$$

The OH^- ion concentration builds up until equilibrium is reached. The H_3O^+ ion concentration becomes less since the product $[H_3O^+][OH^-]$ must remain equal to the ionization constant of the solution, 10^{-14}. Thus the pH is *greater* than 7 and the solution is *alkaline*. In general, *salts formed from weak acids and strong hydroxides hydrolyze in water to form alkaline solutions.*

A solution of ammonium chloride, NH_4Cl, turns blue litmus *red*. This demonstrates that hydrolysis occurs and the solution contains an excess of H_3O^+ ions. Chloride ions show little tendency to combine with hydronium ions in solution. The ammonium ions donate protons to water molecules according to the following equation:

$$NH_4^+ + H_2O \rightleftarrows H_3O^+ + NH_3$$

Equilibrium is established with an increased H_3O^+ concentration. The pH is *less* than 7 and the solution is thus *acidic*.

The metallic ions of many salts are hydrated in water solution. Such hydrated ions may donate protons to water molecules and the solution becomes acidic. For example, aluminum chloride produces the hydrated positive ion

$$Al(H_2O)_6^{+++}$$

Copper(II) sulfate in water solution yields the light blue hydrated positive ion

$$Cu(H_2O)_4^{++}$$

These ions react with water to produce hydronium ions in the following manner:

$$Al(H_2O)_6^{+++} + H_2O \rightleftarrows$$
$$Al(H_2O)_5OH^{++} + H_3O^+$$
$$Cu(H_2O)_4^{++} + H_2O \rightleftarrows$$
$$Cu(H_2O)_3OH^+ + H_3O^+$$

In general, salts formed from strong acids and weak hydroxides hydrolyze in water to form acidic solutions.

Aluminum sulfide, when placed in water, is observed to form both a precipitate and a gas. The reaction is as follows:

$$Al_2S_3 + 6 H_2O \rightarrow 2 Al(OH)_3 \downarrow + 3 H_2S \uparrow$$

Both products are removed from the solution and the hydrolysis therefore runs to completion. *Both ions* of a salt formed from a *weak* acid and a *weak* hydroxide will hydrolyze extensively in water. The salt may undergo complete decomposition. If both ions of the salt hydrolyze equally, the solution will be neutral. Ammonium acetate is such a salt.

Hydrolysis is often very important. Sodium carbonate, washing soda, is widely used as a cleaning agent due to the alkaline properties of the water solution. Sodium hydrogen carbonate forms a mild alkaline solution in water which finds many practical uses. Through the study of hydrolysis we are able to see clearly why the end-point of a neutralization reaction may occur at a pH other than 7 (see Chapter 21, Section 19).

SUMMARY

A state of equilibrium is reached when opposing actions occur simultaneously and at equal speeds. This is true in physical, ionic, and chemical actions. Such equilibria are dynamic, as opposed to static balance.

The speed of chemical action depends on the collision frequency of the reactants and the collision efficiency. There are several factors which affect the speed of a reaction.

The Law of Mass Action is concerned with the relationship between the speed of a reaction and the concentration of reactants. Reaction speed is proportional to the product of the concentrations of the reactants.

When a reversible chemical reaction is in equilibrium, a constant relationship exists between the concentrations of products and original reactants. The ratio of the product of the concentrations of reactants to the product of the concentrations of new substances has a definite numerical value. This ratio is the equilibrium constant. It varies only with temperature for a given system.

A system in equilibrium is disturbed and the equilibrium shifts when subjected to a stress. The principle of Le Chatelier tells us that an equilibrium shifts, when subjected to a stress, in such manner as to relieve the stress. By proper application of this principle, certain equilibrium reactions are made commercially feasible.

Ionic reactions will run to completion if at least one product escapes as a gas, is precipitated as a solid, or is only slightly ionized.

The common ion effect is an application of the Law of Mass Action to ionic equilibria. It may be applied to solutions of weak electrolytes to reduce the ionization of the electrolyte. Solutions of weak acids and alkalies may be buffered against large changes in pH by the use of proper buffer salts.

Water has an ionization constant equal to the product of the concentrations of the H_3O^+ and OH^- ions. This constant, 10^{-14}, remains the same for water solutions as well as pure water. Salts which hydrolyze in water solution may produce an excess of either H_3O^+ ions or OH^- ions in the solution.

TEST YOURSELF ON THESE TERMS

activation energy	contact catalyst	Law of Mass Action
buffer salt	end reaction	pH
carrier catalyst	equilibrium constant	physical equilibrium
chemical equilibrium	hydrolysis	Principle of
collision efficiency	ionic equilibrium	Le Chatelier
collision frequency	ionization constant	reversible reaction
common ion effect	of water	velocity constant

QUESTIONS

Group A

* 1. State three examples of physical equilibrium.
* 2. Write the ionic equations for three examples of ionic equilibrium.
* 3. In order for reactions, other than simple decompositions to occur, what two conditions must be met?
* 4. What is wrong with the following statement? When equilibrium is reached, the opposing reactions stop.
* 5. Name five factors which influence the speed of reaction.
* 6. State the Law of Mass Action.
* 7. An oxidation reaction proceeding in air under standard pressure is transferred to an atmosphere of pure oxygen under the same pressure. (*a*) What is the effect on the speed of the oxidation reaction? (*b*) How can you account for this effect?
* 8. (*a*) State the Principle of Le Chatelier. (*b*) To what kinds of equilibria does it apply?
* 9. (*a*) Name three factors which may disturb, or shift, an equilibrium. (*b*) Which of these affects the value of the equilibrium constant?
*10. What are the three conditions under which ionic reactions involving ionic substances may run to completion? Write an equation for each.

Group B

⋆ 11. The reaction between steam and iron is reversible. Steam passed over hot iron produces magnetic iron oxide and hydrogen. Hydrogen passed over hot magnetic iron oxide reduces it to iron and forms steam. Suggest a method by which this reversible reaction may be brought to a state of equilibrium.

⋆ 12. What is the meaning of the term *dynamic* as applied to an equilibrium state?

⋆ 13. Methanol is produced synthetically as a gas by the reaction between carbon monoxide and hydrogen, in the presence of a catalyst, according to the equilibrium reaction: $CO + 2 H_2 \rightleftarrows CH_3OH + 24$ kcal. Write the expression for the equilibrium constant of this reaction.

⋆ 14. How would you regulate the temperature of the equilibrium mixture of CO, H_2, and CH_3OH of Question 13 in order to increase the yield of methanol? Explain.

⋆ 15. How would you regulate the pressure on the equilibrium mixture of Question 13 in order to increase the yield of methanol? Explain.

⋆ 16. In the reaction, $A + B \rightleftarrows C$, the concentrations of A, B, and C in the equilibrium mixture were found to be 2.0, 3.0, and 1.0 moles per liter respectively. What is the equilibrium constant of this reaction?

⋆ 17. Write the balanced ionic equations for the following reactions in water solution. If a reaction does not take place, write NO REACTION. Omit all *spectator* ions. Show precipitates by ↓ and gases by ↑. Use solubility data in the Appendix as needed. Use a separate sheet of paper. (Do not write in this book.)

(a) $BaCO_3 + HNO_3 \rightarrow$ (f) $FeS + NaCl \rightarrow$
(b) $Pb(NO_3)_2 + NaCl \rightarrow$ (g) $AgC_2H_3O_2 + HCl \rightarrow$
(c) $CuSO_4 + HCl \rightarrow$ (h) $Na_3PO_4 + CuSO_4 \rightarrow$
(d) $Ca_3(PO_4)_2 + NaNO_3 \rightarrow$ (i) $BaCl_2 + Na_2SO_4 \rightarrow$
(e) $Ba(NO_3)_2 + H_2SO_4 \rightarrow$ (j) $CuO + H_2SO_4 \rightarrow$

⋆ 18. Explain why the pH of a solution containing both acetic acid and sodium acetate is higher than that of a solution containing the same concentration of acetic acid alone.

⋆ 19. Complete the following table, using a separate sheet of paper. (Do not write in this book.)

pH	$[H_3O^+]$ (moles/liter)	$[OH^-]$ (moles/liter)	$[H_3O^+][OH^-]$	Property
0				
1				
3				
5				
7	$10^{-7} = 0.0000001$	$10^{-7} = 0.0000001$	10^{-14}	Neutral
9				
11				
13				
14				

PROBLEMS

⋆ **1.** The H_3O^+ ion concentration of a solution is 0.00040 mole per liter. This may be expressed as $H_3O^+ = 4.0 \times 10^{-4}$ mole per liter. What is the pH of the solution?

⋆ **2.** What is the pH of a 0.002-M solution of HCl? (At this concentration HCl is completely ionized.)

⋆ **3.** Find the pH of a 0.02-M solution of KOH.

⋆ **4.** Given a 250 ml volumetric flask, distilled water, and CP grade NaOH, (*a*) state how you would prepare 250 ml of 0.50-M NaOH solution. (*b*) What is the normality of the solution?

⋆ **5.** What quantity of copper(II) sulfate pentahydrate is required to prepare 750. ml of 2.00-M solution?

⋆ **6.** A 0.01000-N solution of acetic acid is found to have a pH of 3.3799 at 18° C. What is the ionization constant of this weak acid?

SOME THINGS FOR YOU TO DO

1. Test the solutions of various salts which you think may hydrolyze in water, with red and blue litmus paper. See if your predictions are correct. Work out a satisfactory explanation in each case.

2. Consult a modern college chemistry text to learn the meaning of *solubility product* and the relationships of solubility products to equilibrium constants. Demonstrate the applications of solubility products to your chemistry class by carrying out several computations for familiar solubility equilibrium systems.

Chapter 23 · OXIDATION-REDUCTION REACTIONS

1. Oxidation. Oxidation in its most common form involves the combination of an element with oxygen. Many substances combine with oxygen to form oxides. *In all of these oxidations, electrons are lost to the oxygen, either partially or completely.* There are many reactions of a similar nature which do not involve the element oxygen. Chemists have found it convenient to classify these types of reactions as oxidations also.

Hydrogen burns in oxygen to form water:

$$2 H_2 + O_2 \rightarrow 2 H_2O$$

Hydrogen also burns in an atmosphere of fluorine to form hydrogen fluoride:

$$H_2 + F_2 \rightarrow 2 HF$$

Hydrogen burns in chlorine to produce hydrogen chloride:

$$H_2 + Cl_2 \rightarrow 2 HCl$$

Iron, when heated, combines with chlorine, forming iron(III) chloride. If iron and sulfur are heated together the product is iron(II) sulfide.

$$2 Fe + 3 Cl_2 \rightarrow 2 FeCl_3$$
$$Fe + S \rightarrow FeS$$

All these reactions are similar to combinations with oxygen. In each, the electropositive element loses one or more electrons, either partially or completely. These elements are said to be *oxidized.* In this general sense, *oxidation is the loss of electrons from an ion, atom, or group of atoms.*

The substance responsible for the removal of electrons during the oxidation process is called the *oxidizing agent.* Hydrogen is oxidized during the formation of hydrogen fluoride; fluorine is the oxidizing agent. In the production of iron(II) sulfide, iron is oxidized to the *iron(II)* state, and sulfur is the oxidizing agent. Iron is oxidized to the *iron(III)* state in the reaction with chlorine. Here, the chlorine is the oxidizing agent. *An oxidizing agent is a substance which takes up electrons during a chemical reaction.*

2. Reduction. Certain metals occur in nature as metallic oxides and may be recovered from such a compound by a

336

process which removes the oxygen. This is the way iron is produced from iron ore in a blast furnace.

Reduction in its most common form involves the removal of oxygen from a compound. The substance responsible for removing the oxygen, is, of course, the *reducing agent.* The only way a metal could combine with oxygen in the first place is by the process of losing electrons. Consequently, the only way a metal can be recovered from its oxide is by returning the lost electrons.

Chemists have extended the meaning of reduction to include all reactions in which electrons are gained, either partially or completely, by reacting substances. In this general sense, *reduction is the addition of electrons to an ion, atom, or group of atoms.* The source of these electrons is considered to be the agent responsible for the reduction. *A reducing agent is a substance which supplies electrons during a chemical action.*

3. Oxidation and reduction occur simultaneously. It is apparent that one substance cannot gain electrons unless another substance loses electrons. If *oxidation* occurs during a chemical action, then *reduction* must occur simultaneously. If one kind of particle is oxidized, another kind of particle must be reduced *to a comparable degree.*

Any chemical process in which there is a transfer of electrons, either partial or complete, is an **oxidation-reduction** *reaction.* This impressive name is often shortened to *"redox" reaction.* Most of the reactions studied in elementary chemistry are oxidation-reduction reactions. In composition reactions having ionic products, and in replacement reactions, the electron transfer is complete. In reactions which form polar covalent bonds the electron transfer is not complete. However, the electrons are shared unequally, with more of them moving in the space around the more highly electronegative element. We may consider the less electronegative substance to be oxidized and the more electronegative substance to be reduced. Few covalent bonds are completely nonpolar.

Reactions in which there are no changes in valence do not involve oxidation-reduction. If sodium chloride is added to the solution of silver nitrate, silver chloride precipitates.

$$Na^+ + Cl^- + Ag^+ + NO_3^- \rightarrow$$
$$Na^+ + NO_3^- + Ag^+Cl^- \downarrow$$

Silver chloride is an ionic compound. Note that the charge of each ion remains the same; no electrons have been transferred. This is *not* an oxidation-reduction reaction.

* Oxidation-reduction reactions sometimes involve electron transfers that are not easily interpreted by our usual application of valence. For example, the *permanganate ion* in a solution of

VOCABULARY

Electrochemical. Pertaining to spontaneous oxidation-reduction reactions used as a source of electric energy.

Electrolytic. Pertaining to forced oxidation-reduction reactions which utilize electric energy from an external source.

Oxidation number. A special valence number assigned to each element to indicate the number of electrons gained, lost, or shared unequally.

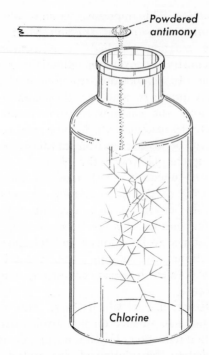

Powdered antimony

Chlorine

Fig. 23-1. The combustion of antimony in chlorine is an oxidation-reduction reaction.

electrons and is oxidized. Another substance gains these electrons and is reduced to a comparable degree. The *state of oxidation* of a substance depends upon the *number of electrons lost or gained*. Loss of electrons produces a more *positive* oxidation state, and gain of electrons produces a more *negative* oxidation state. If all electrons belonging to an atom of an element are present, the oxidation state is *zero* and the atom is assigned the oxidation number 0. All atoms in their elementary form have oxidation numbers of 0. These may be written as: Na^0, K^0, Cu^0, $H_2{}^0$, and $N_2{}^0$.

Observe that the oxidation number 0 was assigned to atoms of diatomic elements as well as monatomic elements. While the bond between the two hydrogen atoms of the H_2 molecule is *real*, it cannot be *polar* since both atoms are electronegative to the same degree. The electron pair is shared equally by both atoms composing the nonpolar covalent molecule.

In the following electronic equations the substances are oxidized:

$$Na^0 \;-\; e^- \rightarrow Na^{+1}$$
$$Fe^0 \;-\; 2\,e^- \rightarrow Fe^{+2}$$
$$Fe^{+2} \;-\; e^- \rightarrow Fe^{+3}$$
$$2\,Cl^{-1} \;-\; 2\,e^- \rightarrow Cl_2{}^0$$

The superscript after each symbol is the oxidation number of that particle. The difference between oxidation numbers indicates the number of electrons lost by each atom or ion. Observe that the chloride ion has the oxidation number −1, a *negative* oxidation state. *Oxidation results in an algebraic increase in the oxidation number* of a substance. A change from −1 to 0 is an algebraic increase in the oxidation number just as is a change from 0 to +1, or +1 to +2. Each of these changes accompanies the loss of 1 electron.

potassium permanganate has a valence of −1, $MnO_4{}^-$. Under proper conditions this ion may be reduced to the *manganese(II) ion*, Mn^{++}. Under other conditions the $MnO_4{}^-$ ion may be reduced to the *manganate ion*, $MnO_4{}^=$.

⋆ If we are to write the equation for one of these reactions, we must know the number of electrons transferred during the chemical action. The common valence of the ion is of little help if the ion consists of two or more different substances. *In order to simplify the task of balancing oxidation-reduction equations, a special kind of valence number is assigned to each element in a compound.* This valence number is commonly called the **oxidation number** of the element.

⋆ **4. Oxidation numbers.** In oxidation-reduction reactions one substance loses

In the electronic equations which follow, the substances are reduced:

$$Na^{+1} + e^- \rightarrow Na^0$$
$$Cl_2{}^0 + 2e^- \rightarrow 2Cl^{-1}$$
$$Fe^{+3} + e^- \rightarrow Fe^{+2}$$
$$Cu^{+2} + 2e^- \rightarrow Cu^0$$
$$Br_2{}^0 + 2e^- \rightarrow 2Br^{-1}$$

The third equation illustrates the reduction of the iron(III) ion, oxidation number +3, to the iron(II) state, oxidation number +2. It further illustrates the distinguishing feature of the Stock nomenclature system coming into general use for ions of variable valence. The Roman numerals III and II as used with iron refer to the oxidation states of the iron atoms. Two additional electrons would be necessary to complete the reduction of the iron(II) ion to the iron atom, oxidation number 0. *Reduction results in an algebraic decrease in the oxidation number of a substance.*

In the illustrations given so far there appears to be no difference between the oxidation numbers assigned and the common valences to which we are accustomed. It is true that the oxidation state of each ion in a binary salt is that indicated by the ionic charge. In binary covalent compounds the oxidation number of each atom is determined by its valence. Shared electrons are arbitrarily assigned to the element having the greater electronegativity. The covalent bonds are polar to some degree, and occur between electropositive, or less electronegative, atoms and more highly electronegative atoms. *Positive* oxidation numbers are assigned to the electropositive atoms and *negative* oxidation numbers are assigned to the electronegative atoms. Thus, in the hydrogen chloride molecule, hydrogen is less elec-

tronegative than chlorine and is given the positive oxidation number: $H^{+1}Cl^{-1}$.

Let us examine a familiar ternary compound, H_2SO_4, with regard to the common valences. We would say that the valence of the hydrogen present is +1 and the valence of the sulfate radical is −2. This is evident from the ionization of a dilute solution of sulfuric acid:

$$H_2SO_4 + 2H_2O \rightarrow 2H_3O^+ + SO_4^=$$

Similarly, sulfurous acid, H_2SO_3, provides the sulfite ion, $SO_3^=$. Obviously all atoms in these two ternary compounds cannot have the same oxidation numbers. The common valences merely tell us that two hydrogen atoms are required for each sulfate radical, or each sulfite radical. *The oxidation state of each atom must be known if we are to balance oxidation-reduction equations involving these substances.* How may the proper oxidation numbers be assigned to the elements in ternary compounds?

Metals in general are electropositive elements and nonmetals are electroneg-

Fig. 23-2. The replacement of the copper(II) ion by zinc is an oxidation-reduction reaction.

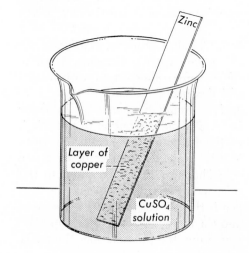

ative. Of all the elements, only *fluorine* is more electronegative than oxygen. Therefore, in combinations with any of the elements except fluorine, oxygen exerts the greater force of attraction on the shared electrons. Hydrogen is the least electronegative of the nonmetals. In combination with other nonmetals, hydrogen is positive. Compounds of metals and hydrogen, called *hydrides*, are relatively unimportant in elementary chemistry.

With these facts in mind a few simple rules can be stated which will enable us to assign oxidation numbers to the elements in any compound.

1. *The oxidation number of an atom of a free element is zero.* Atoms of the same element have the same electronegativity. If bonds do occur between these atoms, they are nonpolar and bond electrons are shared equally.

2. *The oxidation number of a monatomic ion is equal to its charge.* Atoms of metals form ions by losing electrons to the atoms of nonmetals. The simple ions of metals are positively charged, and the simple ions of nonmetals are negatively charged.

3. *In combinations of nonmetals, the oxidation number of the less electronegative element is positive and of the more electronegative element is negative.* Chlorine, bromine, and iodine are the more negative elements in all of their combinations except with oxygen and fluorine.

4. *The oxidation number of hydrogen is +1.* The only exception to this rule is in the formation of metallic hydrides.

5. *The oxidation number of oxygen is −2.* There are three exceptions to this rule. In combination with fluorine, oxygen is the less electronegative nonmetal and therefore is positive. In compounds containing the *peroxide* ion, the oxida-

tion number of oxygen is −1. The oxides of the heavier members of the Group I metals, called *superoxides*, are now believed to contain the O_2^- ion in which the oxidation number of oxygen is $-\frac{1}{2}$.

6. *The algebraic sum of the oxidation numbers of the atoms in the formula of a compound is zero.* We know that both molecular formulas and empirical formulas represent electrically neutral particles of matter. This rule merely tells us that the total of the positive oxidation numbers must *equal* the total of the negative oxidation numbers in any formula.

Now suppose we apply these rules to assign oxidation numbers to each element in the two ternary compounds, H_2SO_4 and H_2SO_3. In each, oxygen is given the oxidation number −2 and hydrogen is given the oxidation number +1. In the sulfuric acid molecule the total contribution of the 4 atoms of oxygen is 4 times −2, or −8; $4(-2) = -8$. The total contribution of the 2 atoms of hydrogen is $2(+1) = +2$. Since the H_2SO_4 molecule is neutral, the oxidation number of the single sulfur atom must be +6. We may write the appropriate oxidation number adjacent to each symbol in the formula. (The numbers are usually placed above the symbols where it is desired not to imply an ionic charge, or where it would cause undue spreading of the formula in a long equation.)

$$\overset{+1 +6 -2}{H_2SO_4}$$
$$2(+1) + 1(+6) + 4(-2) = 0$$

In the sulfurous acid molecule the total contribution of oxygen is $3(-2) = -6$. that of hydrogen is $2(+1) = +2$. Thus the oxidation number of the single atom of sulfur must be +4.

$$\overset{+1+4-2}{H_2SO_3}$$

$$2(+1) + 1(+4) + 3(-2) = 0$$

This is seen to be a reasonable assignment of oxidation numbers by examining the electronic structures of these two molecules. The electron-dot formula of sulfuric acid is as follows:

$$H \overset{\cdot\cdot}{\underset{\cdot\cdot}{O}} \overset{\times\times}{\underset{\times\times}{S}} \overset{\cdot\cdot}{\underset{\cdot\cdot}{O}} H$$

with :O: above and :O: below

Oxygen is the most electronegative element present so we shall assign to oxygen all electrons shared with oxygen. The sulfur atom must contribute all of its six electrons. Hence the oxidation number of sulfur is +6.

The electron-dot formula of sulfurous acid may be written as follows:

$$H \overset{\cdot\cdot}{\underset{\cdot\cdot}{O}} \overset{\times\times}{\underset{\times\times}{S}} \overset{\cdot\cdot}{\underset{\cdot\cdot}{O}} H$$

with :O: below

Observe that one pair of electrons belonging to sulfur is unshared. The atom of sulfur contributes *four* electrons, hence the oxidation number is +4.

Suppose we apply these rules to a ternary salt. Potassium permanganate is composed of potassium ions, K^+, and the complex permanganate ion, MnO_4^-. The empirical formula is $KMnO_4$. Oxygen has the oxidation number -2 as before. The total contribution of the 4 oxygen atoms is $4(-2) = -8$. The K^+ ion is assigned the oxidation number that corresponds to its ionic charge, $+1$. The oxidation number of the manganese atom in the radical group must then be $+7$. The formula showing these oxidation states of the elements can be written as follows:

$$K^{+1}[Mn^{+7}(O^{-2})_4]^{-1}$$

or more simply

$$\overset{+1+7-2}{KMnO_4}$$

Manganese has several important oxidation states. This oxidation number, $+7$, corresponds to the position of the element in Group VII of the Periodic Table and represents its highest oxidation state.

★ 5. Balancing of oxidation-reduction equations. The principal use of oxidation numbers is in balancing equations for oxidation-reduction reactions. In Chapter 12, Section 3, we stated that an orderly procedure is an essential part of equation writing. We must know the *facts:* what the reactants are and what the products are. We must then represent the reactants and products by their *correct formulas.* Finally, we must adjust the coefficients of all reactants and products to be in accord with the *conservation of atoms.* The method used to accomplish this third step is essentially one of trial and error.

Oxidation-reduction reactions are those in which changes in oxidation number occur. *Here we must observe the conservation of electrons, as well as conservation of atoms, in writing equations.* In all but the simplest of these reactions, trial-and-error balancing is a difficult process. This process may be simplified by *balancing the electron shift* between the particles oxidized and the particles reduced *before* adjusting the coefficients for the rest of the equation. The procedure for writing oxidation-reduction equations therefore includes the following steps:

Step 1: Write the skeleton equation for the reaction. To do this we must know the reactants and products and represent each by the correct formula (see Steps 1 and 2 of the general procedure outlined in Chapter 12, Section 3).

Step 2: *Assign oxidation numbers to all elements and determine what is oxidized and what is reduced.*

Step 3: *Write the electronic equation for the oxidation process and the electronic equation for the reduction process.*

Step 4: *Adjust the coefficients in both electronic equations so that the number of electrons lost equals the number gained.*

Step 5: *Place these coefficients in the skeleton equation.*

Step 6: *Supply the proper coefficients for the rest of the equation to satisfy the conservation of atoms (see Step 3 of the general procedure outlined in Chapter 12).*

We shall illustrate the application of these steps by considering a very simple oxidation-reduction reaction. Hydrogen sulfide gas burns in air to form sulfur dioxide and water. These facts, together with our knowledge of valence, enable us to write the skeleton equation.

Step 1:

$$H_2S + O_2 \rightarrow SO_2 + H_2O$$

We now assign oxidation numbers applying the appropriate rules from Section 4. Sulfur is oxidized from the -2 state to the $+4$ state, and oxygen is reduced from the 0 state to the -2 state. Observe that the oxidation number of hydrogen remains the same; thus it plays no part in the primary action of oxidation-reduction.

Step 2:

$$\overset{+1-2}{H_2S} + \overset{0}{O_2} \rightarrow \overset{+4-2}{SO_2} + \overset{+1-2}{H_2O}$$

The difference in the oxidation states

of sulfur requires the loss of 6 electrons; $(-2) - (+4) = -6$. The difference in oxidation states of the oxygen requires the gain of 2 electrons; $(0) - (-2) = +2$. The electronic equations for these two actions are as follows:

Step 3:

$$S^{-2} - 6 \, e^- \rightarrow S^{+4} \text{ (oxidation)}$$
$$O^0 + 2 \, e^- \rightarrow O^{-2} \text{ (reduction)}$$

Free oxygen is diatomic, so 4 electrons must be gained during the reduction of a molecule of free oxygen.

$$O_2^0 + 4 \, e^- \rightarrow 2 \, O^{-2}$$

We are now in a position to adjust the coefficients of the two electronic equations so the number of electrons lost in the oxidation of sulfur equals the number gained in the reduction of oxygen. The smallest number of electrons common to both equations is 12. We can show the gain and loss of 12 electrons in the two equations by multiplying the oxidation equation by 2, and multiplying the reduction equation by 3.

Step 4:

$$2 \, S^{-2} - 12 \, e^- \rightarrow 2 \, S^{+4}$$
$$3 \, O_2^0 + 12 \, e^- \rightarrow 6 \, O^{-2}$$

Hence the coefficients of H_2S and SO_2 are both 2, and the coefficient of O_2 is 3. Notice that the 6 O^{-2} is divided between the two products SO_2 and H_2O. The coefficient, 6, is accounted for with the coefficient 2 in front of each formula. These coefficients are transferred to the skeleton equation.

Step 5:

$$2 \, H_2S + 3 \, O_2 \rightarrow 2 \, SO_2 + 2 \, H_2O$$

We are ready now to adjust the coefficients of the equation in the usual way to satisfy the Law of Conservation of Atoms. In this instance no further adjustments are needed; the equation is balanced.

Step 6:

$$2\ H_2S + 3\ O_2 \rightarrow 2\ SO_2 + 2\ H_2O$$

For a second example, we will use an oxidation-reduction equation that is slightly more difficult to balance. In the reaction between manganese dioxide and hydrochloric acid, water, manganese(II) chloride, and chlorine gas are formed. The skeleton equation is:

$$\overset{+4\ \ -2}{Mn\ O_2} + \overset{+1\ -1}{H\ Cl} \rightarrow \overset{+1\ -2}{H_2\ O} + \overset{+2\ -1}{Mn\ Cl_2} + \overset{0}{Cl_2}$$

We assign oxidation numbers to the elements in the reaction and see that Mn^{+4} is reduced to Mn^{+2}, and some of the Cl^{-1} is oxidized to Cl^0. Hydrogen and oxygen do not take part in the primary action. The electronic equations are:

$$2\ Cl^{-1} - 2\ e^- \rightarrow Cl_2^0$$
$$Mn^{+4} + 2\ e^- \rightarrow Mn^{+2}$$

The number of electrons lost and gained is the same, so we transfer the coefficients to the skeleton equation, which becomes:

$$MnO_2 + 2\ HCl \rightarrow H_2O + MnCl_2 + Cl_2$$

The complete equation may now be balanced by inspection. Two additional molecules of HCl are required to provide the two Cl^- ions of the $MnCl_2$. This requires 2 molecules of water which then accounts for the 2 oxygens of the MnO_2. Our final equation reads:

$$MnO_2 + 4\ HCl \rightarrow 2\ H_2O + MnCl_2 + Cl_2$$

The equations for both of these illustrations can be balanced with little difficulty by trial and error. The step process is applied to a more complicated oxidation-reduction reaction in the Sample Problem on the next page.

The method we have used to balance oxidation-reduction reactions is variously referred to as the *electron-shift, electron-transfer,* and *oxidation-state* method. The use of oxidation numbers in no way implies the existence of ions. Remember that the transfer of electrons may be partial, as in polar covalent bonds, or complete, as in ionic bonds. Oxidation numbers are assigned in either case. Some chemists prefer to use a second method, called the *ion-electron* method. It has the advantage of differentiating between ionic and molecular equations. It is, however, more difficult for students of elementary chemistry to use. For this reason it has not been presented here. Either method, used properly, leads to the correctly balanced equation.

★ **6. Oxidizing and reducing agents.** An oxidizing agent is a substance that takes up electrons during an oxidation-reduction reaction, and a reducing agent is the substance that furnishes the electrons. It is obvious then that the substance oxidized is also the reducing agent, and the substance reduced is the oxidizing agent. An oxidized substance becomes a potential oxidizing agent. Similarly, a reduced substance is a potential reducing agent. It follows, however, that a very active reducing agent (one easily oxidized) becomes a very poor oxidizing agent, and conversely.

The different degrees of attraction that elements have for electrons are referred to as their differences in electronegativity. The relatively large atoms of the Sodium Family of metals, Group I of the Periodic Table, have weak attraction for their valence electrons, form positive ions readily, and are *very active reducing agents.* The lithium atom is the most active reducing agent of all the common elements, based on elec-

★SAMPLE PROBLEM

The oxidation-reduction reaction between hydrochloric acid and potassium permanganate yields the following products: water, potassium chloride, manganese(II) chloride, and chlorine gas. Write the balanced equation.

SOLUTION

We first write the skeleton equation, being careful to show the correct formula of each reactant and each product. Appropriate oxidation numbers are placed above the symbols of the elements.

$$\overset{+1-1}{H\,Cl} + \overset{+1+7-2}{KMnO_4} \rightarrow \overset{+1-2}{H_2O} + \overset{+1-1}{K\,Cl} + \overset{+2-1}{MnCl_2} + \overset{0}{Cl_2}$$

We see that some chloride ions are oxidized to chlorine atoms, and the manganese of the permanganate ions is reduced to manganese(II) ions. Electronic equations are written for these two actions:

$$2\ Cl^{-1} - 2\ e^- \rightarrow Cl_2{}^0$$
$$Mn^{+7} + 5\ e^- \rightarrow Mn^{+2}$$

The electron shift must involve an equal number of electrons in these two equations. This number is 10. The first equation is multiplied by 5 and the second by 2. We now have:

$$10\ Cl^{-1} - 10\ e^- \rightarrow 5\ Cl_2{}^0$$
$$2\ Mn^{+7} + 10\ e^- \rightarrow 2\ Mn^{+2}$$

These coefficients are transferred to the skeleton equation, which becomes:

$$10\ HCl + 2\ KMnO_4 \rightarrow H_2O + KCl + 2\ MnCl_2 + 5\ Cl_2$$

By inspection, 2 $KMnO_4$ produces 2 KCl and 8 H_2O. Now 2 KCl and 2 $MnCl_2$ call for 6 additional molecules of HCl. Our balanced equation then becomes:

$$16\ HCl + 2\ KMnO_4 \rightarrow 8\ H_2O + 2\ KCl + 2\ MnCl_2 + 5\ Cl_2$$

trochemical measurements. The lithium ion, on the other hand, is the weakest oxidizing agent of the common ions. The electronegativity scale suggests that the Group I metals starting with lithium should become progressively more active reducing agents and, with the exception of lithium, this is the case. A possible basis for the unusual activity of lithium is discussed in Chapter 24.

Atoms of the Halogen Family, Group VII of the Periodic Table, have strong attraction for electrons. They form negative ions readily and are *very active oxidizing agents*. The fluorine atom, the most highly electronegative atom, is the most active oxidizing agent among the elements. Because of its strong attraction for electrons, the fluoride ion is the weakest reducing agent.

It is possible to arrange the elements in a table according to their activity as oxidizing and reducing agents. Indeed, the Activity Series in Chapter 12 is such a table. It is arranged to show the relative abilities of metals to replace other metals from their compounds, an oxidation-reduction process. Zinc, for example, is above copper in this series, and is therefore a more active reducing agent than copper. The copper(II) ion, on the other hand, is a more active oxidizing agent that the zinc ion.

A more complete series is shown in the accompanying table. Nonmetals and some important complex ions have been added. In this series, any reducing agent will be oxidized by oxidizing agents below it. You may be interested in observing the similarity between this series and the Activity Series of Chapter 12.

The permanganate, MnO_4^-, ion and the dichromate, $Cr_2O_7^=$, ion are very useful oxidizing agents. They are usually used in the form of their potassium salt. In the presence of an alkali the permanganate ion is reduced to the manganate, $MnO_4^=$, ion. In acid solutions, as we have seen, the permanganate ion is reduced to the manganese(II), Mn^{++}, ion. Dichromate ions, in acid solution, are reduced to chromium(III), Cr^{+++}, ions.

The peroxide ion, $O_2^=$, has a single covalent bond between the two oxygens. The electronic structure may be represented by the following:

$$\left[:\overset{..}{\underset{\times \bullet}{O}} : \overset{..}{\underset{\times \bullet}{O}} : \right]^{=}$$

The structure represents an intermediate state of oxidation between free oxygen and oxides. The oxidation number of oxygen in the peroxide form is −1.

RELATIVE STRENGTH OF OXIDIZING AND REDUCING AGENTS

	Reducing Agents	Oxidizing Agents	
Strong	Li	Li^+	Weak
	K	K^+	
	Ca	Ca^{++}	
	Na	Na^+	
	Mg	Mg^{++}	
	Al	Al^{+++}	
	Zn	Zn^{++}	
	Cr	Cr^{+++}	
	Fe	Fe^{++}	
	Ni	Ni^{++}	
	Sn	Sn^{++}	
	Pb	Pb^{++}	
	H_2	H_3O^+	
	H_2S	S	
	Cu	Cu^{++}	
	I^-	I_2	
	$MnO_4^=$	MnO_4^-	
	Fe^{++}	Fe^{+++}	
	Hg	Hg^+	
	Ag	Ag^+	
	Hg	Hg^{++}	
	NO_2^-	NO_3^-	
	Br^-	Br_2	
	Mn^{++}	MnO_2	
	SO_2	H_2SO_4 (conc.)	
	Cl^-	Cl_2	
	Cr^{+++}	$Cr_2O_7^=$	
	Mn^{++}	MnO_4^-	
Weak	F^-	F_2	Strong

Hydrogen peroxide, H_2O_2, has the interesting property of being able to act as both an oxidizing agent and a reducing agent. As an oxidizing agent, the oxidation number of oxygen changes from −1 to −2. As a reducing agent, the oxidation number of oxygen changes from −1 to 0.

In the decomposition of hydrogen peroxide, both water and molecular oxygen are formed.

$$2\ H_2O_2 \rightarrow 2\ H_2O + O_2 \uparrow$$

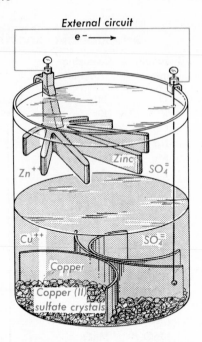

External circuit

e⁻ ⟶

Zn⁺⁺   Zinc   SO₄⁼

Cu⁺⁺   SO₄⁼

Copper

Copper (II) sulfate crystals

Fig. 23-3. The gravity cell. In electrochemical cells, oxidation occurs at the cathode and reduction occurs at the anode.

The peroxide acts simultaneously as an oxidizing agent and as a reducing agent. Such a process is called *auto-oxidation*. Half of the oxygen is reduced to the oxide, forming water. The other half is oxidized to free oxygen. Impurities in a water solution of H_2O_2 act catalytically to accelerate this process.

★ **7. Gram-equivalent weights of oxidizing and reducing agents.** In Chapter 19, Section 8, the gram-equivalent weight of a reactant was referred to as the *mass of the substance that acquires or furnishes the Avogadro number of electrons*. This is the number of electrons that 1 g-atom of hydrogen, the Avogadro number of hydrogen atoms, is capable of releasing or acquiring. If a reactant is oxidized, the mass required to yield the Avogadro number of electrons is the gram-equivalent weight of the substance. If a reactant is reduced, the mass re-

quired to take up the Avogadro number of electrons is the gram-equivalent weight of the substance. Thus, 1 g-equiv. wt. of any reducing agent will always react with 1-g equiv. wt. of any oxidizing agent.

In the case of oxidizing and reducing agents the particular oxidation-reduction reaction must be known in order to express the quantities of reactants in terms of gram-equivalent weights. One atom of iron releases 2 electrons if oxidized to the iron(II), or Fe^{+2}, state and releases 3 electrons if oxidized to the iron(III), or Fe^{+3}, state. One mole of iron, 55.8 g, gives up 2 times the Avogadro number of electrons when oxidized to the +2 oxidation state. Thus the mass of iron that releases the Avogadro number of electrons in such a reaction is one-half mole; the gram-equivalent weight being 55.8 g Fe ÷ 2 = 27.9 g Fe. Similarly, the gram-equivalent weight of iron oxidized to the +3 oxidation state would be 55.8 g Fe ÷ 3 = 18.6 g Fe.

The Fe^{+++} ion in an iron(III) chloride solution is reduced to the +2 oxidation state by the addition of a tin(II) chloride solution, Sn^{++} being the reducing agent. Here 1 g-ion (mole) of Fe^{+++} acquires 1 Avogadro number of electrons in the reduction to Fe^{++}. The gram-equivalent weight of iron in this reaction is 55.8 g ÷ 1 = 55.8 g. The reducing agent Sn^{++}, on the other hand is oxidized to the +4 oxidation state, 1 mole of Sn^{++} ions furnishing 2 times the Avogadro number of electrons. The gram-equivalent weight of tin in this reaction is 118.7 g ÷ 2 = 59.35 g. These relationships are readily apparent from the electronic equations for this oxidation-reduction reaction.

$$2\ Fe^{+3} + 2\ e^- \rightarrow 2\ Fe^{+2}$$
$$Sn^{+2} - 2\ e^- \rightarrow \quad Sn^{+4}$$

$$\text{g-eq.wt. } Fe^{+++} = \frac{2 \, Fe^{+++}}{e^- \text{ gained}}$$

$$= \frac{2 \times 55.8 \text{ g}}{2} = 55.8 \text{ g}$$

$$\text{g-eq.wt. } Sn^{++} = \frac{Sn^{++}}{e^- \text{ lost}}$$

$$= \frac{118.7 \text{ g}}{2} = 59.35 \text{ g}$$

*8. **Electrochemical reactions.***

1. Electrochemical cells. Oxidation-reduction reactions involve a transfer of electrons from the substance oxidized to the substance reduced. Such reactions *that occur spontaneously* can be used as a source of electric energy. If the reactants are in contact, the energy released during the electron transfer is in the form of heat. By separating the reactants in an electrolytic solution, the transfer of electrons may take place through a conducting wire connected between them. Such an arrangement is known as an **electrochemical cell.** *The flow of electrons through the wire constitutes an electric current.*

The *dry cell* is a common source of electric energy in the laboratory. Small dry cells are familiar as flashlight batteries. A zinc container serves as the negative electrode or *cathode.* A carbon rod serves as the positive electrode or *anode.* (In an older nomenclature system still in use in some texts the electrode names are reversed. Since this is simply a matter of choice of definitions, it should not be a source of trouble for the chemistry student.) The carbon rod is surrounded by a mixture of manganese dioxide and powdered carbon. The electrolyte is a moist paste of ammonium chloride which contains some zinc chloride. See Fig. 23-4.

When the external circuit is closed, *zinc atoms are oxidized at the cathode.*

$$Zn^0 - 2 \, e^- \rightarrow Zn^{++}$$

Electrons flow through the external circuit to the carbon anode. Here, *if manganese dioxide were not present,* hydrogen gas would be formed.

$$2 \, NH_4^+ + 2 \, e^- \rightarrow 2 \, NH_3^0 + H_2 \uparrow$$

However, hydrogen is oxidized to water by the manganese dioxide, and *manganese,* rather than hydrogen, *is reduced at the anode.*

$$2 \, MnO_2 + 2 \, NH_4^+ + 2 \, e^- \rightarrow$$
$$Mn_2O_3 + 2 \, NH_3 + H_2O$$

The ammonia is taken up by Zn^{++} ions forming complex $Zn(NH_3)_4^{++}$ ions.

2. Electrolytic cells. Oxidation-reduction reactions *which are not spontaneous* may be forced to occur by means of electric energy supplied externally. The electrolysis of water is such a reaction (see Chapter 20, Section 14). The electrolytic cell for the electrolysis of water

Fig. 23-4. In dry cells, zinc is oxidized at the cathode and manganese(IV) is reduced to manganese(III) at the anode.

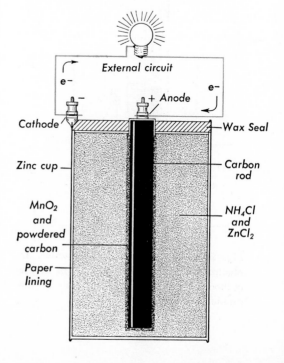

consists of two platinum electrodes immersed in a water solution of an electrolyte such as sulfuric acid. The electrodes may be connected to dry cells, or to various other suitable sources which supply the direct electric current required to force the decomposition reaction. An apparatus for electrolysis of water is shown in Fig. 23-5.

A current of electricity, as produced by a dry cell, is simply a stream of electrons flowing from the negative electrode of the dry cell, through the external circuit, to the positive electrode of the dry cell. The platinum electrode connected to the cathode of the dry cell acquires an excess of electrons and becomes the cathode of the electrolytic cell. The platinum electrode connected to the anode of the dry cell loses electrons to the dry cell and becomes the anode of the electrolytic cell. *Reduction of hydronium ions occurs at the cathode* in the electrolytic cell.

$$2\,H_3O^+ + 2\,e^- \rightarrow 2\,H_2O + H_2^0 \uparrow$$

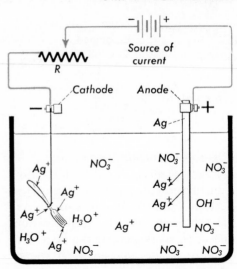

Fig. 23-6. **An electrolytic cell used for silver plating.**

Oxidation of hydroxide ions takes place at the anode.

$$4\,OH^- - 4\,e^- \rightarrow 2\,H_2O + O_2^0 \uparrow$$

Electrolytic cells may be constructed to permit the *electroplating* of certain metals and other substances that conduct electricity. Ions of metals below hydrogen in the electrochemical series of Section 6 are readily reduced at the cathode of an *electroplating cell*. The atoms of the metal thus formed deposit as a smooth plate on the surface of the cathode.

An electroplating cell consists of a solution of a salt of the plating metal, an object to be plated (the cathode), and a piece of the plating metal (the anode). A silver-plating cell consists essentially of a solution of a soluble silver salt, a silver anode, and a cathode of the object to be plated. The silver anode is connected to the positive electrode of a battery or some other source of direct current. The object to be plated is connected to the negative electrode. *Silver*

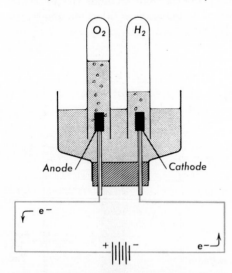

Fig. 23-5. **The electrolysis of water. In electrolytic cells, reduction occurs at the cathode, and oxidation occurs at the anode.**

ions are reduced at the cathode of the cell when electrons flow through the circuit.

$$Ag^+ + e^- \rightarrow Ag^0$$

Silver atoms are oxidized at the anode.

$$Ag^0 - e^- \rightarrow Ag^+$$

Silver ions are removed from the solution at the cathode, being deposited as metallic silver. Metallic silver is removed from the anode as ions to maintain the Ag^+ ion concentration of the solution. Thus, in effect, silver is transferred from the anode to the cathode of the cell during the electrolytic action.

SUMMARY

A substance which loses electrons is said to be oxidized. A substance which gains electrons is said to be reduced. Both processes must occur simultaneously. Reactions of this type are known as oxidation-reduction reactions. Electrons are transferred completely between ionic substances, and partially between covalent substances.

In order to balance the more complicated oxidation-reduction reactions, oxidation numbers are assigned to each element. These numbers may be either negative or positive and are used to indicate the state of oxidation of a substance. The oxidation numbers in binary compounds are indicated by the common valence. In tenary compounds, oxidation numbers may be assigned by use of certain rules.

Complicated oxidation-reduction equations require a detailed balancing procedure. The primary reaction is balanced as to electrons lost and gained prior to adjusting the coefficients of the entire equation.

Lithium and fluorine are respectively the most active reducing and oxidizing agents. Other metals, nonmetals, and ions, arranged in order between these two substances, form an activity series of oxidizing and reducing agents.

Spontaneous oxidation-reduction reactions may be used as a source of electric energy in electrochemical cells. Other oxidation-reduction reactions may be forced by the application of electric energy to electrolytic cells.

TEST YOURSELF ON THESE TERMS

anode	electronic equation	oxidizing agent
cathode	electropositive	polar bond
electrochemical cell	nonpolar bond	redox
electrolytic cell	oxidation	reducing agent
electronegative	oxidation number	reduction

QUESTIONS

Group A

1. (*a*) State a general definition for oxidation. (*b*) For reduction.
2. Why is a substance which undergoes oxidation a reducing agent?
3. Why may a substance which undergoes reduction be considered an oxidizing agent?

4. Which of the following are oxidation-reduction reactions?
    (*a*) $2 Na + Cl_2 \rightarrow 2 NaCl$
    (*b*) $C + O_2 \rightarrow CO_2$
    (*c*) $2 H_2O \rightleftarrows 2 H_2 + O_2$
    (*d*) $NaCl + AgNO_3 \rightarrow AgCl + NaNO_3$
    (*e*) $NH_3 + HCl \rightarrow NH_4^+ + Cl^-$
    (*f*) $2 KClO_3 \rightarrow 2 KCl + 3 O_2$
    (*g*) $H_2 + Cl_2 \rightarrow 2 HCl$
    (*h*) $2 H_2 + O_2 \rightarrow 2 H_2O$
    (*i*) $H_2SO_4 + 2 KOH \rightarrow K_2SO_4 + 2 H_2O$
    (*j*) $Zn + CuSO_4 \rightarrow ZnSO_4 + Cu$
5. For each oxidation-reduction reaction in Question 4 identify: (*a*) the substance oxidized; (*b*) the substance reduced; (*c*) the oxidizing agent; and (*d*) the reducing agent.

Group B

★ 6. Assuming chemical union between the following pairs, indicate in each case which element would have the positive oxidation number: (*a*) Hydrogen-sodium; (*b*) Chlorine-fluorine; (*c*) Chlorine-oxygen; (*d*) Hydrogen-lithium; (*e*) Bromine-hydrogen.
★ 7. What is the oxidation number of each element in the following compounds: (*a*) MnO_2; (*b*) H_3PO_4; (*c*) HNO_3; (*d*) P_4O_{10}; (*e*) $NaOH$?
★ 8. What is the oxidation state of manganese in: (*a*) potassium permanganate, $KMnO_4$; (*b*) manganese(II) sulfate, $MnSO_4$? (*c*) If manganese(II) sulfate is one of the products of a reaction in which potassium permanganate was one of the reactants, what kind of change has it undergone? (*d*) What could you call manganese under such circumstances?
★ 9. The four oxygen-acids of chlorine are: hypochlorous acid, $HClO$; chlorous acid, $HClO_2$; chloric acid, $HClO_3$; and perchloric acid, $HClO_4$. What is the oxidation number of the chlorine atom in each acid of the series?
★10. Verify your conclusions in Question 9 by writing the electron-dot formula for each acid. Use small circles for hydrogen electrons, dots for oxygen electrons, and small crosses for chlorine electrons.
★11. What are the six steps involved in balancing oxidation-reduction equations? List in the proper sequence.
★12. Carry out the first four steps called for in Question 11 for each of the following reactions:
    (*a*) Zinc + hydrochloric acid → zinc chloride + hydrogen.
    (*b*) Iron + copper(II) sulfate → iron(II) sulfate + copper.
    (*c*) Copper + sulfuric acid → copper(II) sulfate + sulfur dioxide + water.
    (*d*) Hydrochloric acid + potassium permanganate → manganese(II) chloride + potassium chloride + chlorine + water.
    (*e*) Bromine + water → hydrobromic acid + hypobromous acid.
★13. The oxidation-reduction reaction between copper and *concentrated* nitric acid yields the following products: copper(II) nitrate, water, and nitrogen dioxide. Write the balanced equation.

⋆14. The oxidation-reduction reaction between copper and *dilute* nitric acid yields the following products: copper(II) nitrate, water, and nitrogen monoxide. Write the balanced equation.

⋆15. Referring to the table of Section 6, the active metals down to magnesium replace hydrogen from water. Magnesium and succeeding metals replace hydrogen from steam. Metals near the bottom of the list will not replace hydrogen from steam. How does this table help to explain this behavior?

SOME THINGS FOR YOU TO DO

1. Ask your instructor for permission to experiment with "clock" reactions. See *Tested Demonstrations in General Chemistry,* Journal of Chemical Education, Vol. 32, No. 8 (August 1955), for some interesting reactions. Your instructor may have directions for others.

CHECK YOUR PROGRESS IN CHEMISTRY

1. What possible explanation can you suggest for the tendency of chemically similar substances to dissolve in each other?

2. What is the freezing point of 250 g of water containing 11.25 g of a non-electrolyte the molecular weight of which is known to be 180?

3. Explain the dissociation of an electrovalent salt in water solution.

4. Explain the ionization of a polar molecular substance in water solution.

⋆ 5. What mass of each of the following chemicals would be needed to prepare 1.00 liter of 0.100-N solution of each: (*a*) NaOH; (*b*) KOH; (*c*) $Ba(OH)_2$; (*d*) H_2SO_4; (*e*) HCl; (*f*) H_3PO_4; (*g*) $HC_2H_3O_2$; (*h*) NaCl; (*i*) $Ca(NO_3)_2$; (*j*) $KMnO_4$; (to be reduced to Mn^{++}).

⋆ 6. Suppose 10.0 ml of vinegar are diluted to 100. ml with distilled water and titrated against 0.010-N sodium hydroxide solution. From the burets, 30.0 ml of the diluted vinegar and 25.0 ml of the solution of the base were withdrawn. What percentage of acetic acid, $HC_2H_3O_2$, did the vinegar contain?

⋆ 7. In the reversible reaction $A + B \rightleftarrows C + D$, k_1 is the velocity constant of the reaction going to the right, and k_2 is the velocity constant of the reaction going to the left for the fixed conditions of the reaction. (*a*) According to the Law of Mass Action, what is the speed of the reaction to the right? (*b*) What is the speed of the reaction to the left? (Each expressed in terms of the concentration of the reactants in moles per liter.) (*c*) If an equilibrium condition is reached, what is the relationship between these two reaction speeds? (*d*) At equilibrium, what is the value of the equilibrium constant, K, in terms of the concentrations of the reacting substances expressed in moles per liter?

⋆ 8. Explain the effect on the equilibrium reaction of Question 7 if the concentration of reactant A is increased.

⋆ 9. Assign oxidation numbers to each element in the following compounds: (*a*) $PbSO_4$; (*b*) H_2O_2; (*c*) $K_2Cr_2O_7$; (*d*) H_2SO_3; (*e*) $HClO_4$.

⋆10. Balance the oxidation-reduction equation: $K_2Cr_2O_7 + HCl \rightarrow KCl + CrCl_3 + H_2O + Cl_2$.

CHALLENGING YOUR KNOWLEDGE

1. If 1 mole of a substance dissolved in 1 kg of water lowers the freezing point 3.60 C°, what can you predict about the nature of the solution? What can you predict about the oxidation numbers of the particles of solute?

2. Name the following unfamiliar compounds: (a) H_2Se; (b) HIO_3; (c) $Ga(OH)_3$; (d) $CsOH$; (e) $RaBr_2$.

★3. The equilibrium constant for the ionization of acetic acid (ionization constant) is 1.8×10^{-5} at 25° C. Explain the significance of this value.

★4. What is the pH of a 0.054-M solution of HCl?

★5. 25.0 ml of 0.150-M NaOH and 50.0 ml of 0.100-M HCl are mixed. What is the pH of the resulting solution?

Unit 7 · THE ACTIVE METALS

The Sodium Family
The Calcium Family

Chapter 24 · THE SODIUM FAMILY

1. The Sodium Family, Group I of the Periodic Table. The Sodium Family includes the metallic elements lithium, sodium, potassium, rubidium, cesium, and francium, as shown in the accompanying table.

Each element in the family has one electron in its outermost shell. The next-to-outermost shell consists of eight electrons, and an outer octet is easily attained in each case by the removal of a single electron. Thus, the ion formed by the loss of one electron has the stable electronic configuration of the preceding inert gas. For example, the sodium ion

has the electron configuration 2–8, the same as that of the neon atom. The electron configuration of the potassium ion, 2–8–8, is the same as that of the argon atom.

The elements of the Sodium Family form hydroxides that are strongly basic, and thus are commonly referred to as the *alkali* metals. They possess certain metallic characteristics to a high degree. Each has a silvery luster, is a good conductor of electricity and heat, and is ductile and malleable. These metals are relatively soft and can be cut with a knife. The properties of the Group I

THE SODIUM FAMILY

Element	Atomic Number	Atomic Weight	Electron Configuration	Oxidation Number	Melting Point, °C	Boiling Point, °C	Density g/cm³	Metallic Radius Å	Ionic Radius Å
Lithium	3	6.939	2, 1	+1	186.	1336	0.53	1.23	0.60
Sodium	11	22.9898	2, 8, 1	+1	97.5	880	0.97	1.57	0.95
Potassium	19	39.102	2, 8, 8, 1	+1	62.3	760	0.86	2.02	1.33
Rubidium	37	85.47	2, 8, 18, 8, 1	+1	38.5	700	1.53	2.16	1.48
Cesium	55	132.905	2, 8, 18, 18, 8, 1	+1	28.5	670	1.87	2.35	1.69
Francium	87	223.	2, 8, 18, 32, 18, 8, 1	+1	. . . .	. . . . .	. . . .	. . . .	. . . .

354

metals can be accounted for by considering their characteristic crystalline lattice structures.

The crystal lattice of the alkali metals is generated by a body centered cubic unit cell made up of metallic ions with a +1 charge, the valence electrons composing a cloud of electron gas that permeates the lattice structure. (See Chapter 19, Section 15.) The good heat and electric conductivity is due to the highly mobile character of these free electrons.

The silvery luster of the Group I metals can be attributed to the free electrons in the crystal surfaces. When light falls on these surfaces the valence electrons absorb energy and are set into vibratory motion re-radiating the energy in all directions as light.

It was stated in Chapter 19, Section 15, that the binding force in the metallic crystal lattice is the attraction between the positive ions and the negative electron cloud permeating the lattice. This force is essentially uniform in all directions, explaining the softness, ductility, and malleability of the alkali metals. Little energy is required to cut these metals or change their shape.

The Group I metals are characterized by low ionization potentials (see Chapter 5, Section 8), the ionization potential decreasing as the atom size increases going down the group. As would be expected, they are vigorous reducing agents. The lithium atom, probably because of the exceptional hydration tendency of its ion, is the strongest reducing agent even though other members of the family have lower ionization potentials.

Electrons which absorb energy from a suitable source become excited, or stepped up to higher energy levels. When excited electrons fall back to their normal energy levels in an atom structure the extra energy is emitted, sometimes as visible light, producing a spectrum characteristic of that atom. Electrons of the Group I metals are quite easily excited to higher energy states, the energy supplied by a Bunsen flame being sufficient to accomplish this. Compounds of these metals impart characteristic colors to flames which serve as the basis of identification tests (known as *flame tests*) for the metallic elements. Lithium compounds produce a crimson (red) flame; sodium, yellow; potassium, lavender (magenta); rubidium, red; and cesium, blue.

Many difficulties are encountered in handling and storing the alkali metals because of their chemical activity. They are usually stored under kerosene or some other liquid hydrocarbon because they react vigorously with water, releasing hydrogen and forming solutions that are strongly basic. The metals do not exist free in nature, but are found only as ions in compounds.

VOCABULARY

Caustic. Capable of converting some types of animal and vegetable matter into soluble materials by chemical action; a substance with such properties.

Spectroscope. An optical instrument used for producing and viewing spectra.

Spectrum. The pattern of colors formed by passing light through a prism.

1. LITHIUM

2. SODIUM

2. Lithium and its compounds. Lithium is a moderately rare element occurring in nature as Li^+ ions in several types of rocks of very complex composition. This element was discovered in 1817 by Johan Arfvedson (1792–1841), a student of Berzelius, but was not isolated until 1855 by Robert W. Bunsen (1811–1899) and Augustus Matthiessen. Lithium, the metal of lowest density, is prepared by electrolyzing fused lithium chloride. It reacts with oxygen, the halogens, hydrogen, and water, forming ionic compounds in all cases. Lithium salts impart a crimson color in the flame test.

Lithium finds many uses in metallurgical processes. Its compounds are used in ceramics, welding, drugs, the manufacture of chemicals, and the synthesis of organic compounds. Lithium, as well as the other alkali metals, dissolves in liquid ammonia.

Fig. 24-1. This worker is dipping molten lithium metal from the electrolytic cell in which it is produced. (Lithium Corporation of America)

3. The occurrence of sodium. Metallic sodium is never found free in nature. However, compounds containing the Na^+ ion and sodium complexes are widely distributed. They are found in soil, in natural waters, and in plants and animals. Sodium is such an abundant element that it is difficult to find an absolutely sodium-free material.

4. The preparation of sodium. Sir Humphry Davy first prepared metallic sodium in 1807 by the electrolysis of moist sodium hydroxide. The metal is prepared today by the electrolysis of fused sodium chloride in an apparatus called the *Downs cell* (see Fig. 24-2). Since sodium chloride has such a high melting point (801° C), calcium chloride is mixed with it, lowering the melting point to 580° C. The molten sodium is collected under oil. The chlorine produced simultaneously is a very valuable by-product.

$$2\ NaCl \xrightarrow{\text{(elect)}} 2\ Na + Cl_2 \uparrow$$

In 1960, the production of sodium metal in the United States totaled approximately 112,000 tons. About 95% of this sodium was produced in the Downs cell.

5. The physical and chemical properties of sodium. Sodium is a silvery-white, lustrous metal that tarnishes rapidly when exposed to air. It is so soft that it can be cut easily with a knife, has a lower density than water, and a low melting point. When a pellet of sodium is dropped into water, it floats on the surface, melts, assumes a spherical shape, and spins around as it reacts with the water to produce sodium hydroxide and hydrogen.

$$2\ Na + 2\ H_2O \rightarrow 2\ NaOH + H_2 \uparrow$$

When exposed to air, sodium unites with the oxygen to form sodium peroxide, Na_2O_2. Of the alkali metals, only lithium reacts directly with oxygen to form the normal oxide. The normal oxide of sodium, Na_2O, can be formed by heating NaOH with sodium.

$$2\ NaOH + 2\ Na \rightarrow 2\ Na_2O + H_2 \uparrow$$

The remaining alkali metals react directly with oxygen to form superoxides of the type $M^{n+}O_2^{-}$, in which the oxygen atoms may be considered to have an oxidation number of $-\frac{1}{2}$. The superoxide of sodium, NaO_2, can be prepared indirectly.

Sodium reacts with all ordinary acids. It burns in an atmosphere of chlorine gas, uniting directly with the chlorine to form sodium chloride.

A flame test of sodium compounds reveals a strong yellow coloration characteristic of vaporized sodium atoms. This is a common identification test for sodium.

6. The uses of sodium. Most of the sodium produced in the United States is used in the production of tetraethyl lead, the antiknock additive for gasolines. It is used as a heat-transfer agent, in the preparation of dyes and other organic compounds, and in sodium vapor lamps.

Important new uses of sodium are continuously being developed, particularly as a chemical reducing agent. Titanium, zirconium, niobium, and tantalum are produced from their fused salts by reduction, using sodium as the reducing agent.

7. The production, properties, and uses of sodium chloride. Sodium chloride is found in sea water, in salt wells, and in deposits of rock salt. Rock salt is mined in many places in the world. New York, Michigan, Kansas, Ohio, Utah,

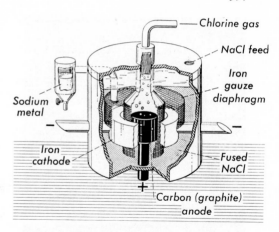

Fig. 24-2. Elementary sodium is produced by the electrolysis of fused sodium chloride in a Downs cell. Chlorine is a valuable by-product.

Louisiana, and several other states contribute to the 30 million barrels of salt produced annually in the United States.

Pure sodium chloride is not deliquescent. However, magnesium chloride, which is very deliquescent, is usually present in salt as an impurity. This explains why common salt becomes wet and sticky in damp weather. Sodium chloride crystallizes in cubes.

Fig. 24-3. The atoms of some metals impart a characteristic color to a colorless gas flame when they are vaporized.

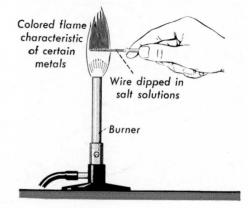

Fig. 24-4. **Crystals of sodium chloride, common table salt, magnified about 80 times. Note the cubic shape of the crystals.** (Morton Salt)

Sodium chloride is essential in the diet of man and animals and is present in certain body fluids. Perspiration contains considerable amounts of it. Consequently, those who perspire freely in hot weather often find it advisable to increase their salt intake by the use of salt tablets.

Thousands of tons of salt are used every year as a preservative in the packing and curing of meat and fish. Mixed with chipped ice, salt makes a good freezing mixture for homemade ice cream. Rock salt is frequently scattered on icy streets and sidewalks in the winter to melt the ice and make travel less hazardous. Since sodium chloride is the cheapest compound of sodium, we find it used as a starting material for making nearly all other sodium compounds.

Fused salt mixtures containing sodium chloride are being used in numerous processes in connection with atomic fuels. For example, a molten mixture of sodium chloride, potassium chloride, and zinc chloride is used to produce electro-refined thorium from spent atomic fuel. With the fused salt mixture as the electrolyte and the spent-fuel alloy as the anode, the operating voltage of the cell is adjusted to deposit thorium at the cathode. Anode elements less positive than thorium settle out as an insoluble anode sludge. Those more positive than thorium remain in solution.

Fig. 24-5. **Sodium chloride, common salt, has many important uses.**

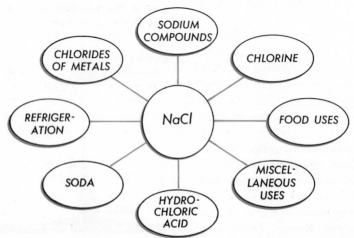

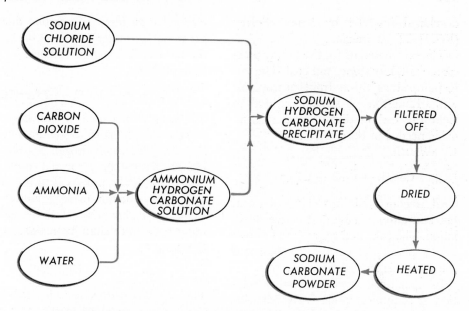

Fig. 24-6. **A flow diagram of the main reactions in the Solvay process. The success of the process depends on the re-use of the by-products, which for simplicity have been omitted here.**

8. The preparation, properties, and uses of sodium hydroxide. Most commercial sodium hydroxide comes as a by-product from the electrolysis of sodium chloride solution.

$$2\,NaCl + 2\,H_2O \xrightarrow{\text{(elect)}} 2\,NaOH + Cl_2\uparrow + H_2\uparrow$$

Considerable amounts are also made by adding calcium hydroxide (slaked lime) to sodium carbonate solution.

$$Na_2CO_3 + Ca(OH)_2 \rightarrow 2\,NaOH + CaCO_3\downarrow$$

The precipitated calcium carbonate is filtered off, and the remaining solution of sodium hydroxide is concentrated by evaporation.

Sodium hydroxide converts some types of animal and vegetable matter into soluble materials by chemical action. It is described as a very *caustic* substance because of its destructive effect on skin, hair, and wool.

Sodium hydroxide is a white crystalline solid that is marketed in the form of flakes, pellets, and sticks. It is very deliquescent, and reacts with water and carbon dioxide from the air, finally producing sodium carbonate. Its water solution is strongly basic.

Sodium hydroxide reacts with fats, forming soap and glycerol. Thus, one of its important uses is for making soap. Sodium hydroxide is also used in the production of rayon and cellulose film, in petroleum refining, and in the production of paper. Sodium hydroxide is sold in cans under the name lye, or caustic soda.

9. The Solvay process. The great bulk of the sodium carbonate and sodium hydrogen carbonate produced in this country and abroad is manufactured by the **Solvay process.** This was developed in 1864 by Ernest Solvay (1838–1922), a Belgian.

The raw materials for the Solvay process are salt, limestone, and coal. The salt is pumped as brine from nearby salt wells. Limestone is strongly heated to yield the carbon dioxide and calcium oxide needed in the process:
Equation 1:

$$CaCO_3 \rightarrow CaO + CO_2 \uparrow$$

Coal is converted into coke, gas, coal tar, and ammonia by destructive distillation. The coke and gas are used as fuel in the plant; the coal tar is sold; and the ammonia is used in the process.

In operation, a cold saturated solution of sodium chloride is treated with ammonia and carbon dioxide. The ammonia dissolves in the water and combines with the carbon dioxide to form ammonium hydrogen carbonate.
Equation 2:

$$NH_3 + H_2O + CO_2 \rightarrow NH_4HCO_3$$

The sodium chloride then reacts with the ammonium hydrogen carbonate and forms sodium hydrogen carbonate (sodium bicarbonate) and ammonium chloride. Sodium hydrogen carbonate is only slightly soluble in this solution and precipitates.
Equation 3:

$$NaCl + NH_4HCO_3 \rightarrow NaHCO_3 \downarrow + NH_4Cl$$

The precipitated sodium hydrogen carbonate is filtered off, dried, and heated to convert it into sodium carbonate.
Equation 4:

$$2\,NaHCO_3 \rightarrow Na_2CO_3 + H_2O \uparrow + CO_2 \uparrow$$

The dried sodium carbonate is packaged and sold. Pure baking soda (sodium hydrogen carbonate) is prepared by dissolving the sodium carbonate in wa-

ter, and then forcing in carbon dioxide gas under pressure. The reaction is just the reverse of *Equation 4* above.
Equation 5:

$$Na_2CO_3 + H_2O + CO_2 \rightarrow 2\,NaHCO_3$$

The ammonia used in the process is more valuable than the sodium carbonate or sodium hydrogen carbonate. Hence it must be recovered and used over again, if the process is to be profitable. The calcium oxide produced in *Equation 1* above is slaked by adding water to form calcium hydroxide.
Equation 6:

$$CaO + H_2O \rightarrow Ca(OH)_2$$

The calcium hydroxide is reacted with the ammonium chloride that was produced in *Equation 3* above.
Equation 7:

$$Ca(OH)_2 + 2\,NH_4Cl \rightarrow$$
$$CaCl_2 + 2\,H_2O + 2\,NH_3 \uparrow$$

The ammonia gas is used over again as shown in *Equation 2*. Calcium chloride produced in *Equation 7* is a by-product that can be sold, although the supply exceeds the demand because it has only limited uses.

10. The properties and uses of sodium carbonate. Sodium carbonate is marketed both as colorless crystals that have the formula $Na_2CO_3 \cdot 10\,H_2O$ and also as an anhydrous white powder, Na_2CO_3. Both forms hydrolyze in water solution, producing a solution with rather strong basic properties. The crystals are sometimes used in the laundry under the name *washing soda*. Anhydrous sodium carbonate is one of the ingredients present in most scouring powders. It is also used in making glass and sodium silicate (water glass). Sodium carbonate makes an effective water softener, known commercially as *soda ash*.

11. The properties and uses of sodium hydrogen carbonate. Sodium hydrogen carbonate reacts with acids and liberates carbon dioxide. For this reason it is used as a leavening agent in baking under the common name of *baking soda.* Sour milk or molasses may be added to the baking soda to set free the carbon dioxide, although most baking powders contain sodium hydrogen carbonate and some acid substance already mixed in the dry state.

The water solution of sodium hydrogen carbonate has weak basic properties due to hydrolysis. It is used to some extent to neutralize excess acid in the stomach, but should not be confused with washing soda, which has much stronger basic properties when dissolved in water.

12. Some other compounds of sodium. Sodium compounds are widely used because they are usually cheap, and because common sodium com-

FAMILIAR SODIUM COMPOUNDS

CHEMICAL NAME	COMMON NAME	FORMULA	COLOR	USES
Sodium nitrate	Chile saltpeter	$NaNO_3$	White, or colorless	As fertilizer; in making nitric acid
Sodium sulfate	Glauber's salt	$Na_2SO_4 \cdot 10 H_2O$	White, or colorless	In making glass; as a cathartic in medicine
Sodium peroxide	None	Na_2O_2	Yellowish white	As oxidizing and bleaching agent; as source of oxygen
Sodium thiosulfate	Hypo	$Na_2S_2O_3 \cdot 5 H_2O$	White, or colorless	As fixer in photography; as antichlor
Sodium cyanide (CAUTION: very poisonous.)	Prussate of soda	$NaCN$	White	To destroy vermin; to extract gold from ores; in silver and gold plating; in case-hardening of steel
Sodium tetraborate	Borax	$Na_2B_4O_7 \cdot 10 H_2O$	White	As a flux; in making glass; as a water softener
Sodium phosphate (normal)	TSP	$Na_3PO_4 \cdot 10 H_2O$	White	As a cleaning agent; as a water softener
Sodium sulfide	None	Na_2S	Colorless	In the preparation of sulfur dyes; for dyeing cotton; to remove hair from hides

pounds are soluble in water. The table on page 361 gives formulas, common names, colors, and important uses of some additional familiar sodium compounds.

3. POTASSIUM

13. The occurrence of potassium. Combined potassium is widely distributed but is not easily available because most deposits of potassium compounds, in the form of feldspar rocks, are insoluble and weather slowly. Large deposits of potassium chloride, crystallized with magnesium and calcium compounds as complex salts, are found in Texas and New Mexico. These deposits, together with some potassium compounds extracted from Searles Lake in California, supply our needs for this element.

14. The discovery and preparation of potassium. Potassium was first pre-

pared by Sir Humphry Davy in 1807 by the electrolysis of fused potassium hydroxide. Today potassium is prepared commercially by electrolyzing fused potassium chloride in a process similar to that for sodium.

$$2 \text{ KCl} \rightarrow 2 \text{ K} + \text{Cl}_2 \uparrow$$

15. Potassium metal closely resembles metallic sodium in its properties. It is soft, of low density, and has a silvery luster that acquires a bluish-gray tarnish in less than a minute when it is exposed to air. It is more active than sodium, usually burning with a lavender flame as it spins around on the surface of water.

Potassium can be identified by the transient lavender or magenta color imparted to a Bunsen flame by the vaporizing potassium atoms. The presence of potassium in a mixture containing both sodium and potassium compounds may be detected by observing the colored

IMPORTANT POTASSIUM COMPOUNDS

CHEMICAL NAME	COMMON NAME	FORMULA	COLOR	USES
Potassium hydroxide	Caustic potash	KOH	White	In making soft soap; in the Edison battery
Potassium chloride	None	KCl	White	As source of potassium; as a fertilizer
Potassium sulfate	None	K_2SO_4	White	As source of potassium; as a fertilizer
Potassium carbonate	Potash	K_2CO_3	White	In making glass; in making soap
Potassium chlorate	None	$KClO_3$	White	As oxidizing agent; in fireworks; in explosives
Potassium nitrate	Saltpeter	KNO_3	White	In black gunpowder; in fireworks; in curing meats
Potassium bromide	None	KBr	White	As a sedative; in photography
Potassium iodide	None	KI	White	In medicine; in iodized salt; in photography
Potassium permanganate	None	$KMnO_4$	Purple	As a germicide; as oxidizing agent

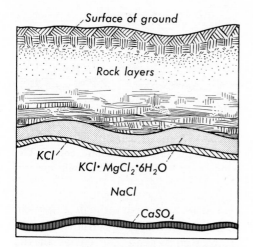

Fig. 24-7. **A cross-section of a salt deposit,** showing how the different minerals were deposited as the sea water evaporated.

flame through cobalt-blue glass. This glass filters out the yellow sodium flame and permits observation of the potassium flame.

16. The compounds of potassium. All common potassium compounds are soluble in water. Potassium hydroxide is prepared by the electrolysis of a solution of potassium chloride. It has the properties of a typical alkali. Potassium nitrate is made by mixing hot, concentrated solutions of potassium chloride and sodium nitrate.

$$KCl + NaNO_3 \rightarrow KNO_3 + NaCl \downarrow$$

When the solutions are mixed, sodium chloride, being the least soluble of the four salts, precipitates and is removed. Then as the solution cools, the potassium nitrate crystallizes from the saturated sodium chloride solution.

The table on the opposite page lists a few of the more important potassium compounds, together with their common names, formulas, color, and uses.

Sodium compounds can often be used instead of potassium compounds. Sodium chlorate is as satisfactory as potassium chlorate for many uses. Sodium hydroxide is as useful for most purposes as potassium hydroxide. It is not only cheaper, but also furnishes more hydroxide ions per gram. Sodium has an atomic weight of 23, and potassium an atomic weight of 39. Thus 56 grams of KOH are needed to furnish 17 grams of hydroxide ions, but only 40 grams of NaOH are needed to furnish the same quantity of hydroxide ions. Sodium carbonate is used most often for making glass, but potassium carbonate yields a more lustrous glass that is preferred for optical uses. Potassium nitrate is used instead of sodium nitrate for making black gunpowder because it is not hygroscopic.

There is one very important use for potassium compounds for which there is absolutely no substitution. Green plants must have these compounds to grow properly, so complete chemical fertilizers always contain a substantial percentage of this necessary element.

4. RUBIDIUM, CESIUM, AND FRANCIUM

17. Rubidium and cesium. Rubidium and cesium were discovered in 1860 by Bunsen, who examined their spectra with the newly invented spectroscope. Because of the great chemical activity of these alkali metals, chemical reduction of the Rb^+ and Cs^+ ions would not seem to be possible. However, the reduction of the Rb^+ ion in fused RbCl with calcium is possible because, at the elevated temperature, rubidium escapes from the reaction environment as a gas. In practice, the metals are produced by the electrolysis of their fused chlorides or hydroxides.

Rubidium and cesium are used in photoelectric cells and to remove the last traces of oxygen from other electronic tubes. Of all the metals, electrons are ejected most easily from cesium by light falling on the metal, a phenomenon known as the *photoelectric effect*.

18. Francium. Francium was discovered by Mlle. M. Perey in 1937, and named for her native country, France. It is a radioactive element formed by the disintegration of an isotope of actinium. Francium has been produced only in very minute quantities and little is known of its properties.

5. SPECTROSCOPY

19. The use of a spectroscope. A *spectroscope* consists of a glass prism, a collimator tube to focus a narrow beam of light rays upon the prism, and a small telescope for examining the light which passes through the prism. When white light is passed through a triangular prism, a band of colors called a *continuous spectrum* is produced due to the unequal bending of light of different wavelengths.

Examination of a sodium flame by means of a spectroscope reveals a characteristic bright-yellow line. Since this yellow line is always in the same relative place in the spectrum, it serves to identify sodium. Potassium produces both red and violet spectral lines. The spectrum chart facing page 310 shows the characteristic color lines of several elements and also the continuous spectrum of white light produced by an incandescent solid.

★ **20. The origin of spectral lines.** A platinum wire held in a Bunsen flame becomes white hot, or incandescent, and emits white light. When the incandes-

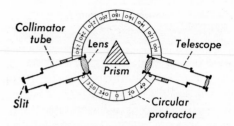

Fig. 24-8. **A spectroscope is used for separating light into its various colors. Elements may be identified by their spectra.**

cent wire is viewed through a spectroscope, a continuous spectrum of colors is observed because the energy of the white light is distributed over a continuous range of light frequencies that includes the entire visible spectrum. Light energy of the shortest wavelength (highest frequency) is bent most to yield the deep violet color characteristic of one extremity of the visible spectrum. Light energy of the longest wavelength (lowest frequency) is bent least to yield the deep red color characteristic of the other extremity of the visible spectrum. Between these two extremities there is a gradual blending from one color to the next making it possible to recognize six elementary colors: red, orange, yellow, green, blue, and violet. In general, incandescent solids and gases under high pressure give continuous spectra.

Luminous gases and vapors under low pressure give discontinuous spectra called *bright line spectra*. These consist of narrow lines of color which correspond to light energy of certain wavelengths. Atoms of different elements produce their own characteristic line spectra.

Electrons in atoms are restricted to energies of only certain values, as discussed in Chapter 4. In normal atoms, electrons occupy the lowest energy levels available to them. The energy of an electron can be changed only as it moves from one discrete energy level to another. A certain amount of energy is absorbed with each jump to a higher energy level, or is emitted with each jump to a lower level. The quantity of energy in each change is equal to the difference between the discrete energy levels involved.

When substances are vaporized in a flame, electrons are raised to higher energy levels by heat energy. When these electrons fall back into the lower energy levels available to them, energy is emitted producing spectral lines characteristic of the wavelengths of the energy emitted. Thus, vaporized sodium atoms produce a spectrum consisting of two narrow yellow lines very close together (seen in the ordinary spectroscope as a single yellow line). Potassium atoms produce two red lines and a violet line. Lithium atoms yield intense red and yellow lines and weak blue and violet lines. Excited atoms produce spectra which serve as their "fingerprints" to enable chemists to identify them by the use of a spectroscope.

Bright lines in the visible portion of the spectrum account for the flame coloration produced by certain metals. The color seen is the combination of light energies of the different wavelengths emitted. Spectral lines produced by excited atoms that fall outside the range of visible wavelengths may be photographed even though they cannot be seen with the unaided eye.

SUMMARY

The Sodium Family includes lithium, sodium, potassium, rubidium, cesium, and francium. Each of these elements has a single electron in its outermost shell. The ions formed from these atoms are very stable. The members of the Sodium Family form electrovalent compounds.

These elements are soft, silvery metals. Because of their activity, they must be stored under oil or kerosene. They react with water, reducing it to hydrogen, and forming solutions with strong basic properties.

Metallic lithium is used in metallurgical processes, while its compounds are used in ceramics, welding, drugs, and the manufacture of chemicals.

Metallic sodium is used in making antiknock gasoline, dyes, and other organic compounds. Sodium has important uses as a reducing agent.

Sodium chloride is obtained from sea water, salt wells, and salt deposits. It is an essential in our diet. Sodium chloride is used as a preservative for meat and fish, as well as a raw material for making sodium compounds.

Sodium hydroxide, or caustic soda, is made by electrolysis of sodium chloride solution, and also by adding calcium hydroxide to sodium carbonate solution. Sodium hydroxide is used in making soap, rayon, and paper.

Sodium carbonate is made by the Solvay process. It is used in the laundry, for making glass, and as a water softener. Sodium hydrogen carbonate, baking soda, is used as a leavening agent.

Potassium compounds are absolutely essential for plant growth. Potassium salts are obtained from deposits in Texas and New Mexico, as well as from the brine of Searles Lake in California.

Flame tests are used to identify members of the sodium family.

TEST YOURSELF ON THESE TERMS

baking soda	cobalt-blue glass	Solvay process
caustic	Downs cell	spectroscope
caustic potash	flame test	spectrum
caustic soda	lye	washing soda

QUESTIONS

Group A

1. Describe the electron configuration of the atoms and ions of the elements in the Sodium Family.
2. Compare the methods of preparing lithium, sodium, and potassium.
3. List three uses for metallic sodium.
4. Distinguish between the terms *caustic* and *corrosive*.
5. (*a*) What are the raw materials for the Solvay process? (*b*) What are the products and by-products?
6. (*a*) What is caustic soda? (*b*) Washing soda? (*c*) Baking soda?
7. Why do molasses and baking soda have a leavening action in cookies?
8. What are the sources of potassium compounds in the United States?
9. (*a*) How are sodium and potassium stored in the laboratory stockroom? (*b*) Why must they be stored in this fashion?
10. Write the balanced formula equation for the reaction of potassium and water.
11. Describe the flame tests for lithium, sodium, and potassium.
12. Why were the names *rubidium* and *cesium* given to these elements?
13. Write three equations to show how sodium carbonate can be produced in the Solvay process.
14. Write three equations for the recovery of ammonia in the Solvay process.

Group B

15. Why are the members of the Sodium Family soft, malleable metals with low melting points and low boiling points?
16. Why is salt necessary in the diet of many animals and man?
17. Why is sodium chloride used as a starting material for preparing metallic sodium and other compounds of sodium?
18. (*a*) Why are sodium compounds more frequently used than potassium compounds? (*b*) For what purpose can sodium compounds not be substituted for potassium compounds?
19. What by-product of the Solvay process has such limited use and yet is produced in such quantity that disposal of it is actually a problem to the manufacturers?
20. For what purposes are spectroscopes used in chemical analysis?
21. Why does table salt become sticky in damp weather when pure sodium chloride is not deliquescent?
22. Explain why potassium has a lower density than sodium, although it consists of heavier atoms.

23. Write a balanced chemical equation for the reaction which occurs when sodium hydroxide is exposed to the air.
24. In the Solvay process, why does the reaction between sodium chloride and ammonium hydrogen carbonate run to completion?
25. Why does a solution of sodium carbonate in water turn red litmus paper blue?
26. Suppose you had a tremendous quantity of acid that had to be neutralized, and that NaOH, KOH, and LiOH were all available at the same price per pound. Which of these three would you use? Why?

PROBLEMS

Group A

1. (*a*) How many grams of sulfuric acid in water solution can be neutralized by 10.0 g of sodium hydroxide? (*b*) 10.0 g of potassium hydroxide?
2. If you have 1.00 kg of sodium nitrate and 1.00 kg of potassium chloride, how much potassium nitrate can you make by reacting these two substances, assuming that all the potassium nitrate can be recovered?
3. If crystallized sodium carbonate, $Na_2CO_3 \cdot 10 H_2O$ sells for 5 cents a pound, what is anhydrous sodium carbonate worth per pound?

Group B

4. How many liters of carbon dioxide can be liberated from 50.0 g of each of the following: (*a*) Na_2CO_3; (*b*) $NaHCO_3$; (*c*) K_2CO_3; (*d*) $KHCO_3$?
★5. How many pounds of sodium chloride and how many cubic feet of carbon dioxide (at S.T.P.) theoretically are required to produce a ton of anhydrous sodium carbonate?

SOME THINGS FOR YOU TO DO

1. Prepare a report describing the purification of sodium chloride for use as table salt. The manufacturers of table salt furnish interesting pamphlets describing the process.
2. Prepare some potassium nitrate by crystallizing it from a hot solution of potassium chloride and sodium nitrate. Add 85 g of sodium nitrate to 75 g of potassium chloride, and dissolve the chemicals in as small an amount of boiling water as possible. Filter the solution to remove any suspended impurities. Allow the solution to cool, preferably in a refrigerator after it reaches room temperature. Pour off the mother liquor and examine the crystals of potassium nitrate produced. From the solubility curves given in Fig. 19-5, explain why potassium nitrate crystallized from solution. The potassium nitrate may be dried, transferred to a bottle, and added to the supplies in the stockroom.
3. Prepare a chart, similar to Fig. 24-6, but in more detail, to show all the reactants and products, as well as the recycling of ammonia and carbon dioxide, for all the reactions of the Solvay process.

Chapter 25 · THE CALCIUM FAMILY

1. The Calcium Family, Group II of the Periodic Table. The Calcium Family comprises the elements beryllium, magnesium, calcium, strontium, barium, and radium. These elements are often called the *alkaline earth metals*.

Because of their uses as metals and in alloys, beryllium and magnesium will be discussed with other light metals in Chapter 34. Radium is important because of its radioactivity. The nature of radioactivity and the properties of radium will be described in Chapter 38. The remaining three elements, calcium, strontium, and barium, have such similar properties that they are described as the Calcium Family in this chapter.

Each of the elements in the Calcium Family has two valence electrons and forms doubly charged ions of the M^{++} type. There is a stronger force of attraction between the metal ions and the electron cloud of the metallic crystal than in the Group I metallic crystals. Consequently, these metals are more dense, harder, and have higher melting points and boiling points than the corresponding members of the Sodium Family.

The atoms and ions of the members of the Calcium Family are smaller than those of the corresponding members of the Sodium Family because of their higher nuclear charge. For example, the magnesium ion Mg^{++} has the same electron configuration as the corresponding

THE CALCIUM FAMILY

Element	Atomic Number	Atomic Weight	Electron Configuration	Oxidation Number	Melting Point, °C	Boiling Point, °C	Density g/cm³	Metallic Radius Å	Ionic Radius Å
Beryllium	4	9.0122	2, 2	+2	1280	2970	1.85	0.889	0.31
Magnesium	12	24.312	2, 8, 2	+2	651	1107	1.74	1.364	0.65
Calcium	20	40.08	2, 8, 8, 2	+2	842	1240	1.55	1.736	0.99
Strontium	38	87.62	2, 8, 18, 8, 2	+2	800	1150	2.54	1.914	1.13
Barium	56	137.34	2, 8, 18, 18, 8, 2	+2	850	1140	3.78	1.981	1.35
Radium	88	226.	2, 8, 18, 32, 18, 8, 2	+2	700	1140	5(?)	....	....

Group I ion Na$^+$, 2 electrons in the K shell and 8 electrons in the L shell. However, Mg^{++} has a nuclear charge of +12 and Na$^+$ has a nuclear charge of +11. The higher nuclear charge of the Mg^{++} ion produces a stronger attraction for electrons resulting in smaller K and L shells.

The alkaline-earth metals form hydrides, oxides or peroxides, hydroxides, and halogenides with general similarities to those of the alkali metals. The hydrides of the alkaline-earth metals are ionic and contain the H$^-$ ion. They react with water to liberate hydrogen gas and form basic hydroxide solutions. In fact, calcium hydride is frequently used as a convenient source of hydrogen.

The oxides of beryllium, magnesium, and calcium have very high melting points and CaO and MgO are used as refractory materials. They are considered to be ionic but are more covalent than alkali-metal oxides. Strontium and barium form peroxides with oxygen, probably because of the large size of their ions.

The hydroxides are formed by adding water to the oxides and, except for Be(OH)$_2$ which is amphiprotic, are completely dissociated in water solution yielding OH$^-$ ions. They are only slightly soluble in water, the solubility increasing with the size of the metallic ion. Thus, the hydroxide solutions have low concentrations of OH$^-$ ions and are weakly basic because of their slight solubility in water and not because of a lack of ionic character.

1. CALCIUM

2. Calcium is widely distributed. Calcium ranks fifth in abundance by weight among the elements in the earth's crust, atmosphere, and surface waters. It is widely distributed over the earth's surface in marble, limestone, dolomite, and gypsum, as well as in many other rocks and minerals.

3. The discovery of calcium. Calcium was first isolated by Sir Humphry Davy in 1808. He prepared metallic calcium by electrolyzing a moist mixture of calcium oxide and mercuric oxide, and then distilling the mercury from the resulting calcium-mercury amalgam.

4. The preparation of calcium. Since calcium occurs as Ca^{++} ions, the metal must be recovered by a reduction process. Calcium is prepared today by

VOCABULARY

Hard water. Water containing ions such as calcium and magnesium which form precipitates with soap.

Ion exchange resin. A resin which can exchange hydronium ions for positive ions; or one which can exchange hydroxide ions for negative ions.

Permanent hardness. Hardness caused by the sulfates of calcium and magnesium, which can be removed by the addition of chemical softeners.

Temporary hardness. Hardness caused by the bicarbonates of calcium and magnesium, which can be removed by boiling the water.

Zeolite. A sodium silicate-aluminate used to soften water.

electrolysis of fused calcium chloride.

$$CaCl_2 \xrightarrow{\text{(elect)}} Ca + Cl_2 \uparrow$$

A graphite crucible, which also serves as the anode, holds the fused chloride. An iron rod cathode dips into the fused salt. As metallic calcium forms on the end of the rod, the rod is slowly raised from the mass. In this way an irregular rod of metallic calcium is produced.

5. The properties and uses of calcium. Metallic calcium is silver-white in color, but a freshly-cut piece tarnishes to a bluish-gray surface within a few hours. It is somewhat harder than lead, but it is only about one-eighth as dense. If a piece of calcium is added to water, it reacts with the water and liberates hydrogen slowly.

$$Ca + 2\,H_2O \rightarrow Ca(OH)_2 + H_2 \uparrow$$

The reaction is much less violent than that of sodium and potassium with wa-

Fig. 25-1. Limestone is an excellent building stone. Here we see a huge block of Indiana limestone being removed from the quarry. (Indiana Limestone)

ter. The calcium hydroxide produced in this reaction is only slightly soluble and coats the surface of the calcium. This coating protects the metal from the rapid interaction with the water which would be expected because of its greater electrochemical activity as compared with sodium. Calcium is a good reducing agent. It burns with a bright, orange-red flame in oxygen, and unites directly with chlorine. Calcium salts yield an orange-red color in flame tests. Sodium contamination often alters the color to orange-yellow. Consequently, the flame test is not very satisfactory in the identification of calcium.

Calcium is used in small amounts to deoxidize copper, and some alloy steels contain small quantities of it. Lead-calcium alloys are used for bearings in machines. Calcium is also used to harden lead for cables and storage battery grids.

6. Calcium carbonate is abundant. Calcium carbonate $CaCO_3$, is found in a number of different forms.

1. Limestone. This is the most common form of calcium carbonate. It was probably formed in past geologic ages from the accumulations of the shells of clams, oysters, and other marine animals. Limestone occurs in layers as a *sedimentary rock*, and is quarried in varying amounts in almost every state in the country. Pure calcium carbonate is white, or colorless, when crystalline. Most deposits, however, are gray because of impurities.

Limestone is used for making glass, as a flux in making iron and steel, and as a source of carbon dioxide. It is used as a building stone, and considerable quantities are used for making roads. Mixed with clay, it can be converted into cement. Powdered or pulverized limestone is used to neutralize acid soils. Large quantities are heated to produce *quicklime,* calcium oxide, CaO.

Fig. 25-2. **The New York Public Library in New York City is constructed of marble.** (New York Convention and Visitors Bureau)

2. *Calcite.* A clear, crystalline form of calcium carbonate is known as calcite. Transparent, colorless specimens are called *Iceland spar.*

3. *Marble.* It is probable that this rock was originally deposited as limestone, and later changed by heat and pressure into marble. Hence it is classed as a *metamorphic rock.* Vermont and Georgia are noted for their fine marble, but it is also quarried in many other states. Marble makes a beautiful building stone.

4. *Shells.* The shells of such animals as snails, clams, and oysters consist largely of calcium carbonate. In some places, large masses of such shells have become cemented together to form a rock called *coquina* (ko-*quee*-na) which is used as a building stone in the southern states. Tiny marine animals, called *polyps,* deposit limestone as they build coral reefs. Chalk, such as that of the chalk cliffs of England, consists of the microscopic shells of small marine animals. Blackboard "chalk," however, contains some claylike material mixed with calcium

carbonate, and should not be confused with natural chalk.

5. *Precipitated chalk.* This form of calcium carbonate is made by the reaction of sodium carbonate and calcium chloride.

$$Na_2CO_3 + CaCl_2 \rightarrow CaCO_3 \downarrow + 2 NaCl$$

It is soft and finely divided. Thus it forms a nongritty scouring powder that is suitable for tooth pastes and tooth powders. Under the name of *whiting* it is used as a filler for paints. When it is ground with linseed oil, it forms putty.

7. Limestone cave formation. Limestone reacts slowly with water that contains carbon dioxide in solution, and forms calcium hydrogen carbonate, which is slightly soluble.

$$CaCO_3 + H_2O + CO_2 \rightleftarrows Ca(HCO_3)_2$$

As the calcium hydrogen carbonate is carried away by the water in which it dissolves, caves or caverns are sometimes formed in the limestone. The Luray Caverns in Virginia, the Mammoth Cave in Kentucky, the Carlsbad Cav-

Fig. 25-3. Carlsbad Caverns contain some of the largest limestone caves found in the United States. (National Park Service)

erns in New Mexico, and the Howe Caverns in New York are famous for their size and the interesting rock formations found in them.

The chemical reaction above is reversible. For that reason, drops of water which hang from the roof of a cave may lose carbon dioxide and redeposit limestone in icicle-shaped masses of limestone, called *stalactites* (stah-*lack*-tytes), which hang from the roof of the cavern. Water dripping from these stalactites may then build up masses of calcium carbonate, called *stalagmites* (stah-*lag*-mytes), on the floor of the cavern.

A similar reaction occurs when water containing dissolved carbon dioxide comes in contact with dolomite,

$CaCO_3 \cdot MgCO_3$. In this case, both calcium hydrogen carbonate and magnesium hydrogen carbonate are formed and dissolve in the water.

$$CaCO_3 \cdot MgCO_3 + 2\,H_2O + 2\,CO_2 \rightleftarrows$$
$$Ca(HCO_3)_2 + Mg(HCO_3)_2$$

8. Hardness in water. Whenever water which contains carbon dioxide in solution soaks through the ground and reaches deposits of limestone or dolomite, some of the calcium carbonate and magnesium carbonate in these rocks is converted to the soluble bicarbonates of these metals. This water, which contains Ca^{++} ions and Mg^{++} ions in solution, is called *"hard water."* This term indicates that it is "hard" to get a lather when soap is added to such water. Conversely, a water that lathers readily with soap is called "soft" water. The terms are not precise, but they are in common usage. Deposits of iron and other heavy metals in the ground may also produce hard water.

Water hardness is of two types: *temporary hardness* in which HCO_3^- ions are present along with the metal ions; and *permanent hardness* in which other negative ions (usually $SO_4^=$) more stable than the HCO_3^- ion are present along with the metal ions.

The principal component of ordinary soap is water-soluble sodium stearate, $NaC_{18}H_{35}O_2$. When soap is added to water containing Ca^{++} ions, the large $C_{18}H_{35}O_2^-$ ions react with the Ca^{++} ions to form the insoluble stearate, $Ca(C_{18}H_{35}O_2)_2$, which deposits as a gray scum.

$$Ca^{++} + 2\ C_{18}H_{35}O_2^- \rightarrow Ca(C_{18}H_{35}O_2)_2 \downarrow$$

The metal ions in hard water react with the soap to form precipitates until all of these ions are removed. Until this occurs, no lasting lather will be produced. Soft water does not contain the ions of these troublesome metals and lathers easily when soap is added.

9. The softening of hard water. Hard water is a nuisance in laundering because the sticky precipitate wastes soap and collects on the fibers of the garments being laundered. In bathing, the hard water does not lather freely, and the precipitate forms a scum on the bathtub. In steam boilers, temporary hard water containing the HCO_3^- ions has a still more serious fault. When this water is boiled, calcium carbonate collects as a hard scale inside the boiler and the steam pipes. It may form a thick crust on these surfaces, acting as a heat insulator and preventing efficient trans-

fer of heat. Thus, for most purposes, hard water should be softened before it is used.

There are several practical methods of softening water. Generally, the nature of the hardness and the quantity of soft water required determine the most economical and effective method.

1. Boiling (for temporary hardness). Hard water containing HCO_3^- ions

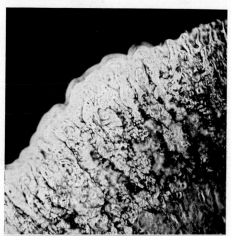

Fig. 25-4. **Photomicrographs of soap in the process of dissolving in hard water (top) and soft water (bottom). In hard water the solution process is inhibited by a barrier of sticky soap curd, but in soft water soap streamers extend into the water, forming a clear solution.** (Permutit)

Fig. 25-5. **The scale of calcium carbonate which has collected on the inside of this pipe cuts down the flow of steam through it and acts as an insulator. Thus, the scale prevents efficient transfer of heat.** (Permutit)

may be softened by boiling. The metal ions precipitate as carbonates according to the following typical reaction:

$$Ca^{++} + 2\,HCO_3^- \rightarrow$$
$$CaCO_3 \downarrow + H_2O + CO_2 \uparrow$$

This reaction is reversible except for the fact that boiling removes the CO_2 and drives the reaction to the right.

2. *Precipitation.* Sodium carbonate, Na_2CO_3, when added to hard water, precipitates Ca^{++} and Mg^{++} ions as insoluble carbonates. The Na^+ ions added to the water, of course, cause no difficulties with soap.

$$Ca^{++} + CO_3^= \rightarrow CaCO_3 \downarrow$$
$$Mg^{++} + CO_3^= \rightarrow MgCO_3 \downarrow$$

The addition of a basic solution such as NH_3-Aq or limewater to temporary hard water supplies OH^- ions which neutralize the HCO_3^- ions and precipi-

tate the objectionable metal ions as carbonates.

$$Ca^{++} + HCO_3^- + OH^- \rightarrow$$
$$CaCO_3 \downarrow + H_2O$$
$$Mg^{++} + HCO_3^- + OH^- \rightarrow$$
$$MgCO_3 \downarrow + H_2O$$

Other precipitating agents such as borax and trisodium phosphate are sometimes used. Both produce basic solutions by hydrolysis and the phosphate salts of calcium and magnesium are insoluble.

3. *Ion exchange.* Certain natural minerals, known as *zeolites*, have porous, three-dimensional networks of silicate-aluminate groups that act as large fixed ions carrying negative charges. Metallic ions such as Na^+ are attached to these complexes to form giant molecules. If hard water is allowed to stand in contact with sodium zeolite, Ca^{++} and Mg^{++} ions replace the Na^+ ions. Since the zeolite ions are immobile, the objectionable metal ions are given up by the water, being exchanged for Na^+ ions.

$$Ca^{++} + Na_2\,zeolite \rightarrow Ca\,zeolite + 2\,Na^+$$

An application of the Law of Mass Action enables the exhausted zeolite to be regenerated and used over and over again. By immersing Ca zeolite in a concentrated sodium chloride solution (high Na^+ concentration), the Ca^{++} ions are replaced, a reversal of the above equation.

$$2\,Na^+ + Ca\,zeolite \rightarrow$$
$$Na_2\,zeolite + Ca^{++}$$

A synthetic zeolite, known as *permutit*, acts more rapidly than natural zeolites and is commonly used today in most household water softeners. Sodium chloride, the cheapest of all sources of Na^+ ions, is used to regenerate the water-softening agent.

Important recent advances in the field of synthetic ion exchanges have enabled chemists to develop ion-exchange resins far superior to the zeolites. One type of resin, called an *acid-exchange resin* or a *cation exchanger*, has large negatively charged organic units whose neutralizing ions in water are H_3O^+ ions. A second type of resin, called a *base-exchange resin* or *anion exchanger*, has large positively charged organic units whose neutralizing ions in water are OH^- ions.

Combinations of the two types of ion-exchange resins make possible the removal of both positive and negative ions in solution in water. Hard water passed through the cation exchanger has the

Fig. 25-6. **This water softening unit enables any laboratory to have a ready supply of soft water.** (Barnstead Still and Sterilizer)

metallic ions (cations) removed and replaced by H_3O^+ ions. The water then passed through the anion exchanger has the negative ions (anions) removed and replaced by OH^- ions. The H_3O^+ and OH^- ions form water by neutralization.

Natural water or a water solution of salts treated by combinations of ion-exchange resins is rendered *ion-free* except for the small equilibrium quantities of H_3O^+ and OH^- ions and is called *deionized* or *demineralized water*. Deionized water is now being used for many processes that formerly required distilled water. In fact, deionized water is as free of ions as the most carefully distilled water, although it may contain some dissolved carbon dioxide.

An acid-exchange resin can be regenerated by running a strong acid such as sulfuric acid through it. Similarly, a base-exchange resin can be regenerated using a basic solution.

10. The preparation of calcium oxide. Calcium oxide is made by heating calcium carbonate to a high temperature.

$$CaCO_3 \rightarrow CaO + CO_2 \uparrow$$

Carbon dioxide is driven off by the heat, and calcium oxide remains. The furnace used for the process may be a vertical kiln, Fig. 25-7, or a rotary kiln, Fig. 25-8.

In the modern rotary kiln, small pieces of limestone are continuously fed into the upper end of a slowly rotating inclined cylinder which may be as large as 8 ft in diameter and 200 ft long. As the lumps move downward by gravity, they meet the hot gases from the burning fuel. By the time they reach the lower end of the kiln, all the carbon dioxide has been driven off by the heat.

11. The properties of calcium oxide. Calcium oxide is a white, ionic solid with a cubic structure and is often

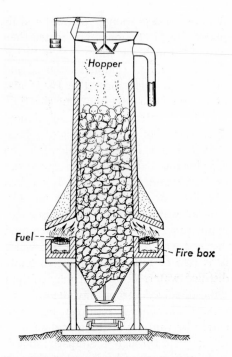

Fig. 25-7. This is a sectional view of a vertical lime kiln. The lime kiln is operated continuously by putting limestone in at the top and withdrawing quicklime from the bottom.

called *quicklime*. It is very refractory since it does not melt or vaporize except at the temperature of the electric arc. It unites chemically with water to form calcium hydroxide, or *hydrated lime*:

$$CaO + H_2O \rightarrow Ca(OH)_2$$

During this process, called **slaking**, the mass swells and large quantities of heat are evolved.

If a lump of quicklime is exposed to air, it gradually absorbs water, swells decidedly, cracks, and crumbles to a powder. It first forms calcium hydroxide, and then slowly unites with carbon dioxide from air to form calcium carbonate. Thus a mixture of calcium hydroxide and calcium carbonate, called *air-slaked lime*, is formed. Such a mixture is valuable for liming soils, but air slaking ruins lime for making mortar and plaster.

12. Calcium hydroxide has many uses. Calcium hydroxide is a white solid which is sparingly soluble in water. Its water solution, called *limewater*, has

Fig. 25-8. As the small pieces of crushed limestone move down through the slowly rotating inclined cylinder of this rotary kiln, they are met by the hot gases from the burning fuel. The high temperature liberates the carbon dioxide and quicklime remains.

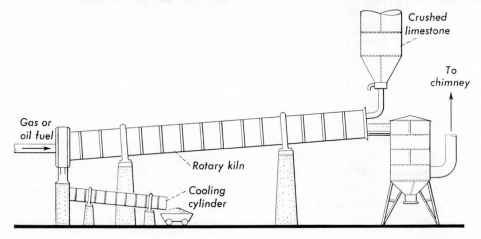

basic properties. A suspension of calcium hydroxide in water is known as milk of lime. Mixed with flour paste or glue, it makes whitewash.

Calcium hydroxide is the cheapest hydroxide. It is used to remove hair from hides before they are tanned, or converted into leather. It is useful for liming soils, for liberating ammonia from ammonium compounds, and for softening temporary hard water. Large quantities are used for making mortar and plaster.

Lime mortar consists of slaked lime, sand, and water. Although mortar of this general composition has been used for many centuries, the process by which it sets to a hard mass is still not fully understood. The first step in the setting is loss of water by evaporation. It appears that the lime and sand slowly react according to the equation:

$$Ca(OH)_2 + SiO_2 \rightarrow CaSiO_3 + H_2O$$

Carbon dioxide from the air reacts with the lime also, as follows:

$$Ca(OH)_2 + CO_2 \rightarrow CaCO_3 + H_2O$$

Mortar becomes harder over a period of many years as chemical changes occur in the center of the mass.

Cement is sometimes added to lime mortar to make it harder and more waterproof. For some construction work, particularly underground, cement is used entirely instead of lime, making a cement mortar.

13. The preparation of cement and concrete. Cement is made from limestone and clay. Powdered limestone and clay are mixed in the proper proportions and heated strongly in a cement kiln. Just as the mixture begins to melt, it forms into pasty masses, about the size of peas, which are called *clinker*. When the clinker is cooled and hardened, it

Fig. 25-9. **A rotary cement kiln 12 feet wide and 450 feet long.** (Permanente Cement)

is ground to a fine powder. The finer the grinding of the clinker, the stronger the cement will be. To prevent too rapid setting, 2% to 3% of gypsum is ground with the clinker.

Sometimes limestone deposits have clay already mixed with the calcium carbonate in about the proportions needed to serve as raw material for making cement. Such rocks are called *natural cement*. Pennsylvania has good deposits of natural cement rock. Cement is sometimes called *hydraulic cement* because it sets or hardens under water.

The hardening of cement is not completely understood. The first step appears to be the union of water with some of the components of the cement to form hydrates. The hydrated crystals seem to become interlocked into a hard mass. Some chemists believe that the action is partly colloidal since the strength increases with the fineness of particle size.

Cement is mixed with sand, crushed stone, and water to make *concrete*. When concrete hardens, it forms a very hard, compact mass which is suitable for many construction purposes. *Reinforced concrete* is strengthened by embedding iron or steel rods in it.

14. The uses of calcium sulfate. Calcium sulfate occurs as the mineral *gypsum* in Kansas, New York, Ohio, Indiana, and Michigan. Transparent crystals of gypsum are called *selenite*.

When gypsum is heated gently, it partially dehydrates and forms a white powder known as plaster of Paris, according to the equation:

$$2\ CaSO_4 \cdot 2\ H_2O \rightarrow$$
$$(CaSO_4)_2 \cdot H_2O + 3\ H_2O \uparrow$$

When plaster of Paris is mixed with water, it forms a paste useful in making molds and casts which set rapidly by uniting with water, the reverse of the above reaction. Gypsum is mixed with lime to make the finish coat of plaster. Large quantities are used in making wallboard or plasterboard.

2. STRONTIUM AND BARIUM

15. Strontium compounds. The sulfate and the carbonate are the chief strontium minerals. Since all the compounds of strontium impart a beautiful scarlet color to a flame, they are used in fireworks displays.

Strontium nitrate, $Sr(NO_3)_2$, when mixed with powdered shellac, makes a red light for fireworks and flares. Strontium salts give an intense scarlet color in flame tests, but the color is not easily obtained with dilute solutions. The inexperienced observer usually has difficulty in distinguishing between lithium and strontium flames.

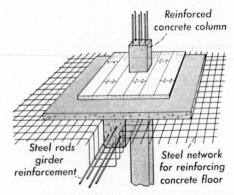

Fig. 25-10. **Steel rods are used in the building industry to reinforce concrete.**

16. Useful compounds of barium. Both the sulfate and the carbonate of barium are found in nature. The compounds of barium are similar in chemical characteristics to the compounds of calcium. The following are most widely used.

1. *Barium sulfate*, $BaSO_4$, is a dense white solid which is used as a filler in making heavy paper and also in paints. It gives more body to paper and makes it less transparent, and it increases the durability of paint.

2. *Barium peroxide*, BaO_2, is used in fireworks, as a vigorous oxidizing agent, and to some extent for making hydrogen peroxide.

3. *Barium nitrate*, $Ba(NO_3)_2$, is a white crystalline solid. All barium compounds impart a yellowish-green color to a flame which may be obscured by sodium impurities. They find considerable use in making flares and fireworks, for which the nitrate is generally used.

The oxides of both barium and strontium are used to coat the filament used in vacuum tubes. A single layer of barium atoms on the surface of the filament is said to multiply the yield of electrons given off by the filament more than one hundred million times.

SUMMARY

The Calcium Family comprises beryllium, magnesium, calcium, strontium, barium, and radium. Each of these elements has two valence electrons. The atoms and ions of the members of the Calcium Family are smaller than the corresponding members of the Sodium Family. The bonding formed by these elements is slightly covalent, and their hydroxides do not produce very strong bases. These elements form hydrates. None of these metals occurs free in nature.

Metallic calcium is silver-white in color, of low density, and relatively hard. It reacts with water, and burns in oxygen with an orange-red light. It is used to harden lead.

Calcium carbonate is an abundant compound that occurs in a number of different forms. Limestone caves are formed by the solvent action of water that contains dissolved carbon dioxide.

Hard water contains compounds of calcium, magnesium, or iron in solution. Water may contain temporary or permanent hardness which can be removed by various methods. The process by which hardness is removed from water is called water softening.

Calcium oxide, or quicklime, unites with water to form calcium hydroxide, or hydrated lime. Calcium hydroxide is used for making mortar, plaster, and for other uses that require the inexpensive formation of a base.

Barium and strontium compounds are used in making fireworks. Barium sulfate is used in paints and to add weight to paper.

TEST YOURSELF ON THESE TERMS

air-slaked lime	gypsum	permanent hardness
anion exchanger	hard water	plaster
calcite	hydrated lime	plaster of Paris
cation exchanger	Iceland spar	quicklime
cement	ion-exchange resin	sedimentary rock
clinker	kiln	slaking
concrete	limestone	temporary hardness
coquina	metamorphic rock	water softener
dolomite	mortar	zeolite

QUESTIONS

Group A

1. Compare the preparation of elementary calcium with that of elementary sodium.
2. What are the important uses for metallic calcium?
3. In what forms is calcium carbonate found in nature?
4. (*a*) What does the term *hard water* mean? (*b*) *Soft water?* (*c*) What is the difference between temporary and permanent hardness of water?
5. What principle is employed to regenerate a zeolite water softener?

6. Distinguish: (*a*) limestone; (*b*) quicklime; (*c*) slaked lime; (*d*) lime; (*e*) hydrated lime.
7. For what gas is limewater used as a test solution?
8. Distinguish between metamorphic and sedimentary rocks.
9. How could you demonstrate that a piece of coral is a carbonate?
10. Write an equation to show the action of water containing dissolved carbon dioxide on limestone.
11. Explain how cement is manufactured from clay and limestone.
12. How are "red fire" and "green fire" made for fireworks?

Group B

13. Why are the members of the Calcium Family denser and harder than the corresponding members of the Sodium Family?
14. Why does calcium chloride exist as a hydrate, $CaCl_2 \cdot 2 H_2O$, while sodium chloride does not occur as a hydrate?
15. Give two reasons why the reaction of calcium with water is not as vigorous as that of potassium and water.
16. (*a*) What metallic ions cause water to be hard? (*b*) What negative ion causes temporary hardness? (*c*) What negative ion usually causes permanent hardness?
17. What type of chemical reaction occurs between soap and hard water?
18. Write an empirical equation to show the softening action of sodium carbonate on hard water containing: (*a*) calcium sulfate; (*b*) magnesium bicarbonate.
19. What chemical changes are thought to take place in the hardening of cement?
20. What are some uses for calcium chloride which is produced in such large quantities as a by-product of the manufacture of Solvay soda?
21. (*a*) How is plaster of Paris made? (*b*) Why does it harden?
22. What are the uses for barium sulfate?
23. What impurity may still remain in water that has been passed through both an acid exchange resin and a base exchange resin?
24. (*a*) Why should cement mortar be used between the cinder block of house foundations? (b) Why may lime mortar be used between the bricks?
25. How can you account for the fact that temporary hard water containing Ca^{++} ions can be softened by the addition of lime water, a solution containing Ca^{++} ions and OH^- ions?

PROBLEMS

Group A

1. How many kilograms of calcium oxide can be produced from 1.00 metric ton of limestone which contains 12.5% of impurities?
2. How much mass will 86.0 kg of gypsum lose when it is converted into plaster of Paris?

Group B

3. How many pounds of carbon dioxide can be obtained from a ton of oyster shells that are 81.0% calcium carbonate?
4. How many liters will the carbon dioxide produced in Problem 3 occupy at S.T.P.?
5. If the carbon dioxide of Problem 4 is measured at 720. mm pressure and 20.° C, what volume does it occupy?

SOME THINGS FOR YOU TO DO

1. Make a collection of as many different forms of calcium carbonate as you can find.
2. Make a paste with plaster of Paris and water. Spread it in a thin layer in a cardboard box, or on a glass square. Rub a little oil on a medal, flat key, or other metallic object, and press it into the plaster of Paris just before it hardens. After a half hour remove the metallic object, and note the clear impression it leaves in the plaster of Paris.
3. Look about your school building and list the ways in which calcium compounds have been used in its construction.
4. Visit one of the large natural caves which are located in various regions of the United States. Try to learn how the cave was formed.
5. Determine the hardness of natural waters by titrating samples of them with a standard soap solution.

CHECK YOUR PROGRESS IN CHEMISTRY

1. How do the structures of graphite and diamond explain the differences in their properties?
2. If you are given a bottle of nitrogen, a bottle of carbon dioxide, and a bottle of carbon monoxide, how can you distinguish them?
3. Name five series of hydrocarbons. Give the general formula for as many of these series as you can.
4. What weight of hydrated copper(II) sulfate, $CuSO_4 \cdot 5 H_2O$, must be used to make up 500. ml of a 0.500-N solution?
5. Distinguish between *dissociation* and *ionization*.
6. Give the modern definitions of *acid* and *base*.
★ 7. Give the expression for the equilibrium constant for the ionization of acetic acid.
★ 8. Balance the following oxidation-reduction equation:
$$Hg + HNO_3 \rightarrow Hg(NO_3)_2 + H_2O + NO \uparrow.$$
9. Compare potassium and calcium as to structure, physical properties, and chemical properties.
10. Why are metals generally good conductors of electricity?
11. Give several uses for elementary lithium.
12. How can you detect potassium in the presence of sodium by a flame test?

13. Write the empirical equation for the preparation of sodium hydroxide from washing soda and slaked lime.
14. Why must the ammonia be recovered in the Solvay process?
15. Define: (*a*) coquina; (*b*) gypsum; (*c*) Iceland spar; (*d*) stalactite; (*e*) temporary hardness.
16. What are the principal uses for limestone?
17. Write the equation for the reaction of sodium carbonate and calcium chloride to produce precipitated chalk.
18. Explain how zeolites soften hard water and how they may be regenerated when exhausted.
19. Describe the operation of a rotary lime kiln.
20. (*a*) What is the composition of a plaster undercoat? (*b*) Of a plaster finish coat?

CHALLENGING YOUR KNOWLEDGE

1. In the Solvay process, sodium hydrogen carbonate is prepared, converted to sodium carbonate, and then reconverted to sodium hydrogen carbonate. Why is this done rather than use the sodium hydrogen carbonate that is first prepared?
2. What optical use is made of crystals of Iceland spar?
3. For what type of solutions would the carbon dioxide which remains dissolved in water after passing through ion exchange resins be objectionable?
4. What important electric discovery had to precede Davy's preparation of metallic sodium, metallic potassium, and metallic calcium?
5. What is *halite?*
6. Why do poultrymen add calcium carbonate to the diet of laying hens?

Unit 8 · THE HALOGENS AND SULFUR

The Halogen Family
Sulfur and Sulfides
The Oxides and Acids of Sulfur

Chapter 26 · THE HALOGEN FAMILY

1. The Halogen Family is Group VII of the Periodic Table. It consists of the nonmetallic elements fluorine, chlorine, bromine, iodine, and astatine, as shown in the table at the bottom of this page.

From this table we see that each of these elements has seven electrons in the outermost shell. In order to attain an outer octet of electrons, a halogen atom must acquire one electron. Since the atoms of these elements are so strongly electronegative, they are all active elements which have never been found free in nature. In the elementary state they exist as covalent diatomic molecules. Fluorine, having the smallest atoms and the greatest affinity for electrons, is the most highly electronegative element. Fluorine, consequently, cannot be prepared from its compounds by any purely chemical reduction. The other halogens, with increasingly larger atoms, are less electronegative than fluorine. As a result, the smaller, lighter halogens are able to replace the larger, heavier halo-

THE HALOGEN FAMILY

Element	Atomic Number	Atomic Weight	Electron Configuration	Principal Oxidation Number	Melting Point, °C	Boiling Point, °C	Color	Density, 10°C	Atomic Radius Å	Ionic Radius Å
Fluorine	9	18.9984	2, 7	−1	−223	−187	pale-yellow gas	1.69 g/l	0.64	1.36
Chlorine	17	35.453	2, 8, 7	−1	−101.6	−34.6	greenish-yellow gas	3.214 g/l	0.99	1.81
Bromine	35	79.909	2, 8, 18, 7	−1	−7.2	58.78	reddish-brown liquid	3.12 g/ml	1.14	1.95
Iodine	53	126.9044	2, 8, 18, 18, 7	−1	113.5	184.35	grayish-black crystals	4.93 g/ml	1.33	2.16
Astatine	85	210.	2, 8, 18, 32, 18, 7							

gens from their compounds. (See Activity Series, Chapter 12, Section 12.) Astatine is a synthetic radioactive halogen produced in 1940 at the University of California by Corson, MacKenzie, and Segre. Very little is known of its properties. However, what study has been made of this element indicates that it is a halogen with properties which correspond to its proper position in the family.

It is evident from the table that there is a regular change in properties shown by the members of this family, proceeding from the smallest and lightest to the largest and heaviest. Refer also to the charts showing ionization potential and electronegatively in Unit 2, Chapters 5 and 6.

Each of the halogens combines with hydrogen. Hydrogen fluoride molecules, because of the great electronegativity difference between hydrogen and fluorine, are so polar that they associate by hydrogen bonding. The remaining hydrogen halogenides with smaller electronegativity differences do not show this property. Each of the hydrogen halogenides is a colorless gas which is ionized in water solution. With the exception of hydrofluoric acid, these acids are highly ionized and are strong acids.

Each of the halogens forms ionic salts with metals. Hence the name *halogens*, which means "salt producers."

1. FLUORINE

2. The preparation of fluorine. Fluorine was first prepared in 1886 by Henri Moissan (1852–1907). He prepared it by electrolyzing a solution of potassium hydrogen fluoride, KHF_2, in liquid anhydrous hydrogen fluoride in a platinum tube, using platinum-iridium electrodes. Today it is prepared by electrolyzing a mixture of potassium fluoride and hydrogen fluoride in a stainless steel or copper electrolytic cell with a graphite anode. The fluoride coating protects these metals from further attack.

3. The properties of fluorine. Fluorine is the most active nonmetallic element. A fluorine atom, with seven electrons in its outer L shell, has a great affinity for an additional electron to complete its octet. An acquired electron is very strongly attracted by the positively-charged nucleus due to the small size of the fluorine atom. This accounts for its extreme electronegativity. It unites with hydrogen explosively, even in the dark. It forms compounds with all elements except the inert gases. There are no known positive oxidation states of fluorine. It forms salts known as *fluorides*. Fluorine reacts with gold and platinum slowly. Special carbon steel containers are used to transport fluorine. These become coated with iron fluoride which resists further action.

VOCABULARY

Antichlor. A substance used to remove traces of chlorine left in bleached goods.

Halogen (*hal*-oh-jen). The name given to the family of elements having seven valence electrons.

Mother liquor. The saturated solution remaining after the separation of a crop of crystals.

Pickling. Removing the surface impurities from a metal by dipping it into an acid bath.

Fig. 26-1. Electrolytic cells used for the production of elementary fluorine from potassium fluoride and hydrogen fluoride. (Allied Chemical and Dye)

4. Fluorine compounds are very useful. The mineral *fluorspar*, CaF_2, is used in preparing most fluorine compounds. Sodium fluoride is used as a poison for destroying roaches and vermin. A trace of sodium fluoride, or the cheaper sodium silico-fluoride, is added to the drinking water of many communities because fluorides help prevent tooth decay. Yet, larger quantities of fluorides in drinking water cause the enamel of the teeth to become spotted. The fluoride ion seems to react with the enamel of children's teeth, but has little effect on the teeth of adults. Fluorides have also been added to some tooth pastes to help prevent tooth decay.

Dichloro-difluoro-methane, commercially called "Freon," CCl_2F_2, is used as a refrigerant. It is odorless, nonflammable, and nontoxic. It is also used as the propellant in spray cans of insecticides. In the production of aluminum, melted cryolite, $AlF_3 \cdot 3\,NaF$, is used as a solvent for aluminum oxide. Uranium is converted to the gaseous uranium hexafluoride, UF_6, for separating the uranium isotopes.

5. The preparation and properties of hydrogen fluoride. This compound, HF, is prepared by treating calcium fluoride with concentrated sulfuric acid:

$$CaF_2 + H_2SO_4 \rightarrow CaSO_4 + 2\,HF \uparrow$$

The colorless gas which is set free by the reaction fumes strongly in moist air. It dissolves in water and forms hydrofluoric acid. This acid is very corrosive, attacking the flesh and forming painful sores which heal slowly. The vapor is very dangerous if inhaled. Hydrofluoric acid reacts with most substances. Wax, lead, platinum, and certain plastics are important exceptions.

At ordinary room temperature, the molar volume of hydrogen fluoride has a mass of about 50. g; thus hydrogen fluoride has an average molecular weight of 50. Since the molecular weight of an HF molecule is only 20., this indicates that hydrogen fluoride contains some molecules more complex than HF. Some scientists believe that gaseous hydrogen fluoride is an approximately equal mixture of H_2F_2 and H_3F_3 molecules, having molecular weights of 40. and 60. respectively. There is some evidence, however, for the existence of even more complex molecules up to and including H_6F_6 in gaseous hydrogen fluoride. At higher temperatures, the molar volume of the gas has a mass of only. 20. g, showing that the gas dissociates into HF molecules. The association of hydrogen fluoride molecules is an example of hydrogen bonding, due to the high electronegativity of fluorine and the resulting polarity of hydrogen fluoride molecules. The hydrogen-fluorine bond is estimated to have about 50 percent ionic character.

Water dipoles can cause only a few

of the H_2F_2 molecules present in hydrofluoric acid at room temperature to ionize as follows:

$$H_2O + H_2F_2 \rightleftarrows H_3O^+ + HF_2^-$$

The hydrogen difluoride ion, HF_2^-, contains the strongest hydrogen bond known; even stronger than the hydrogen bonds in molecules like H_2F_2 and H_3F_3. Because of its slight ionization, hydrofluoric acid is a weak acid. Being a diprotic acid, it forms both acid and normal salts.

$$H_2F_2 + KOH \rightarrow KHF_2 + H_2O$$
$$H_2F_2 + 2 KOH \rightarrow 2 KF + 2 H_2O$$

6. The uses of hydrofluoric acid. The chief uses of hydrofluoric acid are as a catalyst in the manufacture of high-octane gasoline, and in the manufacture of synthetic cryolite for aluminum production.

For many years hydrofluoric acid has been used for etching glass. The surface of the glass is coated with wax or paraffin. A sharp stylus is then used to scratch away the wax from that portion of the surface of the glass which is to be etched. The glass prepared in this manner is then exposed either to hydrogen fluoride gas or to a solution of the gas in water. The excess acid is washed off and the wax removed. If a solution is used for etching, the line etched is likely to be smooth and transparent. If the gas is used, the etched portion is likely to be somewhat rough and translucent. Electric light bulbs may be frosted by exposing the inside surface of the bulb to the fumes of hydrogen fluoride.

2. CHLORINE

7. Chlorine occurs widely in combined form. Because chlorine is a strongly electronegative element, it never occurs free or uncombined in nature. It is found rather abundantly in the form of chlorides of sodium, potassium, and magnesium. Common table salt, sodium chloride, is widely distributed in sea water, in salt brines underground, and in rock salt deposits. Sodium chloride is the commercial source for the preparation of chlorine.

8. The preparation of chlorine. The element chlorine was first isolated in 1774 by Scheele. There are various ways to prepare it: we shall discuss three.

Fig. 26-2. Among the molecules found in hydrogen fluoride at room temperature are H_2F_2, H_3F_3, and H_6F_6 molecules.

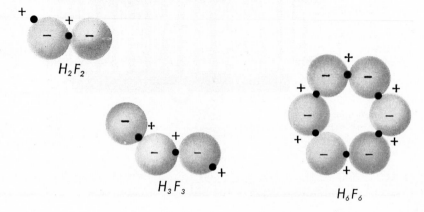

1. By the electrolysis of sodium chloride. There are several commercial methods for preparing chlorine by the electrolysis of sodium chloride in water solution. In all cases the concentration of the solution is such that hydrogen from the water is liberated at the cathode, and chlorine gas is set free at the anode. The gases, hydrogen and chlorine, are kept separate from each other and from the solution by asbestos diaphragms. The sodium and hydroxide ions remaining in the solution are recovered as sodium hydroxide.

$$2\ NaCl + 2\ H_2O \xrightarrow{\text{(elect)}} 2\ NaOH + H_2 \uparrow + Cl_2 \uparrow$$

The most efficient cell for chlorine production is the *Hooker cell.* *Vorce cells* and *Nelson cells* are also used. A small amount of chlorine is prepared by electrolysis of fused sodium chloride, as a by-product of sodium production.

2. By the oxidation of hydrogen chloride. When a mixture of manganese dioxide and hydrochloric acid is heated, the manganese oxidizes half of the chloride ions in the reacting HCl **to** chlorine atoms. Manganese is reduced during the reaction from the +4 oxidation state to the +2 state.

$$MnO_2 + 4\ HCl \rightarrow MnCl_2 + 2\ H_2O + Cl_2 \uparrow$$

This is the method that was used by Scheele in first preparing chlorine. It is a useful laboratory preparation.

In an alternative procedure, manganese dioxide is mixed with sodium chloride and sulfuric acid, and heated. The sodium chloride and sulfuric acid react

Fig. 26-3. **The Hooker cell is the most efficient cell for preparing chlorine by the electrolysis of a solution of sodium chloride.**

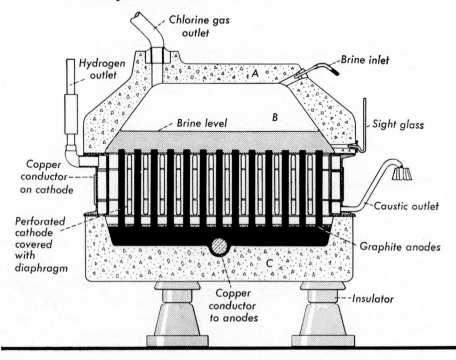

Fig. 26-4. **Chlorine is also prepared commercially in Vorce cells such as these.** (Food Machinery and Chemical)

to form hydrogen chloride, as in *Equation 1.*

Equation 1.

$$2\,NaCl + H_2SO_4 \rightarrow Na_2SO_4 + 2\,HCl$$

The chloride ions are then oxidized by the manganese of the manganese dioxide and free chlorine is liberated.

Equation 2.

$$2\,HCl + MnO_2 + H_2SO_4 \rightarrow$$
$$MnSO_4 + 2\,H_2O + Cl_2\uparrow$$

Combining *Equations 1* and *2* gives the following equation which represents the over-all reaction:

$$2\,NaCl + 2\,H_2SO_4 + MnO_2 \rightarrow$$
$$Na_2SO_4 + MnSO_4 + 2\,H_2O + Cl_2\uparrow$$

3. *By the action of hydrochloric acid on calcium hypochlorite.* This is a convenient laboratory method for the preparation of chlorine, since heat is not needed. Furthermore, the chlorine can be produced in small quantities as required.

Hydrochloric acid is allowed to drop onto calcium hypochlorite powder. Chlorine is liberated and calcium chloride and water are formed.

$$4\,HCl + Ca(ClO)_2 \rightarrow$$
$$CaCl_2 + 2\,Cl_2\uparrow + 2\,H_2O$$

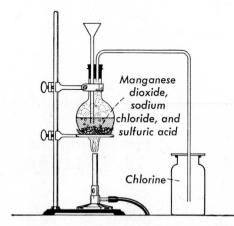

Manganese
dioxide,
sodium
chloride, and
sulfuric acid

Chlorine

Fig. 26-5. **One method of preparing chlorine in the laboratory is by heating a mixture of manganese dioxide, sodium chloride, and sulfuric acid.**

9. **The physical properties of chlorine.** At room temperature chlorine is a greenish-yellow gas, which has a disagreeable, almost suffocating odor. It is about 2.5 times as dense as air, and is moderately soluble in water, forming a pale-yellow solution. Chlorine is easily liquefied and is usually marketed in steel cylinders.

When inhaled in small quantities, chlorine affects the mucous membranes of the nose and throat, producing about the same symptoms as a bad head cold. If inhaled in larger quantities, chlorine is so toxic that it causes death. The bad effects from breathing chlorine are partly alleviated by inhaling either alcohol or ammonia.

10. **Chlorine is very active chemically.** The outer shell of a chlorine atom contains seven electrons. Chlorine undergoes many reactions as it acquires the additional electron to complete the octet. Its chemical properties will be discussed under the following subtopics.

1. *Action with metals.* When powdered antimony is sprinkled into a jar of moist chlorine, the two elements unite spontaneously, emitting a shower of sparks. Antimony trichloride is formed, as represented by the equation:

$$2\ Sb + 3\ Cl_2 \rightarrow 2\ SbCl_3$$

In a similar manner, hot metallic sodium burns in chlorine and forms sodium chloride. Chlorine combines directly with such metals as copper, iron, zinc, and arsenic, if they are heated slightly.
2. *Action with hydrogen.* If hydrogen and chlorine are mixed in the dark, no reaction occurs. But such a mixture explodes violently if it is heated, or if it is exposed to sunlight. The heat or sunlight provides the activation energy. A jet of hydrogen, burning in air, will continue to burn if it is introduced into a bottle of chlorine. Hydrogen chloride gas is produced:

$$H_2 + Cl_2 \rightarrow 2\ HCl \uparrow$$

This is an example of combustion without the presence of oxygen.

Chlorine has such a great affinity for hydrogen that it can take hydrogen from some of its compounds. Chlorine does not support the combustion of wood or paper. A paraffin candle, however, continues to burn in chlorine with a smoky flame. In this reaction the hydrogen of the paraffin unites with the chlorine forming hydrogen chloride, and the carbon is left uncombined. Tur-

Fig. 26-6. **Dyes which can be oxidized to colorless compounds are bleached successfully with chlorine.** (Bennett)

Fig. 26-7. **Chlorine is added to the water in swimming pools to destroy bacteria.** (Monkmeyer)

pentine is a hydrocarbon with the formula $C_{10}H_{16}$. A strip of filter paper moistened with hot turpentine and suspended in a jar of chlorine burns with a sooty flame. Hydrogen chloride is formed, and a dense cloud of soot is set free:

$$C_{10}H_{16} + 8 Cl_2 \rightarrow 10 C + 16 HCl \uparrow$$

3. *Action with water.* A freshly prepared solution of chlorine in water is yellow-green in color. If such a solution stands in sunlight for a few days, both the yellow-green color and the pronounced odor of the chlorine disappear. The chlorine unites with the water to form hypochlorous acid and hydrochloric acid. Hypochlorous acid is unstable and decomposes into hydrochloric acid with the liberation of oxygen. The equation is:

$$2 H_2O + 2 Cl_2 \rightarrow 2 HClO + 2 HCl$$
$$\searrow$$
$$2 HCl + O_2$$

Because of this reaction, chlorine water is a good oxidizing agent.

If no oxidizable material is in contact with hypochlorous acid, its decomposition produces molecules of oxygen as shown by the above equation. However, if an oxidizable material is in contact

with the hypochlorous acid, the liberated oxygen combines directly with the oxidizable material. In bleaching, the oxygen combines with the dye. If the dye can be oxidized to a colorless compound, it will be bleached successfully. However, if the dye cannot be oxidized to a colorless compound, it will not be bleached. Hypochlorous acid will not bleach all dyes or destroy all colors; many dyestuffs are not affected by it at all. Hypochlorous acid usually removes natural colors. It bleaches spots made by ordinary ink, because the resulting compounds are white or pale-colored oxides. It does not affect printers' ink because it cannot oxidize the carbon in this kind of ink.

The bleaching action of chlorine in water (actually of the hypochlorous acid produced) and that of peroxides is similar (see Chapter 10, Section 12). Both decompose and liberate oxygen, which is the actual bleaching agent. Dry chlorine will not act as a bleach.

11. The uses of chlorine.

1. For bleaching. In bleaching cotton goods, the cloth is first boiled in a dilute solution of sodium hydroxide to remove any wax from the fibers. The strip of cloth is then drawn through several vats in succession. The first and third vats contain a bleaching solution, and the second and fourth ones contain dilute sulfuric acid. A bleaching solution of chlorine in water or one of sodium hypochlorite, NaClO, is usually used. The actual bleaching action occurs as the dilute sulfuric acid liberates hypochlorous acid from the bleaching solution absorbed in the fibers of the cloth. The final vat contains an antichlor such as sodium thiosulfate, $Na_2S_2O_3$, to remove the last traces of chlorine which might be left in the cloth. The strip of cloth is then washed, ironed, and rolled.

Many commercial bleaches for home use are now available. Bleaching solutions are generally solutions of sodium hypochlorite. They are made by electrolyzing sodium chloride, and allowing the liberated chlorine to mix with the sodium hydroxide being produced, or they may be made by the reaction between chlorine and sodium carbonate. Dry powdered chlorine bleaches are also available. They generally contain sodium hypochlorite, also.

CAUTION: Chlorine destroys silk or wool fibers. *Commercial bleaches containing hypochlorites must never be used on silk or wool.*

2. *As a disinfectant.* Since moist chlorine is a good oxidizing agent, it destroys bacteria. Large quantities of chloride of lime, $Ca(ClO)Cl$, are used annually as a disinfectant. This compound is made by passing chlorine gas into calcium hydroxide.

$$Ca(OH)_2 + Cl_2 \rightarrow Ca(ClO)Cl + H_2O$$

In city water systems, billions of gallons of water are treated with chlorine to kill disease-producing bacteria. The water in swimming pools is usually treated with chlorine to insure its safety for bathing. Chlorine is also sometimes used to kill bacteria in sewage before it is discharged into lakes or rivers, so the contamination from this source will be at a minimum.

3. *For making compounds.* Because chlorine combines directly with many metals and nonmetals it is used to produce many chlorides. Among these are chloroform, $CHCl_3$; carbon tetrachloride, CCl_4; aluminum chloride, Al_2Cl_6; and disulfur dichloride, S_2Cl_2.

12. The preparation of hydrogen chloride. In the laboratory, hydrogen chloride can be prepared by treating sodium chloride with sulfuric acid. The equation for this reaction is:

$$NaCl + H_2SO_4 \rightarrow NaHSO_4 + HCl \uparrow$$

This same reaction is used commercially, but it is carried out at a higher temperature. Under this condition, a second molecule of HCl may be produced if more NaCl is used.

$$2\,NaCl + H_2SO_4 \rightarrow Na_2SO_4 + 2\,HCl \uparrow$$

Hydrogen chloride is also prepared commercially by the direct union of hydrogen and chlorine which are both obtained by the electrolysis of concentrated sodium chloride solution (see Section 8 of this chapter).

Hydrogen chloride is dissolved in pure water, and sold under the name of hydrochloric acid. Technical grade hydrochloric acid is sometimes called *muriatic acid.*

13. The physical properties of hydrogen chloride. This gas is colorless, but it has a sharp, penetrating odor. It is denser than air and extremely soluble in water. One volume of water at 0° C will dissolve more than 500 volumes of the gas at standard pressure. Hydrogen chloride fumes in moist air. It is so soluble that it condenses water vapor from the air into minute drops of hydrochloric acid.

14. The chemical properties of hydrogen chloride. Hydrogen chloride is a stable compound which does not burn. Some vigorous oxidizing agents react with it to form water and chlorine.

Hydrogen chloride gas does not act as an acid except in the very broad modern sense that it may be a proton donor. Neither does the liquid which is formed by compressing and cooling the gas. But a water solution of the gas forms a strong acid known as *hydrochloric acid.* Hydrogen chloride is a polar covalent compound, but when it is dissolved in water the water dipoles cause it to ionize extensively, forming hydronium ions and chloride ions. Thus the solution has acid properties. The concentrated acid contains about 38% hydrogen chloride by weight, and it is about 1.2 times as dense as water. Hydrochloric acid is a

Fig. 26-8. **A steel strip being drawn from an acid pickling tank. The mixture of acids removes the oxide scale from the steel.** (Jones and Laughlin Steel)

typical nonoxidizing acid. It reacts with many metals and oxides of metals, and neutralizes hydroxides, forming salts and water.

15. The uses of hydrochloric acid. This acid is used in preparing some of the chlorides and in cleaning metals. Many metals must be freed from their oxides and other forms of tarnish before they can be galvanized, enameled, tinned, or plated with other metals. The process of removing such a scale is called *pickling.* The metals are immersed in a mixture of acids, such as hydrochloric and sulfuric, in varying proportions.

Some hydrochloric acid is essential in the process of digestion.

16. There are many chlorides. Theoretically, it is possible to form a chloride of almost any metal. The metallic chlorides form an important group of salts. Nearly all of them are crystalline compounds, and most of them are soluble in water. The chlorides of lead, silver, and mercury(I) are insoluble. Sodium chloride is used for food preservation and seasoning. It is also a very important chemical raw material. Aluminum chloride is employed as a catalyst in the "cracking" of petroleum to increase the yield of gasoline. The tetrachlorides of silicon and titanium are used to make smoke screens. They are also used to produce the smoke used in sky writing. These compounds hydrolyze almost completely in moist air. The hydrogen chloride which is formed by such hydrolysis condenses the moisture of the air and forms a mist. Chlorides of carbon, sulfur, and phosphorus have some important applications. Carbon tetrachloride is just as efficient as gasoline for removing grease spots from clothing, and it has the advantage of being non-flammable. However, good ventilation is required where it is used because its vapors are poisonous. Disulfur dichloride, S_2Cl_2, is used in one process for vulcanizing rubber.

17. The test for a chloride. The test for a soluble chloride is based on the insolubility of silver chloride. Silver nitrate is added to the solution to be tested for chloride ions. The formation of a white precipitate which is soluble in ammonia-water solution, but is reprecipitated when excess nitric acid is added, is a test for the chloride ion.

The ionic equations for the reactions involved in the test for the chloride ion are:

1. Forming the white silver chloride precipitate:

$$Ag^+ + Cl^- \rightarrow Ag^+Cl^- \downarrow$$

2. Dissolving the silver chloride in ammonia-water solution:

$$Ag^+Cl^- + 2 NH_3 \rightarrow Ag(NH_3)_2^+ + Cl^-$$

3. Reprecipitating the silver chloride by adding nitric acid:

$$Ag(NH_3)_2^+ + Cl^- + 2 H_3O^+ + 2 NO_3^- \rightarrow$$
$$Ag^+Cl^- \downarrow + 2 NH_4^+ + 2 NO_3^- + 2 H_2O$$

3. BROMINE

18. The occurrence and discovery of bromine. Several bromides, particularly those of sodium and magnesium, are found in nature. For many years the chief source of bromine was the *mother liquor* left after sodium chloride had been extracted from the brine of salt wells. Now, however, there is such a great demand for bromine in manufacturing antiknock fluids for gasoline that processes have been developed to extract it from sea water.

Bromine was discovered in 1826 by the French chemist Antoine-Jerome Balard (1802–1876). He produced bromine by treating the mother liquor of a natural brine with chlorine gas.

19. Bromine is produced from bromides. In the laboratory bromine can be prepared by using manganese dioxide, sulfuric acid, and sodium bromide. The equation

$$2 NaBr + MnO_2 + 2 H_2SO_4 \rightarrow$$
$$Na_2SO_4 + MnSO_4 + 2 H_2O + Br_2 \uparrow$$

shows that the method is exactly analogous to that for preparing chlorine.

The commercial extraction of bromine from sea water depends on the ability of chlorine to displace bromide ions from solution, as chlorine is more highly electronegative than bromine. The equation follows:

$$2 Br^- + Cl_2 \rightarrow 2 Cl^- + Br_2$$

Large quantities of acidified sea water are treated with chlorine. Bromine is liberated and then blown out of the solution by steam or air. It can be condensed directly, or it may be absorbed in sodium carbonate solution, from

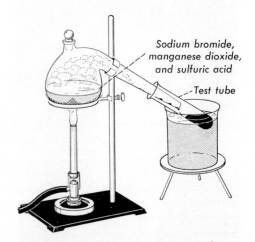

Fig. 26-9. **Bromine may be prepared in the laboratory by heating a mixture of sodium bromide, manganese dioxide, and sulfuric acid in a glass-stoppered retort.**

Fig. 26-10. **An aerial view of a large plant for the extraction of bromine from sea water. The water enters the plant through the flume at the left. The two large rectangular buildings contain the bromine extraction units. In these buildings the sea water is chlorinated and exposed to an air blast that blows out the bromine. In the cylindrical absorption towers just beyond, the bromine is recovered from the air blast. (Dow Chemical)**

which it can be recovered by treatment with sulfuric acid. A similar reaction is used to extract bromine from bromides found in salt wells of Michigan, Ohio, and West Virginia. Bromine may also be prepared by electrolysis of soluble bromides.

20. The physical properties of bromine. Bromine and mercury are the only elements which are liquid at room temperature. Bromine is a dark-red liquid which is about three times as dense as water. It evaporates readily, forming a vapor which is very irritating to the eyes and throat, and very disagreeable in odor. Bromine is moderately soluble in water. Its reddish-brown solution is used in the laboratory under the name of bromine water. It is readily soluble in carbon tetrachloride, carbon disulfide, and in water solutions of bromides.

CAUTION: *Great care must be used in handling bromine; it burns* the flesh and forms wounds which heal slowly.

21. The chemical properties of bromine. Bromine is not as electronegative as chlorine. It unites with hydrogen with difficulty to form hydrogen bromide. It combines with some metals to form bromides. When it is moist, it is a good bleaching agent. Its water solution is a good oxidizing agent, and forms hydrobromic acid and oxygen in the presence of sunlight.

22. The preparation and properties of hydrogen bromide. Pure hydrogen bromide is prepared by the hydrolysis of phosphorus tribromide, as shown in the equation:

$$PBr_3 + 3\,H_2O \rightarrow H_3PO_3 + 3\,HBr \uparrow$$

If we try to prepare hydrogen bromide by a reaction similar to the laboratory preparation of hydrogen chloride, some HBr is formed.

$$NaBr + H_2SO_4 \rightarrow NaHSO_4 + HBr \uparrow$$

However, since hydrogen bromide is a less stable compound than hydrogen chloride, some of it is oxidized by the warm sulfuric acid. The hydrogen bromide is therefore contaminated with sulfur dioxide and free bromine.

Hydrogen bromide dissolves in water to form hydrobromic acid, a strong acid.

23. Several bromides are useful. The bromides of sodium and potassium are employed in medicine as sedatives but they should not be used unless prescribed by a physician. Silver bromide, AgBr, is a yellowish solid which is extensively used as the sensitive salt for making photographic films or plates. Ethylene bromide, $C_2H_4Br_2$, is used to increase the efficiency of lead tetraethyl, $Pb(C_2H_5)_4$, in making antiknock gasoline. Methyl bromide is more toxic to insect larvae and moths than hydrocyanic acid. Xylyl bromide, when present to the extent of only two or three parts per million of air, will cause a copious flow of tears. Bromine compounds, such as xylyl bromide and bromacetone, have been used as tear gases. Other organic bromine compounds are used in the manufacture of dyestuffs.

24. The test for a soluble bromide. Bromine is very soluble in carbon tetrachloride, to which it imparts an orange-red color; chlorine will displace bromine from a bromide. These two facts are used in testing for soluble bromides.

To the solution to be tested for a bromide some carbon tetrachloride, and several milliliters of chlorine water are added and the mixture is shaken vigorously. If *bromide* ions were present, *bromine* molecules are set free by the chlorine. The bromine, being much more soluble in carbon tetrachloride than it is in water, leaves the water. It dissolves mostly in the carbon tetrachloride to which it imparts an orange-red color. The carbon tetrachloride does not mix with the water, but forms a separate layer below the water. While it is Br_2 *molecules* which color the carbon tetrachloride when the test is positive, the only form in which bromine could have existed and be oxidized to free bromine by chlorine was as *Br^- ions*. Therefore, a positive test indicates the presence of bromide ions in the original solution.

4. IODINE

25. The discovery and occurrence of iodine. The element iodine was discovered in 1811 by Bernard Courtois (1777–1838), a French chemist. He noticed the purplish vapor of iodine while investigating the ashes from seaweeds. For many years nearly all iodine was extracted from seaweeds.

At present, the most important domestic source of iodine is the iodides found in California oil well brines. The iodine is liberated from the brine by treatment with chlorine. Some iodine is obtained from Chile, where it is found in the nitrate deposits as sodium iodate, $NaIO_3$.

26. The preparation of iodine. The laboratory preparation of iodine is similar to that of chlorine and bromine. An iodide is heated with manganese dioxide and sulfuric acid.

$$2\,NaI + MnO_2 + 2\,H_2SO_4 \rightarrow$$
$$Na_2SO_4 + MnSO_4 + 2\,H_2O + I_2 \uparrow$$

The iodine is driven off as a vapor. It may be condensed as a solid upon the walls of a cold dish or beaker.

Either chlorine or bromine may be used to displace iodine from a soluble iodide.

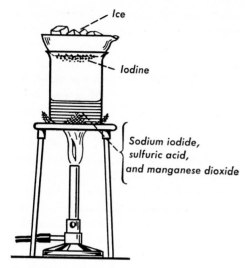

Fig. 26-11. **Iodine is prepared in the laboratory by heating sodium iodide and manganese dioxide with sulfuric acid.**

$$2 \text{ NaI} + \text{Cl}_2 \rightarrow 2 \text{ NaCl} + \text{I}_2$$
$$2 \text{ NaI} + \text{Br}_2 \rightarrow 2 \text{ NaBr} + \text{I}_2$$

27. The physical properties of iodine. Iodine is a steel-gray solid. When heated, it sublimes, or vaporizes without melting, and produces a beautiful violet-colored vapor. The odor of this vapor is irritating, resembling that of chlorine.

Iodine is very slightly soluble in water, but it is much more soluble in water solutions of sodium or potassium iodide with which it forms the complex I_3^- ion. It dissolves readily in alcohol, forming a dark-brown solution. It is very soluble in carbon disulfide and carbon tetrachloride, to which it imparts a rich purple color. Free iodine colors starch paste blue. This color change, caused by some of the iodine being adsorbed on the surface of the starch particles, serves as a test for free iodine. Conversely, an iodine solution may be used to test for starch.

28. The chemical properties of iodine. Iodine is active chemically, though less so than either bromine or chlorine. It combines with metals to form iodides, and it may also unite with some non-metals. If a crystal of iodine is placed on a small piece of white phosphorus, the two elements unite spontaneously with the liberation of light and heat.

29. The uses for iodine. Iodine is used for making certain iodides, especially AgI which is used in photography. It is also used as an antiseptic for cuts and open wounds. Surgeons sometimes use a tincture of iodine to sterilize the skin before making an incision during an operation.

CAUTION: *Iodine is poisonous if taken internally.* Starch paste or starchy foods may be used as an antidote. If a bottle containing tincture of iodine is left unstoppered, some of the solvent will evaporate. The more concentrated tincture which is left may blister the skin. Blistering may also result if a bandage or dressing is placed on the skin after the iodine is applied, or if a second application is used.

30. The preparation of hydrogen iodide. Very little hydrogen iodide is obtained by heating a mixture of an iodide and sulfuric acid because hydrogen iodide is even less stable than hydrogen bromide. It decomposes and reduces the sulfuric acid to sulfur dioxide, sulfur, or even hydrogen sulfide. Any hydrogen iodide which might escape decomposition would be contaminated with iodine and the decomposition products of sulfuric acid. Pure hydrogen iodide may be prepared by hydrolysis of phosphorus tri-iodide:

$$\text{PI}_3 + 3 \text{ H}_2\text{O} \rightarrow \text{H}_3\text{PO}_3 + 3 \text{ HI} \uparrow$$

Hydrogen iodide is a colorless gas which dissolves in water and forms hydriodic acid.

31. The uses of iodides. Potassium iodide, KI, finds some use in medicine. Iodine is present in the thyroid gland of the body. The thyroid manufactures the iodine-containing compound, *thyroxine*, which controls the rate at which the body uses food energy. If the diet is deficient in iodine, the thyroid gland may become enlarged. This condition is known as simple goiter. Iodine compounds may be added to the water in certain localities where simple goiter is common. Either sodium iodide, NaI, or potassium iodide, KI, is added to common salt to make *iodized salt*. Silver iodide, AgI, finds some use in photography. Di-iodine pentoxide, I_2O_5, is used as an indicator to detect the presence of carbon monoxide, and to determine its amount. Iodoquinine sulfate, is used in making Polaroid light-polarizing film.

32. The test for soluble iodides. To the solution to be tested, a few milliliters of carbon tetrachloride and a few milliliters of chlorine water are added, and the mixture is shaken vigorously. If an iodide was present, the carbon tetrachloride globule which sinks to the bottom is colored purple due to the presence of free iodine. Here again, as in the test for bromides, the liberation of the *free halogen* constitutes a positive test for the presence of the corresponding *halogenide ion* in the solution tested.

SUMMARY

The Halogen Family consists of the highly electronegative elements, fluorine, chlorine, bromine, iodine, and astatine. Each of these has seven electrons in its outermost shell. None occurs free in nature. In the elementary state they exist as covalent molecules.

Fluorine is prepared by the electrolysis of a mixture of potassium fluoride and hydrogen fluoride. The other three common halogens are prepared in the laboratory by oxidizing their binary acids with manganese dioxide. Commercially, chlorine is made by the electrolysis of brine; bromine is extracted from sea water; and iodine is obtained from oil well brines.

Hydrogen fluoride and hydrogen chloride are prepared by treating a salt of the acid with sulfuric acid. Hydrogen bromide and hydrogen iodide are prepared by the hydrolysis of phosphorus tribromide and phosphorus triiodide. Hydrogen fluoride molecules associate by hydrogen bonding. Each of the hydrogen halogenides is a colorless gas which is ionized in water solution.

Fluorine compounds are used for etching glass. Chlorine is used for bleaching, disinfecting, and for making chlorides. Bromine is used in the dye industry, for making medicines, in photography, and for making antiknock gasoline. Iodine is used in photography and in medicine.

TEST YOURSELF ON THESE TERMS

antichlor	fluorspar	iodized salt
bleaching action	Freon	mother liquor
chloride of lime	halogen	muriatic acid
cryolite	Hooker cell	pickling

QUESTIONS

Group A

1. What does the term *halogen* mean?
2. (*a*) What kind of container must be used for fluorine? (*b*) For hydrofluoric acid?
3. What are the most important uses for hydrofluoric acid?
4. Describe the physiological effects of chlorine.
5. (*a*) Define combustion. (*b*) Must oxygen be present for combustion to occur? Explain.
6. What is an *antichlor*?
7. What method of collection is used when preparing hydrogen chloride in the laboratory?
8. How can you test an unknown solution for the chloride ion?
9. Why is bromine produced in large quantities today?
10. What are the physical properties of bromine?
11. (*a*) What is xylyl bromide? (*b*) For what is it used?
12. What is the most important source of iodine in the United States?
13. What is the danger of using tincture of iodine that has been in the medicine cabinet for several years?
14. (*a*) For what purpose does the body require iodine? (*b*) From what sources may it be obtained?
15. Why are none of the halogens found free in nature?
16. List the halogens in order of increasing activity.
17. Compare the ionic characters of the bonds between hydrogen and each of the four common halogens.
18. Why are sodium chloride and calcium chloride ionic salts, while aluminum chloride is molecular?

Group B

19. Why do hydrogen fluoride molecules exhibit hydrogen bonding?
20. Write the equation for the preparation of fluorine from hydrogen fluoride by electrolysis.
21. What is Freon?
22. Describe the process of placing the graduations on a buret.
23. Why must the hydrogen, chlorine, and sodium hydroxide produced in a Hooker cell be kept separated from each other?
24. Write the equation for the laboratory preparation of chlorine from manganese dioxide and hydrochloric acid.
25. (*a*) For which does chlorine have greater affinity, carbon or hydrogen? (*b*) What experimental evidence can you give to support your answer?
26. (*a*) Why is freshly prepared chlorine water yellow-green in color? (*b*) Why does it become colorless after standing in sunlight?
27. What element does the bleaching when chlorine is used as a bleach?
28. Is liquid hydrogen chloride an acid? Explain.
29. What type of chemical reaction is involved in the commercial preparation of bromine from sea water?
30. Why is it not possible to prepare pure hydrogen bromide from sodium bromide and sulfuric acid?

31. What constitutes a positive test for bromide ions in a solution?

32. Compare the colors of: (*a*) solid iodine; (*b*) iodine in alcohol; (*c*) iodine in carbon tetrachloride; (*d*) iodine vapor.

33. The reactions between water molecules and molecules of the hydrogen halogenides to form hydronium ions and halogenide ions are reversible reactions. (*a*) Qualitatively, at equilibrium, what are the relative concentrations of the particles involved? (*b*) What does this indicate about the relative stability of the hydrogen halogenide molecules compared with the stability of the ions which can be formed from them?

PROBLEMS

Group A

1. What weight of sodium hydroxide is formed while making 710. lb of chlorine by the electrolysis of sodium chloride?

2. A quantity of 10.0 g of bromine is needed for an experiment. What mass of sodium bromide is required to produce this bromine?

3. (*a*) What mass of calcium hydroxide is required for making 250. g of bleaching powder, $Ca(ClO)Cl$? (*b*) What mass of chlorine is also required?

4. Hydrogen bromide is to be prepared by hydrolysis of phosphorus tribromide. How much phosphorus tribromide is needed to produce 40.5 g of hydrogen bromide?

Group B

5. How many grams of hydrogen fluoride can be obtained when an excess of sulfuric acid acts on 390. g of calcium fluoride?

6. Calculate the percentage of bromine in ethylene bromide, $C_2H_4Br_2$.

7. How many liters of chlorine at S.T.P. can be obtained from 468 g of sodium chloride?

8. A laboratory experiment requires five 250.-ml bottles of chlorine, the gas being measured at S.T.P. What mass of sodium chloride will be required?

SOME THINGS FOR YOU TO DO

1. Test pieces of colored cotton cloth with commercial bleaching solution. How do the dyes compare in fastness?

2. Visit your community water purification plant and observe how chlorine is added to kill harmful bacteria.

3. Attach a metal plate to the negative terminal of a battery of two dry cells joined in series. Cover the plate with a sheet of filter paper, and then pour over the paper a dilute solution of starch paste to which a little potassium iodide solution has been added. Attach one end of a copper wire to the positive terminal of the battery, and use the free end of the wire to write in the starch paste. What happens? Explain the action.

Chapter 27 · SULFUR AND SULFIDES

1. SULFUR

1. The occurrence of sulfur. Sulfur is one of the elements known since ancient times. It is naturally associated with volcanic regions because considerable amounts of sulfur are mined in regions where volcanoes were formerly active. The sulfur mines in Sicily are of this type and have been worked for centuries. Japan and Mexico also produce some sulfur, but the United States is the greatest producer of sulfur for world markets. Sulfur occurs in nature as the free element or combined with other elements in sulfides and sulfates.

Immense deposits of nearly pure sulfur occur about 500 feet below the surface of the ground in Texas and Louisiana, near the Gulf of Mexico in a non-volcanic region. These deposits are now the world's greatest source of sulfur.

2. The mining of sulfur. The sulfur beds in Texas and Louisiana are as much as 200 feet thick. Between the surface of the ground and the sulfur there is a layer of quicksand which makes it difficult to sink a shaft to the sulfur so that it can be mined by the common methods.

Herman Frasch (1852–1914), an American chemist, devised a method to obtain the sulfur by driving pipes down through the quicksand to the sulfur beds below. Sulfur melts at 114.5° C, and water boils at 100° C under atmospheric pressure. Obviously, water at 100° C is not hot enough to melt sulfur. However, by heating water in a closed container, it can be raised to a much higher temperature without boiling. *Such water, heated above its normal boiling temperature under pressure, is **superheated** water.* Frasch found that superheated

VOCABULARY

Fungicide. A chemical material that kills non-green plants known as fungi.

Superheated water. Water heated under pressure to a temperature above its normal boiling point.

401

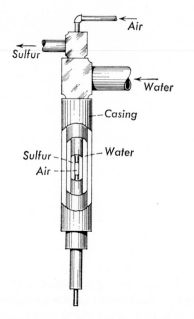

Fig. 27-1. **The system of concentric pipes used in the Frasch process of mining sulfur.**

water would melt the sulfur, which could then be raised to the surface by compressed air.

As a casing to protect the other pipes, a 12-inch pipe is driven down to the sulfur. Inside the casing are three concentric pipes, 6 inches, 3 inches, and 1 inch in diameter, respectively. Superheated water at a temperature of 170° C is forced down the 6-inch pipe and hot air down the 1-inch pipe. As a result, a foamy mass of melted sulfur, steam, and air is forced up the 3-inch pipe (the middle one) to the surface. Figure 27-1 shows the system of pipes used in this process. The melted sulfur flows into molds which may be as much as 100 feet long, 20 feet wide, and 50 feet high. After the sulfur has solidified, the sides of the mold are removed and the block is broken into pieces for shipment, as shown in Fig. 27-2.

Fig. 27-2. **Crude sulfur being loaded for shipment.** (Texas Gulf Sulphur)

3. The purification of sulfur. The sulfur obtained from Texas and Louisiana is about 99.5% pure. Further purification is, therefore, unnecessary for ordinary commercial purposes. When sulfur must be further purified, it is distilled in large iron retorts connected to a brick chamber. Some sulfur vapor condenses, forming a fine powder on the walls. This is called *flowers of sulfur*. A pool of liquid sulfur collects on the floor of the chamber. The liquid sulfur is poured into cylindrical molds, which, after cooling, yield *roll sulfur*.

4. The physical properties of sulfur. Common sulfur is a yellow, *odorless* solid which is practically insoluble in water and is twice as dense as water. It dissolves readily in carbon disulfide and in carbon tetrachloride. Sulfur is converted into soluble polysulfides by solutions of strong bases. When an acid is added to such a solution, *lac sulfur*, or *milk of sulfur* is precipitated as a fine white powder.

Sulfur melts at a temperature of 114.5° C, forming a pale-yellow mobile liquid. When it is heated to a still higher temperature, instead of becoming more mobile, as liquids usually do, it becomes thicker, or more viscous, and

does not flow freely. At a temperature of about 250° C, the melted sulfur becomes so thick that it hardly flows from an inverted tube. As the temperature rises, the color changes from a light yellow to a reddish-brown, and then almost to black. Near the boiling point the fluidity increases and the liquid again flows freely. Sulfur boils at 445° C. This unusual behavior is due to the existence of the different allotropic forms of liquid sulfur.

5. The allotropic forms of sulfur. Sulfur is in the same family of the Periodic Table as oxygen. Just as oxygen exists in the allotropic forms of oxygen and ozone, so sulfur also exists in several different solid and liquid allotropic forms. These are produced by different arrangements of groups of sulfur atoms. *1. Rhombic sulfur.* This form of solid sulfur is stable at ordinary temperatures. It consists of eight-membered puckered rings of sulfur atoms, as shown in Fig. 27-4. The sulfur atoms are connected in these rings by single covalent bonds. Crystals of rhombic sulfur may be prepared by dissolving roll sulfur in carbon disulfide, and then allowing the solvent to evaporate slowly. The specific gravity of rhombic sulfur is 2.06.

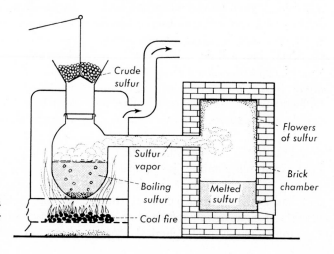

Fig. 27-3. **Crude sulfur can be freed from impurities by distillation.**

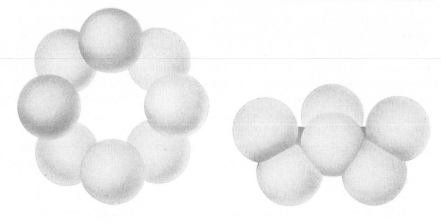

Fig. 27-4. **The structure of S_8 molecules of sulfur.**

2. *Monoclinic sulfur.* Sulfur can also be crystallized in the form of long needle-like monoclinic crystals that have two crystal axes at right angles to each other. The third axis is perpendicular to one of these but tilted toward the other. Monoclinic crystals can be prepared by first melting some sulfur in a crucible at as low a temperature as possible. It is next allowed to cool slowly until a crust just begins to form. If the crust is then broken and the liquid sulfur remaining poured off, a mass of monoclinic crystals will be found lining the walls of the crucible. Heat energy must be added to form this type of sulfur, and when such crystals cool below 95° C they gradually change back into the rhombic form. However, monoclinic sulfur still consists of eight-membered rings of sulfur atoms but in a different crystalline arrangement. The specific gravity of monoclinic sulfur is 1.96.

3. *λ-sulfur.* (*Lambda-sulfur.*) This is the liquid allotropic form of sulfur which is produced at temperatures just above the melting point of sulfur. It is quite fluid and has a straw-yellow color. It, too, consists of eight-membered rings of sulfur atoms. The almost spherical shape of these S_8 molecules enables them to roll over one another easily, and gives this form of sulfur its fluidity.

4. *μ-sulfur.* (*Mu-sulfur.*) If λ-sulfur is heated to about 200° C, it darkens to a reddish, and then almost black liquid. The molten sulfur becomes so thick and viscous that it will not flow. The heating imparts enough energy to the sulfur atoms to open some of the eight-membered rings. When a ring of sulfur atoms breaks open, the sulfur atoms on either side of the break are each left with an unshared electron. These sulfur atoms form bonds with similar sulfur atoms from other open rings, and produce long chains. These chains are another allotropic form of sulfur, μ-sulfur. The color of μ-sulfur arises from the greater absorption of light by electrons which formerly completed the ring structure but which are now free and migrate along the chain structure. The high viscosity of μ-sulfur is caused by the tangling of the chains of sulfur atoms. However, as the temperature is raised still further, these chains break up into smaller groups of atoms and the fluidity of the mass increases. The color becomes still darker because the break-

ing-up of the chains produces more free electrons.

Sulfur vapor, produced when sulfur boils at 445° C consists again of S_8 molecules. If sulfur vapor is heated to a higher temperature, these molecules gradually dissociate into S_2 molecules. Monatomic molecules of sulfur are produced at very high temperatures.

5. *Amorphous sulfur.* Amorphous sulfur is a rubbery, plastic mass that is made by pouring boiling sulfur into cold water. It is dark-brown, or even black in color, and is elastic, like rubber. At the boiling point of sulfur, the long enmeshed chains have largely broken down, and the sulfur is fluid again. Eight-membered rings of sulfur atoms and chains are now in equilibrium. The S_8 rings are evaporating. When this boiling mixture is suddenly cooled, the chains of μ-sulfur have no time to reform into rings, and amorphous sulfur is produced. A mass of amorphous sulfur soon loses its elasticity, becoming hard and brittle. In the cooled amorphous sulfur the transformations into successive allotropic forms proceed in reverse order. Finally, it once again becomes the S_8 ring configuration of the stable rhombic variety. Amorphous sulfur is insoluble in carbon disulfide.

6. The chemical properties of sulfur. At room temperature, sulfur is not very active chemically. When heated, it unites with oxygen to produce sulfur dioxide.

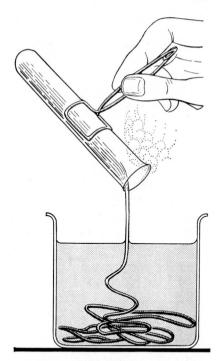

Fig. 27-6. **The sudden cooling of mu-sulfur produces amorphous sulfur.**

$$S + O_2 \rightarrow SO_2 \uparrow$$

Traces of sulfur trioxide, SO_3, are also formed when sulfur burns in air. Sulfur can be made to combine with nonmetals such as hydrogen, carbon, and chlorine, but such compounds are formed with some difficulty, and are not very stable. The differences in electronegativity between sulfur and hydrogen, carbon, and chlorine are so small that the bonding in such compounds is predominantly covalent.

Fig. 27-5. **A chain of sulfur atoms as found in mu-sulfur.**

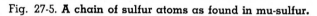

SIMILARITIES BETWEEN SULFUR AND OXYGEN

Hydrogen sulfide	H_2S	Hydrogen oxide	H_2O
Carbon disulfide	CS_2	Carbon dioxide	CO_2
Copper(I) sulfide	Cu_2S	Copper(I) oxide	Cu_2O
Copper(II) sulfide	CuS	Copper(II) oxide	CuO
Mercury(II) sulfide	HgS	Mercury(II) oxide	HgO
Zinc sulfide	ZnS	Zinc oxide	ZnO

From the formulas SO_3, SO_2, and H_2S, we see that sulfur may have an oxidation number of $+6$, or $+4$ when it combines with oxygen, and of -2 when it combines with hydrogen. Electron-dot formulas for these compounds are shown below. Notice that the actual molecules of sulfur trioxide and sulfur dioxide are resonance hybrids of the possible structures given.

Sulfur trioxide

Sulfur dioxide   Hydrogen sulfide

Sulfur is similar to oxygen in the manner in which it combines with other elements, as can be seen by the table at the top of this page.

Powdered zinc and sulfur combine vigorously. The heat produced when iron filings and sulfur unite causes the whole mass to be heated to incandescence. Copper unites with the vapor of boiling sulfur to form copper(I) sulfide. If the oxide of any metal is insoluble, as a rule the sulfide of that metal is insoluble also.

7. Sulfur has many uses. This element is used in making sulfur dioxide, carbon disulfide, sulfuric acid, and other sulfur compounds. Several million tons are used annually in the manufacture of sulfuric acid. Matches, fireworks, and black gunpowder all contain either sulfur or sulfur compounds. Sulfur is also used in the preparation of certain dyes.

A mixture of four parts of sulfur and one part of lead arsenate makes an excellent fungicide for controlling blights, mildews, and other diseases of plants. Or, it may be used alone without lead arsenate. When sulfur is boiled with lime and water, it forms a red liquid which consists essentially of the polysulfides of calcium, such as CaS_x. This lime-sulfur solution is used widely to destroy scale insects, and also as a general fungicide.

Sulfur finds important uses in medicine. It is also used in the vulcanization of rubber. This process will be discussed in Chapter 44.

2. HYDROGEN SULFIDE

8. Hydrogen sulfide is formed by natural processes. Sulfur is present in some proteins. When such compounds decay, hydrogen sulfide is one of the products formed. The odor of decayed eggs is due to the formation of hydrogen sulfide. Coal is seldom entirely free from sulfur. As coal burns, sulfur dioxide and some traces of hydrogen sulfide pass off into the air. Some mineral waters also contain hydrogen sulfide.

9. The preparation of hydrogen sulfide. When hydrogen is bubbled through molten sulfur, some hydrogen sulfide is formed. The action is reversible, however, and is not practical for preparing hydrogen sulfide in any considerable quantity.

A metallic sulfide and either hydrochloric or sulfuric acid can be used to prepare hydrogen sulfide. Iron(II) sulfide, FeS, is suitable for the purpose. The following equations show that exchange reactions occur when these acids are used:

$$FeS + 2 HCl \rightarrow FeCl_2 + H_2S \uparrow$$
$$FeS + H_2SO_4 \rightarrow FeSO_4 + H_2S \uparrow$$

Hydrogen sulfide is a gas, and the exchange reactions go to completion. The gas is usually collected by upward displacement of air since it is denser than air and moderately soluble in water.

10. The physical properties of hydrogen sulfide. The gas is colorless, but it has the very disagreeable odor of decayed eggs. Hydrogen sulfide is poisonous when inhaled. When diluted with air, it causes nausea, headache, and dizziness. In concentrated form, it is a violent poison, which may cause death if inhaled.

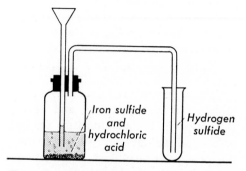

Fig. 27-7. **The laboratory method of preparing hydrogen sulfide.**

11. The chemical properties of hydrogen sulfide.

1. Hydrogen sulfide burns. When hydrogen sulfide burns, the products that are formed depend on the relative amounts of hydrogen sulfide and oxygen present. If an abundance of oxygen is available, 2 volumes of hydrogen sulfide react with 3 volumes of oxygen.

$$2 H_2S + 3 O_2 \rightarrow 2 SO_2 \uparrow + 2 H_2O \uparrow$$

When 2 volumes of hydrogen sulfide react with 2 volumes of oxygen, half the sulfur does not burn.

$$2 H_2S + 2 O_2 \rightarrow 2 H_2O \uparrow + SO_2 \uparrow + S \downarrow$$

If only 1 volume of oxygen is available for burning 2 volumes of hydrogen sulfide, the hydrogen combines with the oxygen, and all the sulfur is set free.

$$2 H_2S + O_2 \rightarrow 2 H_2O \uparrow + 2 S \downarrow$$

2. Hydrogen sulfide is a reducing agent. Because sulfide ions give up their electrons readily to oxidizing agents, hydrogen sulfide is a good reducing agent. To show the properties of hydrogen sulfide as a reducing agent, the gas may be bubbled through a solution of hydrogen peroxide. The oxygen in hydrogen peroxide is reduced from peroxide to oxide, while the sulfide ions are oxidized to sulfur in the form of a fine white powder which remains suspended in the water.

$$H_2O_2 + H_2S \rightarrow 2 H_2O + S \downarrow$$

3. Hydrogen sulfide forms a weak acid. When hydrogen sulfide dissolves in water, it forms a weak acid called hydrosulfuric acid. This weak acid turns blue litmus red, and neutralizes hydroxides to form sulfides and water.

$$Cu(OH)_2 + H_2S \rightarrow CuS \downarrow + 2 H_2O$$

4. Hydrogen sulfide acts on metals. The tarnishing of some metals is due to the formation of a coating of a sulfide of the metal. Such foods as eggs and mustard form enough hydrogen sulfide to produce a tarnish of black silver sulfide on silver tableware.

12. Some tests for the presence of a sulfide. Any soluble sulfide furnishes sulfide, $S^=$, ions in solution. Such ions unite with silver, lead, or copper to form a black precipitate. A drop of a soluble sulfide solution applied to a silver coin forms a brownish-black stain.

When hydrochloric acid is added to a moderately insoluble sulfide, hydrogen sulfide is set free. It can usually be recognized by its odor.

A strip of filter paper moistened with a solution of lead acetate, $Pb(C_2H_3O_2)_2$, quickly turns brownish-black when exposed to hydrogen sulfide in water solution or as a gas.

$$Pb(C_2H_3O_2)_2 + H_2S \rightarrow PbS \downarrow + 2 HC_2H_3O_2$$

13. Hydrogen sulfide is used in chemical analysis. Hydrogen sulfide is used frequently to analyze minerals or metals. When it is added to a solution containing the ions of certain metals, insoluble sulfides of those metals are deposited as precipitates.

$$Cu^{++} + S^= \rightarrow CuS \downarrow$$
$$2 As^{+++} + 3 S^= \rightarrow As_2S_3 \downarrow$$
$$Cd^{++} + S^= \rightarrow CdS \downarrow$$
$$2 Sb^{+++} + 3 S^= \rightarrow Sb_2S_3 \downarrow$$

Copper, lead, silver, mercury, and some other metals form black sulfides. The sulfides of arsenic and cadmium are yellow. Antimony sulfide is orange. Zinc sulfide is white in color. But analysis is not so easy as such facts may indicate, because it is possible to have in one solution the ions of several metals. If such a mixture is to be analyzed, it is necessary to separate the sulfides after they have been precipitated by finding reagents in which some of them will dissolve, but not the others. For example, the sulfides of zinc and manganese are soluble in dilute acids; the sulfides of arsenic and antimony are soluble in ammonium sulfide; the sulfides of copper and lead are soluble in hot dilute nitric acid, but mercury(II) sulfide is insoluble.

3. OTHER SULFIDES

14. Metallic sulfides are found in nature. Many important ores are found in nature as sulfides. Large quantities of copper sulfide are found in Montana. Zinc sulfide is one of the important sources of zinc; nearly all of our lead comes from lead sulfide. The sulfides of such metals as silver, nickel, arsenic, antimony, and iron are found in nature. Sulfides of iron are a source of sulfur and sulfur compounds, but are not important as a source of iron.

15. The preparation and properties of carbon disulfide. When sulfur vapor is passed over heated charcoal in an electric furnace, carbon and sulfur unite to form a vapor which condenses to an almost colorless liquid. Its formula is CS_2, analogous to that of carbon dioxide. The commercial product has a disagreeable odor, somewhat resembling boiled cabbage. The liquid does not mix with water. It has a very low kindling temperature and burns rapidly. Its vapor burns explosively when mixed with air.

$$CS_2 + 3 O_2 \rightarrow CO_2 \uparrow + 2 SO_2 \uparrow$$

Carbon disulfide is a good solvent for rubber, phosphorus, waxes, and resins. It is used in the manufacture of varnishes and matches, and in one step of the process of manufacture of viscose rayon. It is also used in the preparation of carbon tetrachloride.

SUMMARY

Sulfur occurs both free, and combined as sulfides and sulfates. It is mined in Texas and Louisiana by the Frasch process, and may be purified by distillation. It is marketed as lump sulfur, roll sulfur, flowers of sulfur, and lac sulfur.

Sulfur exists in several allotropic forms. The solid allotropes are rhombic, monoclinic, and amorphous sulfur. The liquid allotropes are lambda- and mu-sulfur. Ordinary sulfur is a yellow solid which is practically insoluble in water. It dissolves in carbon disulfide and in carbon tetrachloride. Sulfur is not very active chemically, but when heated with oxygen it burns with a blue flame and forms sulfur dioxide, with traces of sulfur trioxide. Zinc, iron, and copper unite with sulfur at elevated temperatures, forming sulfides of the metals. Sulfur is used for making sulfur dioxide, carbon disulfide, sulfuric acid, and other sulfur compounds.

Hydrogen sulfide is a foul-smelling, poisonous, combustible gas. It is produced when coal which contains sulfur as an impurity is burned. It reacts with silver, forming a black tarnish of silver sulfide. In water solution, it forms a weak acid known as hydrosulfuric acid, which reacts with metallic salts to form insoluble sulfides. It is used in analysis to detect the presence of metals.

The sulfides of many metals occur in nature. Some are important ores of the metals. Carbon disulfide is a good solvent for rubber and is used in making carbon tetrachloride.

TEST YOURSELF ON THESE TERMS

amorphous sulfur	lac sulfur	resonance hybrid
flowers of sulfur	λ-sulfur	rhombic sulfur
Frasch process	milk of sulfur	roll sulfur
fungicide	monoclinic sulfur	sulfides
hydrosulfuric acid	μ-sulfur	superheated water

QUESTIONS

Group A

1. Describe the location of the sulfur deposits in the United States.
2. (*a*) What is the odor of sulfur? (*b*) Of hydrogen sulfide?
3. (*a*) What is the formula for a molecule of rhombic sulfur? (*b*) Why do we not usually use this formula in equations?
4. (*a*) What is plastic sulfur? (*b*) How is it produced?
5. What are the uses of sulfur?
6. Write the formulas for: (*a*) iron(III) sulfide; (*b*) diarsenic pentasulfide; (*c*) copper(II) sulfide; (*d*) mercury(II) sulfide; (*e*) silver sulfide.
7. What use is made of sulfur in fungicides?

8. Describe two natural processes which release hydrogen sulfide into the air.
9. (*a*) Write the formula equation for the laboratory preparation of hydrogen sulfide. (*b*) What type of chemical reaction is this?
10. What metals have important sulfide ores?
11. (*a*) Give several uses for carbon disulfide. (*b*) What property of carbon disulfide is involved in each use?
12. (*a*) What is the function of the superheated water in the Frasch process? (*b*) The function of the compressed air? (*c*) Why is this process used instead of more conventional methods?

Group B

13. Distinguish between *flowers of sulfur* and *lac sulfur*.
14. Explain the changes in color and fluidity of sulfur between its melting point and boiling point.
15. A pupil prepared some nearly-black plastic sulfur in the laboratory. The next week when he examined it, it had become brittle and much lighter in color. Explain.
16. What is meant by *resonance?*
17. Draw electron-dot formulas to show the possible resonating structures in sulfur dioxide.
18. How are the products of combustion of hydrogen sulfide related to the amount of oxygen available?
19. Explain why there is usually a yellowish-white deposit on the ground around a sulfur spring.
20. Write equations to show the reactions between hydrogen sulfide and solutions of the chlorides of mercury, lead, and antimony.
21. (*a*) What are the characteristics of λ-sulfur? (*b*) Of μ-sulfur? (*c*) What explanation can you give for these differences?
22. Iron pyrites, or "fool's gold," has the formula FeS_2. How could you prove that it is not gold?
23. Look up the heat of formation of carbon disulfide in the Appendix. (*a*) What does this heat of formation tell you about the reaction by which it is prepared? (*b*) What does it tell you about the stability of carbon disulfide?
* 24. Balance the equation for the oxidation of hydrogen sulfide by hydrogen peroxide by the electron transfer method.

PROBLEMS

Group A

1. How many pounds of sulfur dioxide may be produced by burning 1.0 ton of pure sulfur?
2. What mass of iron(II) sulfide is required to prepare 170. g of hydrogen sulfide?
3. What volume of oxygen is required for the complete combustion of 5.0 liters of hydrogen sulfide?

Group B

4. Calculate the percentage composition of lead sulfide, PbS.
5. How many liters of carbon dioxide are formed by burning 39.0 g of carbon disulfide?
6. Calculate the mass in grams of 500. ml of hydrogen sulfide measured at 27° C and 740. mm pressure.

SOME THINGS FOR YOU TO DO

1. Write a report on the Frasch process for obtaining sulfur. Include some information about Frasch himself. Read your report to the class.
2. Bubble some hydrogen sulfide through solutions of chlorides of Co^{++}, Ni^{++}, Pb^{++}, Hg^{++}, Mn^{++}, Bi^{+++}, Sb^{+++}, Zn^{++}, Cu^{++}. If no precipitate is produced, add a little ammonia-water solution to the test tubes. Note the color of each sulfide produced.
3. Use some carbon disulfide outdoors to get rid of a pest such as a ground mole. Pour a few teaspoonfuls of the carbon disulfide down the burrow, and ignite it. Cover the burrow with earth to hold the suffocating gases within the burrow.
4. Consult an encyclopedia, college chemistry textbook, and recent scientific magazines to learn about the properties and uses of the other members of Group VI, selenium and tellurium.

Chapter 28 · THE OXIDES AND ACIDS OF SULFUR

1. THE OXIDES OF SULFUR

1. The occurrence of sulfur dioxide. Traces of sulfur dioxide may be found in the air for several reasons. Sulfur dioxide occurs in some volcanic gases and in some mineral waters. Coal contains sulfur as an impurity, and, as coal is burned, the sulfur is burned to sulfur dioxide. The heating of sulfide ores in the presence of air is the first step in extracting the metal from such ores. This process, called *roasting*, converts the sulfur of the ore into sulfur dioxide. The sulfur dioxide is sometimes expelled into the air, although modern smelting plants convert it into sulfuric acid.

2. The preparation of sulfur dioxide.

1. *By burning sulfur.* The simplest way to prepare sulfur dioxide is to burn sulfur in air or in pure oxygen. The gas produced by burning sulfur in air is mixed with nitrogen, but this is not objectionable for many operations.

$$S + O_2 \rightarrow SO_2 \uparrow$$

2. *By roasting sulfides.* Enormous quantities of sulfur dioxide are produced when sulfide ores are roasted. The roasting of *sphalerite*, ZnS, is typical.

$$2\,ZnS + 3\,O_2 \rightarrow 2\,ZnO + 2\,SO_2 \uparrow$$

Sulfur dioxide is a by-product in this operation. Iron pyrite, FeS_2, is roasted to produce sulfur dioxide for making sulfuric acid.

3. *By the reduction of sulfuric acid.* In one of the laboratory methods of preparing this gas, a rather inactive metal

such as copper is heated with concentrated sulfuric acid (see Fig. 28-1). The hot, concentrated acid is a vigorous oxidizing agent. The copper is oxidized and the sulfur in sulfuric acid is reduced. Sulfur dioxide, copper(II) sulfate, and water are the products.

$$Cu + 2 H_2SO_4 \rightarrow$$
$$CuSO_4 + 2 H_2O + SO_2 \uparrow$$

4. By the decomposition of sulfites. In this second laboratory method, pure sulfur dioxide may be prepared by the action of a strong acid on a sulfite. When sodium sulfite reacts with sulfuric acid, the following reaction occurs:

$$Na_2SO_3 + H_2SO_4 \rightarrow$$
$$Na_2SO_4 + H_2O + SO_2 \uparrow$$

Sulfurous acid, H_2SO_3, is first formed; it then decomposes into water and sulfur dioxide (see Fig. 28-2).

3. The physical properties of sulfur dioxide. Pure sulfur dioxide is a colorless gas with a suffocating, choking odor. It is more than twice as dense as air, and is very soluble in water. It is one of the easiest gases to liquefy, since it becomes

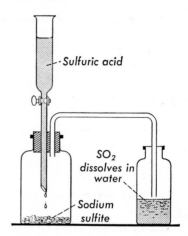

Fig. 28-2. **An acid added to a sulfite forms unstable sulfurous acid which decomposes into sulfur dioxide and water.**

liquid at room temperature under a pressure of about two atmospheres. Liquid sulfur dioxide is commercially available in steel cylinders.

4. The chemical properties of sulfur dioxide.
1. It is an acid anhydride. Sulfur dioxide is the anhydride of sulfurous acid. As it dissolves in water, it also reacts with the water:

$$H_2O + SO_2 \rightleftarrows H_2SO_3$$

This accounts, in part at least, for the high solubility of sulfur dioxide in water. Sulfurous acid is a weak acid, which will turn litmus paper red, neutralize hydroxides, and form bisulfites and sulfites. The reaction is reversible, and the acid decomposes into water and sulfur dioxide again when the water solution is warmed. A solution of sulfurous acid, if exposed to the air, will react slowly with oxygen and form sulfuric acid.

If sulfur dioxide is allowed to escape into the air in the waste gases from smelting or from any other chemical operations, it combines with moisture in the air and forms sulfurous acid. This

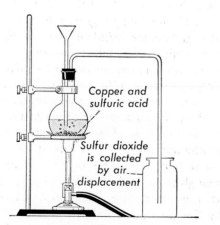

Fig. 28-1. **Sulfur dioxide may be prepared in the laboratory by reducing hot, concentrated sulfuric acid with copper.**

acid, if not neutralized by alkaline dust in the air, may be oxidized to sulfuric acid. If this falls as a mist on the earth, it may kill all of the plant life in the area.

2. *It is a stable gas.* Sulfur dioxide does not burn. In the presence of a suitable catalyst, it may be oxidized to sulfur trioxide.

$$2 SO_2 + O_2 \rightleftarrows 2 SO_3$$

5. The uses for sulfur dioxide and sulfurous acid.

1. *For making sulfuric acid.* Tremendous quantities of sulfur dioxide are oxidized to form sulfur trioxide which can be combined with water to form sulfuric acid (see Section 7).

2. *As a preservative.* Dried fruits, such as apricots and prunes, are treated with sulfur dioxide which acts as a preservative.

3. *In the petroleum industry.* Liquid sulfur dioxide is used in the treatment of kerosene and light lubricating oils.

4. *For making sulfites.* Sulfurous acid is diprotic and reacts with hydroxides to form bisulfites and sulfites.

5. *For bleaching.* Sulfurous acid does not harm the fibers of wool, silk, straw, and paper, and can be used to bleach them. It is believed that the sulfurous acid converts the colored compounds in these materials to white sulfites. The bleaching is not permanent, however, and the natural yellow color of the fiber reappears after some time.

6. *In preparing paper pulp.* Sulfurous acid reacts with limestone to form calcium hydrogen sulfite, $Ca(HSO_3)_2$. When wood chips are heated in this bisulfite solution, the lignin which binds the cellulose fibers together is dissolved, leaving the fibers unchanged. The fibers are then processed to form paper (see Chapter 43).

6. Sulfur trioxide. Sulfur trioxide, SO_3, is useful for one purpose—it is the anhydride of sulfuric acid. Therefore, it is an intermediate product in the manufacture of sulfuric acid. Sulfur trioxide is a white, crystalline solid at room temperature. It reacts with water to form sulfuric acid:

$$SO_3 + H_2O \rightarrow H_2SO_4$$

2. SULFURIC ACID

7. The preparation of sulfuric acid. Sulfuric acid is made by either the contact process or the chamber process. Between 75% and 80% of the sulfuric acid produced in the United States is made by the contact process; the remainder is made by the chamber process.

1. *The contact process.* In this process, sulfur dioxide may be prepared by burning sulfur or by roasting iron pyrites, FeS_2. Impurities which might poison the catalyst are then removed from the gas. The purified sulfur dioxide is mixed with air, and passed through heated iron pipes which contain the catalyst. This close "contact" of the sulfur dioxide and the catalyst gives the contact process its name. While in contact with the catalyst, the sulfur dioxide combines with the oxygen of the air mixed with it, to form sulfur trioxide. Divanadium pentoxide, V_2O_5, is now generally used as the catalyst (see Fig. 28-3).

The oxidation of sulfur dioxide is an exothermic process. It is carried out at about 400° C. This temperature is high enough to cause the reaction to proceed at a practical rate. The heat evolved by the reaction is used to preheat the entering reactants. This prevents the temperature in the catalyzer from becoming high enough to promote the de-

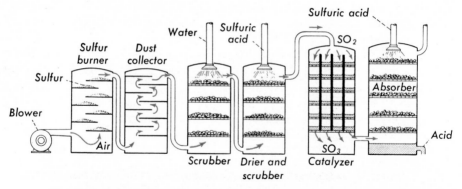

Fig. 28-3. **In making sulfuric acid by the contact process, sulfur is burned to form sulfur dioxide. The gas is freed from dust, scrubbed, dried, and passed through a catalyst where it is converted into sulfur trioxide. The sulfur trioxide is then absorbed in 97% sulfuric acid in which it is readily soluble.**

composition of the sulfur trioxide produced.

Gaseous sulfur trioxide does not unite readily with pure water. Consequently, sulfur trioxide is absorbed in 97% sulfuric acid, in which it is readily soluble. The sulfur trioxide combines with the 3% water and forms 100% sulfuric acid. Part of this may be drawn off, and the remainder diluted with water to make 97% acid for the absorption of more sulfur trioxide. Very pure, highly concentrated sulfuric acid is produced by the contact process.

★ *2. The chamber process.* This method is used for making sulfuric acid for commercial uses that do not require very pure or highly concentrated acid, especially for the production of superphosphate fertilizer. Sulfur dioxide is converted to sulfuric acid by the action of nitrogen dioxide, NO_2, and water.

$$H_2O + SO_2 + NO_2 \rightarrow H_2SO_4 + NO \uparrow$$

The nitrogen monoxide or nitrogen(II) oxide, NO, which is produced, is recovered. It is allowed to react with oxygen

to produce nitrogen dioxide for use over again.

$$2\,NO + O_2 \rightarrow 2\,NO_2 \uparrow$$

Thus the nitrogen monoxide serves as a *carrier* of oxygen, taking it from the air and giving it up to the sulfur dioxide to form sulfuric acid. The chemical reactions take place in huge lead-lined chambers into which steam is introduced. Concentrated sulfuric acid is used to dissolve the oxides of nitrogen and prevent their escape, so that they can be used again.

Let us refer to Fig. 28-4. The sulfur dioxide, which is formed by burning sulfur or by roasting iron pyrites, enters the Glover tower. As it rises through the tower, it meets a shower of moderately concentrated sulfuric acid mixed with oxides of nitrogen. The tower is filled with lumps of quartz, or some acid-resisting brick, to retard the upward flow of gas and expose it for a longer time to the sulfuric acid which trickles down. This is an example of the use of *countercurrents* in industrial chemistry. Some sulfuric acid is formed in the

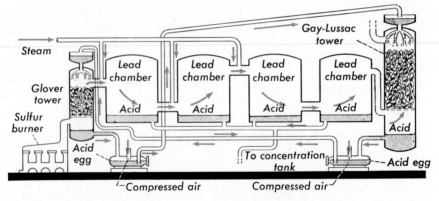

Fig. 28-4. **The chamber process for producing sulfuric acid is used to manufacture acid that is moderately concentrated and suitable for commercial use, but not chemically pure.**

Glover tower, and it becomes quite concentrated by the time it reaches the bottom of the tower. It is drawn off into a container called an *acid egg.*

The main reactions occur in the lead chambers, which may be 100 ft long, 40 ft high, and 20 ft wide. During the complicated reactions, the exact course of which chemists are not sure, sulfur dioxide, air, and oxides of nitrogen from the Glover tower react with steam introduced into the lead chamber to form sulfuric acid. The acid collects in the bottom of the lead chambers. Sulfuric acid does not react with the lead until it becomes fairly concentrated, about 75%. For certain industrial purposes, sulfuric acid of this strength is sufficient, and no further concentration is necessary.

Those reactions which are not completed in the first lead chamber are continued in the second, third, and fourth chambers. The Gay-Lussac tower is used to recover the oxides of nitrogen. In this tower, sulfuric acid which is made in the Glover tower and forced by compressed air from the acid egg to the top of this tower, trickles down over layers of coke. It meets the oxides of nitrogen and re-

acts with them forming nitrosylsulfuric acid, which remains dissolved in the excess sulfuric acid.

$$NO + NO_2 + 2\ H_2SO_4 \rightarrow$$
$$2\ SO_2(OH)(ONO) + H_2O$$

This mixture of acids, called "nitrose acid," flows into another acid egg. From this egg, the "nitrose acid" is forced to the top of the Glover tower where it is diluted with water which releases the oxides of nitrogen. While care is taken to prevent the loss of oxides of nitrogen, some must continually be replaced. They are prepared from ammonia, NH_3, by oxidation.

8. The physical properties of sulfuric acid. Concentrated sulfuric acid is a dense, oily liquid which is sometimes called *oil of vitriol.* The concentrated acid, which contains only about 2% water, has a specific gravity of about 1.84 and a boiling point of 338° C. Pure sulfuric acid is colorless, but commercial acid may have a yellow color, or it may be brown or almost black because of the presence of impurities, especially organic matter.

When sulfuric acid is added to water (*you must never add water to sulfuric acid*) a great deal of heat is evolved because of the formation of the hydrates $H_2SO_4 \cdot H_2O$ and $H_2SO_4 \cdot 2 H_2O$.

9. The chemical properties of sulfuric acid.

1. Its acid properties. Sulfuric acid, being a diprotic acid, ionizes in dilute water solution in two stages:

$$H_2SO_4 + H_2O \rightleftarrows H_3O^+ + HSO_4^-$$
$$HSO_4^- + H_2O \rightleftarrows H_3O^+ + SO_4^=$$

At 18° C, 0.1-N H_2SO_4 is 90% ionized in the first stage and 60% ionized in the second stage. Sulfuric acid can react with hydroxides to form bisulfates and sulfates. It reacts with metals and with the oxides of metals. Because it is more highly ionized, *dilute* sulfuric acid reacts with metals above hydrogen in the activity series more vigorously than *cold, concentrated* sulfuric acid does.

2. Its oxidizing properties. Hot, concentrated sulfuric acid is a vigorous oxidizing agent. The sulfur is reduced from the +6 oxidation state to the +4 or −2 oxidation state depending on the strength of the acid and the reducing agent with which it reacts. Thus with copper, sulfur dioxide is produced (see Section 2). With zinc and hot, slightly diluted acid, hydrogen sulfide is the gaseous product.

$$4 Zn + 5 H_2SO_4 \rightarrow$$
$$4 ZnSO_4 + H_2S \uparrow + 4 H_2O$$

3. Its dehydrating properties. The strong affinity of sulfuric acid for water makes it an excellent *dehydrating* agent. Gases may be dried by bubbling them through concentrated sulfuric acid. Lumps of pumice stone soaked in sulfuric acid may be used in the lower part of a desiccator. In fact, sulfuric acid is such an active dehydrating agent that it will take hydrogen and oxygen, in the proportion

needed to form water, from such substances as sugar, $C_{12}H_{22}O_{11}$, or cellulose, $(C_6H_{10}O_5)_n$, leaving the carbon uncombined.

$$C_{12}H_{22}O_{11} + 11 H_2SO_4 \rightarrow$$
$$12 C + 11 H_2SO_4 \cdot H_2O$$

In the same manner, concentrated sulfuric acid chars wood, paper, cotton, starch, and other organic compounds.

In making some products commercially, water is formed as a by-product. Let us illustrate this with the reaction for making nitroglycerin, $C_3H_5(NO_3)_3$.

$$C_3H_5(OH)_3 + 3 HNO_3 \rightarrow$$
$$C_3H_5(NO_3)_3 + 3 H_2O$$

In the manufacture of this explosive, concentrated nitric acid is used. Since the nitric acid is reacting with a non-electrolyte, the reaction is slow. To prevent dilution of the acid, which would cause the reaction to proceed still more slowly, sulfuric acid is always mixed with the nitric acid. The sulfuric acid acts as a dehydrating agent. It absorbs the water as fast as it is formed and thus maintains the rate of the reaction. This same principle is applied to many other reactions involving nonelectrolytes where water, formed as a product, would slow down the rate of reaction.

Fig. 28-5. The floor plan of a chamber process sulfuric acid plant.

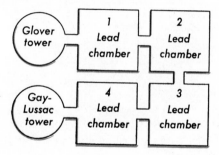

In the laboratory preparation of carbon monoxide, sulfuric acid is used to dehydrate formic acid (see Chapter 17, Section 10).

CAUTION: *Sulfuric acid burns the flesh severely.* Great care must be used in the handling of sulfuric acid so that it does not come in contact with the skin.

10. The uses of sulfuric acid. Calcium phosphate, $Ca_3(PO_4)_2$, is quarried in great amounts in Florida, Tennessee, and other states, for use as a fertilizer. The rock phosphate, even when finely pulverized, is too insoluble to be of immediate use to growing plants. Sulfuric acid is used to convert the rock phosphate into a more soluble product. About four million tons of the acid are used each year to make *superphosphate* fertilizer.

Sulfuric acid is used also in the preparation of other acids and various sulfates. For example, hydrochloric acid may be made by treating common salt with sulfuric acid. Copper(II) sulfate, sodium aluminum sulfate (alum), and iron(II) sulfate have wide uses. Many other chemicals are made from sulfuric acid.

The iron and steel industries use large quantities of sulfuric acid to remove a coating of oxide from the surface of iron or steel before the metal is plated, or before it is coated with an enamel. Bathtubs are "pickled" in sulfuric acid before being glazed. The enamelware used for kitchen utensils is similarly treated.

Sulfuric acid is used in the refining of petroleum products to remove certain organic impurities. The electrolyte in automobile batteries is usually dilute sulfuric acid.

Sulfuric acid is necessary in the manufacture of many explosives. It serves as a dehydrating agent in the production of smokeless powder and nitroglycerin. It is used in the manufacture of photographic film, in making nitrocellulose plastics, in manufacturing rayon, paints and pigments, cellophane, and in innumerable articles of commerce.

11. Some sulfates are important. Sulfuric acid reacts with many metals to form sulfates. Some of the most important sulfates are those of copper, iron, zinc, calcium, barium, and aluminum. Copper(II) sulfate is used in copper plating and to produce mordants in dyeing. Iron(II) sulfate finds use in water purification and in the manufacture of ink. Zinc sulfate is used to make lithopone, a white paint pigment. Hydrated calcium sulfate is the mineral gypsum. Barium sulfate and aluminum sulfate are used in preparing other compounds of these elements. Nearly all sulfates are soluble in water, those of calcium, strontium, barium, and lead(II) being the

Fig. 28-6. **An aerial view of a plant for producing contact process sulfuric acid. Note the stockpile of sulfur at the top of the picture; the maze of tanks, pipes, and buildings of the plant itself; and the storage tanks where the sulfuric acid is kept before being transferred to the waiting railroad cars. (Allied Chemical and Dye)**

chief exceptions. The bisulfates are not very important.

12. The test for a sulfate. When a solution of barium chloride is added to sulfuric acid or to any soluble sulfate, a white precipitate of barium sulfate is formed.

$$Ba^{++} + SO_4^= \rightarrow BaSO_4 \downarrow$$

Barium sulfate is insoluble in hydrochloric acid. White precipitates of barium oxalate or barium phosphate which might be confused with the barium sulfate precipitate are soluble in hydrochloric acid. Thus the addition of hydrochloric acid when performing the test prevents the formation of these interfering precipitates.

Fig. 28-7. **When a white precipitate that is insoluble in hydrochloric acid is formed after the addition of barium chloride solution, the presence of a sulfate is indicated.**

SUMMARY

Sulfur dioxide may be prepared: *1.* by burning sulfur; *2.* by roasting sulfides; *3.* by the reduction of sulfuric acid; *4.* by the decomposition of sulfites. It is a dense, suffocating gas that is extremely soluble in water and is easily liquefied. Sulfur dioxide is the anhydride of sulfurous acid. It does not burn and is a fairly stable compound. In the presence of a suitable catalyst, sulfur dioxide can be oxidized to sulfur trioxide.

Sulfur dioxide is used for making sulfuric acid and sulfites. It is used as a preservative, for treating kerosene and light oils, for bleaching, and in preparing paper pulp.

Sulfur trioxide is useful as the anhydride of sulfuric acid.

Sulfuric acid may be made by the contact process or by the chamber process. It is a dense, oily liquid which mixes with water in all proportions. When dilute it acts as an acid; when hot and concentrated, it is a vigorous oxidizing agent. It is also a good dehydrating agent. Sulfuric acid is one of the most important industrial chemicals. Many sulfates are common chemical compounds.

TEST YOURSELF ON THESE TERMS

acid anhydride	countercurrents	roasting
bisulfate	dehydrating agent	sulfate
bisulfite	diprotic acid	sulfite
carrier	divanadium pentoxide	sulfuric acid
chamber process	"nitrose" acid	sulfurous acid
contact process	oil of vitriol	superphosphate

Group A

1. From what sources does sulfur dioxide as an impurity in the air come?
2. What is mean by *roasting* an ore?
3. Write balanced chemical equations for: (*a*) a commercial preparation of sulfur dioxide; (*b*) a laboratory preparation of sulfur dioxide.
4. (*a*) What method of gas collection is used in a laboratory preparation of sulfur dioxide? (*b*) What properties of sulfur dioxide determine this choice?
5. What is the principal use for sulfur dioxide?
6. Why is the contact process for producing sulfuric acid so named?
7. Compare contact sulfuric acid with chamber sulfuric acid.
8. Why is sulfur trioxide absorbed in sulfuric acid rather than in water in the contact process?
9. What is the proper method of diluting sulfuric acid?
10. Why are large quantities of sulfuric acid used in the iron and steel industry?
11. Name four important sulfates and give their uses.
12. Give two reasons why boiling concentrated sulfuric acid burns the flesh so badly.

Group B

13. Is sulfur dioxide easy to liquefy or hard to liquefy? Explain.
14. Why is sulfur dioxide so soluble in water?
15. How does nitrogen monoxide act as a carrier of oxygen in the chamber process?
16. Why is a mixture of nitric acid *and sulfuric acid* used in making nitroglycerin?
17. Write balanced chemical equations to show the formation from sulfurous acid and sodium hydroxide of: (*a*) sodium hydrogen sulfite; (*b*) sodium sulfite.
18. How is sulfuric acid used in making superphosphate?
19. How can you test a soluble salt to determine whether it is a sulfate?
20. What is meant by the *countercurrent principle* in industrial processes?
21. Compare the bleaching action of sulfur dioxide with that of hydrogen peroxide.
22. Explain the heat exchange needed in the catalyst chamber of a contact sulfuric acid plant.
23. What is the function of the Gay-Lussac tower in the chamber process?
★24. Using the electron-transfer method, balance the following equation:
$$Hg + H_2SO_4 \rightarrow HgSO_4 + SO_2 \uparrow + H_2O$$
25. What is the purpose of the concentrated hydrochloric acid in the test for a soluble sulfate?
26. Why must boiling concentrated sulfuric acid be handled with extreme care?
★27. Balance the following oxidation-reduction equation:
$$Cu_2S + O_2 \rightarrow Cu_2O + SO_2$$

PROBLEMS

Group A

1. How many pounds of sulfuric acid can be prepared from 1.00 ton of sulfur that is 99.5% pure?
2. How many liters of sulfur dioxide may be produced by the roasting of 1200. kg of iron pyrites, FeS_2?
3. If 140. lb of scrap iron is added to a large vat of dilute sulfuric acid, how many pounds of iron(II) sulfate can be produced?
4. Calculate the percentage composition of H_2SO_4.

Group B

5. How many grams of sodium sulfite are required for the production of 1.00 liter of sulfur dioxide by reaction with sulfuric acid?
6. How many liters of sulfur dioxide can be prepared from a mixture of 100. g of copper and 100. g of H_2SO_4?
7. A lead smelter processes 500. tons of zinc sulfide, ZnS, each day. If no sulfur dioxide is lost, how much sulfuric acid could be made in the plant daily?

SOME THINGS FOR YOU TO DO

1. Bleach a moist red carnation in a bottle of sulfur dioxide gas. The flower must be dripping wet to bleach well. Why?
2. Make a solution of sulfur dioxide in water. Put one or two dried apricots in the solution and allow it to stand for a day or two. What color change do you notice in the apricots?
3. Sulfuric acid usually comes to the laboratory in five-pint bottles with plastic tops that hold nine pounds of sulfuric acid. Examine such a bottle of concentrated acid. Note how heavy it is, but be careful not to drop it. Read the label closely, and see how much information is given as to quantity, specific gravity, impurities, etc.

CHECK YOUR PROGRESS IN CHEMISTRY

1. In making a solution of copper(II) sulfate from coarse lumps of $CuSO_4 \cdot 5\ H_2O$, what procedures could you follow to shorten the time required?
2. Explain the anode and cathode reactions which occur in the electrolysis of very dilute sulfuric acid solution.
3. Write equations showing the stages in the ionization of the triprotic acid, H_3PO_4.
★ 4. How are catalysts believed to alter the rate of chemical reactions?
★ 5. What is the oxidation number of sulfur in: (*a*) H_2S; (*b*) $NaHSO_3$; (*c*) $KHSO_4$; (*d*) H_2SO_3; (*e*) H_2SO_4?

6. Which furnishes more carbon dioxide, 50. g of Na_2CO_3 or 50. g of $NaHCO_3$?
7. Write the equations for the production of hydrated lime from limestone.
8. Draw electron-dot formulas for molecules of fluorine, chlorine, bromine, and iodine.
9. For what purpose are fluoride ions added to drinking water?
10. How does an ink eradicator which produces a hypochlorous acid solution work?
11. What are the sources of bromine in the United States?
12. What do we mean when we say that iodine *sublimes?*
13. Draw a sketch showing a cross-section of the pipes which go down to a sulfur deposit. Indicate what flows through each pipe and the direction in which it goes.
14. (*a*) What are the solid allotropic forms of sulfur? (*b*) How do they differ in crystal structure?
15. Draw electron-dot formulas to show the possible resonating structures in sulfur trioxide.
16. How can you test for the presence of a sulfide?
17. Show by an equation that sulfur dioxide is an acid anhydride.
18. Sulfur trioxide is an important compound to chemical manufacturers, yet it is rarely seen in laboratory stockrooms. Why?
19. What catalyst is used in the contact process for making sulfuric acid?

CHALLENGING YOUR KNOWLEDGE

1. What do you believe was the reason for the relatively late isolation of fluorine as compared with the other common halogens?
2. (*a*) What effect will freshly prepared chlorine water have on blue litmus paper? (*b*) What effect will chlorine water stored in a clear glass bottle on a shelf in the laboratory for a week have on blue litmus paper?
3. How do reactions of metals with oxygen and metals with sulfur compare in the amount of energy evolved?
4. Why is white lead, a basic carbonate of lead, never used for making the paint to be used on the walls of a chemical laboratory?
5. What deviations from ideal gas behavior would you expect to be shown by chlorine, hydrogen sulfide, and sulfur dioxide?
6. Sulfuric acid is made by both the contact and the chamber processes. Why can both processes persist in competition with each other?
7. If equal masses of $NaCl$ and $CaCl_2 \cdot 2 H_2O$ are used with equal volumes of water, which produces the greater freezing point lowering?

Unit 9 · THE NITROGEN FAMILY

The Atmosphere
Nitrogen and Its Compounds
Phosphorus, Arsenic, Antimony, and Bismuth

Chapter 29 · THE ATMOSPHERE

1. THE COMPOSITION AND PROPERTIES OF AIR

1. Air is a mixture of gases. *The atmosphere is the layer of gases which surrounds the earth.* Its density is greatest near the surface of the earth, and decreases with increasing altitude because of the lower gravitational attraction of the earth.

Near the earth's surface, *the air is a mixture of oxygen, nitrogen, carbon dioxide, and argon and several other inert gases,* of rather constant composition. It is colorless, odorless, and tasteless. At high altitudes, its composition gradually changes. The outer limit of the atmosphere probably consists of widely scattered molecules of hydrogen.

Since smoke and other gases are constantly escaping into the air, traces of such impurities as carbon monoxide, hydrogen sulfide, sulfur dioxide, and ammonia are likely to be found in the air. Water vapor in varying quantities is always present in it. Ozone is formed in small quantities during thunderstorms. Particles of dust, bacteria, and the spores of plants are also nearly always present. The table on the opposite page shows the percentage composition of air near the earth's surface.

One liter of dry air at S.T.P. has a mass of 1.29 g. This is slightly less than the mass of one liter of oxygen. Dry air is $\frac{1}{773}$ as dense as water.

2. Proofs that air is a mixture. There are several ways to prove that air is a mixture of gases and not a single compound.

1. The composition of the air varies slightly in different localities, and in the same locality at different times. If it were a compound, it would always have a definite composition by weight.

2. There is no evidence of any chemical action when the components of air are mixed in the same proportion in which they are present in air. No heat or light is produced.

3. The air which surrounds us is about one fifth oxygen by volume. When cold water is slowly warmed, bubbles of gas come out of the solution. If these bubbles are analyzed they are found to consist of about one third

424

COMPOSITION OF AIR

Component	Percentage by Volume	Percentage by Weight
Nitrogen	78	75.5
Oxygen	21	23.2
Argon and Other Inert Gases	0.94	1.3
Carbon Dioxide	0.04	0.05
Water Vapor	Varies, small fraction to 2% or more	Varies

oxygen by volume. The change in composition is due to the difference in the solubility of the gases which make up the air. If air were a single compound, the bubbles which escape from the water would have the same composition as undissolved air.

4. When liquid air boils, the nitrogen boils off first, leaving nearly pure liquid oxygen. The liquid oxygen then boils off at a somewhat higher temperature. Air must be a mixture because it can be separated into its components by this purely physical method.

5. The gases in the air react chemically with other substances the same way the pure gases do. Carbon burns in air, combining with the oxygen of the air to produce carbon dioxide. Carbon burns in pure oxygen to form carbon dioxide. Burning magnesium ribbon in air produces a mixture of magnesium oxide and magnesium nitride. Magnesium burns in pure oxygen to form magnesium oxide. Heated magnesium combines with pure nitrogen to form magnesium nitride. If air were a compound, different products would be formed by the reactions of a single substance with air and with the gases which air contains.

3. The liquefaction of gases. Michael Faraday (1791–1867) discovered that it is possible to liquefy certain gases by cooling them and compressing them at the same time. He used a thick-walled sealed tube of the type shown in Fig. 29-1 to liquefy chlorine, sulfur dioxide, and some other gases. One end of the glass tube containing the chlorine gas

VOCABULARY

Atmosphere. The layer of gases which surrounds the earth.

Critical pressure. The pressure required to liquefy a gas at its critical temperature.

Critical temperature. The highest temperature at which it is possible to liquefy a gas with any amount of pressure.

Critical volume. The volume occupied by one mole of a gas at its critical temperature and critical pressure.

Fractional distillation. The separation by carefully controlled vaporization of the components of a mixture which have slightly different boiling points.

Liquefaction. The process of converting a gas or solid to a liquid.

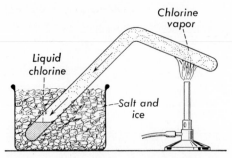

Fig. 29-1. **By using a tube like the one above, Faraday succeeded in liquefying chlorine, sulfur dioxide, and several other gases which have high critical temperatures.**

was strongly heated. That caused the gas in the heated end of the tube to expand and exert pressure on the gas in the other end of the tube, which was cooled by being packed in a freezing mixture. Such cooling and compression converted the gaseous chlorine into liquid chlorine.

In order to liquefy a gas, it is necessary first to compress the gas and then to absorb the heat of compression. The second step is to permit the cool, compressed gas to expand rapidly. If the expansion is sufficiently rapid, it will cool the remaining part of the gas to a temperature at which some of it will liquefy.

Compressing a gas always raises its temperature since energy is acquired by the molecules of a gas when work is done on them to push them closer together. In liquefying gases this heat of compression is absorbed by a suitable refrigerant. The gas molecules thereby lose the energy acquired during compression. Thus the compressed gas is reduced to the same temperature that it had before compression. The molecules possess the same energy they had prior to compression.

When a compressed gas is permitted

to expand, the molecules lose energy as they do work in spreading apart against the force of molecular attraction. This energy loss by the molecules is observed as a decrease in the temperature of the gas. Since the temperature of the compressed gas was that which it had before compression, the expanded gas is now at a much lower temperature than originally. By repetition of this compression, cooling, and expansion cycle the temperature of the gas is reduced still further.

The liquefaction of gases is accomplished by the combined efforts of lowered temperature and increased pressure. The increased pressure crowds the gas molecules together. The lowered temperature slows their movement. Ultimately, they are slowed down and crowded together so closely that the attractive forces between the molecules cause them to condense to a liquid.

Scientists have found that above a certain temperature it is impossible to liquefy a gas by pressure alone because the kinetic energy of the molecules is great enough to overcome the attracting forces between them. Thus the gas will not liquefy however great the pressure applied. *The highest temperature at which it is possible to liquefy a gas with any amount of pressure is called its critical temperature. The pressure required to liquefy a gas at its critical temperature is called its critical pressure. The volume occupied by one mole of a gas under these conditions is called its critical volume.* The critical temperature and critical pressure of several common gases is given in the table at the bottom of page 427.

From these data it is easy to see that in order to liquefy a gas its temperature must be lowered below its critical temperature . Simultaneously its pressure must be raised above the vapor pressure of the liquefied gas at this temperature.

4. Critical temperature and molecular attraction. Since the critical temperature of a gas is the temperature above which it cannot be liquefied no matter how great the pressure, the magnitude of the critical temperature serves as a measure of the attractive forces between molecules. The higher the critical temperature of a gas the greater is the attractive force between its molecules, and the lower the critical temperature of a gas the less is the attractive force between its molecules.

The high critical temperature of water shown in the table below indicates that the forces of attraction between polar water molecules are so great that they can cause the liquefaction of water vapor even at 374° C. The critical temperature of sulfur dioxide is less than that of water. Thus the attractive forces between sulfur dioxide molecules must be less than those between water molecules. This we would expect because sulfur dioxide molecules are less polar than water molecules. Consequently, sulfur dioxide can be condensed to a liquid only below 157° C.

The attractive forces between nonpolar covalent molecules such as chlorine, carbon dioxide, oxygen, nitrogen, and hydrogen are van der Waals forces. They are of a different nature and usually weaker than the forces between polar molecules. They vary with the number of electrons and the tightness with which they are held in the molecules. The greater the number of electrons and the less tightly they are bound, the greater are the attractive forces between the nonpolar molecules. Thus, generally, the higher the molecular weight of a nonpolar molecule, the higher its critical temperature will be. This is borne out by the order of the critical temperatures of chlorine, carbon dioxide, oxygen, nitrogen, and hydrogen shown in the table below at the left.

5. The production of liquid air. Air will change into a liquid if it is cooled sufficiently. Small amounts of liquid air were first produced in France in 1877. Today it is produced in large amounts as a preliminary step in separating the components of the air.

Figure 29-2 is a simplified diagram of a liquid air machine. By means of a compressor, the air is first put under a pressure of from 3000 to 4000 lb/in². This hot compressed air then flows through a coiled pipe in a condenser through which water circulates to absorb the heat of compression. In the liquefier, the gas flows out through a needle valve, and expands rapidly. This expansion cools the gas decidedly. The cool gas then flows back through the outer of the two pipes of the liquefier, cooling still further the gas in the inner tube of the liquefier. The expanded gas is recycled. The continuous expansion of cooler and cooler gas in the liquefier finally produces a low enough temperature to liquefy some of the gas. The liquid air collects in the reservoir at the bottom of the liquefier.

CRITICAL TEMPERATURES
AND PRESSURES

Gas	Critical Temperature (° C)	Critical Pressure (atm)
Water	374.0	217.7
Sulfur dioxide	157.2	77.7
Chlorine	144.0	76.1
Carbon dioxide	31.1	73.0
Oxygen	−118.8	49.7
Nitrogen	−147.1	33.5
Hydrogen	−239.9	12.8

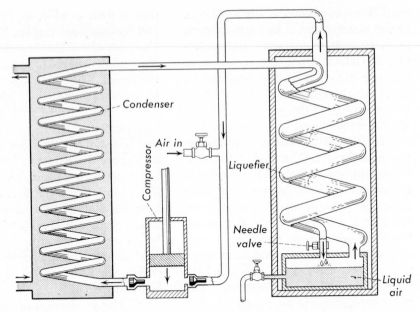

Fig. 29-2. **This diagram shows how a liquid air machine operates.**

6. The properties of liquid air. Liquid air resembles water in appearance. Under ordinary atmospheric pressure, liquid air boils at a temperature of about −190° C. Its boiling temperature is not constant, because it is a mixture of liquid nitrogen which boils at −195.8° C, and of liquid oxygen which boils at −182.7° C. Because it has the lower boiling point, nitrogen boils away first and leaves nearly pure oxygen.

A test tube of alcohol immersed in liquid air will soon be frozen solid. Mercury freezes so hard that it can be used as a hammer for driving nails. Carbon dioxide solidifies in liquid air. A rubber ball immersed in liquid air, and then thrown on the floor, breaks as if it were glass. In liquid air, tin and rubber become brittle and lead becomes elastic.

To get an idea of how cold liquid air really is, a vessel of liquid air may be placed upon a cake of ice. The ice is so

hot, comparatively, that the liquid air is likely to boil over. Remember that boiling water is only 100 Centigrade degrees hotter than ice, yet ice is about 190 Centigrade degrees hotter than liquid air. These facts will give you a clearer idea of the extremely low temperature of liquid air.

Fig. 29-3. **Liquid air boils vigorously when placed on a cake of ice.** (Union Carbide)

7. The storage of liquid air. Large glass vacuum bottles are used to store liquid air. These bottles are double-walled, with the space between the walls evacuated. This vacuum prevents the conduction of heat from the outside through the walls of the flask to the liquid inside. The glass is silvered to prevent radiant heat rays from passing through. Even with these precautions, enough heat gets in to keep the liquid boiling slowly. Liquid air containers should never be stoppered. The pressure of the air as it vaporizes would either blow out the stopper or burst the container.

8. The uses of liquid air. Liquid air is useful for producing low temperatures. It is a commercial source of both oxygen and nitrogen. Processors who prepare oxygen and nitrogen for the market also separate from the liquid air such products as neon and argon.

2. THE INERT GASES

9. Inert gases in the air. In 1893 Lord Rayleigh (1842–1919), an English physicist, was investigating nitrogen prepared by removing oxygen and the other known gases from the air. He found that the density of nitrogen prepared in this way was slightly higher than that of the nitrogen chemically prepared from nitrogen compounds. Lord Rayleigh suspected that there must be some other substance mixed with the nitrogen from the air which produced this discrepancy. He turned the problem over to his friend, Sir William Ramsay (1852–1916), who was a chemist. Ramsay carefully analyzed the air, and found that about 1% of an air sample could not be removed by chemical methods. Later Ramsay and his co-workers found that

Fig. 29-4. **Sir William Ramsay, an English scientist, discovered the inert gases, neon, argon, krypton, and xenon.** (Brown Brothers)

this unreactive residue of the air consisted of five inert gases, helium, neon, argon, krypton, and xenon. These gases, along with radon, which is formed by radioactive disintegration of radium, constitute Group VIII of the Periodic Table.

As noted in Chapter 5, each member of Group VIII has an outer shell with a stable electron configuration. These elements show no tendency to form chemical compounds by the usual methods of electron transfer or electron sharing. As a consequence also, each of these gases is monatomic. Their atomic weights and molecular weights are the same.

All of these elements have low melting points indicating that the attraction between atoms is slight. In fact, helium solidifies at $-272.2°$ C only when subjected to a pressure of 26.2 atmospheres. The energy of motion of the helium atoms which cannot be removed as heat prevents them from assuming the orderly arrangement of a solid unless such high pressure is applied.

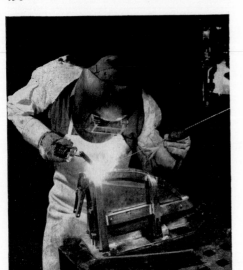

Fig. 29-5. **This worker is welding magnesium by using a helium-shielded electric arc. The helium prevents oxidation of the magnesium during the welding process.** (Dow Chemical)

The very narrow range of temperatures in which each of these elements exists as a liquid is also of interest. The amount of attraction between atoms is so small that once they acquire sufficient energy to overcome the orderly arrangement of a solid, very little more energy is required before the atoms can take up separate independent existence as gas particles. These relationships are summarized in the table below.

10. The discovery and production of helium. Helium was first discovered through spectrographic analysis of the sun's atmosphere in 1868 by Sir Norman Lockyer (1836–1920). It was named *helium* from the Greek word meaning sun. Later, Sir William Ramsay found it in small amounts in the earth's atmosphere.

The natural gas from some wells in Texas, Oklahoma, and Kansas contains as much as 2% helium. If this natural gas is compressed and cooled, the helium, which does not liquefy, may be separated from the other components of the gas and compressed into steel cylinders for storage or shipment.

11. The properties of helium. This colorless, odorless, and tasteless gas has two special properties which make it useful. It is only one-seventh as dense as air, and it does not burn. In spite of the fact that helium is twice as dense as hydrogen, it is still 93% as efficient as hydrogen as a buoyant agent (refer to Chapter 8, Section 8). Remember that the buoyancy of any gas is equal to the difference between the weight of a given volume of gas and that of the same volume of air.

12. The uses of helium. The importance of helium for filling balloons and airships depends on the fact that it is nonflammable and has a low density. Helium is less soluble in the blood

THE INERT GASES

Element	Atomic Number	Atomic Weight	Electron Configuration	Oxidation Number	Melting Point, °C	Boiling Point, °C	Density, g/l
Helium	2	4.0026	2	0	−272.2	−268.9	0.177
Neon	10	20.183	2, 8	0	−248.7	−245.9	0.899
Argon	18	39.948	2, 8, 8	0	−189.2	−185.7	1.784
Krypton	36	83.80	2, 8, 18, 8	0	−157	−152.9	3.708
Xenon	54	131.30	2, 8, 18, 18, 8	0	−112	−107.1	5.85
Radon	86	222.	2, 8, 18, 32, 18, 8	0	−71	−61.8	9.73

stream than nitrogen. Accordingly, divers and men who work in tunnels in an atmosphere of compressed air breathe a special mixture of helium and oxygen. This prevents the common disease of such occupations known as "the bends," which is caused by the formation of gas bubbles in the body tissues when the pressure is reduced. Helium is also used as an inert atmosphere to surround magnesium while it is being electrically welded. This prevents oxidation of the magnesium. Liquid helium is used in the study of the properties of materials at very low temperatures.

13. Neon is used in advertising signs. Neon is present in the air to the extent of about 18 parts per million by weight. It is produced by the fractional distillation of liquid air. *Fractional distillation is the separation of the components of a mixture which have slightly different boiling points by carefully controlled vaporization.*

Neon signs are usually manufactured on special order for a particular purpose. First, electrodes are sealed into the ends of glass tubes which are bent to the desired shape. Then the air is pumped out of the tubes. Finally, neon gas under a pressure of about 10 mm is introduced into the tube. As the neon vapor conducts electricity through the tube, the tube is filled with an orange-red light. The electricity energizes the electrons of the neon atoms. This increase in energy causes the electrons to move away from the nucleus and temporarily occupy normally vacant energy levels. As these electrons return to their usual energy levels, they give up their energy as light energy. Neon tubes are used not only in signs but also on airport landing fields as runway and boundary markers.

14. The preparation, properties, and uses of argon. Argon is prepared commercially from liquid air by fractional distillation. The impure argon which is obtained by this process is passed over hot copper. This removes any remaining traces of oxygen, leaving practically pure argon.

Argon is a colorless, odorless, and tasteless gas. It is present in the air to the extent of about 10,000 parts per million by weight, or about 1% by volume.

Argon is used in electric light bulbs. The gas-filled tungsten filament bulbs contain a mixture of nitrogen and argon, in some cases as much as 80% argon. The argon does not combine with the tungsten wire used for the filament, and it keeps the hot tungsten from evaporating rapidly. Its pressure inside the bulb equalizes the atmospheric pressure outside and helps prevent the seepage of air into the bulb. Oxygen in the air would oxidize the tungsten and make the lamp less efficient. Argon is used extensively as an inert shielding atmosphere during electric arc welding. It is also used, together with mercury vapor, in fluorescent tubes.

Fig. 29-6. Argon provides an inert atmosphere in this equipment for producing titanium metal from titanium tetrachloride by reduction with metallic sodium. (Union Carbide)

15. The other inert gases. *Krypton* (*krip*-ton) comprises about 1 part per million and xenon (*zee*-non) about 0.1 part per million by weight of air. Some flash tubes used in photography contain a mixture of these gases. The gases are produced by fractional distillation of liquid air. In 1962 scientists at Argonne National Laboratory prepared crystalline xenon tetrafluoride.

Radon (*ray*-don) is so closely connected in its chemistry with radium that it will be studied with other radioactive elements in Chapter 38.

SUMMARY

Air is a mixture of colorless, odorless, and tasteless gases. About 99% of it is a mixture of nitrogen and oxygen. Argon comprises about 1%. Smaller amounts of neon, helium, krypton, and xenon are present, together with carbon dioxide and variable amounts of water vapor. By compression and cooling, air can be liquefied. Liquid air has a very low temperature. It is used as a commercial source of nitrogen, oxygen, argon, and neon.

The highest temperature at which it is possible to liquefy a gas with any amount of pressure is called its critical temperature. The pressure required to liquefy a gas at its critical temperature is called its critical pressure. The magnitude of the critical temperature serves as a measure of the attractive forces between molecules.

The inert gases are elements with stable outer shell configurations. They show little tendency to form chemical compounds by the methods of electron transfer or electron sharing. Each gas is monatomic. Helium is used for balloons, and, mixed with oxygen, is breathed by divers. Neon is used for neon signs and for airplane beacons. Argon is used in electric light bulbs.

TEST YOURSELF ON THESE TERMS

argon	critical volume	liquefaction
atmosphere	fractional distillation	liquid air
critical pressure	helium	neon
critical temperature	inert gas	van der Waals forces

QUESTIONS

Group A

1. What are the important gases in air?
2. Name the gases which are present as impurities in the air.
3. What non-gaseous impurities are there in the air?
4. What proofs are there that air is a mixture and not a single compound?
5. (*a*) Which has the higher boiling point, liquid nitrogen or liquid oxygen? (*b*) What practical use is made of this difference in boiling points?
6. Define: (*a*) critical temperature; (*b*) critical pressure; (*c*) critical volume.

7. Why will a beaker of liquid air boil very rapidly when placed on ice?
8. How are liquid air containers constructed to prevent heat transfer to the liquid air?
9. (*a*) To which group of the Periodic Table do the inert gases belong? (*b*) Why are they placed in this group?
10. (*a*) What is an important aeronautical use for helium? (*b*) What properties make it so useful for this purpose?
11. Why is argon used in electric light bulbs?

Group B

12. Why does air which has been dissolved in water consist of about one-third oxygen, when the atmosphere contains only about one-fifth oxygen?
13. (*a*) Why does compressing a gas raise its temperature? (*b*) Why does a gas become colder when it is allowed to expand?
14. What conditions must be met in order for a gas to be liquefied?
15. Where, in a liquid air machine, is the heat removed from the air?
16. What evidence caused Rayleigh to suspect that there were yet undiscovered gases in the air?
17. Why are the inert gases monatomic, while other common gases are diatomic?
18. Distinguish: *fractional distillation, destructive distillation,* and *distillation.*
19. (*a*) Can carbon dioxide be liquefied at 100.° C? (*b*) Can chlorine be liquefied at 100.° C?
20. Why must a difference in a physical property, such as boiling point, be used in separating neon from liquid air?

PROBLEMS

1. What is the weight of 22.4 liters of air at S.T.P.?
2. What is the weight of 22.4 liters of helium at S.T.P.?
3. What is the lifting power of 22.4 liters of helium?

SOME THINGS FOR YOU TO DO

1. Consult recent magazine articles dealing with studies of the upper atmosphere made by using rockets and earth satellites. Report to the class on changes in the composition and temperature of the atmosphere found at increasing altitudes above the earth's surface.
2. Cryogenics is the study of low temperature phenomena. Learn what unusual physical properties materials possess at the temperature of liquid helium by reading a book such as *Saturday Science,* by scientists of the Westinghouse Research Laboratories, Dutton, 1960.
3. Visit a plant where neon signs are made. Note the skill of the workmen in shaping the glass tubes into intricate designs.
4. Read Part IV, "The Canopy of Air," in the Life Magazine book, *The World We Live In,* and report to the class on the sections related to chemistry.

Chapter 30 · NITROGEN AND ITS COMPOUNDS

1. NITROGEN

1. The occurrence of nitrogen. We have already recognized that about four-fifths of the air is elementary nitrogen. Combined nitrogen is also widely distributed. It is found in the proteins of both plants and animals. Natural deposits of both potassium nitrate and sodium nitrate are raw materials for the production of other nitrogen compounds.

2. The discovery of nitrogen. Several scientists played a part in the discovery of nitrogen. In 1772 Daniel Rutherford (1749–1819), a Scottish physician, published an account of his study on the products of breathing of small animals in a closed vessel. After he had separated the gas which we know as carbon dioxide from the exhaled air, he found that a colorless gas remained. This remaining gas would support neither life nor burning. This was the first separation of relatively pure nitrogen from the air.

Priestley, Cavendish, Scheele, and Lavoisier also made contributions to the discovery of nitrogen. Lavoisier was the first to recognize it as a distinct element present in the air. He called it *azote*, which means "without life," but the name was later changed to nitrogen because it is present in *niter*, which is the common name for potassium nitrate.

3. The preparation of nitrogen.
1. By fractional distillation of liquid air. This is the commercial method for producing nitrogen (see Chapter 29, Section 8).
2. By chemically removing oxygen from the air. This laboratory method produces nitrogen which is contaminated with

434

carbon dioxide and the inert gases. A small piece of phosphorus is put in a small crucible and the crucible floated on water, as shown in Fig. 30-1. The phosphorus is ignited and immediately a bell jar is placed over it. As the phosphorus combines with the oxygen of the air in the bell jar, the water rises in the bell jar to take the place of the oxygen which was removed. Impure nitrogen remains in the bell jar. The diphosphorus pentoxide which is formed dissolves in the water and does not contaminate the nitrogen.

Several other substances can be used to remove the oxygen from the air in similar experiments, including heated mercury, iron filings, steel wool, hot copper gauze, or hot carbon.

3. *By decomposing ammonium nitrite.* Pure nitrogen can be prepared in the laboratory by gently heating ammonium nitrite, NH_4NO_2, which decomposes into nitrogen and water.

$$NH_4NO_2 \rightarrow N_2 \uparrow + 2 H_2O$$

Ammonium nitrite is too unstable to store in the laboratory. Usually, it is pre-

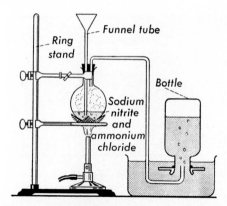

Fig. 30-2. **Pure nitrogen can be prepared by the decomposition of ammonium nitrite. The flask must be heated gently to prevent too rapid decomposition.**

pared by heating gently a mixture of ammonium chloride and sodium nitrite solutions. The ions form ammonium nitrite which then decomposes to yield nitrogen.

$$NH_4Cl + NaNO_2 \rightarrow NH_4NO_2 + NaCl$$
$$\searrow$$
$$N_2 \uparrow + 2 H_2O$$

4. The physical properties of nitrogen. Nitrogen is a colorless, odorless, and tasteless gas. It is slightly less dense than air, and is only slightly soluble in water. Its density shows that its molecules are diatomic, N_2.

5. The chemical properties of nitrogen. The triple covalent bond between the atoms of nitrogen in a molecule

$$^\circ_\circ N ^{\circ\circ}_{\circ\circ\circ} N \mathbf{:}$$

is a very strong one. As a result, elementary nitrogen is rather inactive. It unites with other elements with difficulty. Three other chemical properties of this gas are:

1. Nitrogen does not burn in oxygen. However, when a lightning discharge passes through the air, or when nitrogen and oxygen are passed through an

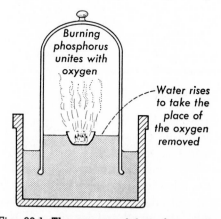

Fig. 30-1. **The gas remaining after oxygen is removed from air by burning phosphorus is nitrogen contaminated with small amounts of carbon dioxide and inert gases.**

Fig. 30-3. **The nodules attached to the roots of this clover plant contain nitrogen-fixing bacteria. These bacteria produce nitrates from the nitrogen of the air which surrounds the soil particles through which the roots grow.** (U. S. Department of Agriculture)

electric arc, nitrogen monoxide, NO, is formed.

2. By the use of a catalyst, nitrogen can be made to combine with hydrogen to form ammonia, NH_3. This method of making ammonia will be described later in Section 10.

3. At a high temperature, nitrogen combines directly with such metals as magnesium, titanium, and aluminum to form *nitrides*.

6. The uses of elementary nitrogen. Substances burn rapidly in pure oxygen, but nitrogen does not support combustion. Therefore, nitrogen in the air serves as a diluting agent and makes combustion much less rapid. Nitrogen gives bulk to the air and helps increase both its pressure and its buoyant force.

Because of its inertness, nitrogen is used to produce a blanketing atmosphere

during the processing of food to prevent oxidation which would cause food to spoil or which would affect its natural taste. It is used by chemical, petroleum, and paint industries in a similar fashion to prevent fires or explosions. Nitrogen is used with argon for filling electric lamps. It is also used in metalworking operations to control furnace atmospheres. Large amounts of nitrogen are taken from the air for use in making ammonia, nitric acid, and other nitrogen compounds.

7. The test for nitrogen. The best test for nitrogen depends on the fact that magnesium combines with it when heated and forms magnesium nitride, Mg_3N_2. If water is added to magnesium nitride, ammonia is produced and can be detected by its odor.

$$Mg_3N_2 + 6\,H_2O \rightarrow 3\,Mg(OH)_2 + 2\,NH_3 \uparrow$$

8. Nitrogen fixation. Besides *free or elementary nitrogen*, which is in the air, all living things contain nitrogen compounds. The nitrogen in these compounds is called *combined or fixed nitrogen. Any process that converts free nitrogen into nitrogen compounds is called* **nitrogen fixation.** Such processes are important because nitrogen compounds in the soil make it possible to grow more food plants. Some processes of nitrogen fixation are:

1. *One natural method* is to grow certain crops which will put nitrogen compounds into the soil. Many crops, such as wheat, corn, oats, and lettuce, remove nitrogen compounds from the soil rapidly. On the other hand, certain other crop plants, belonging to the bean and pea family, have small *nodules*, or swellings, on their roots (see Fig. 30-3). Certain types of bacteria known as **nitrogen-fixing bacteria** grow in these nodules. If the soil is alkaline, these bacteria have

the ability to take free nitrogen from the air and convert it into nitrogen compounds which the plants can use.

2. Another *natural method* of nitrogen fixation occurs during electric storms. Lightning discharges furnish sufficient energy to cause some of the nitrogen and oxygen of the air to unite, forming an oxide of nitrogen. After a series of changes, nitrogen compounds are washed down into the soil in the ensuing rain.

3. The chief *artificial method* of nitrogen fixation is the manufacture of ammonia from a mixture of nitrogen and hydrogen. The ammonia so produced in chemical works can then be oxidized to nitric acid. The nitric acid, in turn, can be converted into nitrates suitable for fertilizer.

4. Another *artificial method* is the manufacture of calcium cyanamid, $CaCN_2$. In this process, nitrogen is passed over white-hot calcium carbide.

$$CaC_2 + N_2 \rightarrow CaCN_2 + C$$

The cyanamid may be used directly as a nitrogen fertilizer, or it may be converted into ammonia by means of super-heated steam.

$$CaCN_2 + 3 H_2O \rightarrow CaCO_3 + 2 NH_3 \uparrow$$

2. AMMONIA AND AMMONIUM COMPOUNDS

9. The occurrence of ammonia. Very small traces of ammonia, NH_3, are found in the air. These are formed when the complex proteins in plant and animal bodies are decomposed in the operation of the nitrogen cycle. An odor of ammonia is always noticeable around barns and stables where farm animals are housed. Bacteria break down the nitrogen compounds in manures to form ammonia.

10. The preparation of ammonia. 1. By decomposing ammonium compounds. In the laboratory, ammonia is prepared by heating a mixture of calcium hydroxide and an ammonium compound, usually ammonium chloride or ammonium sulfate.

$$Ca(OH)_2 + 2 NH_4Cl \rightarrow$$
$$CaCl_2 + 2 NH_3 \uparrow + 2 H_2O$$
$$Ca(OH)_2 + (NH_4)_2SO_4 \rightarrow$$
$$CaSO_4 + 2 NH_3 \uparrow + 2 H_2O$$

The mixture may be heated in a test tube fitted with an L-shaped delivery tube, as shown in Fig. 30-4. Ammonia is so soluble that it cannot be collected by water displacement, but it can be collected by downward displacement of air in an inverted container.

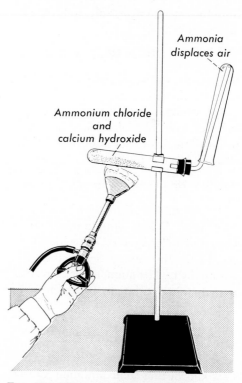

Ammonia displaces air

Ammonium chloride and calcium hydroxide

Fig. 30-4. When the mixture of ammonium chloride and calcium hydroxide in the test tube is heated, ammonia is evolved.

Fig. 30-5. **These absorbing and scrubbing towers are used for purifying nitrogen and hydrogen before their synthesis into ammonia.** (E. I. du Pont)

In either reaction, the ammonium ion, NH_4^+, from the ammonium salt, reacts with the hydroxide ion, OH^-, from the calcium hydroxide, to form ammonia and water.

$$NH_4^+ + OH^- \rightarrow NH_3 \uparrow + H_2O$$

Heating drives the reaction to the right since ammonia is a gas.

Any strong hydroxide may be used instead of calcium hydroxide. For example, sodium hydroxide and ammonium chloride react as follows:

$$NaOH + NH_4Cl \rightarrow NaCl + NH_3 \uparrow + H_2O$$

2. *By destructive distillation of bituminous coal.* When bituminous coal is heated in a closed container without access to air, ammonia is one of the gaseous products. The ammonia is converted to ammonium sulfate by treatment with sulfuric acid.

$$2 NH_3 + H_2SO_4 \rightarrow (NH_4)_2SO_4$$

3. *By the Haber process.* Chemists have long known that some ammonia can be prepared by passing an electric spark through a mixture of nitrogen and hydrogen. But the reaction is reversible:

$$N_2 + 3 H_2 \rightleftarrows 2 NH_3$$

Only a very small percentage of ammonia is produced. The problem of increasing that percentage was solved in 1913 by Fritz Haber (1868–1934), a German chemist.

The reaction between nitrogen and hydrogen is exothermic, and higher temperatures, which would be desirable for increasing the rate at which the molecules of nitrogen and hydrogen react, shift the equilibrium toward the left. However, four volumes of reactants produce only two volumes of products, so increased pressure shifts the equilibrium toward the right. Haber found that by using a catalyst to increase the speed of reaction, and by using a temperature of about 600° C and a pressure of about 200 atmospheres, he could obtain a yield of about 8% ammonia.

Today, the yield from the Haber process has been improved to about 40%. This has been brought about by using pressures as high as 1000 atmospheres, and an improved catalyst which is a mixture of porous iron and the oxides of potassium and aluminum.

The ammonia, produced in special

chrome-vanadium steel bombs which are needed to withstand the tremendous pressure, is separated from the unreacted nitrogen and hydrogen by being dissolved in water, or by being cooled until it liquefies. The uncombined gases are returned to the bombs to be exposed again to the action of the catalyst.

11. The physical properties of ammonia. Ammonia is a colorless gas with a characteristic, penetrating odor. It is less dense than air and is easily liquefied when sufficiently cooled. Liquid ammonia, which has a boiling point of $-34°$ C at atmospheric pressure, is sold in steel cylinders.

One of the unusual properties of ammonia is its great solubility in water. One liter of water at 20° C dissolves about 700 liters of ammonia. At 0° C

Fig. 30-6. **A flow diagram of the Haber process. Ammonia gas produced in the catalyst chamber is condensed into a liquid in the cooler. The uncombined nitrogen and hydrogen are recirculated through the catalyst chamber.**

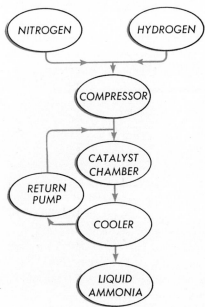

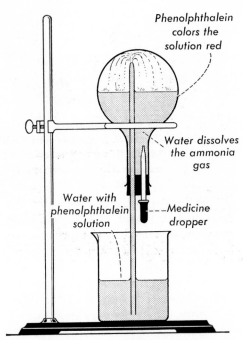

Fig. 30-7. **When a few drops of water are squeezed from the medicine dropper into the flask, the ammonia dissolves in the water and reduces the pressure in the flask. The atmospheric pressure forces water with phenolphthalein solution up the glass tube. More ammonia dissolves in this water, further reducing the pressure and causing the action to continue. Since ammonia-water solution has basic properties, the phenolphthalein turns red.**

nearly 1200 volumes of ammonia can be dissolved in one volume of water.

The structural formula for ammonia is:

$$H \!:\! \overset{\circ\circ}{\underset{\overset{\bullet\bullet}{H}}{N}} \!:\! H$$

For a compound with such a simple molecular structure, ammonia has an unusually high melting point and a high boiling point. You will remember from the study of water that water shows these properties to an even more marked

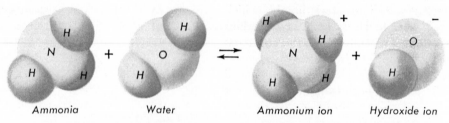

Fig. 30-8. **Ammonia reacts with water to form ammonium ion and hydroxide ion. In this reaction water acts as an acid (proton donor) and the ammonia acts as a base (proton acceptor).**

extent. Just as in the case of water, the high melting point and high boiling point are explained by the formation of hydrogen bonds between molecules of ammonia when in the solid and liquid states. The three hydrogen atoms are not symmetrically bonded to the nitrogen atom. Consequently, ammonia molecules are polar molecules. Hydrogen atoms from one ammonia molecule form hydrogen bonds to the nitrogen atom in adjacent ammonia molecules. The polar nature of both water and ammonia molecules is also believed to be the reason for the high solubility of ammonia in water.

12. The chemical properties of ammonia. Gaseous ammonia does not support ordinary combustion or burn in air, but it will burn in pure oxygen. At ordi-

Fig. 30-9. **The direct addition of synthetic ammonia is a useful method of supplying carefully regulated amounts of nitrogen to the soil. The process is called nitrogation. (Shell Oil)**

nary temperatures it is a stable compound, although it is decomposed into nitrogen and hydrogen at high temperatures. When ammonia is dissolved in water, most of the ammonia forms a simple solution. A small part of the ammonia reacts with water and ionizes, according to the reaction:

$$NH_3 + H_2O \rightleftarrows NH_4^+ + OH^-$$

This mixture of molecules and ions is commonly called *ammonium hydroxide;* a better name is *ammonia-water* solution. Ammonia-water solution is weakly basic.

Do not confuse the *ammonium ion,* NH_4^+, with the *ammonia molecule.* While the ammonium ion may act like a metallic ion such as sodium ion or potassium ion in its compounds, it cannot be isolated as NH_4^+. All attempts to separate ammonium from ammonium compounds have resulted in the decomposition of the compound into ammonia and other products.

13. The uses of ammonia and ammonium compounds.

1. *As fertilizers.* Ammonium compounds have long been used to supply nitrogen to the soil for growing plants. Recently, techniques have been worked out to use ammonia directly as a fertilizer. See Fig. 30-9.

2. *As a cleaning agent.* Ammonia-water solution makes a satisfactory cleaning agent because it is weakly basic, emulsifies grease, and leaves no residue to be wiped up. The water and ammonia simply evaporate. Ammonia-water solution is used for cleaning windows and the surface of porcelain tile.

3. *As a refrigerant.* Ammonia is used in factories which make ice. A compressor is used to liquefy ammonia gas, as shown in Fig. 30-10. The heat liberated during the compression of the gas is absorbed by water which flows down over the cooling and condensing coils. At this high pressure and lowered temperature, the ammonia liquefies. The cold, liquid

Fig. 30-10. The absorpton of the heat needed to evaporate and expand the liquid ammonia lowers the temperature of the fresh water until it freezes into ice.

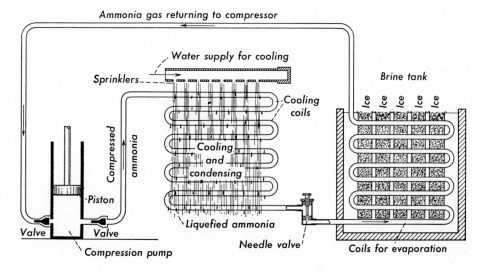

Ammonia gas returning to compressor

Water supply for cooling

Sprinklers

Brine tank

Cooling coils

Compressed ammonia

Cooling and condensing

Ice Ice Ice Ice Ice

Piston

Valve   Valve

Liquefied ammonia

Needle valve

Coils for evaporation

Compression pump

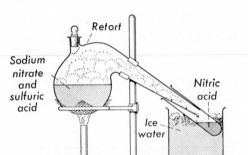

Fig. 30-11. **Nitric acid may be prepared in the laboratory by the action of sulfuric acid on sodium nitrate.**

ammonia then flows to a tank of brine in which are suspended the cans of fresh water to be frozen. As the liquid ammonia passes through a needle valve into coils of pipe immersed in the brine where reduced pressure is maintained, it evaporates and expands. This cools the brine to a temperature of about −10° C, well below the freezing point of fresh water.

In cold storage rooms, frozen food locker plants, or ice cream plants, brine is cooled by the evaporation of liquid ammonia, as in the making of ice. Then the cold brine is pumped through coils of pipes to the freezing and storage rooms. Just as hot water flowing through coils of pipe may warm a room, so cold brine flowing through a similar set of coils may cool a room.

4. For making other compounds. Great quantities of ammonia are oxidized to make nitric acid, as explained later in Section 15 of this chapter. It is also used in the production of nylon and one type of rayon, and as a catalyst in the preparation of several types of plastics. Ammonia is used in the synthesis of sulfa drugs, vitamins, and antimalarials, as a neutralizing agent by the petroleum in-

dustry, and in the rubber industry to prevent the coagulation of latex during transportation.

14. Hydrazine is another compound of nitrogen and hydrogen. Hydrazine, N_2H_4, is produced by oxidizing ammonia-water solution with sodium hypochlorite. It burns readily, and finds considerable use as a fuel for rockets and as a strong reducing agent.

3. NITRIC ACID

15. The preparation of nitric acid. Two methods are commonly used to prepare this important acid.
1. From nitrates. Small amounts of nitric acid may be prepared in the laboratory by heating a nitrate with sulfuric acid. The reaction is carried out in a glass-stoppered retort because of the corrosive action of nitric acid on apparatus with rubber stoppers or rubber connectors. The equation for the reaction, using sodium nitrate, is

$$NaNO_3 + H_2SO_4 \rightarrow NaHSO_4 + HNO_3 \uparrow$$

The nitric acid vapor is condensed in the side arm of the retort and collected in the receiver. Any nitrate may be used. Sodium nitrate is commonly used because it is inexpensive.
2. From ammonia. Wilhelm Ostwald (1853–1933), a German chemist, learned how to oxidize ammonia to nitric acid with the aid of a catalyst at about the same time that Haber developed the process for the synthesis of ammonia. These two processes fit together perfectly. Ammonia is made by synthesis from nitrogen and hydrogen. The ammonia is then oxidized to nitric acid in another part of the same plant. Some of the nitric acid may be neutralized with additional ammonia producing ammonium

nitrate, a useful fertilizer and explosives ingredient.

In the Ostwald process, a mixture of ammonia and air is heated to a temperature of 600° C. It is then passed through a tube containing platinum gauze, which serves as the contact catalyst. On the surface of the platinum, the ammonia is oxidized by the oxygen of the air to nitrogen monoxide, NO.

$$4 \, NH_3 + 5 \, O_2 \rightarrow 4 \, NO + 6 \, H_2O$$

This reaction is exothermic and raises the temperature of the mixture of gases to about 1000° C. Now more air is mixed with the nitrogen monoxide to oxidize it to nitrogen dioxide, NO_2.

$$2 \, NO + O_2 \rightarrow 2 \, NO_2$$

The nitrogen dioxide is cooled and absorbed in water, forming nitric acid.

$$3 \, NO_2 + H_2O \rightarrow 2 \, HNO_3 + NO \uparrow$$

The nitrogen monoxide produced in this reaction is also oxidized to nitrogen dioxide and absorbed in water.

Today almost all of the nitric acid used in industry is made by the oxidation of ammonia.

16. The physical properties of nitric acid. Pure HNO_3 is a colorless liquid, about 1.5 times as dense as water. It fumes in moist air and boils at 86° C. Pure HNO_3 is unstable, and for that reason, the concentrated nitric acid of commerce is a 68% solution of HNO_3 in water, which boils at 120° C. A more dilute solution boils at a lower temperature, losing water, and becoming more concentrated.

17. The chemical properties of nitric acid.
1. Stability. Nitric acid is not very stable. When boiled, or even when exposed to sunlight, it decomposes to some extent. Water and nitrogen dioxide are two products of its decomposition. The deep yellow color of laboratory bottles of nitric acid is caused by small amounts of dissolved nitrogen dioxide which are formed when the acid is exposed to light. In water solution the acid is more stable. *Fuming nitric acid,* a very corrosive liquid, has a red color due to considerable amounts of dissolved nitrogen dioxide. It fumes in moist air and burns the skin painfully.

2. Acid properties. Dilute nitric acid has the usual properties of acids. It reacts with metals and the oxides of metals. It reacts with hydroxides, forming salts known as *nitrates.*

Nitric acid stains the skin yellow, forming xanthoproteic (zan-thoh-proh-*tee*-ik) acid. It produces the same effect with any protein, and for that reason is used as a *test* for proteins. A drop of nitric acid added to a slice of hard-boiled egg white will show the test perfectly. The color deepens to a bright orange when treated with ammonia-water solution.

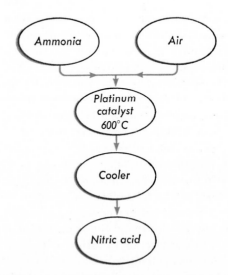

Fig. 30-12. **Flow diagram of the Ostwald process for the oxidation of ammonia into nitric acid.**

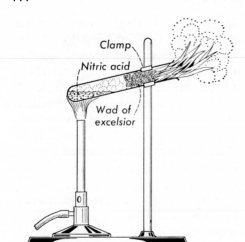

Fig. 30-13. Excelsior is oxidized very rapidly by boiling fuming nitric acid.

3. As an oxidizing agent. The decomposition of nitric acid molecules furnishes oxygen which unites with various materials that may be in contact with the acid. Nitric acid is a powerful oxidizing agent. To illustrate, let us put 5 ml of fuming nitric acid in a test tube and clamp the tube in a slightly inclined position. Now, with forceps, we slide a loose plug of excelsior down into the tube until it comes within an inch of touching the surface of the acid. When the acid is boiled, the excelsior is oxidized by the acid vapors and burns within the tube with a brilliant glow.

CAUTION: *Be sure that the open end of the test tube is not directed toward anyone.*

Nitric acid may break up in a variety of ways. The concentration of the acid, the activity of the reducing agent that is mixed with it, and the temperature at which the reaction is carried out determine what products are formed. Under ordinary conditions, moderately dilute nitric acid is reduced to nitrogen monoxide. If concentrated nitric acid is re-

duced, nitrogen dioxide is the product. With other reducing agents and different conditions for the reaction, such other reduction products as N_2O, dinitrogen monoxide (commonly called nitrous oxide), N_2, and NH_3 may be formed by the decomposition of nitric acid.

4. *Action with metals.* Nitric acid is such a vigorous oxidizing agent that hydrogen gas is *not usually* set free when this acid is added to common metals. *Very dilute nitric acid* reacts with such active metals as sodium, calcium, or magnesium, forming a nitrate and setting hydrogen free.

$$Mg + 2 HNO_3 \rightarrow Mg(NO_3)_2 + H_2 \uparrow$$

In reactions with less active metals, such as zinc and copper, the hydrogen appears in the water product and the nitrogen of the nitric acid is reduced. Copper reacts with cold, dilute nitric acid according to the following equation:

$$3 Cu + 8 HNO_3 \rightarrow$$
$$3 Cu(NO_3)_2 + 2 NO \uparrow + 4 H_2O$$

With concentrated nitric acid, copper reacts as follows:

$$Cu + 4 HNO_3 \rightarrow$$
$$Cu(NO_3)_2 + 2 NO_2 \uparrow + 2 H_2O$$

Nitric acid does not react with gold or platinum because of the stability of these metals. It reacts with aluminum and iron very slowly, probably because of the formation of semi-protective surface coatings. When nitric acid reacts with a metal, the nitrate of that metal is usually formed. The nitrates of the various metals are crystalline compounds which are readily soluble in water.

18. **The test for a nitrate.** To 5 ml of the solution to be tested in a test tube, an equal volume of a solution of

iron(II) sulfate, $FeSO_4$, is added. With the test tube held in an inclined position, a few milliliters of concentrated sulfuric acid is added slowly, so that it runs down the inclined wall of the test tube very gradually and settles to the bottom, not mixing with the other mixture in the tube. If the solution being tested does contain a nitrate, a *brown layer* containing nitrosyl iron(II) sulfate, $Fe(NO)SO_4$, forms at the junction of the acid and the other mixture (see Fig. 30-14).

19. **Aqua regia reacts with gold.** No single acid reacts with gold or platinum, but a mixture of nitric acid and hydrochloric acid reacts with these metals, forming chlorides. Such a mixture was named *aqua regia*, which means "royal water," by the early chemists because it reacts with gold, the king of metals. The most common mixture of aqua regia contains one part of concentrated nitric acid mixed with three parts of concentrated hydrochloric acid.

20. **The uses of nitric acid.**
1. *For making fertilizers.* About 75% of the nitric acid produced in the United States is used in the manufacture of fertilizers. Ammonium nitrate is the most important nitrate so used, and is readily manufactured in plants using the combined Haber-Ostwald processes. Sodium nitrate and potassium nitrate are also used as fertilizer ingredients which supply nitrogen to soils.
2. *For making explosives.* Practically all modern explosives are made directly or indirectly from nitric acid. The acid itself is not an explosive, but many of the compounds derived from it form the most violent explosives known. Among these are nitroglycerin, smokeless powder, and TNT.
3. *For making dyes.* Nitric acid reacts with several products obtained from coal

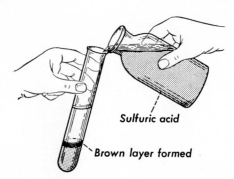

Fig. 30-14. **The brown layer formed when sulfuric acid is added slowly to a solution of iron(II) sulfate containing nitrate ions, serves as a test for the nitrate ions.**

tar, forming *nitro compounds*. One of these coal tar products is benzene, with which nitric acid reacts to form nitrobenzene, $C_6H_5NO_2$. Aniline, $C_6H_5NH_2$, a compound used in making different dyes, is made by reducing nitrobenzene with hydrogen.
4. *For making plastics.* Cotton, which consists mainly of cellulose, $(C_6H_{10}O_5)_n$, is treated with a mixture of nitric acid and sulfuric acid to make nitrocellulose plastics. A variety of products is formed, depending on the amount of nitric acid used, the temperature, and the length of time the acid is allowed to act on the cellulose. Manufacturers use sulfuric acid to absorb the water that is formed in the reaction. Celluloid, pyroxylins, photographic film, and many other products are made from such nitrocellulose plastics.

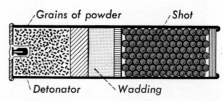

Fig. 30-15. **A cross-section of a shotgun shell such as is used for hunting game.**

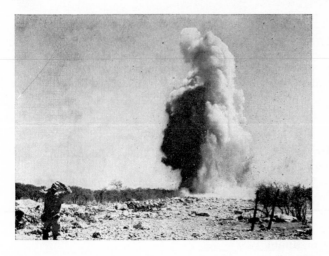

Fig. 30-16. **Small scale dynamite explosions such as the one shown here enable petroleum prospectors to map the underlying rock formations.** (Standard Oil of New Jersey)

4. EXPLOSIVES

21. Characteristics of explosives. *Explosives are compounds or mixtures which decompose suddenly and produce large volumes of gases.* Most explosives are nitrogen compounds which may be set off by ignition or shock. Explosives are used for blasting rock, digging ditches and tunnels, and many other purposes. Their military value is well known. Terrible accidents have occurred through the unintentional discharge of explosives. *It is never wise for inexperienced persons to handle them, and under no conditions should an amateur ever try to make an explosive.*

22. Black gunpowder. Gunpowder is a mixture of potassium nitrate, charcoal, and sulfur. Black gun powder is set off by ignition. This explosive is used today in fireworks and for rock blasting.

23. Nitroglycerin and dynamite. Nitroglycerin is made by treating glycerol (glycerin) with a mixture of nitric and sulfuric acids. It is a dense, oily liquid that is extremely sensitive to shock. The slightest jarring may be sufficient to cause it to decompose with enormous force.

Dynamite is a solid mixture made by absorbing nitroglycerin in wood pulp mixed with ammonium nitrate. The dynamite is usually encased in cardboard cylinders to form "sticks." In this way the hazardous property of nitroglycerin is lessened, while its usefulness is retained. Dynamite is especially useful for blasting rock.

24. Smokeless powder. Smokeless powder, or nitrocellulose, is made by treating cellulose with nitric and sulfuric acids. It differs from nitrocellulose plastics in that the cellulose is more thoroughly nitrated.

When smokeless powder burns, the colorless products, carbon dioxide, carbon monoxide, water vapor, and nitrogen, are formed. Almost no smoke is produced. Hence the name "smokeless" powder. It is principally used as a propelling charge for small arms and artillery.

25. Shell-fillers and detonators. The explosive used inside an artillery shell must be able to stand the shock of the propellant which starts it on its course. It must also be capable of exploding with great force when it reaches its target. Explosives of this type, requiring severe shock to set them off, are called *shell-fillers.* Trinitrotoluene (try-ny-troh-*tol*-you-een), usually abbreviated TNT, is the most commonly used shell-filler for military purposes.

Detonators are extremely sensitive explosives which are set off by a shock and which decompose with almost incredible rapidity. They are used in small amounts in cartridges and shells to start the main explosion. Mercury fulminate and lead azide are well-known detonators. They are very sensitive explosives that may be set off by heat, friction, or shock.

5. THE OXIDES OF NITROGEN

26. Five different oxides of nitrogen are known. Dinitrogen monoxide (nitrous oxide) has the formula N_2O; nitrogen monoxide (nitric oxide) has the formula NO; dinitrogen trioxide, which is the anhydride of nitrous acid, is written N_2O_3; nitrogen dioxide has the formula NO_2; and dinitrogen pentoxide, the anhydride of nitric acid, has the formula N_2O_5. In these oxides, nitrogen has oxidation numbers of +1 to +5.

27. The preparation and use of dinitrogen monoxide. Dinitrogen monoxide is prepared by gently heating ammonium nitrate.

$$NH_4NO_3 \rightarrow N_2O \uparrow + 2 H_2O$$

This gas was formerly called "laughing gas" because of the mild hysteria it induces. Mixed with oxygen, it is used by dentists and surgeons as an anesthetic.

28. The properties of dinitrogen monoxide. Dinitrogen monoxide is a colorless gas which has a somewhat sweet odor and taste. It is about 1.5 times as dense as air and moderately soluble in cold water. It is easily liquefied, and is usually sold as a liquid compressed in steel containers.

At ordinary temperatures, dinitrogen monoxide is stable, but it decomposes into oxygen and nitrogen when heated slightly. Even a glowing splint is hot enough to decompose the gas. Then the splint continues to burn almost as well as it does in oxygen. This is because the mixture of gases formed by decomposing dinitrogen monoxide contains 1 part of

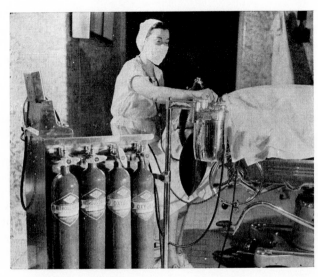

Fig. 30-17. **Dinitrogen monoxide (nitrous oxide) is mixed with oxygen and administered as an anesthetic during minor surgical operations.** (Air Reduction)

oxygen to 2 parts of nitrogen and this is twice as rich as the proportion of oxygen to nitrogen in air, 1 to 4. Dinitrogen monoxide can be distinguished from oxygen because barely ignited, feebly burning sulfur is extinguished in dinitrogen monoxide although it burns more vigorously when thrust into oxygen. Vigorously burning sulfur continues to burn in either gas.

29. The preparation and properties of nitrogen monoxide. Nitrogen monoxide is produced naturally during thunderstorms. We may prepare it for laboratory use by the reaction of dilute nitric acid on copper (see Section 17).

Nitrogen monoxide is a colorless gas which is only slightly denser than air, and almost insoluble in water. Its most important chemical property is its ability to unite directly with the oxygen of the air to form nitrogen dioxide.

$$2\ NO + O_2 \rightarrow 2\ NO_2 \uparrow$$

30. The uses of nitrogen monoxide. Nitrogen monoxide readily combines with oxygen from the air. The nitrogen dioxide that is formed then gives up oxygen in the presence of a reducing agent. Thus nitrogen monoxide acts as a *carrier of oxygen*. It is used to convert sulfur dioxide to sulfur trioxide in the manufacture of sulfuric acid by the chamber process (see Chapter 28, Section 7).

31. Nitrogen dioxide. At ordinary temperatures the color of this gas is reddish-brown. Its density indicates a molecular formula, NO_2. It has a disagreeable, suffocating odor, and is very poisonous. When cooled to lower temperatures, its color almost disappears and its density increases markedly, showing that two NO_2 molecules have associated to form a molecule with the formula N_2O_4.

$$2\ NO_2 \rightleftarrows N_2O_4$$

Nitrogen dioxide dissolves in water, and reacts with it to form a mixture of nitrous and nitric acids. Nitrogen dioxide is one of the decomposition products of nitric acid. Because it gives up its oxygen readily to other substances, it is a vigorous oxidizing agent.

SUMMARY

Nitrogen can be obtained from the air by fractional distillation, or by removing the oxygen with phosphorus or hot metals. Pure nitrogen is obtained by heating a mixture of ammonium chloride and sodium nitrite. Nitrogen is slightly less dense than air and only slightly soluble in water. Elementary nitrogen is rather inert. Nitrogen does not burn. It is difficult to make nitrogen unite with other elements and its compounds are not very stable. Under proper conditions, nitrogen can be combined with hydrogen to make ammonia. The conversion of free nitrogen into nitrogen compounds is called nitrogen fixation.

Ammonia is formed by the decay of animal and vegetable matter. It is prepared by heating calcium hydroxide with an ammonium compound. It is obtained as a by-product in the destructive distillation of bituminous coal, or is made synthetically by the Haber process from nitrogen and hydrogen.

Ammonia is a colorless gas with a penetrating odor. It is less dense than air and is extremely soluble in water. Ammonia-water solution is weakly basic. The ammonium ion acts like a metallic ion and combines with negative ions to form salts.

Ammonia is used as a refrigerant. Ammonia-water solution is used as a cleaning agent. Ammonia and ammonium compounds are used as fertilizers.

Nitric acid is prepared in the laboratory by heating a mixture of sodium nitrate and sulfuric acid. Commercially, it is prepared by the oxidation of ammonia in the presence of a catalyst. It is a dense, colorless liquid. The pure acid is unstable, but a solution containing about 68% nitric acid is fairly stable. The concentrated acid is a vigorous oxidizing agent. It reacts with metals, and hydroxides, and forms salts called nitrates. Nitric acid is used for making fertilizers, for making explosives, in the dye industry, and for making nitrocellulose plastics.

Explosives are compounds or mixtures which decompose suddenly and produce large volumes of gases.

Five oxides of nitrogen are known. Dinitrogen monoxide is mixed with oxygen and used as an anesthetic during minor operations. Nitrogen monoxide is used as a carrier of oxygen in the manufacture of sulfuric acid by the chamber process. Nitrogen dioxide is a good oxidizing agent.

TEST YOURSELF ON THESE TERMS

ammonia
ammonium
aqua regia
black gunpowder
calcium cyanamid
destructive distillation
detonator
dynamite
explosive

fixed nitrogen
fractional distillation
Haber process
hydrazine
hydrogen bond
laughing gas
niter
nitride
nitrocellulose

nitrogen fixation
nitrogen-fixing bacteria
nitroglycerin
Ostwald process
protein
shell-filler
smokeless powder
test for nitrate
test for proteins

QUESTIONS

Group A

1. (*a*) Where are large quantities of elementary nitrogen found? (*b*) In what kinds of compounds does combined nitrogen occur naturally?
2. (*a*) Who first isolated relatively pure nitrogen? (*b*) Why was the gas given the name nitrogen?
3. (*a*) Write the balanced equation for the production of nitrogen from ammonium chloride and sodium nitrite. (*b*) Of what type of reaction is this an example?
4. What is meant by *nitrogen fixation?*
5. (*a*) What are two natural methods of nitrogen fixation? (*b*) Name two artificial methods.
6. Write a balanced equation for the reaction between calcium hydroxide and ammonium nitrate for producing ammonia.
7. (*a*) What is the purpose of high pressure in the Haber process? (*b*) What is the function of the catalyst?
8. Why is *ammonia-water solution* a better name for the solution of ammonia in water than *ammonium hydroxide?*

9. Why is a glass-stoppered retort used for the laboratory preparation of nitric acid?
10. Why may zinc be used with either hydrochloric or sulfuric acids for producing hydrogen, but not with nitric acid?
11. You are given a colorless solution of a salt. Tell how you would test it to determine whether the salt is a nitrate or not.
12. What is the difference between a detonator and a shell-filler?
13. (*a*) How is dinitrogen monoxide prepared? (*b*) How is it administered as an anesthetic?
14. How could you prove that a metal is gold and not yellow brass?

Group B

15. What structural feature of the nitrogen molecule accounts for its stability?
16. How can you test a bottle of colorless gas to determine whether or not it is nitrogen?
17. Give two reasons why ammonia-water solution makes a good window cleaner.
18. What condition must be met for the reaction between sodium nitrate and sulfuric acid to run to completion?
19. Why can we remove oxygen from air by means of phosphorus without contaminating the air?
20. What must be the condition of the soil for nitrogen-fixing bacteria to be most effective?
21. What is the xanthoproteic test for proteins?
22. Why does concentrated nitric acid turn yellow in the laboratory?
23. Why might a farmer alternate crops of corn and lima beans on one of his fields in successive years?
24. Write three equations to show the steps in the production of nitric acid from ammonia.
25. The equation for the reaction of copper and dilute nitric acid indicates that nitrogen monoxide is one of the products. Yet when we carry out this reaction in an evaporating dish, a dense reddish-brown gas billows over the rim of the dish. Explain.
26. What is the oxidation number of nitrogen in: (*a*) NH_3; (*b*) N_2H_4; (*c*) N_2; (*d*) HNO_2; (*e*) HNO_3?

PROBLEMS

Group A

1. How many grams of ammonia will be produced by the reaction of steam on 160. g of calcium cyanamid?
2. What volumes of nitrogen and hydrogen are required for the preparation of 200. liters of ammonia?
3. If 15 g of HNO_3 are needed for a laboratory experiment, what mass of sodium nitrate is required for its preparation?
4. How many liters of dinitrogen monoxide may be prepared by heating 400. g of ammonium nitrate?

Group B

5. What volume of nitrogen at S.T.P. can be prepared from a mixture of 10. g of NH_4Cl and 10. g of $NaNO_2$?
6. How many grams of nitric acid can be prepared from 50.0 g of potassium nitrate of 80.0% purity?
7. (*a*) What mass of copper(II) nitrate may be prepared from 254 g of copper by reaction with nitric acid? (*b*) What volume of nitrogen monoxide is also produced?

SOME THINGS FOR YOU TO DO

1. Examine the roots of a clover plant and see if you can find the nodules that contain the nitrogen-fixing bacteria.
2. Test a sample of "household ammonia" and find the percentage of ammonia in the sample. Different brands may give interesting results. Burets and acid of known normality can be obtained from the instructor.
3. React a piece of copper with concentrated nitric acid (outdoors). Note the vigorous action of concentrated nitric acid. Do not breathe the brown fumes that are produced, and be careful not to get the nitric acid on your fingers or clothing.
4. Under the supervision of your instructor, make up a small quantity of aqua regia. Put a crumpled piece of gold foil in the aqua regia and observe the action. CAUTION: Use a hood or perform the experiment outdoors because the fumes evolved are poisonous. Do not get the acid on your skin or clothing.

Chapter 31 · PHOSPHORUS, ARSENIC, ANTIMONY, AND BISMUTH

1. The Nitrogen Family of elements is Group V of the Periodic Table. In addition to nitrogen, which we have already described, this group consists of phosphorus, arsenic, antimony, and bismuth. The table on page 453 lists certain properties of all the members of this family.

In a family of nontransition elements, the metallic properties of the elements increase as their atomic number, atomic weight, and atomic size increase. This is shown most clearly by the elements of Group V. Nitrogen and phosphorus are typical nonmetals. They show nonmetallic properties, such as covalent bonding with other atoms, and are found in the negative ions of acids. Bismuth is a typical metal in its properties. Its bonding with other elements is more ionic,

and in solution it forms hydrated positive ions. Arsenic and antimony are intermediate in character, sometimes showing metallic properties and sometimes showing the properties of non-metals.

Each of these elements has five electrons in its outer shell. Two of these electrons fill the first orbital of the outer shell. If the other three electrons are shared, the element has an oxidation number of +3. If the two electrons which already complete an orbital are also shared with two other atoms (as they may be in all the elements of this family but nitrogen) the element has an oxidation number of +5. Nitrogen and the other members of this family also attain an oxidation number of +5 by forming a double bond and two single

VOCABULARY

Alloy. A material composed of two or more metals.
Antifriction alloy. An alloy which reduces friction.
Fusible alloy. An alloy which has a low melting temperature.
Mordant. A substance which, by combining with a dye, produces a fast color in a textile fiber.

452

THE NITROGEN FAMILY

Element	Atomic Number	Atomic Weight	Electron Configuration	Principal Oxidation Numbers	Melting Point, ° C	Boiling Point, ° C	Density, 15° C
Nitrogen	7	14.0067	2, 5	−3, +3, +5	−209.9	−195.8	1.25 g/l
Phosphorus	15	30.9738	2, 8, 5	−3, +3, +5	44.1	280.	1.82 g/cm³ (white)
Arsenic	33	74.9216	2, 8, 18, 5	−3, +3, +5	814. (36 atm)	615. (sublimes)	5.73 g/cm³
Antimony	51	121.75	2, 8, 18, 18, 5	−3, +3, +5	630.5	1380.	6.69 g/cm³
Bismuth	83	208.980	2, 8, 18, 32, 18, 5	−3, +3, +5	271.3	1560.	9.75 g/cm³

bonds with three atoms. For example, the nitrate ion has the structure

$$\left[\begin{array}{c} \ddot{\text{O}} \vdots \ddot{\text{N}} \ddot{\vdots} \ddot{\text{O}} \\ \ddot{\text{O}} \end{array} \right]^{-}$$

Nitrogen, surprisingly, is the most stable member of the family. This is due to the strength of the triple bond between the two atoms in a molecule. Phosphorus is so active that one form of it will catch fire spontaneously in the air. The other elements in the family will burn when heated in air.

1. PHOSPHORUS

2. The occurrence and discovery of phosphorus. Because phosphorus is such an extremely active element, it is not found free in nature. Its most important mineral source is rock phosphate, which is composed mostly of calcium phosphate, $Ca_3(PO_4)_2$. Extensive areas of rock phosphate are found in Florida, Tennessee, and other southern states. Scientists think these deposits were produced from the accumulation of bones of prehistoric animals. Other deposits of rock phosphate have been discovered in the northern Rocky Mountains near Yellowstone Park, and in northern Af-

rica. The bones and teeth of vertebrate animals contain calcium phosphate. Phosphorus, in the form of phosphates, is also found in protoplasm, seeds, and egg yolks.

Phosphorus was discovered in 1669 by Hennig Brand, a German alchemist. The name *phosphorus*, from a Greek word meaning "light-giver," was given to the element because it glows in the dark.

3. The preparation of phosphorus. Phosphorus is prepared by heating a mixture of calcium phosphate, sand, and coke in an electric furnace. An electric arc between the two electrodes near the bottom of the furnace produces the heat energy needed for the reaction. The following equations represent the action:

$$2\ Ca_3(PO_4)_2 + 6\ SiO_2 \rightarrow$$
$$P_4O_{10} + 6\ CaSiO_3$$
$$P_4O_{10} + 10\ C \rightarrow P_4 \uparrow + 10\ CO \uparrow$$

or, combining these two equations:

$$2\ Ca_3(PO_4)_2 + 6\ SiO_2 + 10\ C \rightarrow$$
$$6\ CaSiO_3 + 10\ CO \uparrow + P_4 \uparrow$$

The sand combines with the calcium to form a calcium silicate slag which is drawn off from the bottom of the furnace. The P_4O_{10} which is thus produced

Fig. 31-1. **The mining of an extensive deposit of phosphate rock in Florida.** (International Mineral)

is reduced to elementary phosphorus by the coke. The P_4 vapors are conducted from the furnace and condensed under water. The molten phosphorus is run into molds where it solidifies in the form of sticks.

Phosphorus vapor, as well as liquid phosphorus and one of the solid allotropes, exists in the form of P_4 molecules. Frequently in equations, however, we represent phosphorus merely by its symbol, P, rather than by its molecular formula, P_4.

4. The properties of phosphorus. There are two important allotropic forms of phosphorus, *white phosphorus*, and *red phosphorus*. Their properties are so different that they will be discussed separately.

1. White phosphorus. White phosphorus is produced in the electric furnace, as described above. It is a waxy, translucent solid, with a density about twice that of water. White phosphorus is not very stable at room temperature, and on standing acquires a lemon-yellow color because of partial conversion to the more stable red allotrope. White phosphorus melts at 44° C, but since its kindling temperature is only about 35° C, the melting must be done under

water to prevent its combustion by contact with oxygen in the air.

This form of phosphorus is soft enough to be easily cut with a knife. It must always be cut under water to prevent the heat due to friction from kindling it. White phosphorus is insoluble in water, but dissolves readily in carbon disulfide and in oils.

Phosphorus vapor and liquid and solid white phosphorus all consist of P_4 molecules. In these molecules each phospho-

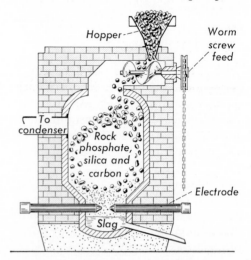

Fig. 31-2. **Phosphorus is prepared from calcium phosphate in an arc-type electric furnace.**

rus atom forms covalent bonds with the other three atoms, as shown in Fig. 31-3.

White phosphorus oxidizes readily in air, giving off dense fumes of P_4O_{10}. This compound is usually named diphosphorus pentoxide, corresponding to its empirical formula, P_2O_5, even though the molecules actually have the composition P_4O_{10}. If the oxidation of white phosphorus occurs in a dark room, a faint glow, or phosphorescence, can be seen. Phosphorus burns rapidly in air, and in oxygen with dazzling brilliancy. White phosphorus can be changed to red phosphorus by heating it to a temperature of 250° C without access to air, with a small amount of iodine as a catalyst.

CAUTION: *White phosphorus must never be handled with the fingers. It must be stored under water. It is exceedingly poisonous if taken internally.*

2. *Red phosphorus.* This allotropic form of phosphorus is a dark-red powder, believed to consist of molecules containing a large number of phosphorus atoms. It is slightly more than twice as dense as water, and insoluble in water or carbon disulfide. Pure red phosphorus is not poisonous, and it does not take fire when exposed to the air. If heated to its kindling temperature, about 250° C, it ignites and forms diphosphorus pentoxide as it burns. If heated without access to air to a temperature of about 290° C, it sublimes. White phosphorus is formed as it condenses.

5. The uses of phosphorus. Much phosphorus is converted into phosphoric acid, and its salts, the phosphates. Small quantities of phosphorus are used in making special alloys such as phosphor tin or phosphor bronze. The latter alloy is used for ship propellers, since it is not corroded by sea water. Most phosphorus, however, is used in the match industry and the fertilizer industry.

6. The manufacture of matches. The two types of matches in common use are the friction match, which can be ignited on any rough surface, and the safety match, which can be ignited by rubbing it on a prepared surface.

1. *The friction match.* By the use of continuous-operating machines, match sticks are first cut and then dipped into an ammonium phosphate solution. This prevents afterglow and lessens the danger of fire from careless handling of matches. The head end of the match is next dipped in melted paraffin. Then the first part of the head is applied. This consists of a paste containing glue, coloring matter, oxidizable matter such as sulfur, and an oxidizing agent such as potassium chlorate. The smaller portion of the head, called the tip, consists largely of tetraphosphorus trisulfide, P_4S_3. When a match is struck, the heat produced by the friction ignites the tip. This, in turn, ignites the head, the paraffin, and finally the wood of the match itself. More than a million matches an hour can be made by one of the huge match-making machines.

2. *The safety match.* The head of a safety match contains diantimony trisulfide, glue, and an oxidizing agent.

Fig. 31-3. **The structure of P_4 molecules of phosphorus.**

The striking surface upon which it is to be scratched is covered with a layer of red phosphorus, powdered glass, and glue. Such matches do not ignite easily unless rubbed against the striking surface on the box or packet.

7. **The use of phosphorus in fertilizers.** Calcium phosphate deposits are the main source of phosphorus for fertilizer. Rock phosphate itself is too insoluble to be of much value as a fertilizer, though it is used to a small extent. Commonly, rock phosphate is treated with sulfuric acid to convert it to a more soluble material called *superphosphate.* Superphosphate contains an amount of available phosphorus equivalent to 18–20% diphosphorus pentoxide.

The demand for fertilizers richer in phosphorus has encouraged the production of enriched superphosphates (23–41% P_4O_{10}) and triple superphosphate (45–48% P_4O_{10}). These products are made by reacting rock phosphate with a mixture of phosphoric and sulfuric acids or with phosphoric acid alone.

Phosphorus in fertilizers is needed especially for raising seed crops such as corn.

8. **The oxides and acids of phosphorus.** If phosphorus burns in a limited supply of air, diphosphorus trioxide, P_4O_6, is formed. (Here again, the name given to the compound corresponds to its empirical formula, P_2O_3, even though the actual composition of the molecule is P_4O_6.) P_4O_6 is the anhydride of phosphorous acid. Diphosphorus pentoxide, P_4O_{10}, is a white solid formed by burning phosphorus in a plentiful supply of air or oxygen. It is the anhydride of phosphoric acid. Its great affinity for water makes it useful for drying gases. It is also used in the manufacture of chemically resistant glassware.

Of the several acids formed by phosphorus, phosphoric acid, H_3PO_4, is the most important. It may be prepared by treating its anhydride, P_4O_{10}, with water or by the reaction of calcium phosphate and sulfuric acid.

$$Ca_3(PO_4)_2 + 3 H_2SO_4 \rightarrow$$
$$3 CaSO_4 + 2 H_3PO_4$$

Phosphoric acid is used in the food, dyeing, drug, and petroleum industries.

Phosphorous acid, H_3PO_3, metaphosphoric acid, HPO_3, and hypophosphorous acid, H_3PO_2, are best known through the usefulness of their salts.

9. **Some useful salts of the acids of phosphorus.** Since phosphoric acid is triprotic, it may form three different kinds of salts. For example, H_3PO_4 may ionize to furnish the $PO_4^{\equiv}$ ion, the $HPO_4^{=}$ ion, or the $H_2PO_4^{-}$ ion. It forms such salts as trisodium phosphate, Na_3PO_4; disodium hydrogen phosphate, Na_2HPO_4; or sodium dihydrogen phosphate, NaH_2PO_4.

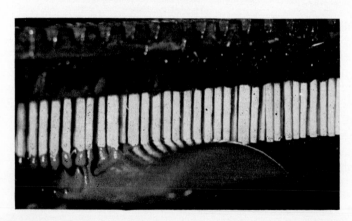

Fig. 31-4. **A close-up view of safety match sticks passing over the composition dip roll.** (Diamond Match)

Fig. 31-5. Dusting a field of cotton with calcium arsenate to reduce insect damage. (Pennsalt Chemicals)

Trisodium phosphate is used in washing powders as a water softener and detergent. Ammonium phosphate is used for fireproofing. Monocalcium phosphate is used in one type of baking powder. Phosphates, as well as certain hypophosphites, are used in medicine. Sodium hexametaphosphate, $(NaPO_3)_6$, is used for softening hard waters. It softens water without leaving a precipitate in the water.

2. ARSENIC

10. The occurrence and preparation of arsenic. Some arsenic is found uncombined in nature. It is also found in ores containing arsenic and sulfur. It is prepared from these sulfide ores by roasting them to form oxides which are then reduced with carbon to obtain metallic arsenic. Arsenic is also present as an impurity in many metallic ores. It is recovered from the chimney stacks of the smelters when these ores are processed. This is the most important source of arsenic in the United States.

11. The properties of arsenic. Metallic arsenic is a brittle, gray solid. When freshly cut, it has a bright metallic luster which rapidly tarnishes in moist air. It exists in three allotropic forms. Chemically it may act as a metal and form oxides and chlorides. It may also act as a nonmetal and form acids which are analogous to those of phosphorus. When heated, arsenic sublimes and forms a yellow vapor, As_4, which has the odor of garlic.

When ignited, arsenic burns with a pale-blue flame and forms diarsenic trioxide, As_4O_6. (As was the case with the oxides of phosphorus, the name corresponds to the empirical formula, even though the actual formula is As_4O_6.) Arsenic unites indirectly with hydrogen to form arsine, AsH_3, a compound analogous to ammonia, which is a deadly poisonous gas.

12. The uses of arsenic and its compounds. Metallic arsenic is little used. A small amount is added to lead used for making shot. It hardens the shot and makes it more nearly spherical.

Diarsenic trioxide is used in producing other compounds of arsenic and in making some kinds of glass. A third use is as a preservative of animal skins that are to be mounted. Some medicines contain small quantities of arsenic compounds.

CAUTION: *While very small amounts of arsenic have medicinal value, larger quantities are extremely poisonous.*

Arsenic compounds make excellent insecticides. Paris green, a compound of copper and arsenic, is used to destroy certain beetles and other insect pests. However, it is now being replaced by the arsenates of lead and calcium. Enormous quantities of lead arsenate, $Pb_3(AsO_4)_2$, are used every year for spraying fruit trees and other plants. Calcium arsenate, $Ca_3(AsO_4)_2$, is also used as an insecticide.

3. ANTIMONY

13. The occurrence and preparation of antimony. Some antimony is found free in nature. Its most important ore is *stibnite*, a sulfide of antimony, Sb_2S_3. Antimony is usually prepared from stibnite by reduction with iron. While China has been the chief source of antimony, deposits in Bolivia and Mexico are now being developed. Since very little antimony is found in the United States, most of this element must be imported.

14. The properties of antimony. Antimony is a dense, brittle, silver-white metal with a bright metallic luster. It is less active than arsenic, and exists in several allotropic forms. When strongly heated in air, antimony forms a white oxide, diantimony trioxide, Sb_4O_6. (Again the name corresponds to the empirical formula, not the actual one.) This compound is amphiprotic. It reacts with hydroxides to form antimonites, and with acids to form antimony(III) salts. Pure antimony is not affected by hydrochloric acid, but reacts readily in aqua regia and forms antimony penta-

Fig. 31-6. **This slug of type metal contains antimony, tin, and lead.** (Mergenthaler)

chloride, $SbCl_5$. Antimonates, which are compounds analogous to the phosphates and arsenates, are also known.

15. The nature of an alloy. If two or more metals are melted together, an alloy may be formed. In some cases, the alloy seems to be a mixture of the metals. In a few cases, the proportion is definite, and a compound appears to have been formed. In still other cases, alloys contain interlocking crystals of the pure elements. In the majority of cases, the alloy is a solid solution of one or more metals dissolved in another metal.

An alloy may have properties unlike those of any of its constituents. Its properties may also be intermediate, somewhat like each constituent. Usually the melting point of the alloy is lower than the average melting point of its constituents. In many cases it is lower than the melting point of any one of them. This is easily explained when we remember that the melting point of a solution is lower than that of the pure solvent.

16. The uses of antimony. Type metal contains antimony, tin, and lead. Antimony is important for type metal because it causes this alloy to expand when it solidifies. The edges of the type which is cast from this alloy thus are sharp and distinct.

An antifriction alloy of lead and antimony is used between the bearing surfaces of the moving parts of machinery.

The friction of steel sliding over this antifriction alloy is much less than the friction of steel sliding over steel.

An alloy of lead and antimony is used for the plates in storage batteries. This alloy is stronger and more resistant to acids than is lead alone. Thus battery plates made from the alloy are more durable.

17. Some compounds of antimony. Only a few of the compounds of antimony are used extensively. The sulfides are used in matches, and as pigments. Red rubber contains diantimony trisulfide. Tartar emetic, potassium antimonyl tartrate, $KSbOC_4H_4O_6$, is used as a mordant in the dyeing of cotton goods. A mordant is generally an insoluble gelatinous material which fastens itself to the fibers of a fabric. When this mordanted cloth is later dyed, the dye in some way, perhaps by adsorption, unites with the mordant. Thus the mordant helps to make the dye fast by producing a strong dye-to-fabric linkage.

CAUTION: *The soluble compounds of antimony are nearly as poisonous as the compounds of arsenic. Tartar emetic, $KSbOC_4H_4O_6$,*

containing antimony, must not be confused with cream of tartar, potassium hydrogen tartrate, $KHC_4H_4O_6$, which is used in baking powder.

4. BISMUTH

18. The sources, preparation, and properties of bismuth. Bismuth, which is found in certain regions of Bolivia and Canada, generally resembles antimony. However, it is denser and has a pinkish tinge. In the United States it is obtained principally as a by-product in the smelting of copper, lead, and zinc ores. Its acid-forming properties are less marked than those of antimony, but it forms bases more readily. It exists in two allotropic forms. Like antimony, bismuth expands when it solidifies.

19. The uses of bismuth. The chief use of bismuth is in the manufacture of fusible alloys. Two such alloys, Wood's metal and Rose's metal, melt below the temperature of boiling water. The automatic valves used in sprinkler systems in factories, stores, and warehouses contain plugs made of fusible alloys. If a fire starts, the fusible plug in the valve melts and releases the water automatically to extinguish the fire. Bismuth may be melted and used to make castings. It can be shaped if it is first heated above 225° to make it more malleable and ductile.

20. Some compounds of bismuth. If water is added to bismuth nitrate, $Bi(NO_3)_3$, hydrolysis occurs and bismuthyl nitrate, $BiONO_3$, is formed. It is used medicinally for relieving digestive disturbances. Bismuthyl carbonate is used for similar purposes. Other compounds of bismuth are used in paints and pottery glazes.

Fig. 31-7. An antifriction alloy is packed in a bearing to help reduce the friction produced when the shaft turns in the bearing. (Cleveland Graphite)

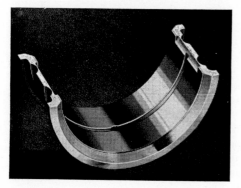

SUMMARY

The Nitrogen Family consists of nitrogen, phosphorus, arsenic, antimony, and bismuth. As the elements of this family increase in atomic number, atomic weight, and atomic size, their properties undergo a transition from nonmetallic to metallic nature.

Phosphorus occurs in nature as calcium phosphate. It is extracted by heating the calcium phosphate with sand and coke in an arc-type electric furnace. Of the allotropic forms of phosphorus, white phosphorus and red phosphorus are most common. White phosphorus is active, even at room temperature. It burns with a hot flame, forming diphosphorus pentoxide. Red phosphorus is inactive at low temperatures. Phosphorus is used in making alloys, in the match industry, and as phosphates in fertilizers.

Arsenic is used for hardening shot. Its compounds are used in medicines and as insecticides.

Antimony is used in alloys. Its compounds are used in matches, as pigments, and to form mordants in dyeing.

Bismuth is used in the manufacture of fusible alloys. Its salts are used in medicine.

TEST YOURSELF ON THESE TERMS

alloy	Paris green	safety match
antifriction alloy	phosphor bronze	stibnite
friction match	phosphor tin	tartar emetic
fusible alloy	red phosphorus	type metal
mordant	rock phosphate	white phosphorus

QUESTIONS

Group A

1. What is the principal mineral source of phosphorus?
2. What foods are important sources of phosphorus?
3. What precautions must always be observed when handling white phosphorus?
4. Why does white phosphorus become lemon-yellow on standing?
5. (a) How is white phosphorus converted to red phosphorus? (b) How can red phosphorus be changed to white phosphorus?
6. What are the two most important uses for phosphorus?
7. Give two uses for diphosphorus pentoxide.
8. Should the preparation of arsenic be classed as a product or a by-product of smelting operations?
9. Why must extreme care be used in handling arsenic and its compounds?
10. Explain how fusible alloys are used in automatic sprinkling devices.
11. What is the function of a mordant in dyeing?
12. What bismuth compounds are used in medicine?

Group B

13. Describe the commercial production of phosphorus from rock phosphate.
14. (*a*) What is the formula for a molecule of solid white phosphorus? (*b*) Why do we usually not use this formula in equation writing?
15. Explain what happens when a friction match is struck.
16. Why are "safety" matches given this name?
17. Give the formulas and names of the three possible potassium salts of phosphoric acid.
18. (*a*) In what ways do metals form alloys? (*b*) How do the properties of an alloy compare with those of the metals of which it is composed?
19. Diphosphorus pentoxide is usually stored in glass, plastic-capped bottles, which have been sealed with wax. Why is this so?
20. (*a*) What are the electronegativity values for the members of the Nitrogen Family? (*b*) How do these correlate with the observed transition from nonmetallic to metallic properties with increasing atomic number?

PROBLEMS

Group A

1. How many pounds of phosphorus may be prepared from 620. lb of $Ca_3(PO_4)_2$ in an electric furnace?
2. What mass of calcium phosphate must be heated with sulfuric acid to produce 49.0 g of H_3PO_4?
3. Calculate the percentage composition of calcium arsenate.

Group B

4. How many grams of $SbCl_3$ can be prepared by the reaction of 10.0 g of antimony with chlorine?
5. Assume that P_4O_{10}, when used as a dehydrating agent, forms H_3PO_4 according to the following equation: $P_4O_{10} + 6 H_2O \rightarrow 4 H_3PO_4$. What mass of water can be combined with 50.0 g of P_4O_{10}?
6. A compound contains 96.15% arsenic and 3.85% hydrogen. Its vapor has a specific gravity, air standard, of 2.695. What is the molecular formula of the compound? Use accurate atomic weights.

SOME THINGS FOR YOU TO DO

1. Under the direction of your instructor, dissolve a piece of white phosphorus no bigger than a small match head in 5 ml of carbon disulfide. Lay a sheet of filter paper on an asbestos board, pour enough of the solution over it to moisten the paper, and stand back to await results. CAUTION: *Keep flames away from carbon disulfide. Do not save any of the solution of phosphorus in carbon disulfide.*
2. Pour a few ml of a 5% solution of $CuSO_4$ over a small piece of burning phosphorus. The phosphorus becomes incased in copper, preventing further combustion. This technique is used in treating phosphorus burns.

CHECK YOUR PROGRESS IN CHEMISTRY

1. What are the principal chemical properties of the members of the Sodium Family?
2. What are the main differences in chemical properties between the elements of the Calcium Family and those of the Sodium Family?
3. What are the principal chemical properties of the members of the Halogen Family?
4. How do the reactions of oxygen and sulfur with metals compare with the reactions of the halogens with metals?
5. What property of the inert gases constitutes their chemistry?
6. In what important ways does the Nitrogen Family differ from both the Sodium Family and the Halogen Family?
7. What unusual property does carbon have that is not shown by any other element we have yet described?
8. (*a*) In what way is hydrogen like the members of the Sodium Family? (*b*) Give several ways in which its behavior differs.
9. (*a*) What are the important gases of the air? (*b*) What is the percentage of each by volume in air?
10. Give several examples of striking changes in properties shown by common materials when chilled in liquid air.
11. Does the usefulness of the inert gases depend upon their physical properties or their chemical properties? Explain.
12. You are given some white crystals which the flame test shows is a sodium compound. How could you tell whether it is sodium chloride, sodium carbonate, sodium sulfite, or sodium nitrate?
13. For what purposes is elementary nitrogen used?
14. Draw electron-dot formulas for ammonia and ammonium ion.

CHALLENGING YOUR KNOWLEDGE

1. Measure the length, width, and height of your chemistry laboratory in meters. Read and record the barometric pressure and the temperature. Calculate the mass of the air in the laboratory under your recorded conditions.
2. Why do you think Faraday failed to liquefy oxygen, hydrogen, and nitrogen, yet he was successful in liquefying chlorine and sulfur dioxide?
3. Why do steel companies often market ammonium sulfate for use as a fertilizer?
4. Why would you expect anhydrous ammonia to be a very poor conductor of electricity?
5. A laboratory bottle contains many small pieces of white phosphorus. How can you mold them into a single chunk?

Unit 10 · THE COLLOIDAL STATE

Colloidal Suspensions
Suspensoids and Emulsoids

Chapter 32 · COLLOIDAL SUSPENSIONS

1. THE COLLOIDAL STATE

1. Colloidal suspensions. In 1861 a Scottish scientist, Thomas Graham (1805–1869), performed a series of experiments with starch, glue, and sugar in water. He enclosed these materials in parchment bags which he suspended in water, as in Fig. 32-1. He observed that substances that crystallize easily passed through the parchment readily. He called these materials *crystalloids*. Sticky substances, on the other hand (starch and glue in water), passed through the membrane hardly at all. He called these materials *colloids*, from the Greek word for glue. Sugar and salt form *true solutions* when added to water, because they are dispersed through the liquid as molecules or ions. Colloids only *appear* to go into solution when added to water. Actually, they are dispersed as particles larger than ordinary molecules, and are too large to pass through the parchment. Since Graham's time *the word colloid has been broadened to include any dispersion of particles of very small size that are larger than simple*

molecules. We still call such mixtures colloids, although they may not have anything to do with sticky substances such as those which Graham investigated.

Later investigations showed that some materials, under certain conditions, were nondiffusing and colloidal in behavior. Yet under different conditions, they were crystalline in nature. About 65 years ago enough evidence was available

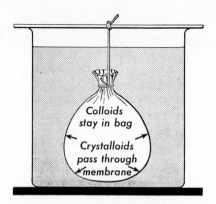

Fig. 32-1. **A colloidal dispersion is held back by the parchment membrane, permitting it to be separated from substances in solution. This process is called dialysis.**

464

to prove that *the state of subdivision, rather than the chemical nature of a material, determines whether it forms a suspension or a true solution when dispersed in a second medium.* Sodium chloride may form a colloidal suspension if the sodium ions and chloride ions are brought together in a medium in which sodium chloride is not soluble.

A true solution is formed when a solute, as molecules or ions, diffuses throughout the solvent to form a homogeneous mixture. It consists of a *single phase.* The solute is said to be soluble in the solvent. *A colloidal suspension, on the other hand, is a two-phase system having dispersed particles rather than a solute, and a dispersing medium rather than a solvent.* The dispersed substance (*internal phase*) cannot be soluble in the dispersing medium (*external phase*). It must consist of finely divided particles which remain suspended in the medium.

2. The range of colloidal size. The colloidal state has been called *the world of neglected dimensions.* It lies between true solutions which are homogeneous, and temporary mixtures which separate on standing. Colloidal size has no fixed limits. However, particles between mo-

lecular size and a size great enough to be seen in the optical microscope are said to be colloidal. This includes particles with diameters ranging from approximately 10 Å to 1000 Å. (The Ångstrom has been used in earlier chapters in describing the diameters of molecules; $1 \text{ Å} = 10^{-8}$ cm.) Ordinary simple molecules are only a few Ångstroms in diameter. The diameter of protein macromolecules may approach 100 Å and their molecular weights may be several hundred thousand. Viruses, known to be large protein molecules, may have molecular weights between one million and one billion. These macromolecular substances are well within the colloidal range.

If the size of the dispersed particles is at the lower limit of the colloidal range, a dispersion may begin to have the characteristics of a solution. As the size of the dispersed particles approaches the upper limit of the colloidal range, a dispersion may begin to show the properties of an ordinary suspension. Thus we see that there is no definite division between the true solution and the colloidal state on one hand, and the colloidal state and the ordinary suspension on the other.

VOCABULARY

Adsorption. The concentration of a gas, liquid, or solid on the surface of a solid or liquid.

Colloidal state. A state of subdivision of matter ranging between the dimensions of ordinary molecules and microscopic particles.

Colloidal suspension. A two-phase system having dispersed particles suspended in a dispersing medium.

Dispersion. A scattering, or state of being scattered.

Emulsoid. A colloidal system in which there is a strong attraction between the dispersed substance and the dispersing liquid.

Suspensoid. A colloidal suspension in which there is little attraction between the dispersed substance and the dispersing liquid.

Hydrogen   Average Colloidal   Visible
atom   molecule particle   particle

(not drawn to scale)

Fig. 32-2. The colloidal range of particle size lies between that of simple molecules and visible particles.

3. Types of colloidal suspensions. Since there are three (physical) states of matter—gas, liquid, and solid—we might assume that there are nine possible types of dispersions. However, all gases consist of simple molecules, and molecules of one gas may mix completely in any proportion with the molecules of another gas. Therefore, disperse systems of *gas-in-gas* cannot occur. The eight possible types of colloidal systems are listed in the accompanying table together with typical examples of each.

Colloidal Dispersion	Example
Liquid in gas	Fog, clouds
Solid in gas	Smoke
Gas in liquid	Whipped cream
Liquid in liquid	Cream, mayonnaise
Solid in liquid	Glue, India ink
Gas in solid	Floating soap
Liquid in solid	Opal, jelly
Solid in solid	Ruby glass

The properties of most colloidal systems fall into two general patterns of behavior. These depend primarily on the relationship which exists between the internal and external phases.

1. *Lyophobic* (ly-oh-*foh*-bik) *systems.* Suppose we prepare a dispersion of diarsenic trisulfide, As_2S_3, in water. Since water can disperse only a small amount of diarsenic trisulfide, *the concentration of the internal phase (the diarsenic trisulfide) is low.* The dispersed particles have negligible attraction for the water. Consequently this dispersion *has the same fluidity (viscosity) as pure water.* The particles of diarsenic trisulfide become negatively charged due to adsorption of hydroxide ions. If a solution of an electrolyte such as hydrochloric acid is added, *the dispersion coagulates and precipitates due to the loss of the charge.* The behavior of this diarsenic trisulfide dispersion is typical of *lyophobic colloids,* called **suspensoids.**

2. *Lyophilic* (ly-oh-*fih*-lik) *systems.* If a relatively large amount of powdered gelatin is mixed in water and the dispersion is allowed to stand, it *sets* to form a firm *gel* or *jelly.* The dispersed particles of gelatin have a strong attraction for the dispersing medium (the water) and become thoroughly hydrated. This traps the water in such a way that *the viscosity of the system increases.* The relative concentration of gelatin is high and *small additions of solutions of electrolytes have little effect on the jelly.* The behavior of gelatin in water is typical of *lyophilic colloids,* which are called **emulsoids.**

Because of this significant difference between lyophobic colloids and lyophilic colloids, their characteristics and properties will be considered separately in Chapter 33.

Since the dispersed phase of colloidal systems consists of extremely finely divided particles, the surface area of this phase is enormous. Under such circumstances actions peculiar to *surface* will be most important. Therefore some of the characteristics of surface behavior should be examined before specific colloidal suspensions are considered. *This study of surface properties is called surface chemistry.*

2. SURFACE CHEMISTRY

4. The effect of subdivision on the properties of substances. Colloidal particles have a tremendous *specific surface*. *Specific surface is the ratio of the surface area of the particles to their volume.* If a one-inch cube of soft clay is divided across the middle of each face, eight smaller cubes are formed (see Fig. 32-3). The surface area of the one-inch cube was 6 in², but the total surface area of the eight smaller cubes is 12 in². The total surface area has been doubled by this division, but the total volume of material has remained the same. *Thus the specific surface has been doubled.* If each of the half-inch cubes is divided as before, the specific surface is again doubled. If we proceed in this manner until the original volume of material has been reduced to colloidal dimensions, the surface area will be more than 200 acres!

This great increase in surface results in a corresponding increase in the number of surface molecules, or ions, or atoms, as the case may be. Surface molecules are those which are no longer surrounded on all sides by molecules similar to themselves. This increase in the number of surface molecules is always accompanied by changes in physical properties and the appearance of new properties.

It is the appearance of these new properties with the subdivision of matter that characterizes the colloidal state. Changes may occur in solubility, melting point, heat of solution, and color of the subdivided material. With this vast increase in surface there appears a peculiar phenomenon called adsorption.

5. The nature of adsorption. *Adsorption may be defined as the concentration of a gas, liquid, or solid on the surface of a liquid or solid with which it is in contact.* The adsorption of a gas on a solid is sometimes referred to as *occlusion.* The material providing the surface upon which adsorption occurs is known as the **adsorbent.** The material adsorbed is called the **adsorbate.** Because of the tremendous surface of particles of colloidal dimensions, a remarkable amount of adsorption may occur. One volume of palladium black (finely divided palladium metal) adsorbs nearly 1000 volumes of hydrogen. A gas cylinder, first filled with activated charcoal and then with nitrogen under pressure, discharges over 65% more nitrogen than

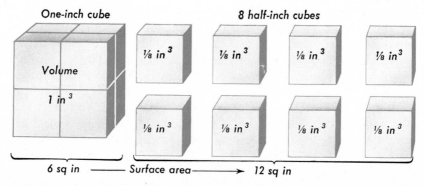

Fig. 32-3. **The specific surface of a substance is increased when the surface area is increased and the volume remains constant.**

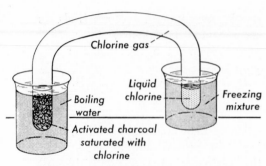

Fig. 32-4. **Liquefaction of chlorine. Ad-sorbed chlorine is released as the temperature of the charcoal is raised; the pressure of the chlorine gas increases and liquid chlorine forms in the upper end of the tube.**

it would without the charcoal. An ad-sorbent is *activated* by heating it to free its surface of adsorbed gases.

Adsorption is selective. This means that a given adsorbent shows a preference for one adsorbate over another. Activated coconut charcoal used in gas mask canisters selectively adsorbs most toxic gases in preference to oxygen and nitrogen even though the poisons may be present in the atmosphere in relatively minor proportions. In general, *gases of low volatility are adsorbed more readily then those of higher volatility.*

Adsorption is specific. The extent to which any substance is adsorbed under any given set of conditions depends on the physical and chemical natures of the adsorbent and adsorbate. We may, however, list two general rules which apply to adsorption of gases on solids.

1. *Effect of pressure.* The adsorption of a gas on a solid *increases* with *increase* in pressure.

2. *Effect of temperature.* Adsorption is *increased* as the temperature of a system is *decreased*.

6. **Some practical applications of adsorption.** The use of activated char-

coal in gas cylinders to store nitrogen and in gas masks has been mentioned. Several different *ad*sorbents may be used together with selected *ab*sorbents in gas mask canisters to provide protection against various combinations of gases which may be irritating or toxic.

Activated charcoal is used in liquefying gases, to obtain extremely high vacuums, and in the separation of gases. Helium is the least readily adsorbed of any known substance. It may be separated from the other inert gases by permitting them to be adsorbed on cold activated charcoal. Activated alumina, Al_2O_3, made by moderately heating aluminum hydroxide, is an effective adsorbent for water vapor. It is useful for removing water vapor from various gases. Activated alumina is often used in the chemistry laboratory as a desiccant. A considerable saving in fuel is realized by passing air through silica gel before it is forced into blast furnaces.

You have probably seen evidence of the adsorption of gases from the atmosphere on glass. Two pieces of glass tubing may be welded together by bringing them into contact in the flame of a Bunsen burner. The rise in temperature causes the gas molecules to be released from the glass surfaces. This enables the surfaces of the two tubes to make contact and cohere.

A liquid adsorbed on the surface of a solid is said to *wet* the solid. Water will wet clean glass but mercury will not. It is possible to float powders on water because of the slowness with which the particles adsorb water. This is the basis for *flotation processes* used in the concentration of ores. Diamonds are separated from *blue earth* by passing it over greased tables.

Exhausted oil sands have been made productive again by the addition of water or sodium carbonate solution. These are strongly adsorbed on the surface of the sand and displace more oil. Formations of glazes on pottery and of baked enamels on metals depend on the molten *frit* being adsorbed on the surface and remaining there after it cools.

The relative sizes of the particles of two solids seems to determine which is adsorbed on the other. If one is much finer than the other the finer will be adsorbed on the coarser. If the two solids are of different colors, the mixture will have the color of the one adsorbed. This fact is taken into account in the manufacture of paints.

Slow-setting cement consists of finely powdered gypsum which is adsorbed on the coarser cement particles. Manufacturers of chewing gum have made use of the fact that the first taste of a mixture of sugar and paprika is very sweet if the sugar in the mixture is very finely powdered.

★ A *hydrogen electrode* may be used as a reference electrode in an electrochemical cell. A layer of finely divided platinum is deposited on a platinum wire or foil by electrolysis. The electrode is then placed in the solution and hydrogen gas is passed over it. Hydrogen is adsorbed on the relatively great surface of the platinum. Thus, in effect, the electrode presents a surface of hydrogen to the solution and acts as a "metallic" hydrogen electrode. The hydrogen electrode provides chemists with a direct method of determining the pH of solutions. An electrochemical series such as that shown in Chapter 23 is compiled using the hydrogen electrode as a reference.

7. Contact catalysts are important in industry. Many reactions are brought about, or speeded, by contact with the surface of certain solids. As these solids are not permanently altered by the re-

actions in which they are involved we may consider them to be catalytic agents. Due to the nature of the catalytic action they are known as *contact catalysts* or simply **contact agents.**

If even a minute quantity of the catalyst is subdivided to collodial size, it presents a very great surface area to the reacting substances. The reactants are then adsorbed on the surface of the contact agent, effecting an increase in the concentration of the reacting substances. This produces a corresponding increase in the reaction speed. Many chemical industries are vitally interested in catalytic research. Consequently, catalytic agents, as well as the way in which they are used, are sometimes closely guarded trade secrets.

In the Haber process for the synthesis of ammonia, a contact agent, usually iron with the oxides of aluminum and

Fig. 32-5. Hydrogen electrode, the standard reference electrode for the electrochemical series.

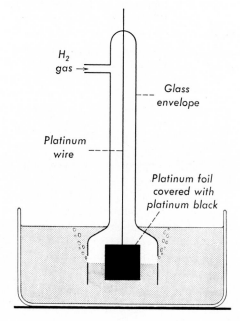

H₂ gas →

Glass envelope

Platinum wire

Platinum foil covered with platinum black

potassium, is necessary to make the process economically feasible. Platinum gauze is employed as a contact agent in the synthesis of nitric acid by the Ostwald process. Finely divided vanadium pentoxide, or platinum, is similarly used in the contact process for manufacturing sulfuric acid.

The hydrogenation of vegetable oils to form solid fats is accomplished by using colloidal nickel. The semisolid vegetable shortenings used in many American homes are partially hydrogenated products from such liquid fats as cottonseed oil. Complete hydrogenation forms hard, brittle fats. Methanol is sometimes referred to as wood alcohol because it was originally produced by the destructive distillation of wood.

Methanol is now made synthetically from carbon monoxide and hydrogen in the presence of zinc chromite.

8. Catalytic poisoning. Chemical reactions that employ contact catalysts must be very carefully controlled. The presence of even slight amounts of certain foreign substances may seriously retard, or even stop, the chemical action. Chemists believe that these materials are preferentially adsorbed on the surface of the contact agent and prevent the molecules or ions of the reactants from reaching the surface of the catalyst. Such substances are known as *catalytic poisons*. Partial poisoning of a catalyst may be deliberately induced as a means of controlling the activity of a contact agent.

SUMMARY

A colloidal suspension is a two-phase system of a dispersed phase and a dispersing medium. The dispersed substance is known as the internal phase, and the dispersing medium is known as the external phase. Colloidal systems are characterized by insolubility rather than solubility as in true solutions. The collodial state is one of physical subdivision rather than chemical nature.

Colloids fall into an intermediate position between molecular size and visible size, and range in diameters from 10 to 1000 Ångstroms. There is no fine line of demarcation between solutions and colloidal suspensions, and between colloidal suspensions and temporary suspensions.

Colloidal suspensions may be grouped into two general systems depending on the relationship between the internal and external phases. These are called lyophobic colloids, or suspensoids, and lyophilic colloids, or emulsoids.

The subdivision of materials results in a great increase in specific surface. Adsorption is a surface phenomenon of prime significance in the realm of colloids. Adsorption is both selective and specific. The adsorption of a gas on a solid is known as occlusion. Occlusion is influenced by both temperature and pressure. There are many practical applications of adsorption throughout the chemical industry.

Contact catalysts may be colloidal in nature. By occlusion, the concentration of gaseous reactants may be increased, resulting in a corresponding increase in reaction speed. Catalytic poisoning may result from the presence of slight amounts of impurities. Poisoning of a catalyst may be deliberately induced to retard or stop a reaction.

TEST YOURSELF ON THESE TERMS

activated
adsorbate
adsorbent
adsorption
catalytic poison
colloid
colloidal state

colloidal suspension
contact agent
dispersed particles
dispersing medium
dispersion
emulsoid
external phase

internal phase
lyophilic colloid
lyophobic colloid
occlusion
specific surface
surface chemistry
suspensoid

QUESTIONS

Group A

1. What is the colloidal range of particle size?
2. Name eight possible types of colloidal suspensions.
3. Why is it not possible to have a colloidal suspension of a gas in a gas?
4. List three characteristics which are typical of lyophobic colloids.
5. List three characteristics typical of lyophilic colloids.
6. Distinguish between a true solution and a colloidal suspension.
7. Distinguish between the *internal* phase and the *external* phase of a colloidal system.
8. (*a*) What is the meaning of *specific surface?* (*b*) What is the relationship between the specific surface and the extent of subdivision of a substance?
9. Distinguish between *adsorption* and *absorption*.
10. How is an adsorbent activated?

Group B

11. What distinction did Graham make between *crystalloids* and *colloids?*
12. Explain why we now consider the colloidal state to depend on the subdivision rather than the chemical nature of a substance.
13. How can you account for the changes in physical properties and the appearance of new properties which accompany the subdivision of a substance to colloidal dimensions?
14. What conditions of temperature and pressure would you maintain if you were interested in causing a large volume of a gas to be adsorbed on a solid?
15. How would you treat a lump of charcoal in preparing it to act as an adsorbent for a gas?
16. Explain why an army gas mask is effective in removing poison gases from the air breathed by the soldier wearing it.
17. A solid which is more dense than water may be floated on the surface of the water if it is first reduced to a fine powder. Explain.
18. Given two solids each capable of adsorbing the other, what determines which will be adsorbed on the surface of the other when they are mixed?
19. Explain how a contact catalyst may act to bring about or speed up a chemical reaction.
★20. Explain how a hydrogen electrode is formed.

21. Explain why the viscosity of a suspensoid is quite similar to that of the dispersing medium alone.
22. A suspensoid is formed with pure water acting as the dispersing medium. The particles of the internal phase are found to have acquired a negative charge. What possible source of this negative charge can you suggest?
23. It is found that the addition of a very small quantity of an electrolyte such as hydrochloric acid to the negatively charged suspensoid of Question 22 causes the dispersion to precipitate. What does this reveal about the concentration of the internal phase of the suspensoid?

SOME THINGS FOR YOU TO DO

1. Prepare a demonstration illustrating different types of colloidal suspensions. Improvise from materials which are readily available. Your instructor may be able to provide you with some tested demonstrations.
2. Prepare a colloidal suspension of iron(III) hydroxide in water by adding dropwise a small amount of iron(III) chloride solution to boiling water. Place in a cellophane bag suspended in a beaker of water. Place a solution of copper(II) sulfate in a second bag similarly suspended in a beaker of water. Observe over a period of several days. How can you account for the difference in behavior you observe?

Chapter 33 · SUSPENSOIDS AND EMULSOIDS

1. SUSPENSOIDS

1. The characteristics of suspensoids. *Lyophobic colloidal* systems, or suspensoids, were described in Section 3, Chapter 32. Several different media are used for suspending the colloidal particles. When water is the suspending medium the term *hydrosol* is used. Thus a colloidal dispersion of metallic gold in water is called a gold hydrosol. In *organosols* an organic liquid makes up the external phase. *Aerosols* are suspensoids in which a gas is the dispersing medium. This type of suspensoid is produced when an insecticide is released from a spray bomb.

2. The properties of suspensoids. The size of colloidal particles, together with the resulting vast specific surface, is responsible for the unusual properties of colloidal dispersions. Some of these properties are:

1. Brownian movement. In 1827 Robert Brown, an English botanist, observed the haphazard motion of pollen dust in water while viewing the suspension through his microscope. He suspected

that the motion was in some way associated with the life process. However, when he examined other suspended materials, which could in no way be related to living matter, he observed similar motion.

With the invention of the *ultramicroscope* about 1900 by the German chemist Richard Zsigmondy (1865–1929),

Fig. 33-1. **When an aerosol bomb is used, a suspensoid is produced in which air is the dispersing medium. The propellent is usually "Freon."** (du Pont)

the colloidal range could be studied directly. Brownian movement was rediscovered by Zsigmondy in a gold hydrosol. He described the astonishing motion of the tiny gold particles as "a swarm of dancing gnats in a sunbeam." Careful investigations have eliminated all possible outside factors as the cause of these random motions. *Thus we may conclude that the forces which act upon the dispersed particles are the result of collisions between these particles and the molecules of the dispersing medium.* This offers an excellent proof of the kinetic theory of matter.

We see here the *first* of three general reasons why colloidal suspensions do not settle. *The influence of gravity is not great enough to overcome the collision forces of the dispersing medium on particles which show Brownian movement.* Consequently they do not settle. A gold hydrosol prepared by Michael Faraday over one hundred years ago still exists as a colloidal suspension. The two remaining reasons for the stabilization of colloidal suspensions will appear later in this chapter.

2. *Tyndall effect.* If a beam of light is directed into a darkened room, a surprising amount of dust is observed suspended in the air of the room. Rays of light are deflected sidewise, or *scattered*, from the surfaces of the dust particles. If the particles responsible for the scattering are extremely small, the scattered light will be somewhat bluish. Smoke suspended in air sometimes appears blue and distant haze usually has a bluish tint. The blue sky and, in certain instances, the blue color of bodies of water are due to the scattering of light.

Suppose a strong beam of light is directed through a true solution, or through pure water, in a darkened room. There is little evidence of scattering; the beam is practically invisible. When light is passed through a colloidal dis-

VOCABULARY

Aerosol (*a*-er-oh-sol). A suspensoid in which gas is the dispersing medium.

Biocolloid. Lyophilic colloidal systems existing within plant and animal organisms.

Gangue (gang). Worthless rock or earthy material in which valuable minerals occur.

Gel (jel). A jelly-like mass consisting of a colloidal suspension of a liquid in a solid.

Hydrosol (*hy*-droh-sol). A suspensoid in which water is the dispersing medium.

Organosol (or-*gan*-oh-sol). A suspensoid in which an organic liquid is the dispersing medium.

Protective agent. A colloidal substance which when adsorbed on suspended particles stabilizes the system.

Scattering. The deflection of rays of light sidewise by particles of suspended matter.

Ultramicroscope. A microscope in which the object is illuminated by a light source at right angles to the optical axis of the microscope.

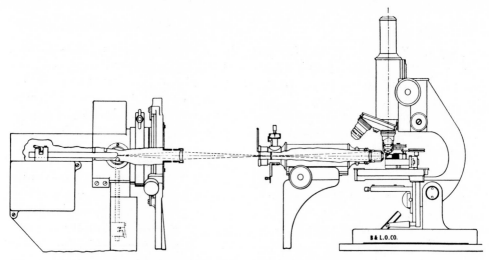

Fig. 33-2. **The path of light through a slit ultramicroscope. The ultramicroscope makes it possible to observe the light scattered by colloidal particles too small to be seen with an ordinary microscope.** (Bausch and Lomb)

person, however, the beam is plainly visible. This diffusion of light by colloidal particles is known as the **Tyndall effect,** after the English physicist John Tyndall (1820–1893). It may be used to detect suspended particles.

3. *Structural colors.* A physical chemist might classify all colors under two headings: *pigment* colors and *structural* colors. Pigment colors are due to the absorption by the pigment of some portions of the white light illuminating a substance. The color observed is the complement of that absorbed. Colored inorganic substances generally contain elements found in the central region of the Periodic Table. The halogenides of

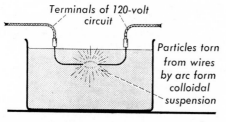

Terminals of 120-volt circuit

Particles torn from wires by arc form colloidal suspension

Fig. 33-3. **A Bredig arc. Less active metals may be used to form hydrosols. More active metals form organosols.**

the Sodium and Calcium Families are colorless. Anhydrous copper(II) sulfate is not colored, but water solutions prepared from anhydrous copper(II) sulfate or from the crystalline hydrate, $CuSO_4 \cdot 5\,H_2O$, are blue. Observe that it is the $Cu(H_2O)_4^{++}$ ion that is colored. Scientists believe that pigment colors are associated with the electronic arrangement of particles.

Structural colors, on the other hand, are due to the physical structure of the mass. They are not dependent upon the electronic configuration of the substance. The color of colloidal suspensions is usually structural. There is no blue pigment in the blue feathers of birds. Tiny air bubbles dispersed throughout the solid matter of the feathers are responsible for the scattering of light. There are no blue pigments in the irises of blue eyes. Green and gray eyes result from the combined effect of structural blue, and yellow and brown pigments. The eye of the albino lacks both structural and pigment colors.

A very dilute solution of $FeCl_3$ possess a faint yellow pigment color due to the hydrated Fe^{+++} ion. If such a solution is boiled, colloidal $Fe(OH)_3$ is formed, resulting in a rich deep-red structural color. The quantity of iron present remains the same.

4. Electric charge. Scientists have learned that the dispersed particles of lyophobic colloids are electrically charged in a stable system. Some types possess positive charge and others negative charge. However, within a system all suspended particles have the same kind of electric charge. Since particles with like charge repel each other, their mutual repulsion prevents them from joining together and settling out. Thus the system tends to remain stable. Here we have the *second* reason why colloidal suspensions do not settle: *The accumulation of similar charges on the suspended particles holds them apart thus stabilizing the system.*

The charge is generally acquired by adsorbing positive or negative ions from the dispersing medium. The external phase has the charge opposite to that on the dispersed particles and the system as a whole is neutral. Most colloidal metals, sulfides, and acid dyestuffs acquire a *negative* charge. Most colloidal oxides and hydroxides of metals and basic dyestuffs become *positively* charged. Proteins appear to gain either a positive or a negative charge with equal ease.

We should expect such colloidal dispersions to be *precipitated* by the addition of solutions having a high concentration of ions of charge opposite to those which are adsorbed. An interesting result of this action is the formation of deltas at the mouths of large rivers. Colloidal sediment suspended in the river water flowing into the sea is precipitated by ions of the salt water. Fresh water is less dense than sea water. Thus, when fresh water first encounters the sea wa-

ter, it fans out over the sea water in a surface layer. The deposition of the precipitated silt and clay eventually produces a fan-shaped delta. The large delta at the mouth of the Mississippi River is the result, in part at least, of this precipitating action.

3. The preparation of suspensoids. The colloidal state is dependent on the size of the suspended particles. There are two general methods by which particles may be brought to colloidal size.

1. The size of solute particles, which is below the colloidal range, may be increased. This is known as **condensation.** Condensation of solute particles to colloidal size may be accomplished by hydrolysis, oxidation, or reduction reactions. Very rapid precipitation or crystallization in an insoluble environment may produce colloidally suspended microcrystals of the solute. Colloidal iron(III) hydroxide is prepared by the hydrolysis of iron(III) chloride in hot water.

$$Fe^{+++} + 6\,H_2O \rightarrow Fe(OH)_3 + 3\,H_3O^+$$

Colloidal gold may be prepared by adding a reducing agent such as tin(II) chloride or iron(II) sulfate to a dilute solution of gold chloride.

$$2\,Au^{+++} + 3\,Sn^{++} \rightarrow 2\,Au^0 + 3\,Sn^{++++}$$

The color of the gold hydrosol which results depends on the size of the gold particles but is usually purple.

If hydrogen peroxide, an oxidizing agent, is added to a water solution of hydrogen sulfide, sulfur is precipitated according to the following reaction:

$$H_2S + H_2O_2 \rightarrow S + 2\,H_2O$$

The particles of sulfur are found to be colloidal when an attempt is made to filter the suspension. The sulfur particles pass through the filter paper along with the water. Frequently, colloidal suspensions formed by condensation methods interfere with analytic procedures since ordinary filtration does not remove the precipitated material.

2. *The size of visible particles, which is above the colloidal range, may be reduced.* This is known as **dispersion.** The dispersion method of producing colloidal particles may involve the use of an electric arc, mechanical methods such as grinding, shaking, or homogenizing, or the addition of a third substance. An electric arc may be produced under water by momentarily placing two energized conductors together and then separating them slightly so as to maintain the arc. If the conductors are made of gold, a purple gold dispersion will result from the disintegration of the ends of the electrodes within the arc. In a similar manner platinum electrodes will yield a brownish-black dispersion, and silver a brownish-green dispersion.

Many grinding and powdering operations are carried out in the chemistry laboratory with a mortar and pestle. Coarse particles may be so reduced in size that some colloidal suspensions are prepared in this way. In commercial operations, large grinding and shearing machines, called **colloid mills,** are used to break down coarse particles to the desired colloidal size.

Cement manufacturers use colloid mills to reduce cement particles to colloidal size because they know that the final hardness of concrete depends largely on the fineness of the cement particles used. Colloidal dispersions may be produced by introducing the coarse particles and the dispersing medium into the colloid mill together.

Suppose a few drops of oil are added to water in a test tube and the mixture is shaken vigorously. The oil is broken down into tiny droplets which remain suspended for a short time in the water before coalescing and rising to the surface. If these oil droplets are made much smaller, their separation from the water can be delayed considerably. Milk is *homogenized* by breaking down the fat globules into particles of such small dimensions that they do not readily join together. Thus they do not rise to the surface as cream.

Colloidal dispersions are sometimes

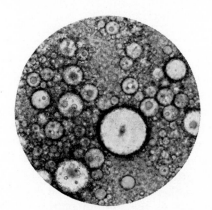 

Fig. 33-4. **Left, an emulsion of oil in water produced by an ordinary mixer. Right, the same emulsion after passing through a colloid mill.** (Premier Mill)

prepared by adding a third substance to the system. This substance acts upon the particles and reduces them to colloidal dimensions. Such a substance is called a *peptizing agent* and the process is known as **peptization**. Certain of the pre-digestive processes involve peptization.

4. Precipitation of suspensoids. The formation of river deltas by the introduction of an opposite electric charge into a colloidal dispersion has already been mentioned. In the manufacture of soap, the product is formed in the colloidal state. The soap is precipitated, or *salted out*, by adding sodium chloride to the suspension. The salting-out process is frequently used in the precipitation of proteins. The opposite charge of iron(III) hydroxide and diarsenic trisulfide suspensions results in the precipitation of both when they are mixed.

Acids are sometimes used as coagulating agents. The milky colloid called *latex*, which is obtained from the rubber tree, is coagulated by the addition of acetic acid. Ammonia water, on the other hand, prevents coagulation of the latex.

Heat coagulates some colloids. If the colloidal dispersions produced during chemical analysis are boiled, the internal phase may coagulate. Then it can be removed by ordinary filtration. Egg albumen, a lyophilic colloid, is coagulated by hot water or hot grease in the poaching or frying of eggs.

5. The Cottrell precipitator. In various manufacturing processes large volumes of smoke, dust, and mist were formerly expelled into the air. These waste products were a nuisance to people who lived near the factories. Certain smelters (plants for extracting metals from their ores) gave off chimney dust containing diarsenic trioxide, a poisonous compound. This dust was scattered by the wind, and some eventually settled on pasture lands, poisoning the cattle which grazed there. The smelter operators were confronted with a serious problem which they solved by using the Cottrell precipitator.

Dr. Frederick G. Cottrell (1877–1948), an American chemist, devised a means of precipitating colloidal dust using high voltage electricity. The dispersed particles in the waste gases are passed into a high potential electrostatic field before reaching the flue or smoke stack. Here they acquire an electric charge. As charged particles they are attracted to a collecting electrode where they are discharged and deposited as dust in the bottom of the precipitator.

Some of these precipitated dusts contain valuable by-products. The diarsenic

Fig. 33-5. The Cottrell precipitator is used to recover suspended particles from flue gases.

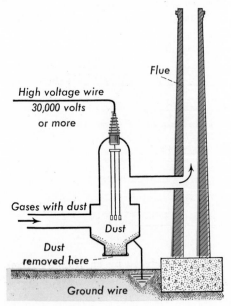

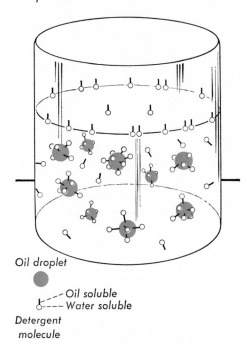

Oil droplet

--- Oil soluble
--- Water soluble

Detergent molecule

Fig. 33-6. A detergent will stabilize an oil-in-water emulsion.

trioxide from flue dust is used in making insecticides. Potassium salts are removed from the dust of cement kilns, and acid mists are recovered from sulfuric acid plants. These are just a few examples of the economic importance of Cottrell precipitators. Today there is little excuse for air pollution in industrial areas because of the discharge of dust, smoke, or mists from factory chimneys.

Precipitators operating on the same general principle are available for home use. Dust, pollen, and other objectionable suspended particles may be removed from the air in the home. This helps reduce house cleaning and provides relief to those who are allergic to pollen in the air. Dust filters, made of spun polyethylene, are now available which acquire an electrostatic charge as a result of the passage of air through

them. They are more effective in removing suspended particles than the disposable filters normally used in air conditioners and heating systems.

6. Protective colloids. In some colloidal systems the precipitation of the internal phase may be prevented by the addition of a second colloid known as a *protective agent.* When a pharmacist prepares an emulsion he makes an intimate mixture of the oil and the dispersing medium with gum arabic or gum tragacanth. The protective agent is adsorbed on the surface of the dispersed particles, coating them and thus preventing actual contact and subsequent coagulation. Here we have the *third* reason why colloidal suspensions do not settle: *a protective layer of adsorbed material stabilizes the suspended particles.*

Gelatin added to milk tends to prevent curdling. When added to an ice cream mix, it prevents the formation of objectionable ice crystals, producing a smoother product. A protective colloid such as glue is added to electroplating baths to secure a smoother surface. Glue or starch added to boiler water acts to prevent the deposition of scale.

Detergents (cleaning agents) are used to stabilize grease and water emulsions. A detergent molecule has a long hydrocarbon portion and an ionic portion. The hydrocarbon part of the molecule is insoluble in water but is soluble in oils. The ionic part is insoluble in oils but is soluble in water. A small amount of soap added to water forms a colloidal suspension. The hydrocarbon ends of groups of detergent molecules cluster together leaving the ionic ends in contact with the water. If grease or oil is introduced, and the system is agitated, the oil droplets are stabilized by the detergent as a colloidal suspension of oil

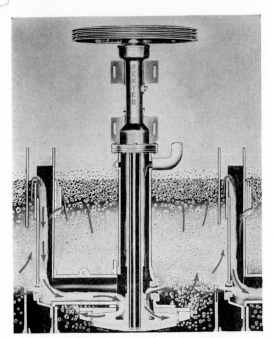

Fig. 33-7. Diagram of a flotation cell. (Denver Equipment)

in water. In this condition the grease or oil is easily floated away.

Mayonnaise is salad oil colloidally dispersed in vinegar, using egg as an emulsifying agent. The egg stabilizes the oil droplets by forming a protective coating around them to prevent their coalescence.

7. The flotation process. *Foam* is a colloidal dispersion of a gas in a liquid. A very small quantity of an oil may act as a foam stabilizer, particularly in the presence of finely divided solids. Many metallic ores are found in nature in low concentrations. These are usually sulfides mixed with earthy materials known as *gangue*. Before the metal in such an ore may be extracted profitably the ore must be concentrated.

This concentration is often accomplished by a process called *flotation.* Flotation depends on the fact that the gangue is preferentially wetted by water while the unwetted ore particles become attached to the oil-covered air bubbles.

The low grade ore is ground very fine, then mixed with water, oil, and air to form a foamy, frothy mixture. The water-wetted particles of gangue settle to the bottom. The unwetted ore particles are carried to the surface in the frothy suspension of air bubbles and are skimmed off.

In our present day economy the demand for minerals and metals steadily increases. Consequently the reserve of high grade minerals and ores steadily declines. This situation has stimulated the development of new flotation techniques. Chemists are able to change the composition of the flotation mixture so that various substances are made floatable. Specific chemical additives, called *collectors,* may be introduced. These are selectively adsorbed by the particles to be floated. The collector provides the proper kind of surface for these particles and enables them to adhere to air bubbles in the froth.

It is even possible to control the surface wetting of mixtures of desirable minerals. The minerals may be floated, one at a time, and thus concentrated and separated in the same operation. A low grade copper ore, *chalcopyrite*, containing copper, iron, and sulfur, is often found mixed with *pyrite*, a sulfide of iron. Suppose we wish to separate the two ores and recover them in concentrated form.

The raw ore is first pulverized with water in colloid mills to make a thick *slurry* which is pumped into a flotation cell along with water and very small quantities of certain chemicals. One chemical substance acts as a collector for the chalcopyrite, another causes the pyrite to be wetted. As air is blown through the cell only the copper ore particles stick to the air bubbles. They float to the surface and are skimmed off.

Fig. 33-8. **A flotation cell. The ore is carried to the surface by air bubbles in the froth.** (Philadelphia Quartz)

The gangue and pyrite, both water wetted, are pumped to a second cell. Here the mixture is treated with another collector chemical. This displaces the water from the pyrite surfaces and makes them water-repellent. The frothing action is repeated and the pyrite particles are separated from the gangue.

Chemists have found flotation procedures for concentrating all solid mineral substances. Flotation techniques are also employed in sewage disposal and in many areas in the chemical industry. The rapid strides made recently in flotation chemistry are largely the result of radioactive tracer studies of the behavior of the chemicals used as collectors.

2. EMULSOIDS

8. The characteristics of emulsoids. The internal phase of *lyophilic colloidal systems,* known as *emulsoids,* shows a marked attraction for the external phase. The intermingling of internal and external phases makes the viscosity of the system greater than that of the external phase alone. The system *sets* to form a gelatinous mass called a *gel.* Gels may become sufficiently rigid to retain the shape of the container in which the setting occurs.

In general, this class includes those substances which naturally form colloidal suspensions. They are usually organic materials, while most suspensoids are inorganic. Some emulsoids are reversible. That is, they will redisperse in a liquid after having been separated from it. Brownian movement and the Tyndall effect are much less noticeable in emulsoids. The dispersed particles of emulsoid systems carry an electric charge, usually negative. However, they are not easily precipitated by electrolytes, as are suspensoids.

A second factor, known as *solvation,* contributes to the stability of emulsoids. The internal phase becomes *solvated* in the presence of the dispersing liquid. The dispersed particles adsorb molecules of the dispersing liquid and thus become surrounded by a protective layer. Solvation is a general term which may be applied regardless of the identity of the

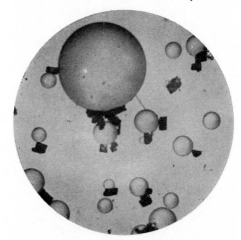

Fig. 33-9. **Ore particles stick to the air bubbles in the flotation cell as shown by this photomicrograph.** (Philadelphia Quartz)

dispersing liquid. If the liquid is water, the more specific term *hydration* may be used.

Solvation accounts for the change in viscosity of emulsoids. It is the basic distinction between lyophilic and lyophobic colloidal systems. The setting, or formation of gels, is due to proper conditions of concentration, temperature, and hydronium-ion concentration.

9. Some common gels. Gelatin desserts are gels consisting of hydrated suspensions of gelatin, a protein, to which certain flavors have been added.

Fruit jellies consist of fruit acids, sugar, and *pectin*. Pectin, in the presence of fruit acids, produces the gel. During setting, the colloidal particles are thought to link together, forming a network of fibrils that entrap the liquid medium in which they are suspended (see Fig. 33-10). Enough pectin is present in some fruits, such as apples and grapes, to cause a jelly to set. However, the pectin content of berry juices is usually insufficient, so apple juice or a commercial pectin product is generally added in the preparation of berry jellies.

When 15 ml of a saturated solution of calcium acetate are added to 85 ml of denatured alcohol, a jelly-like mass

Fig. 33-10. A gel forms a network of fibrils that entrap the liquid.

forms which is known as *solid alcohol*. Unless stabilized, however, the gel breaks down on standing. For this reason it is sometimes referred to as a *false gel*. Solid alcohol, commonly known as "canned heat," is sold in small cans as a fuel for outdoor fires.

Gelatin dynamite and photographic film are gels. Silica gel is formed by dehydrating gelatinous silicic acid. It has a remarkable capacity for the adsorption of many gases and vapors.

10. Biocolloids. Lyophilic colloidal systems are of great importance in physiology and biology. Life processes depend on natural colloidal substances, called **biocolloids**, which compose the protoplasm of living cells.

The biocolloids include nearly all of the energy foods: starches (insoluble carbohydrates), proteins, and fats. Together with water they are the chief constituents of living matter. Included also are the biocatalysts: enzymes, hormones, and vitamins. These stimulate and control the various chemical reactions involving the biocolloids. Thus the reactions within living organisms take place in matter that is colloidal in nature.

The biocolloids are the stable parts of the body, while the soluble substances are the migrating parts. The colloidal starches, proteins, and fats cannot pass through the tissue membranes but their soluble components do so freely.

Sugar circulates in the vein system of the plant. However, on entering the cells it is either utilized or converted, by catalytic action, to starch for storing. Similarly, in the animal body the blood sugar is converted to *glycogen* (animal starch) in the liver and muscles. The process is reversed, again by catalytic action, whenever this stored food is required.

The digestive process prepares food substances for passage through the membranous walls of the intestine into the blood stream. Colloidal starches are acted upon by enzymes to produce water-soluble simple sugar. Colloidal proteins, during digestion, are broken down to soluble *amino acids*. Colloidal fat substances are reduced to soluble *fatty acids* and *glycerin*. Upon entering the blood stream these soluble food substances are distributed to the body tissues. Within the living cells they may be changed back into the colloidal state.

Much of food-cooking involves the colloidal state. Bread becomes stale largely because of the adsorption of moisture by the colloidal materials of the ruptured cells.

The condition of the body tissues may be associated with the degree of dispersion of the colloidal proteins composing them. Salts dissolved in the watery fluids of the body are the electrolytes which maintain the proper degree of dispersion of these colloidal systems. Certain mental disorders and diseases involving tissue swelling may be directly related to the degree of dispersion of the colloidal proteins in the organs and tissues of the body.

SUMMARY

Suspensoids are lyophobic colloidal systems which show no strong attracting forces between the internal and external phases. The haphazard Brownian motion observed in colloidal dispersions of very small particles is due to the molecular bombardment of the suspending medium. The Tyndall effect offers a means of distinguishing between colloidal suspensions and true solutions.

Pigment colors result from removal of portions of white light by absorption. Structural colors are due to the physical structure of the mass. Structural colors may vary with the size of the dispersed particles.

Colloidal suspensions are stablized by Brownian movement, the acquisition of an electric charge, or the addition of a protective agent. Suspensoids are prepared by condensation methods and dispersion methods. They may be precipitated by the introduction of the opposite electric charge, coagulating agents, or heat. The Cottrell precipitator is useful in removing suspended matter from the air by discharging the particles as they pass through a high-potential electric field.

The flotation process is an important means of concentrating many low grade ores and minerals. It depends on the fact that the gangue is readily wettable and the mineral fraction can be made water-repellent. Chemical additives, called collectors, make it possible to control the wettability of ores.

Emulsoids differ from suspensoids in that the internal phase becomes solvated by the adsorption of molecules of the dispersing liquid. Such systems form gels by entrapping the liquid medium in which they are suspended.

The life processes involve many natural emulsoids. These lyophilic colloids are known as biocolloids. They are very important in the areas of biology and physiology.

TEST YOURSELF ON THESE TERMS

aerosol	fatty acid	protective agent
amino acid	flotation	salting out
biocolloid	gangue	scattering
Brownian movement	gel	slurry
colloid mill	hydrosol	solvation
condensation method	organosol	structural color
Cottrell precipitator	peptization	Tyndall effect
dispersion method	pigment color	ultramicroscope

QUESTIONS

Group A

1. What is meant by Brownian movement?
2. Describe the Tyndall effect.
3. Distinguish between pigment colors and structural colors.
4. State three general reasons why colloidal suspensions do not settle on standing.
5. (a) What dispersions acquire a negative electric charge? (b) A positive charge?
6. What are four common properties of suspensoids?
7. What are the two general methods by which suspensoids may be prepared?
8. What are three different methods by which suspensoids may be precipitated?
9. Why is the Cottrell precipitator of great value to operators of smelters?
10. What kind of colloidal suspensions are usually formed by organic materials?

Group B

11. (a) Explain how a colloidal suspension of diarsenic trisulfide in water may acquire a negative charge. (b) What would be the result of adding hydrochloric acid to the suspensoid?
12. (a) Define peptization. (b) What does the fact that a peptizing agent is involved in certain pre-digestive processes suggest concerning the nature of these processes?
13. Explain how soap can act as a protective colloid to stabilize oil in water.
14. On what basic fact does the ore-flotation process depend?
15. Explain the function of collectors in the flotation process.
16. Suggest a possible reason why Brownian movement is less noticeable in emulsoids than in suspensoids.
17. Why do colloidal suspensions sometimes cause difficulties in chemical analysis procedures?
18. Account for the formation of deltas at the mouths of large rivers.
19. What would you expect to occur as a result of mixing colloidal suspensions of iron(III) hydroxide and diarsenic trisulfide? Explain.

SOME THINGS FOR YOU TO DO

1. Prepare colloidal gold by adding a reducing agent, such as tin(II) chloride solution, to a dilute solution of gold(III) chloride. [If gold(III) chloride is not available, it may be prepared by adding gold leaf to a few drops of aqua regia.] The colloidal gold suspension varies in color (why?), but is usually purple.

2. Coagulate rubber from latex by adding dilute acetic acid. Half fill a small beaker of latex, and then add a convenient amount of dilute acetic acid. Stir the mixture with a glass rod. The rubber coagulates and collects in a ball on the end of the glass rod.

3. Prepare some "canned heat," as described in Section 9 of this chapter. Stir the mixture, and note how it jells to a solid mass. Scoop out some of the "solid alcohol," place it on an asbestos square, and ignite it.

CHECK YOUR PROGRESS IN CHEMISTRY

1. The speed of light is approximately 300,000 kilometers per second. Express this speed in centimeters per second using the scientific notation form for large and small numbers.

2. (*a*) State the Law of Definite Composition; (*b*) the Law of Multiple Proportions.

3. What is the empirical formula of potassium iodide which is found to contain 76.5% iodine?

4. What is the percentage composition of water of hydration in sodium carbonate, $Na_2CO_3 \cdot 10\ H_2O$?

5. Write the balanced equation for each of the following reactions:
   (*a*) copper + silver nitrate →
   (*b*) iron(III) oxide + carbon monoxide →
   (*c*) calcium carbonate + hydrochloric acid →
   (*d*) potassium chlorate →
   (*e*) ammonium nitrate + potassium hydroxide →

6. How many moles of barium sulfate can be produced by a reaction between an excess of sodium sulfate and 100. g of barium chloride?

7. We wish to produce 100. g of carbon dioxide using limestone, which is 80.5% pure, and hydrochloric acid. (*a*) What mass of limestone is required? (*b*) What volume of concentrated hydrochloric acid must be measured out if it is 36.0% HCl by weight and has a specific gravity of 1.18?

8. Find the specific gravity (air standard) of carbon dioxide.

9. What is the volume of a gas at S.T.P. if 112 ml were collected at a temperature of 25° C and a pressure of 730. mm?

10. A gas is found to be 75.0% carbon and 25.0% hydrogen. It has a density of 0.715 g/l. What is the correct formula?

11. How many liters of oxygen are required to produce 50 liters of carbon dioxide during the combustion of coke?

★12. How many grams of zinc are required in a reaction with sulfuric acid to yield 2.00 liters of hydrogen collected over water at 740. mm pressure and 23° C? (Vapor pressure of water at 23° C is 21 mm.)

13. Calculate: (*a*) the freezing point; and (*b*) the boiling point of water in which 50.0 g of cane sugar, $C_{12}H_{22}O_{11}$, are dissolved per 100.0 g of water.

★14. It is found that 27.0 ml of 0.200N HCl are required to neutralize 40.0 ml of NaOH solution. What is the normality of the basic solution?

★15. What is the pH of a 0.020-M HCl solution assuming complete ionization?

★16. List three conditions under which ionic reactions may go to completion.

★17. Describe a practical application of the principle of Le Chatelier.

★18. Zinc reacts with dilute nitric acid to form zinc nitrate, water, and ammonium nitrate. Balance the equation for this oxidation-reduction reaction.

19. How can you account for the appearance of new properties and changes in the common physical properties as a result of a substance being subdivided to colloidal dimensions?

20. Explain the operation of the Cottrell precipitator.

CHALLENGING YOUR KNOWLEDGE

1. Black drawing ink is a colloidal suspension of carbon in water. Suggest a way of preventing the carbon from settling out as a precipitate.

2. Why is peanut butter sometimes homogenized? Suggest how this might be accomplished.

3. How does the licorice used in foam-type extinguishers stabilize the foam?

4. When doing accurate work, why should a beaker containing a suspension of silver chloride be heated to boiling before it is filtered?

Unit 11 · THE LIGHT METALS

Beryllium, Magnesium, Aluminum, and Titanium

Chapter 34 · BERYLLIUM, MAGNESIUM, ALUMINUM, TITANIUM

1. Comparisons of the light metals. Beryllium, atomic number 4, and magnesium, atomic number 12, are the first two members of Group II of the Periodic Table. The other metals of Group II, calcium, strontium, barium, and radium, were discussed in Chapter 25.

Aluminum, atomic number 13, is the second member of Group III which is headed by boron and includes gallium, indium, and thallium. All are typically metallic except boron which is classed as a metalloid. The difference in the character of boron as an element and in its compounds from the other Group III elements stems primarily from the small size of its atom. Boron resembles silicon and germanium and its chemistry is presented in Chapter 40.

Titanium, atomic number 22, is the first member of a subgroup of transition elements called the titanium subgroup which includes zirconium and hafnium. Each has unfilled next-to-outermost shells characteristic of all transition elements.

Beryllium, magnesium, aluminum, and titanium are grouped together in this chapter because they are commercially important low-density metals. Each is used structurally as the pure metal, as an alloy with other light metals, or as an alloy with such heavy metals as copper and iron. Beryllium and magnesium follow their corresponding alkali metals lithium and sodium in their chemical behavior. Aluminum in Group III follows directly its cor-

Element	Atomic Number	Atomic Weight	Electron Configuration	Oxidation Number	Melting Point, °C	Boiling Point, °C	Density g/cm³	Metallic Radius Å	Ionic Radius Å
Beryllium	4	9.0122	2, 2	+2	1280	2970	1.85	0.889	0.31
Magnesium	12	24.312	2, 8, 2	+2	651	1107	1.74	1.364	0.65
Aluminum	13	26.9815	2, 8, 3	+3	660	2057	2.70	1.248	0.50
Titanium	22	47.90	2, 8, 10, 2	+2, +4	1800	>3000	4.5	1.324	0.68

488

responding alkaline-earth metal, magnesium. However, the Group III metals below aluminum are separated from their Group II counterparts by the intervening transition metals of which titanium is an important member.

The first member of a periodic group often exhibits properties somewhat diffrent from those of the remaining elements of the group. These elements are in the second series across the Periodic Table and have only the K shell containing 2 electrons beneath their valence shell. All elements below this series have their valence electrons backed up by a shell populated by at least 8 electrons. The beryllium atom is quite small and the 2 valence electrons are held rather firmly. Bonds formed by beryllium with other substances tend to be more covalent than ionic. Lithium is a stronger reducing agent than its position in Group I would suggest. Boron is a metalloid while all other Group III elements are metals. Nitrogen, oxygen, and fluorine likewise differ in important ways from the other members of their respective groups.

Even though a difference in valence exists between such diagonally arranged pairs of elements on the Periodic Table as lithium and magnesium, and beryllium and aluminum, their similar atomic and ionic radii give them quite similar properties under certain circumstances. Some important physical data on the light metals are given in the table on the opposite page.

1. BERYLLIUM

2. The preparation, properties, and uses of beryllium. Beryllium is not a common element. It occurs in the mineral beryl, $Be_3Al_2Si_6O_{18}$. The aquamarine and emerald are varieties of beryl which are prized as gems. Beryllium can be isolated by the electrolysis of a fused mixture of sodium and beryllium chlorides. It has a specific gravity of 1.85, is silvery-white, and very hard.

Beryllium, with copper, forms nonsparking alloys that are used for electric switches and for tools. Beryllium-copper springs are practically unbreakable. Beryllium is used for making windows for X-ray tubes because these rays readily pass through elements with low atomic numbers. Of the low atomic number elements, beryllium can be best fabricated for this purpose. The addition of beryllium to light-metal alloys makes them easier to work. Beryllium oxide, BeO, is used in the nuclear reactors in which plutonium is made.

Beryllium compounds are somewhat covalent. This is an important difference between beryllium compounds and the compounds of the other members of Group II. Furthermore, beryllium salts are extensively hydrolyzed in water. These characteristics show that nonmetallic properties begin to appear in the Period 2 elements even near the extreme left of the Periodic Table. Beryllium and its compounds are exceedingly poisonous.

VOCABULARY

Self-protective metal. A metal which forms a nonporous, nonscaling coat of tarnish.

Thermite reaction. The reaction by which a metal is prepared from its oxide by reduction with aluminum.

Fig. 34-1. **An aerial view of an open pit asbestos mine in the province of Ontario, Canada.** (Johns Manville)

2. MAGNESIUM

3. The occurrence of magnesium. Magnesium compounds are widely distributed on land and in the sea. Magnesium sulfate is found in the ground in many places, notably British Columbia and the state of Washington. A double chloride of potassium and magnesium is mined from the potash deposits of Texas and New Mexico. Sea water contains a significant quantity of magnesium compounds in solution.

Dolomite, $CaCO_3 \cdot MgCO_3$, is a double carbonate of magnesium and calcium which is often found in the United States and Europe. It is an excellent building stone, and is useful for lining steel furnaces. Pulverized dolomite neutralizes soil acids and also supplies magnesium for the growth of plants.

Talc and asbestos are silicates of magnesium. Asbestos, which is mined in Ontario and Quebec, Canada, is a remarkable mineral. It has a high melting point, is nonflammable, and is a good heat insulator. Its fibrous structure permits the mineral to be spun into threads and woven into cloth. It is mixed with cement for making asbestos shingles. With magnesium oxide it is used for covering steam pipes and furnaces. Asbestos is also used for making automobile brake linings, fireproof curtains and clothing, and as an electric insulator.

Elementary magnesium was first prepared by Davy in 1807, in the series of experiments which resulted in the isolation of sodium, calcium, and similar active metals.

4. The extraction of magnesium. *1. From magnesium chloride.* The sea provides an almost inexhaustible supply of magnesium. The first step in obtaining magnesium from sea water is to treat it with lime made from oyster shells, which are inexpensive and readily available. This treatment causes the magnesium ions to be precipitated as magnesium hydroxide.

$$Mg^{++} + 2\ OH^- \rightarrow Mg(OH)_2 \downarrow$$

The magnesium hydroxide is separated from the water by filtration. The addition of hydrochloric acid converts the magnesium hydroxide to magnesium chloride.

$$Mg(OH)_2 + 2\ HCl \rightarrow MgCl_2 + 2\ H_2O$$

Magnesium is liberated by electrolysis of fused magnesium chloride.

$$MgCl_2 \xrightarrow{\text{(elect)}} Mg + Cl_2 \uparrow$$

Most magnesium today is made by electrolyzing a fused mixture of magnesium chloride, calcium choride, and sodium chloride at about 700° to 750° C. Magnesium is also prepared by electrolyzing fused magnesium chloride obtained from natural underground brine.

2. *From magnesium oxide.* In the United States some magnesium is prepared from magnesium oxide by reducing it with ferrosilicon, an alloy of iron and silicon. The reduction is carried out at a temperature of about 1150° C in a vacuum. At this high temperature and low pressure, the magnesium evaporates, is condensed, and cast into molds.

5. Magnesium has interesting properties. Magnesium is a silver-white metal with a specific gravity of 1.74. When heated, it becomes ductile and malleable. Its tensile strength is not quite as great as that of aluminum.

Magnesium is not acted upon by dry air, but in moist air a coating of basic magnesium carbonate forms on the surface. Because this coating is not porous, it protects the metal underneath from further tarnishing. *A metal which forms a nonporous, nonscaling coat of tarnish is said to be a* **self-protective metal.**

When heated in air to the kindling point, magnesium burns with an intensely hot flame and gives off a dazzling light. The products of the combustion are magnesium oxide, MgO, and magnesium nitride, Mg_3N_2. Magnesium is one of the few metals which combines directly with nitrogen. Boiling water reacts with magnesium slowly, and hydrogen is set free. All the common acids react with it.

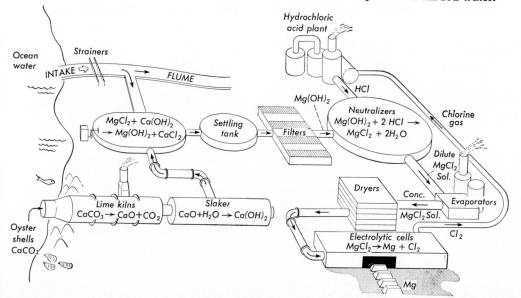

Fig. 34-2. Diagram of a plant for production of magnesium from sea water.

Fig. 34-3. **Many of the structural parts of this helicopter are made of magnesium.** (Dow Chemical)

6. Magnesium has many uses. The brilliant white light produced by burning magnesium makes it useful for flares and fireworks. Magnesium forms light, strong alloys with aluminum, such as magnalium and Dowmetal. Other alloying metals are zinc and manganese. Magnesium alloys are used for making tools and fixtures, for the beams of delicate chemical balances, and for automobile and airplane parts. The growth of the airplane industry has produced a much greater demand for magnesium. The table below lists a few of the more common magnesium compounds with which you should be familiar.

COMMON MAGNESIUM COMPOUNDS

Chemical Name	Common Name	Formula	Appearance	Uses
Magnesium carbonate	None	$MgCO_3$	White, usually fluffy	For lining furnaces; in making the oxide
Basic magnesium carbonate	Magnesia alba	$Mg_4(OH)_2(CO_3)_3 \cdot 3 H_2O$	Soft, white powder 85% pores	In tooth cleansers; "85% magnesia" for pipe coverings
Magnesium oxide	Magnesia	MgO	White powder	As refractory; for lining furnaces
Magnesium chloride	None	$MgCl_2$	White, crystalline solid	With asbestos for stone flooring
Magnesium sulfate	Epsom salts	$MgSO_4 \cdot 7 H_2O$	White, crystalline solid	In laxatives, cathartics; in dye industry
Magnesium hydroxide	Milk of magnesia	$Mg(OH)_2$	White, milky suspension	As antacid; in laxatives

3. ALUMINUM

7. The occurrence of aluminum.
Aluminum is the most abundant metal in the earth's crust. It is found in many clays, rocks, and other mineral materials. While the aluminum industry is working on processes by which aluminum may be economically extracted from clay, none has yet proved successful. Such a process would make the United States less dependent on foreign sources of aluminum ore. At present, bauxite, an impure aluminum oxide ore, is imported from Jamaica, Surinam, and British Guiana. It is also mined in certain areas in Georgia, Alabama, Tennessee, and Arkansas.

8. A famous discovery. Friedrich Wöhler, the German chemist, first isolated aluminum. As late as 1855 aluminum sold at $90 per pound; but by

Fig. 34-5. The "crown jewels" of Oberlin College. The first nuggets of aluminum prepared by Charles Martin Hall. (Alcoa)

1870 the price had fallen to $12 per pound. In 1886 a newer process of reduction by sodium lowered the price of aluminum to about $2 per pound, but this was still too expensive to enable its full potential as a structural and household metal to be developed.

It remained for a young American, Charles Martin Hall, to develop a cheap practical method of aluminum production. While still a student at Oberlin College, Hall discovered that aluminum could be separated from its oxide by electrolysis. His process, commercialized in 1889, reduced the price of aluminum to about 20¢ per pound. Today aluminum is one of our most widely used metals.

9. The preparation of aluminum.
Fused salt electrolysis has great commercial significance, being used to produce alkali and alkaline-earth metals as well as aluminum and related metals in huge quantities. The production of aluminum in the United States during 1960 exceeded 2 million tons.

Fig. 34-4. Charles Martin Hall, the young American who discovered the electrolytic process for producing aluminum. (Alcoa)

Aluminum is extracted by electrolyzing aluminum oxide (refined bauxite) dissolved in molten cryolite, Na_3AlF_6, at a temperature slightly below 1000° C. The process was developed in the United States in 1886 by Charles Martin Hall (1863–1914) and independently in France in the same year by Paul Héroult.

The electrolytic cell, shown in Figure 34-6, consists of an iron box lined with graphite which serves as a cathode. Graphite rods serve as the anode, and cryolite-aluminum oxide is the electrolyte. Enough heat is produced by the large current in the cell to melt the cryolite which dissolves the aluminum oxide and to maintain the aluminum metal in the bottom of the cell in a molten state for convenient removal.

The electrode reactions are complex and are not understood completely. Aluminum is reduced at the cathode, possibly from a complex ion structure composed of aluminum, oxygen, and fluorine. Carbon dioxide is the major product at the anode, which is gradually consumed. This suggests that oxygen is formed at the anode by oxidation of the $O^=$ ion or some complex containing oxygen in the negative oxidation state. The following electrode reactions are probably oversimplifications of the reaction mechanism, but serve to summarize the oxidation-reduction processes.

Cathode: $4\ Al^{+3} + 12\ e^- \rightarrow 4\ Al^0$
Anode: $6\ O^{-2} - 12\ e^- \rightarrow 3\ O_2^0$
   $3\ C\ \ \ + 3\ O_2 \rightarrow 3\ CO_2 \uparrow$

The consumption of electric energy is high; approximately 10 kilowatt-hours per pound of aluminum recovered. Therefore, aluminum reduction plants are located where large quantities of electric energy can be generated cheaply.

10. The physical properties of aluminum. Aluminum is silver-white in color and has a specific gravity of 2.7. It is ductile and malleable, but is not so tenacious as brass, copper, or steel. It ranks with the best conductors of electricity, being surpassed only by silver, copper, and gold. Aluminum can be welded, cast, or spun, but it can be soldered only with difficulty by the use of a special solder.

11. The chemical properties of aluminum. Aluminum takes a high polish, but soon becomes covered with a thin layer of aluminum oxide. This oxide layer is adherent and impervious; hence aluminum is a self-protective metal. Hydrochloric and sulfuric acids react with

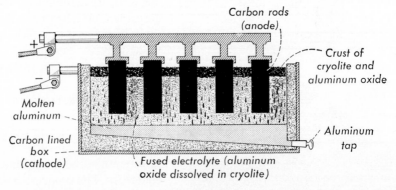

Fig. 34-6. **Aluminum is produced by electrolysis. Purified aluminum oxide is dissolved in melted cryolite, sodium aluminum fluoride.**

aluminum readily and form salts of the respective acids. Nitric acid hardly affects aluminum at all. Salt water corrodes it rapidly, especially when it is hot. Such a strong alkali as sodium hydroxide reacts with aluminum forming sodium aluminate and liberating hydrogen.

$$2 \text{ Al} + 6 \text{ NaOH} \rightarrow 2 \text{ Na}_3\text{AlO}_3 + 3 \text{ H}_2 \uparrow$$

Aluminum is an excellent reducing agent although it is not so active as the Group I and Group II metals.

$$\text{Al}^0 \rightarrow \text{Al}^{+3} + 3 \text{ e}^-$$

The Al^{+3} ion is quite small and carries a large positive charge. The ion hydrates vigorously in water solution and is usually written $\text{Al}(\text{H}_2\text{O})_6^{+++}$. Water solutions of aluminum salts are generally acidic due to hydrolysis of the Al^{+3} ion.

12. Aluminum is a very useful metal. Aluminum is sometimes used in place of copper for electric conductors. Its electric conductivity is only about 0.6 that of copper, but is less than one-third as dense. Hence electric power lines may be made of thicker aluminum wire to increase conductivity and still put less strain on the supporting poles or towers than copper wire.

Photographic flash bulbs contain fine aluminum wire and enough oxygen to burn the wire completely. The wire burns with an intensely brilliant flash when ignited by a momentary current.

Powdered aluminum is used in paint to protect the surface of iron. Aluminum foil is used for wrapping candy bars, cheese, soap, and many other products, and as a heat insulator. Aluminum is also used for making various novelty articles, and for parts of airplanes and automobiles.

Aluminum is very popular for cooking utensils. It is light and durable, is a

Fig. 34-7. Corrugated aluminum sheet is one of the many building materials fabricated from aluminum. (Reynolds Metals)

good conductor of heat, does not tarnish noticeably, and is easily kept clean. Aluminum cooking utensils are easily bent or dented and will melt in a gas flame if the utensil boils dry.

Aluminum is used extensively to form alloys with other metals. Magnalium, an alloy of aluminum and magnesium, has already been mentioned. Several other alloys of aluminum and copper are known under the name of aluminum bronze. The color of such bronzes varies with the relative proportions of the metals used. One resembles silver, another gold, and both take a high polish.

Duralumin is an alloy that contains about 95% aluminum, 4% copper, 0.5% manganese, and 0.5% magnesium. It is less than half as dense as steel, yet is nearly as strong. This alloy is used extensively for airplane parts where a strong, light alloy is required.

13. The thermite reaction. A mixture of powdered aluminum and iron oxide, raised to a high enough temperature to start the reaction, produces a tremendous amount of heat. Such a re-

Fig. 34-8. **The thermite demonstration makes a striking spectacle. Dry sand should be used to protect the table top, and spectators must keep a safe distance away as the sparks travel several feet. In the photograph, the contrasting black and white shows the brilliance of the molten iron.**

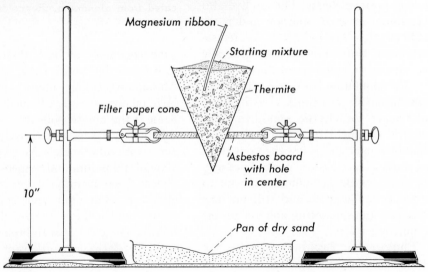

Magnesium ribbon

Starting mixture

Thermite

Filter paper cone

Asbestos board with hole in center

10"

Pan of dry sand

action between aluminum and the oxide of a less active metal is called the **thermite reaction.**

Table 6 in the Appendix shows that 390 kilocalories of heat are set free during formation of one mole of aluminum oxide. The heat of formation of iron (III) oxide is 191 kilocalories. When the thermite reaction occurs, an amount of heat equal to the difference between these values is set free for each mole of aluminum oxide formed. The equation is:

$$2 \text{ Al} + \text{Fe}_2\text{O}_3 \rightarrow$$
$$\text{Al}_2\text{O}_3 + 2 \text{ Fe} + 199 \text{ kilocalories}$$

The liberation of such a large amount of heat so suddenly produces a very high temperature, estimated at 3500° C. Reactions of this type are sometimes called *aluminothermy* or *aluminothermics.*

14. Some metals are reduced by the thermite reaction. It is not practical to use aluminum to reduce cheaper metals. However, the thermite reaction may be used when it is desirable to produce a small quantity of carbon-free metal. A more important use of this reaction is to reduce metallic oxides which are not readily reduced with carbon. Chromium, manganese, titanium, tungsten, and molybdenum may be extracted from their oxides by the thermite reaction. All of these metals are used in making alloy steels of high quality. Uranium, which is used for producing nuclear energy, may also be reduced by the thermite reaction.

15. Thermite welding. The high temperature produced by the thermite reaction makes it possible to use such a mixture for welding. Massive steel parts, such as propeller shafts and rudder posts on a ship, or crankshafts of heavy machinery, can be repaired quickly by means of thermite. A mixture of powdered aluminum and either Fe_2O_3 or Fe_3O_4 is placed in a cone-shaped crucible above the metals to be welded. A little starting mixture consisting of barium peroxide and powdered magnesium is placed in a slight depression in the top of the mixture. Within a few seconds after the starting mixture is ignited, the white-hot molten iron flows out through the bottom of the cone and surrounds the broken ends.

16. The uses of aluminum oxide. Bauxite, the chief ore of aluminum, is an oxide of aluminum. Corundum and emery are also natural oxides of this metal, and are used as abrasives. Emery is used in the form of emery paper, emery cloth, or emery grinding wheels.

Rubies and sapphires are aluminum oxide colored by traces of metallic oxides. Synthetic rubies and sapphires are made by fusing pure aluminum oxide in the flame of an oxyhydrogen blow torch. In making clear sapphires, no coloring matter is added. Synthetic

rubies are colored by the addition of a tiny quantity of chromium.

Alundum is an oxide of aluminum made by fusing bauxite. It is used for making grinding wheels and other abrasives, crucibles, funnels, tubing, and other pieces of laboratory apparatus.

17. The chemical behavior of aluminum hydroxide. If a little sodium hydroxide solution is added to a solution of an aluminum salt, such as aluminum chloride, a white gelatinous precipitate of aluminum hydroxide is formed.

$$AlCl_3 + 3\ NaOH \rightarrow Al(OH)_3\downarrow + 3\ NaCl$$

Aluminum hydroxide is insoluble in water, but if an excess of sodium hydroxide is added, soluble sodium aluminate is formed. In this reaction aluminum hydroxide acts as an acid, H_3AlO_3.

$$H_3AlO_3 + 3\ NaOH \rightarrow Na_3AlO_3 + 3\ H_2O$$

If, on the other hand, hydrochloric acid is added to aluminum hydroxide, the

Fig. 34-9. The thermite reaction is used to repair breaks in heavy steel structures. Here a thermite crucible is being used to weld a broken steel rail. (Burbank Photo Service)

Fig. 34-10. **These crucibles are made of Alundum, an artificial oxide of aluminum.** (Norton)

aluminum hydroxide acts as a hydroxide, $Al(OH)_3$.

$$Al(OH)_3 + 3\ HCl \rightarrow AlCl_3 + 3\ H_2O$$

These reactions show the amphiprotic nature of aluminum hydroxide.

Aluminum hydroxide is so weakly basic that its salts with weak acids are almost completely hydrolyzed. If sodium carbonate is added to a solution of aluminum chloride, aluminum carbonate might be expected to precipitate. It is possible that aluminum carbonate may be first formed, but, if so, it immediately hydrolyzes and forms aluminum hydroxide. A precipitate of aluminum hydroxide is always formed when a soluble carbonate, or even a soluble sulfide, is added to a solution of an aluminum salt.

18. The uses of aluminum hydroxide. Aluminum hydroxide may be used to remove suspended matter from drinking water. It also finds use as a mordant. As a rule, aluminum hydroxide is precipitated on the fibers before they are dyed (see Chapter 43, Section 17).

Colored pigments for use in the paint industry are sometimes made by precipitating a dye with aluminum hydroxide in a large vat. The insoluble compound, which contains the dye, is then filtered off. Such pigments are known as lakes.

Aluminum hydroxide is used medicinally as an antacid.

19. Aluminum forms double salts known as alums. If solutions of potassium sulfate and aluminum sulfate are mixed, a double salt, $KAl(SO_4)_2 \cdot 12\ H_2O$, crystallizes when some of the water is evaporated. Any double sulfate formed in such a manner and having similar properties is called an *alum*.

Instead of potassium sulfate, either ammonium sulfate or sodium sulfate may be used. The sulfates of such trivalent metals as chromium or iron may be used instead of aluminum sulfate. The general formula, $M^+M^{+++}(SO_4)_2 \cdot 12\ H_2O$, in which M^+ is some univalent element or radical, and M^{+++} is some trivalent metal, is used to represent the alums. The different alums are used to form mordants.

20. Some silicates of aluminum are useful. Fuller's earth is a silicate of aluminum which is a good adsorbent. It is used for clarifying oils by filtration and for removing spots and stains from textile fabrics.

Mica is a potassium aluminum silicate which is translucent and infusible. It is used for the translucent tops of fuse plugs. As an electric insulator, it is used in the commutators of motors and dynamos.

The feldspars are complex silicates which usually contain aluminum silicate with the silicates of either sodium or potassium. They fuse rather easily. When water or carbon dioxide brings about the weathering of the feldspars, the alkalies are leached out as the soluble silicates or carbonates. Hence the disintegration of a feldspar may add potassium to the soil. The insoluble portion is a fine white clay, or hydrated aluminum silicate, known as kaolin. Colored clays usually owe their color to traces of iron compounds.

21. Clay is used to make pottery. Clay becomes plastic when mixed with water, and can then be molded into any desired shape. When the plastic mass is dried and baked at a high temperature it shrinks and forms a hard, porous mass capable of resisting considerable pressure. These properties of clay make it suitable for use in the pottery industry. The particular use to which the clay is put depends on its purity.

In making bricks, an impure clay is used. Field tile is made from the same material. In making vitrified brick the temperature used is high enough to start the fusion of the clay at the surface. The

Fig. 34-12. **Clay is used in making pottery. Here a potter is shaping the clay into a vase on a potter's wheel.** (Monkmeyer)

glaze thus produced fills the pores at the surface. Firebricks contain both clay and sand.

Earthenware and tile are made from coarse clays, and a low temperature is used in firing them, in order to keep the mass porous. Flowerpots are examples of such ware. If such clays are heated hot enough so they become vitrified throughout, they form stoneware. The cheaper kinds of stoneware and crockery are glazed by throwing salt into the furnace. The product of sodium and aluminum silicate which forms at the surface has a rather low melting point. It fuses and closes the pores.

Porcelain or china (dinnerware) is made from a very pure white clay mixed with powdered feldspar. It is usually fired twice. After the first firing the porous bisque or biscuit is dipped into water containing in suspension a mixture of powdered feldspar and kaolin. During the second firing the feldspar

Fig. 34-11. **A sheet of mica 1.5 mm thick, partially separated to show its layered structure. Sheets of mica are used as insulation in electric equipment.** (S. E. De-Berry)

melts and fills the pores to make the porcelain impervious to liquids.

Ohio and New Jersey produce the most pottery. New York, California, and Pennsylvania are also large producers. Fine chemical laboratory porcelain is produced in Colorado.

4. TITANIUM

22. The occurrence of titanium. Titanium is the ninth most abundant element, comprising an estimated 0.6% of the earth's crust. It is found as rutile, TiO_2, and in titanates, such as ilmenite, $FeTiO_3$. Traces of titanium are almost always found in sand, clay, soil, mineral waters, and plant and animal tissue.

23. The preparation of titanium. Metallic titanium is prepared commercially by the reduction of titanium tetrachloride with magnesium or sodium at 750° to 900° in an atmosphere of argon or helium. The powder thus formed, titanium sponge, is carefully melted to form a mass of metallic titanium. Some titanium is prepared as an alloy with iron for use in the production of special steels.

24. The properties of titanium. Titanium can be purified and treated to produce a strong, ductile metal which can be forged, drawn, and fabricated. It is stable in air, but when heated to 600° C it takes fire and burns with a brilliant light.

Titanium is the first transition metal of the transition subgroup which bears its name and has the following electronic configuration:

1s	2s	2p	3s	3p	3d	4s
2	2	6	2	6	2	2

Removal of the two 4s electrons gives titanium the +2 oxidation state. Further removal of one or two 3d electrons gives the +3 and +4 oxidation states. Of these the +4 state is the most common. Observe that titanium has an octet of electrons remaining in the M-shell when in the +4 oxidation state.

The Ti^{++} and Ti^{+++} compounds are colored, having unpaired electrons. These ions are good reducing agents.

25. The uses of titanium and its compounds. Titanium is used with iron in making alloy steels which are resistant to shock and corrosion. Titani-

Fig. 34-13. **Zone refining of titanium. Energy from a high frequency generator melts a narrow zone in the titanium bar and impurities in the metal dissolve in the melted portion. The molten zone is shifted along the bar, taking the impurities as it goes and leaving highly purified titanium metal. (Union Carbide)**

um also alloys with copper and bronzes. An alloy of nickel, chromium, and titanium is used in the combustion chambers of jet engines. Titanium also shows promise of being used in alloys with very great strengths per unit of weight.

Titanium dioxide, TiO_2, is used in the manufacture of enamels, glazes, white rubber, paper, and face powders. Its most important use is as a paint base. It possesses great covering power, lightness, permanence, a nonpoisonous nature, and is easily mixed with oil.

Titanium tetrachloride is used with ammonia in skywriting. When released to the air, titanium tetrachloride hydrolyzes with the moisture of the air to form hydrochloric acid which then reacts with ammonia to form clouds of white ammonium chloride.

Fig. 34-14. **A titanium alloy compressor for a jet engine is 443 pounds lighter than one made of steel.** (Pratt and Whitney)

SUMMARY

Beryllium, magnesium, aluminum, and titanium are four commercially important low density metals. Each of them is used for structural purposes.

Beryllium is not a common element. It is used for making nonsparking alloys with copper. Its compounds are somewhat covalent.

Magnesium compounds are widely distributed. Sea water contains magnesium compounds in solution. Dolomite, a double carbonate of calcium and magnesium, is used as a building stone, and for neutralizing soil acids. Talc and asbestos are silicates of magnesium.

Magnesium metal is obtained by the electrolysis of fused magnesium chloride, and by the reduction of magnesium oxide with ferrosilicon. It is a silver-white metal with a density less than twice that of water. Magnesium forms a self-protective coating of tarnish. It is used for making alloys of low specific gravity, and for making flares and fireworks.

Aluminum is a silver-white metal with a density 2.7 times as great as water. It is ductile and malleable and a good conductor of electricity. Aluminum forms a self-protective coating of tarnish. Aluminum reacts with hydrochloric and sulfuric acids, but nitric acid hardly affects it. Strong alkalies react with aluminum.

Aluminum is used for making electric transmission cables and cooking utensils. Powdered aluminum is used to make "silver" paint for metallic surfaces. Duralumin is an aluminum alloy that is used for making airplane parts. Aluminum is used as a reducing agent with the oxides of less active metals. Its oxide, as corundum or emery, is used as an abrasive.

Aluminum hydroxide is used in water purification, in mordant dyeing, and in the preparation of lakes.

Feldspars are complex silicate rocks. Water and carbon dioxide bring about the weathering of feldspars to form clay. Bricks, earthenware, tile, and stoneware are made from clay. Porcelain or china is made from pure white clay mixed with powdered feldspar.

Titanium is prepared by the reduction of titanium tetrachloride with magnesium or sodium in an inert atmosphere. It is used in alloys which resist shock and corrosion. Titanium dioxide is used in paints.

TEST YOURSELF ON THESE TERMS

alum	corundum	magnalium
aluminothermy	cryolite	mica
alundum	dolomite	nonsparking alloy
amphiprotic	Dowmetal	porcelain
anode	duralumin	rutile
asbestos	feldspar	self-protective metal
bauxite	fuller's earth	thermite reaction
beryl	kaolin	tile
cathode	lake	titanium sponge

QUESTIONS

Group A

1. Why are beryllium, magnesium, aluminum, and titanium grouped together for study?
2. What useful alloy is made from beryllium and a heavy metal?
3. List some of the common uses for asbestos.
4. (*a*) What is dolomite? (*b*) For what purposes is it used?
5. Since magnesium is an active metal, why do objects made from it not corrode to a mass of rust as iron does?
6. What are the uses for magnesium metal?
7. In what materials does aluminum occur in nature?
8. What are the physical properties of aluminum?
9. Why is aluminum so popular for cooking utensils?
10. What are two important alloys of aluminum and magnesium?
11. How do *vitrified brick, stoneware,* and *earthenware* differ?
12. For what purposes is titanium used?

Group B

13. Write three balanced chemical equations to show the steps in the preparation of magnesium from sea water.
14. What is the chemical nature of corundum and emery?
15. Why must aluminum oxide be dissolved in fused cryolite before it can be decomposed by electricity?
16. Why are certain metallic oxides reduced with aluminum rather than with carbon?
17. Write the chemical formulas for four different alums.

18. In terms of atomic structure, describe how titanium attains an oxidation number of $+4$.

19. Why must the reduction of magnesium oxide by ferrosilicon be carried out in a vacuum?

20. What reaction occurs when aluminum is placed in: (*a*) hydrochloric acid solution; (*b*) sodium hydroxide solution?

21. How do beryllium compounds differ from those of other Group II elements?

22. Write equations to show the net anode and cathode reactions during the electrolysis of aluminum oxide.

23. Write balanced formula equations to show the amphiprotic nature of aluminum hydroxide.

PROBLEMS

Group A

1. Calculate the percentage of beryllium in beryl, $Be_3Al_2Si_6O_{18}$.

2. What quantity of magnesium can be prepared from a metric ton of magnesium oxide, MgO?

3. A cubic mile of sea water contains in solution enough minerals to form about 35 million pounds of magnesium chloride. How much metallic magnesium could be obtained from this?

4. How much aluminum and how much iron(III) oxide must be used in a thermite mixture to produce 10.0 kg of iron for a welding job?

Group B

5. If dolomite is 95.0% a double carbonate of calcium and magnesium, together with 5.0% of impurities such as iron and silica, what is the percentage of magnesium in the sample? (Compute to 3 significant figures.)

6. What is the percentage of aluminum in sodium alum which crystallizes with 12 molecules of water of hydration?

7. How many liters of hydrogen can be prepared by the reaction of 50. g of aluminum and 100. g of sodium hydroxide in solution?

SOME THINGS FOR YOU TO DO

1. Make a batch of "Milk of Magnesia." Add 100 ml of 10% sodium hydroxide solution to a large flask. Add 10% magnesium sulfate solution, a little at a time, as long as a precipitate is formed. Shake the mixture and allow it to settle. Pour off the clear solution above the white precipitate. Fill the flask with water, shake, and allow it to settle again. Now pour off the clear liquid to wash away excess of either magnesium sulfate or sodium hydroxide. Repeat the washing process several times. The milky precipitate left is a suspension of magnesium hydroxide which is called "milk of magnesia." It is not advisable to use this milk of magnesia.

2. Clean some silverware by the aluminum process. Use an old aluminum pan. Put the silverware in the pan and cover with water. Now add a teaspoonful of baking soda for each quart of water. Boil the liquid for twenty minutes. Remove the silver. Rinse thoroughly under hot and cold water. Dry with a clean, soft cloth.

3. Prepare insoluble pigments called lakes. Add 50 ml of 2% alizarin solution to an equal volume of saturated solution of aluminum sulfate. Then add the same amount of 10% ammonia-water solution. The precipitate which forms is colored and is known as a lake. Filter off the precipitate and dry it in a warm oven. Grind the residue that results to a fine powder in a mortar. Cochineal solution may be used instead of alizarin. Salts of chromium and tin yield different colored lakes from those produced by aluminum salts.
4. Prepare a report on the life and work of Charles Martin Hall.

CHECK YOUR PROGRESS IN CHEMISTRY

(*Write balanced formula equations for the following reactions.*)

1. Priestley's production of oxygen.
2. The reaction between sodium and water.
3. The reduction of copper(II) oxide by hydrogen.
4. The reaction between aluminum sulfate and calcium hydroxide in a sedimentation basin.
5. The production of carbonic acid from its acid anhydride.
6. The preparation of oxygen from potassium chlorate.
7. The reaction between marble chips and hydrochloric acid.
8. The synthesis of methanol.
9. The laboratory preparation of acetylene (ethyne) using calcium carbide.
10. The production of 1,2-dibromoethane from ethylene (ethene).
11. The loss of water of hydration on heating $BaCl_2 \cdot 2\,H_2O$.
12. The ionization of hydrogen chloride producing hydronium ions and chloride ions.
13. The anode and cathode reactions during the electrolysis of water.
14. The reaction between zinc and hydrochloric acid.
15. The hydrolysis of hydrated copper(II) ion, $Cu(H_2O)_4{}^{++}$.
16. The reaction between sodium chloride and ammonium hydrogen carbonate.
17. The laboratory preparation of plaster of Paris from gypsum.
18. The laboratory preparation of chlorine from chloride of lime.
19. The over-all reaction for the production of sulfuric acid by the contact process from sulfur, oxygen, and water.
20. The reaction between copper and dilute nitric acid.

CHALLENGING YOUR KNOWLEDGE

1. Explain why magnesium is a self-protective metal.
2. What double function does pulverized dolomite perform for the farmer?
3. Why do we import bauxite from the West Indies and South America when almost any clay bank in the United States contains aluminum?
4. Write the equation for the reaction which occurs when a flash bulb containing Al is set off.
5. What geographic conditions affect the location of plants for the production of aluminum from purified bauxite?

Unit 12 · THE HEAVY METALS

The Iron Family
The Copper Family
Zinc, Cadmium, Mercury, Tin, and Lead

Chapter 35 · THE IRON FAMILY

1. The Iron Family of transition elements. The Iron Family consists of the well-known heavy metals *iron, cobalt,* and *nickel.* They are in the fourth series and each is the first member of the subgroup of transition metals that bears its name. The iron subgroup includes iron (atomic number 26) in the fourth series, *ruthenium* (atomic number 45) in the fifth series, *osmium* (atomic number 76) in the sixth series. The cobalt subgroup includes cobalt (atomic number 27) in the fourth series, *rhodium* (atomic number 46) in the fifth series, and *iridium* in the sixth series. The nickel subgroup includes nickel (atomic number 28) in the fourth series, *palladium* (atomic number 47) in the fifth series, and *platinum* (atomic number 78) in the sixth series.

Within each series of transition elements electron expansion occurs generally in the shell below the outermost with the result that considerable similarity exists along each horizontal series. In fact, the similarities between iron, cobalt, and nickel are more pronounced than those within each of the three subgroups they head. The remaining six members of these three subgroups have properties similar to platinum and may be considered to be members of the *Platinum Family*. They are noble metals —rare and expensive.

Iron is by far the most important member of the Iron Family. Alloys of iron, cobalt, and nickel are important structural metals. Significant properties of the metals of the Iron Family are listed in the following table.

THE IRON FAMILY

Element	Atomic Number	Atomic Weight	Electron Configuration	Oxidation Numbers	Melting Point, °C	Boiling Point, °C	Density, g/cm³
Iron	26	55.847	2, 8, 14, 2	+2, +3	1535	3000	7.86
Cobalt	27	58.9332	2, 8, 15, 2	+2, +3	1495	2900	8.90
Nickel	28	58.71	2, 8, 16, 2	+2, +3	1455	2900	8.90

The Iron Family is located in the midst of the transition elements where atoms have less than the maximum number of electrons beneath the valence shell. Each member exhibits the +2 and +3 oxidation states. The +3 oxidation state of iron tends generally to be more stable than the +2 state. This tendency decreases through cobalt to nickel, the latter occurring only rarely in the +3 oxidation state. The electron population of iron, cobalt, and nickel sublevels is shown in the table at the right in which paired and unpaired electrons of the $3d$ and $4s$ sublevels are represented by paired and unpaired dots.

The two $4s$ electrons are removed with the relative ease characteristic of metals to form the Fe^{++}, Co^{++}, or Ni^{++} ion. In the case of iron, one $3d$ electron is also easily removed to form the Fe^{+++} ion since the five remaining $3d$ electrons constitute a half-filled sublevel. (Recall that filled and half-filled sublevels have extra stability.) It becomes progressively more difficult to remove a $3d$ electron from cobalt and nickel to form the Co^{+++} and Ni^{+++} ions, possibly because of the increasing nuclear charge of these atoms and the fact that neither a half-filled nor filled sublevel is left.

All three metals of the Iron Family have a magnetic property commonly re-

ELECTRON POPULATION OF THE IRON FAMILY

Sublevel	1s	2s	2p	3s	3p	3d	4s
Maximum population	2	2	6	2	6	10	2
Iron	2	2	6	2	6	:	:
Cobalt	2	2	6	2	6	: : . . .	:
Nickel	2	2	6	2	6	: : : . .	:

ferred to as *ferromagnetism* because of the unusual extent to which it is possessed by iron. Cobalt is strongly magnetic; nickel is the least magnetic of the group. The magnetic nature of iron, cobalt, and nickel is related to peculiarities in the incomplete M-shell.

Electrons revolving around the nucleus of an atom are thought to spin on their own axes. Physicists believe that magnetism in metals is associated with this electron spin. Each spinning electron is a tiny magnet and electron pairs are formed by two electrons spinning in opposite directions. The electronic magnetisms of such a pair of electrons neutralize each other. The members of the Iron Family have incomplete M-shells containing unpaired electrons giving the atoms a net magnetic effect. Groups of such atoms may be so aligned as to form a small magnetized region, called a

VOCABULARY

Alnico (*al*-nih-ko). A strongly ferromagnetic alloy of iron, nickel, aluminum, and cobalt.

Carboloy (*kar*-bol-oy). An extremely hard alloy of cobalt and tungsten carbide.

Flux. A material used to promote the fusion of minerals.

Nitralloy (*nye*-tral-oy). An alloy steel that has been treated with ammonia.

Permalloy (*per*-mal-oy). A high-nickel alloy of steel that is easily magnetized.

Stellite. A hard alloy of cobalt and chromium.

domain. Ordinarily magnetic domains within the metallic crystals point in random directions and cancel one another so that the net magnetism is zero. A piece of iron becomes magnetized when an outside force aligns the domains in the same direction.

1. IRON

2. The occurrence of iron. Iron is the fourth element in abundance by weight in the earth's crust. Nearly 5% of this crust consists of iron. It is the second most abundant metal, being surpassed only by aluminum. Meteors are known to contain iron. This fact, together with the knowledge of the magnetic nature of the earth itself, has led scientists to believe that the core of the earth may be composed mainly of iron.

Unfortunately, much of the iron in the crust of the earth cannot be removed profitably. Only those iron-bearing minerals from which the iron can be recovered by a practical and profitable method are considered to be *iron ores.*

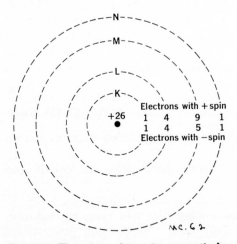

Fig. 35-1. **The atom of iron is magnetic because the electron spins in the M-shell are not all counterbalanced.**

Fig. 35-2. **Magnetite is rich in iron and has magnetic properties. Pieces of this ore were once used in magnetic compasses.** (American Museum of Natural History)

The most abundant ore is *hematite*, Fe_2O_3, a reddish-brown substance. *Limonite*, $2 Fe_2O_3 \cdot 3 H_2O$, is a hydrated oxide which yields a yellow powder when it is crushed. *Magnetite*, Fe_3O_4, is a magnetic ore which is rich in iron. Pieces of magnetite will attract iron filings like an ordinary magnet. These were the lodestones of ancient times. *Siderite*, $FeCO_3$, is a carbonate of iron that is also mined as an ore. *Pyrite*, FeS_2, called fool's gold, is an abundant iron mineral used in the production of sulfuric acid. It is of minor importance as an iron ore.

Iron ore is mined in nearly half of the states of the United States. Minnesota and Michigan produce many millions of tons each year. Alabama has a thriving iron and steel industry which is favored by the fact that iron ore, coal for making coke, and limestone are all located within a few miles of each other. New York, Pennsylvania, West Virginia, Ohio, and Missouri also produce considerable amounts of iron ore.

The largest deposits of iron ore in the world are those of hematite in the Lake

Superior region of the United States. Over 90 million tons of ore are shipped through the Great Lakes from this area each year. It is estimated that, at the present rate of consumption, these reserves of high grade hematite will be exhausted by 1970.

New fields in Labrador and Quebec are now yielding several million tons of rich ore each year. A veritable mountain of high grade hematite, the Cerro Bolivar of Venezuela, was discovered in 1947 by American geologists. It contains more than 400 million tons of ore of about 58% iron. When developed it is expected to yield 10 million tons annually. A 30-million-ton mountain of perhaps the richest iron ore on earth is being developed for mining in the Liberian jungle of Africa by American and Dutch interests.

In addition to the high grade hematite deposits of the Lake Superior region, there is an abundance of low grade ore, *taconite*, which is a mixture of hematite and magnetite in a matrix of rock. The proportions are two parts magnetite to one part hematite. The magnetite is recovered by magnetic separation; the hematite and rock are discarded as waste.

3. Iron is extracted from its ores by reduction. Coke is the reducing agent. About one ton of coke is required to produce one ton of iron. Limestone is ordinarily used as a *flux* in the reaction. The flux unites with impurities in the ore to form an easily melted *slag*.

Prior to reduction, some ores are improved by a process called **beneficiation.** This is a general term applied to any process, physical or chemical, which renders the ore more suitable for reduction. The magnetic separation of magnetite from low grade ores is an example of *physical beneficiation*. By roasting a low grade of hematite in a reducing atmosphere, it may be converted to magnetite. This is *chemical beneficiation*.

$$6\ Fe_2O_3 + C \rightarrow 4\ Fe_3O_4 + CO_2 \uparrow$$

4. The operation of the blast furnace. Iron oxide is reduced to iron in a giant structure called a **blast furnace.** The furnace is about 100 ft high, with an internal diameter of about 25 ft. It has a steel shell lined with firebrick. A blast of hot air, sometimes enriched with oxygen in the most modern furnaces, is forced into the base of the furnace through blowpipes called **tuyères** (twee-*yair*).

Fig. 35-3. In this typical beneficiation process, heavy water-borne ore particles are separated from lighter impurities by centrifugal force. (Steelways)

The charge which is put into the blast furnace consists of iron oxide, coke, and a flux, in the proper proportions as calculated from an analysis of the raw materials. Usually the flux is limestone, because silica or sand is the most common impurity in the iron ore. Some iron ores contain limestone as an impurity and, in such cases, the flux added is sand.

A single blast furnace may produce 1500 tons of iron, 500 tons of slag, and 2000 tons of flue gas daily. The United States now produces nearly 100 million tons of iron each year. This tonnage is being increased constantly by improving blast furnace technology.

A large blast furnace requires about 50,000 cubic feet of hot air every minute for the air blast. This air is heated in gigantic stoves that are almost as tall as the furnace itself. The exhaust gas contains carbon monoxide which is burned in the stoves to heat more air for the blast furnace.

5. Chemical reactions within the blast furnace. The blast furnace reduces the iron ore to iron and removes the earthy gangue as slag. Coke is required

Fig. 35-4. **A battery of stoves serves these two blast furnaces.** (Ewing Galloway)

for the first function and the limestone for the second. The products of the blast furnace are *pig iron, slag,* and *flue gas.*

The chemical changes which occur are complex. The coke is ignited by the blast of hot air and some of it burns forming carbon dioxide.

$$C + O_2 \rightarrow CO_2 \uparrow$$

As the carbon dioxide which is formed just above the tuyères rises through the furnace, it comes in contact with hot coke and is reduced to carbon monoxide.

$$CO_2 + C \rightarrow 2\,CO \uparrow$$

The carbon monoxide thus formed is actually the reducing agent that reduces the iron oxide to metallic iron.

$$Fe_2O_3 + 3\,CO \rightarrow 2\,Fe + 3\,CO_2 \uparrow$$

To prevent the possibility of any reversal of the reactions, the operation is so controlled that there will be a large excess of carbon monoxide. For that reason, the exhaust gases contain from 20 to 30% carbon monoxide.

The white-hot liquid iron flows to the bottom of the furnace as it is reduced. Every 4 or 5 hours it is tapped off. It may be cast into molds to form *pig iron,* or it may go directly to a furnace or converter where it is made into steel.

In the middle region of the furnace, the limestone decomposes into calcium oxide and carbon dioxide.

$$CaCO_3 \rightarrow CaO + CO_2 \uparrow$$

The calcium oxide combines with silica to form a calcium silicate slag which is more readily fused than silica.

$$CaO + SiO_2 \rightarrow CaSiO_3$$

This glassy slag also collects in a pool at the bottom of the furnace. Since it has a much lower density than liquid

Fig. 35-5. **Tapping the blast furnace.** (United States Steel)

iron, it floats on top of the melted iron and prevents the reoxidation of the iron. The melted slag is tapped off every few hours. Usually the slag is thrown away, although it is sometimes used for making Portland cement.

6. **Impurities in cast iron.** Not all of the impurities in the iron ore find their way into the slag. Manganese, phosphorus, silicon, and sulfur are usually present in minute quantities in the reduced iron. Pig iron may contain from 2 to 5% carbon, and as much as 1% manganese, 0.1% phosphorus, 3% silicon, and 0.3% sulfur. The carbon may be present either as free carbon in the form of graphite, or as the very hard iron carbide, Fe_3C, which is called *cementite*. *White cast iron* is cooled quickly and contains much cementite. *Gray cast iron* is cooled slowly and has more graphite.

7. **The properties of wrought iron.** *Wrought iron*, the purest form of iron which is used commercially, is made by heating cast iron in a furnace lined with iron oxide (see Fig. 35-6). The oxygen from the iron oxide lining unites with the excess carbon in the cast iron, and the oxides of carbon escape. Other im-

purities in the cast iron are similarly oxidized and form a slag. As the purity of the iron increases, the melting point rises, and the iron is collected as a pasty mass. Most of the slag is removed by hammering the iron while still plastic.

8. **The uses of the different kinds of iron.** Several varieties of iron are prepared for commercial uses by different types of heat treatment and purification processes. Steel contains more carbon than wrought iron, as a rule, and less carbon than cast iron. Steel varies decidedly in its carbon content, ranging from 0.05% to 1.7% carbon. In fact,

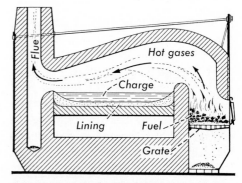

Fig. 35-6. **In the reverberatory furnace the hot gases are deflected down on the charge in the bed of the furnace.**

steel which contains from 0.05 to 0.4% carbon is often spoken of as *low-carbon steel*. *Medium-carbon steel* contains from 0.4 to 0.8% carbon. Steel which contains from 0.8 to 1.7% carbon is called *high-carbon steel*.

As one would infer from its name, cast iron is used for making castings. The molten iron is poured into sand molds and allowed to cool. Over 75% of the cast iron produced is used every year in making steel.

Wrought iron is used to some extent for making high-grade steel. It is used for blacksmith iron, chains, ornamental furniture, and wire, although the cheaper low-carbon steel has replaced it for many purposes. Wrought iron water pipes resist corrosion better than those of steel or cast iron.

Steel is used for many purposes that require a metal of great tensile strength, such as railroad rails, structural steel for buildings, bridges, automobiles, and ships.

2. STEEL PRODUCTION

9. The processes for making steel. The relatively high carbon content of cast iron makes it very hard and brittle. It is very brittle at low temperatures due to the presence of phosphorus. It is also very brittle at high temperatures due to the presence of sulfur. *The conversion of cast iron to steel is essentially a purification process in which the impurities are removed by oxidation.* Near the end of the process the proper amounts of carbon and selected alloying substances are added to give the desired properties to the steel.

Three important methods of producing steel are in use today. *The Besse-*

mer process accounts for about 5% of the steel produced in the United States. Air, or oxygen, is used as the oxidizing agent. *The open-hearth process* accounts for about 85% of the steel produced in this country. Iron(III) oxide is used as the oxidizing agent. *The electric-furnace process* accounts for about 10% of the total steel production. Electric-furnace steel is very high in quality. Iron(III) oxide is used as the oxidizing agent.

Nearly 150 million tons of steel were produced by these processes in the United States in 1960, and the demand for steel is increasing yearly.

The modern Age of Steel began with the development of the *Bessemer process* a century ago. The great advantage of this process is that tons of steel can be made in approximately 20 minutes from pig iron. The *open-hearth process*, which was developed later, produces even larger batches, but 6 to 12 hours are required for converting the iron into steel. The *electric-furnace process* is a still more recent development that is growing in importance, especially for steels of high quality.

10. The Bessemer process. In this process, the cast iron is poured into an egg-shaped *converter* which is large enough to hold from 15 to 20 tons. The converter is mounted on pivots which permit it to be turned down on its side to receive the charge of cast iron. The air blast is then turned on, and the converter is turned almost to a vertical position, as shown in Fig. 35-7. The oxygen unites with the carbon and the other impurities, forming products which either escape as gases or unite with the lining of the converter.

In about 15 or 20 minutes the process is complete. The converter is then turned down on its side, and a measured amount of *spiegeleisen* (*spee*-g'l-eyezun), or *ferromanganese*, is added to the iron in the converter. These alloys are rich in carbon and manganese. The carbon thus added gives a steel having the proper carbon content. The manganese unites with the oxygen left in the steel from the blast of air.

Sir Henry Bessemer (1813–1898), who developed this process, found it hard to tell just when to turn off the air blast so as to leave exactly the right amount of carbon in the finished steel. The problem was solved by burning out all of the carbon, and then adding a small quantity of iron alloy that is rich in carbon. This explains why ferromanganese is added in making steel by the Bessemer process.

Another problem that confronted Bessemer was how to get rid of phosphorus. Phosphorus, present as an impurity in some iron ores, makes steel brittle when it is cold. Sulfur is another undesirable impurity because it makes hot steel brittle. Sulfur is burned out of the steel and escapes as a volatile gas, sulfur dioxide. But phosphorus forms a solid oxide, diphosphorus pentoxide, which is not eliminated so easily. Finally, two English chemists, Thomas and Gilchrist, suggested lining the converter with dolomite, $CaCO_3 \cdot MgCO_3$. When dolomite is heated, it yields the basic anhydrides, CaO and MgO. These compounds react with diphosphorus pentoxide, which is an acid anhydride. The reactions are shown in the following equations:

$$6\ CaO + P_4O_{10} \rightarrow 2\ Ca_3(PO_4)_2$$
$$6\ MgO + P_4O_{10} \rightarrow 2\ Mg_3(PO_4)_2$$

The slag that is formed contains phosphates which are poured off from the converter. Ground to a fine powder, this slag is used as a phosphate fertilizer.

Fig. 35-7. **A Bessemer converter "blowing off."** (American Iron and Steel Institute)

One of the faults of Bessemer steel is the speed by which it is made. Although this process produces about 20 tons of steel in 20 minutes, it is hard to control the composition of the steel with precision. All the steel in one batch is homogeneous, and all gases must be expelled completely, otherwise weak spots would be present in the finished steel. These faults have caused the Bessemer process to be superseded largely by the *open-hearth process* today. This slower process allows frequent testing of the steel while it is in process, which insures a more reliable quality in the finished product.

11. The open-hearth process.
1. *The furnace.* The open-hearth furnace holds a pool of molten steel 30 to 80 feet in length, 12 to 15 feet in width, and about 2 feet in depth. From 50 to 200 tons are made in one batch. The furnace is built of steel plates covered with a thick lining of either limestone or silica. The choice of the lining depends on whether the cast iron has acid

or basic impurities. At the end of the process, the melted steel is poured out into a large ladle.

2. *The heating system.* A high temperature is necessary to burn out the impurities from the cast iron, and to melt the steel scrap which forms part of the charge. Producer gas is used as the fuel. Both the gas and the air needed for its combustion are preheated before they enter the furnace by passing them over a checkerwork of hot firebrick. As the gas burns inside the furnace, the heat from the flames is reflected down on the charge. The hot waste products of combustion pass out of the furnace through a second checkerwork of firebrick, heating it to a high temperature.

At intervals of about twenty minutes, the valves are reversed to direct the incoming gas and air through the checkerwork just heated. Thus a very hot flame is supplied continuously by the burning of the preheated gas in preheated air. Since the heat is supplied from an external source, the temperature can be controlled more accurately than in the Bessemer converter.

3. *The charge.* The charge for an open-hearth furnace consists of melted iron from the blast furnace, scrap steel, iron ore, and limestone. The melted iron is poured into the furnace from ladles. A machine picks up scrap steel, iron ore, and limestone, and dumps them into the furnace. The iron ore supplies oxygen to unite with the carbon in the liquid iron from the blast furnace. The limestone unites with impurities to form a slag which is drained off. Scrap steel may form as much as 50% of the charge.

The impurities in the pig iron are oxidized in the following way:

$$3\ C\ +\ Fe_2O_3 \rightarrow 3\ CO \uparrow +\ 2\ Fe$$
$$3\ Mn\ +\ Fe_2O_3 \rightarrow 3\ MnO\ +\ 2\ Fe$$
$$12\ P\ +\ 10\ Fe_2O_3 \rightarrow 3\ P_4O_{10}\ +\ 20\ Fe$$
$$3\ Si\ +\ 2\ Fe_2O_3 \rightarrow 3\ SiO_2\ +\ 4\ Fe$$
$$3\ S\ +\ 2\ Fe_2O_3 \rightarrow 3\ SO_2 \uparrow +\ 4\ Fe$$

The limestone flux decomposes as in the blast furnace:

$$CaCO_3 \rightarrow CaO + CO_2 \uparrow$$

Calcium oxide and the oxides of the impurities, except those of carbon and sulfur which escape as gases, react to form the slag:

$$P_4O_{10} + 6\ CaO \rightarrow 2\ Ca_3(PO_4)_2$$
$$SiO_2\ +\ CaO \rightarrow\ CaSiO_3$$
$$MnO\ +\ SiO_2 \rightarrow\ MnSiO_3$$

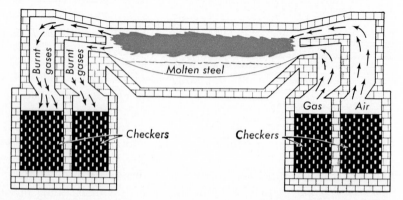

Fig. 35-8. Sectional diagram of an open-hearth furnace for the manufacture of steel.

Fig. 35-9. The electric furnace pictured here is tilted while a heat of high grade steel is being tapped. These furnaces may draw 12,000 amperes at 40 volts to produce the heat required to make stainless steel and other alloy steels. (Crucible Steel)

12. The electric-furnace process. In one common type of electric furnace for making steel, carbon electrodes about 10 feet long and 15 inches in diameter extend through the top of the furnace (see Fig. 35-9). The furnace is lined with dolomite. The charge usually consists of scrap steel, cast iron, and iron ore.

When the electric current is turned on, an arc forms through the charge between the electrodes, producing the heat necessary to carry out the process. There is no electrolysis. This process produces high grade steel. It allows for testing of the steel at various intervals before it is finished. Purer raw materials are also used in the charge. Furthermore, the operation is carried on in a reducing atmosphere, which prevents oxidation of the steel.

Sometimes a duplex process of making steel is used. Because of its speed, the Bessemer process is first used. Before the reaction is complete, the charge is transferred to either an open-hearth furnace or an electric furnace where it is finished more slowly.

13. Working steel. As the steel comes from the furnace, it is usually drawn off into a huge ladle from which it is poured into ingot molds. Then the molds are stripped from the ingots of red-hot steel and the ingots are placed in *soaking pits* where they are kept at a uniform high temperature until removed to be worked.

The ingots, at the proper temperature, may be put through a series of rolls. They may be *rolled* into any desired thickness, shape, or length.

Sometimes steel is treated by *drop-forging*. In this treatment, the steel is placed on a block and hammered with a powerful mechanical hammer.

Steel is often shaped in a hydraulic press. Some of the huge presses used for *stamping* out automobile bodies, or armor plate, are capable of exerting a force of from 12,000 to 14,000 tons.

A *hot extrusion* process has recently been perfected which enables hot billets of steel to be extruded into long seamless tubes. This is a development of great importance for atomic power plants, jet engines, and petroleum refineries. In these industries tough steel tubes are needed to contain liquids and gases under very high temperatures and pressures.

IRON ORE

LIMESTONE

COAL

COKE

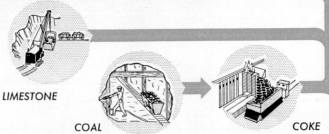

Open hearth furnace

Charging box being dumped

Open-hearth furnace cut-away to show method of charging

1650°C

Slag

Steel ladle

Charging machine

Charging boxes hold limestone, iron ore or scrap

Molten steel

Slag ladle

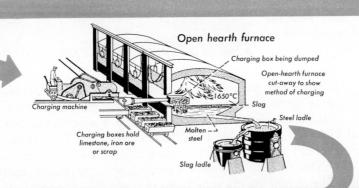

Teeming ingots

Stripping ingots

Stripper crane

Ingot mold

Ingot mold

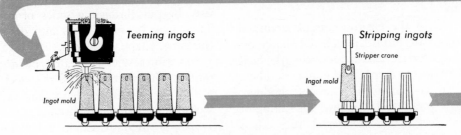

Blooms

Bloom

Blooming mill

Structural steel and rails

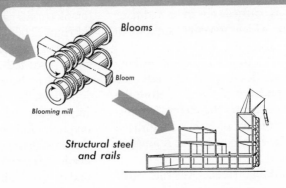

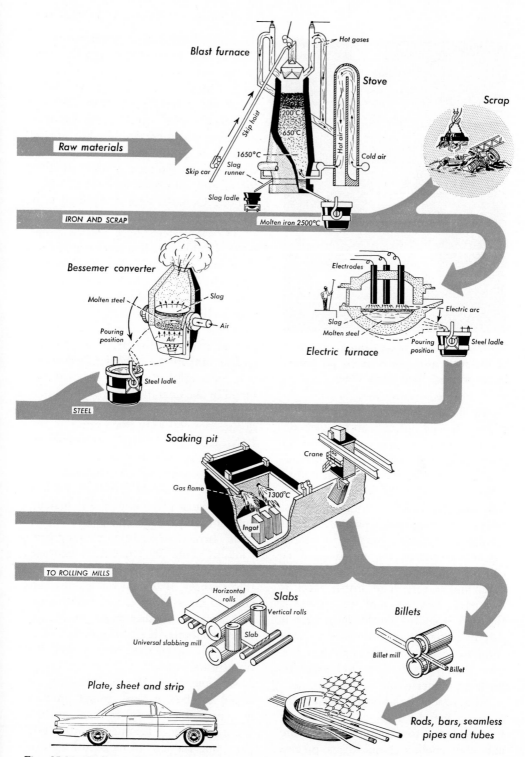

Fig. 35-10. **A flow chart showing the various processes in the manufacture of steel.**

Fig. 35-11. **A steel ingot heated to 1300° C is removed from the soaking pit before being worked.** (Bethlehem Steel)

14. Tempering steel. The properties of steel depend not only on the percentage of carbon it contains, but also on the manner in which the carbon is held.

When a high-carbon steel is heated to a bright cherry-red heat, about 670° C, iron carbide, Fe_3C, is formed. It dissolves in the iron that is present. If such a solution is cooled quickly by plunging it into water, oil, or some other coolant, the carbide does not decompose, and a very hard brittle steel is formed. If the solution of iron carbide in the iron is cooled slowly, by letting it cool in air for example, some of the iron carbide decomposes and the product contains iron carbide, iron and graphite. Such a product is soft and tough.

All grades of hardness between these extremes may be obtained by reheating hardened steel to a definite temperature and then cooling it quickly; a process called *tempering*. A piece of hard, brit-

tle steel reheated to a temperature of 220° C, and then cooled quickly, will not be quite so hard or quite so brittle. Such a steel is hard enough for razor blades. If the steel is preheated to 280° C, and then cooled quickly, the product formed is still more flexible, but not so hard. It might be suitable for making watch springs. To get a product suitable for making handsaws and other woodworking tools the steel is reheated to a temperature of 300° C to 350° C.

15. Alloy steels have special properties. Ordinary carbon steel is really an alloy, but the name *alloy steel* is traditionally given to steels to which certain metals, or nonmetals, have been added. Just before the steel is drawn from the furnace, a number of metals may be added to the batch to produce special properties in the finished product. Such alloy steels are in great demand by the manufacturers of tools, machines, automobiles, and airplanes. Some of the common alloy steels are:

1. Nickel steel. A small percentage of nickel added to steel makes an alloy steel that is not easily corroded and combines toughness with hardness. Such a strong, elastic steel is used for making automobile parts, bridges, and armor plate. *Invar* is a nickel-steel alloy that contains about 36% nickel. It expands and contracts very little with temperature changes. It is used for making surveyor's tapes and clock pendulums. *Permalloy* is another nickel-iron alloy which contains about 80% nickel. It is very easily magnetized and is used for transformer cores.

2. Chrome steel. When chromium is added to steel, a hard, tough product is formed. It is useful for making ball bearings, roller bearings, automobile parts, and the jaws of rock-crushing machinery. *Stainless steel* contains about

14% chromium. It resists corrosion very well and is popular for making cutlery, surgical instruments, and nontarnishing metal trim.

3. *Chrome-nickel steel.* Steel that contains about 4% chromium and 4% nickel is exceedingly hard and tough. It is used for making plowshares, crankshafts, files, and gear teeth. Alloy steel, known as "18-8" in the trade, contains 18% chromium and 8% nickel. It does not tarnish.

4. *Chrome-vanadium steel.* Alloy steel that contains both chromium and vanadium withstands severe strains and shocks without breaking. For this reason it is used for making some automobile parts and wrenches.

5. *Manganese steel.* Steel containing considerable amounts of manganese is exceedingly hard. Such manganese steel is used for making burglar-proof safes, and the teeth of the scoops on power shovels and dredging equipment.

6. *Silicon steel.* Silicon, a nonmetal, is also added to make a special kind of alloy steel which is easily magnetized

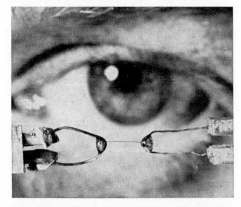

Fig. 35-12. **A tiny "whisker" of pure iron, free of the structural imperfections of the ordinary metal, provides scientists with a means of studying the nature of the enormous forces which bind atoms tightly together.** (Westinghouse)

and demagnetized. Hence it is used for making the cores of transformers and electromagnets.

7. *Tungsten steel.* The addition of considerable tungsten to steel produces an alloy that can be heated red-hot and still retain a hard cutting edge. It is used for making cutting tools for lathes, and for making hacksaw blades.

8. *Molybdenum steel.* Molybdenum alloy steel is very strong. Usually molybdenum is added in small amounts to other alloying metals to produce a strong, tough steel that will resist strains without breaking. Such alloys are used for making automobile parts.

9. *Nitralloy steel.* Nitralloy steels are made by treating a special steel that contains some aluminum with ammonia gas at a temperature of about 500° C. Nitralloy steel is extremely hard and is used on motor parts that are subjected to heavy wear.

3. IRON AND ITS COMPOUNDS

16. Pure iron is seldom seen. Pure iron is a metal that is seldom seen. It is silver-white, soft, ductile, tough, and does not tarnish readily. It melts at 1535° C. Commercial iron contains carbon and other impurities that alter its properties. Cast iron melts at about 1150° C. All forms of iron corrode, or rust, in moist air, so it is not a self-protective metal. The rust that forms is brittle and scales off, leaving the metal underneath exposed to corrosion.

In many cases the corrosion of iron seems to be an electrochemical process. A carbon particle in contact with a piece of moist iron causes the iron to rust rapidly. The carbon acts as the positive element of a miniature electrochemical

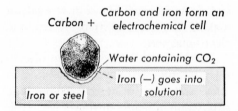

Fig. 35-13. **Iron and steel contain impurities and corrode readily unless covered by a protective coating.**

cell, and the iron becomes the negative element (see Fig. 35-13). Rain water containing dissolved carbon dioxide enhances the action.

Merely a difference in the amount of oxygen over the surface of wet iron will result in rusting. A single drop of rain containing dissolved carbon dioxide sets up a tiny cell between the iron at the center of the drop and the iron around the edge. Iron(II) hydroxide is formed and is readily converted to iron(III) hydroxide. By loss of water the familiar red rust, $Fe_2O_3 \cdot X\,H_2O$ is formed.

Dilute acids generally act readily on iron, but alkalies do not react with it. Concentrated nitric acid does not react with iron. In fact, dipping iron into concentrated nitric acid renders the iron *passive*, or *inactive*, with respect to its behavior toward other chemicals. Concentrated sulfuric acid has little effect on iron.

17. The protection of iron.
1. *Coating it with other metals.* In the galvanizing process, iron is coated with zinc or cadmium. In tinware, sheet iron is covered with a thin layer of tin.
2. *Coating it with metallic compounds and lacquers.* Some kinds of paint, such as red lead or zinc chromate, protect iron against corrosion. Lacquers and varnishes are also used to prevent the corrosion of iron.
3. *Alloying it with other metals.* Silicon

alloys and stainless steel are alloys of iron or steel which do not tarnish.
4. *Using chemicals to form a surface coating.* By treating red-hot iron with steam, a thin coating of magnetic iron oxide, Fe_3O_4, is formed on the surface. This coating is adherent and nonporous. It protects the metal underneath from corrosion. The product, which is called *Russia iron,* is used for making stovepipes. The blue-black oxide on handsaws is similar in its nature.

Iron is "Parkerized" by dipping it into a hot alkaline solution of sodium phosphate. The phosphate forms a thin coating of basic phosphate of iron.
5. *Attaching a more active metal.* Iron pipes lying in acid soil may be attached to blocks of magnesium which is more active than iron. As the magnesium corrodes, the attached iron is maintained at a negative potential and does not corrode. Magnesium rods are sometimes placed in hot-water heaters where electrochemical action between iron and copper or brass fittings would cause the iron to corrode.

18. There are three oxides of iron. Of the three oxides of iron, *iron(II) oxide,* FeO, is of little importance since it changes rapidly, when exposed to the air, into *iron(III) oxide,* Fe_2O_3. This oxide is the most important ore of iron, and it is used as a cheap red paint pigment known as red ocher, Venetian red, or Indian red. It is used for grinding and polishing glass under the name of *rouge*.

Limonite is a natural *hydrated iron(III) oxide* which is pulverized and used as a pigment called yellow ocher. When it is heated or roasted, it forms pigments known as *siennas* and *umbers. Magnetic iron oxide,* Fe_3O_4, is an important ore of iron. It is composed of Fe_2O_3 and FeO, and may be considered to be iron(II,III) oxide.

19. Reactions of the Fe⁺⁺ ion. Hydrated iron(II) sulfate, $FeSO_4 \cdot 7 H_2O$ is the most important compound of iron in the +2 oxidation state. It is commonly called *green vitriol* or *copperas*. It is used to form a mordant, and for making blue-black inks. Iron(II) sulfate may be prepared by the action of dilute sulfuric acid on iron. The crystalline hydrate, on exposure to air, loses water of hydration and turns brown due to oxidation. Iron(II) sulfate in solution is gradually oxidized to the iron(III) state by dissolved oxygen. The formation of a brown precipitate of basic iron(III) sulfate is evidence of this change.

$$4 \; FeSO_4 + O_2 + 2 \; H_2O \rightarrow$$
$$4 \; Fe(OH)SO_4 \downarrow$$

By making the solution acidic with sulfuric acid and adding a small amount of metallic iron, the Fe⁺⁺ ion may be maintained in the reduced state. Hydrated iron(II) ammonium sulfate, $Fe(NH_4)_2(SO_4)_2 \cdot 6 H_2O$, is a better source of Fe⁺⁺ ions in the laboratory because it is stable in contact with air.

Iron(II) salts are readily oxidized to iron(III) salts by use of the corresponding acid and an oxidizing agent. In the case of the nitrate, nitric acid meets both requirements.

$$3 \; Fe(NO_3)_2 + 4 \; HNO_3 \rightarrow$$
$$3 \; Fe(NO_3)_3 + NO \uparrow + 2 \; H_2O$$

Crystals of hydrated iron(II) chloride, $FeCl_2 \cdot 2 H_2O$, are blue as long as the reduced state is maintained. Gradual oxidation to the iron(III) state is evident as a green color develops. Iron(II) chloride may be prepared by the action of hydrochloric acid on iron.

Iron(II) hydroxide is formed as a white precipitate when sodium hydroxide is added to a solution of an iron(II) salt. The precipitate is first green, in the presence of air, and finally brown as the iron(III) hydroxide is formed.

We may show the oxidation of the Fe⁺⁺ ion in the use of an iron ink (ordinary blue-black ink). If a freshly prepared solution of iron(II) sulfate is added to a solution of tannic acid, the nearly colorless compound, *iron(II) tannate*, is formed. It slowly oxidizes to form the black compound, *iron(III) tannate*. Usually a blue dye is added to an iron ink, which also contains dextrin to make it wet the pen and the paper.

Iron inks are easily removed by the use of a reducing agent, such as oxalic acid, or salt and lemon juice. Skimmed milk applied at once to fresh ink stains, and then followed by cold water, will usually remove nearly all the stain.

20. Reactions of the Fe⁺⁺⁺ ion. Iron(III) chloride, $FeCl_3 \cdot 6 H_2O$, is the most important compound of iron in the +3 oxidation state. The anhydrous salt may be recovered as black crystals in the composition reaction between iron and chlorine. The hydrated Fe⁺⁺⁺ ion, $Fe(H_2O)_6^{+++}$, imparts a pale violet color which usually is not seen because of hydrolysis. Hydrated iron(III) chloride has a yellow-brown color.

The Fe⁺⁺⁺ ion undergoes hydrolysis in water solutions of iron(III) salts. The solutions are acidic.

$$Fe^{+++} + 2 \; H_2O \rightleftarrows FeOH^{++} + H_3O^+$$
$$FeOH^{++} + 2 \; H_2O \rightleftarrows Fe(OH)_2^+ + H_3O^+$$
$$Fe(OH)_2^+ + 2 \; H_2O \rightleftarrows Fe(OH)_3 + H_3O^+$$

The hydrolysis is extensive when it occurs in boiling water and the blood-red colloidal suspension of iron(III) hydroxide is formed.

Iron(III) ions are removed from solution by the addition of a solution containing hydroxide ions. A red-brown gelatinous precipitate of iron(III) hydroxide is formed. By evaporating the water, red Fe_2O_3 remains. It is the pigment, Venetian red, or the polishing powder, rouge, referred to in Section 18.

$$Fe^{+++} + 3\ OH^- \rightarrow Fe(OH)_3 \downarrow$$

21. Tests for the iron ions. Potassium hexacyanoferrate(II), $K_4Fe(CN)_6$ (also called potassium ferrocyanide), is a light yellow crystalline salt containing the complex hexacyanoferrate(II) ion (ferrocyanide ion), $Fe(CN)_6^{\equiv}$. The iron is in the +2 oxidation state. It may be formed by adding an excess of cyanide ions to a solution of an iron(II) salt.

CAUTION: *Solutions containing the cyanide ion are deadly poisons and should never be handled by inexperienced chemistry students.*

$$6\ KCN + FeCl_2 \rightarrow K_4Fe(CN)_6 + 2\ KCl$$

The iron of the $Fe(CN)_6^{\equiv}$ ion may be oxidized by chlorine to the +3 state to form the hexacyanoferrate(III) ion (ferricyanide ion) $Fe(CN)_6^{=}$.

$$2\ K_4Fe(CN)_6 + Cl_2 \rightarrow$$
$$2\ K_3Fe(CN)_6 + 2\ KCl$$

The oxidation of the iron from the +2 state to the +3 state is accompanied by the reduction of the chlorine from the 0 to the −1 state. Potassium hexacyanoferrate(III), $K_3Fe(CN)_6$ (known also as potassium ferricyanide), is a dark red crystalline salt.

When Fe^{++} ions and $Fe(CN)_6^{=}$ ions are brought together a deep blue precipitate forms. *The pigment color is due to the presence of iron in two different oxidation states.* This insoluble substance is called Turnbull's blue, and is now considered to have the composition $KFeFe(CN)_6 \cdot H_2O$.

$$FeSO_4 + K_3Fe(CN)_6 + H_2O \rightarrow$$
$$KFeFe(CN)_6 \cdot H_2O \downarrow + K_2SO_4$$

or simply

$$Fe^{++} + K^+ + Fe(CN)_6^{=} + H_2O \rightarrow$$
$$KFeFe(CN)_6 \cdot H_2O \downarrow$$

Similarly, Fe^{+++} ions and $Fe(CN)_6^{\equiv}$ ions form a deep blue precipitate. Again the color is a pigment color and is due to the presence of *two different* oxidation states of iron. The precipitate is called Prussian blue, and is now recognized as having the same composition as Turnbull's blue, $KFeFe(CN)_6 \cdot H_2O$.

$$Fe^{+++} + K^+ + Fe(CN)_6^{\equiv} + H_2O \rightarrow$$
$$KFeFe(CN)_6 \cdot H_2O \downarrow$$

Fe^{++} ions and $Fe(CN)_6^{\equiv}$ ions form a white precipitate of $K_2FeFe(CN)_6$, if precautions have been taken to prevent the oxidation of any Fe^{++} ions. Of course, on exposure to air, it begins to turn blue due to oxidation. Fe^{+++} ions and $Fe(CN)_6^{\equiv}$ ions give only a brown solution. From these reactions it is evident that we have a means of detecting the presence of the two oxidation states of iron.

1. *Test for the Fe^{++} ion.* Suppose a few drops of $K_3Fe(CN)_6$ solution are added to a solution of iron(II) sulfate (or iron(II) ammonium sulfate). The characteristic dark blue precipitate, $KFeFe(CN)_6 \cdot H_2O$ forms.

$$Fe^{++} + SO_4^{=} + 3\ K^+ + Fe(CN)_6^{\equiv} + H_2O \rightarrow$$
$$KFeFe(CN)_6 \cdot H_2O \downarrow + 2\ K^+ + SO_4^{=}$$

The two potassium ions and the sulfate ion are merely spectator ions in this reaction. The *formation of a blue precipitate when $K_3Fe(CN)_6$ is added to a solution suspected of containing the iron (II) ion serves as a test for the Fe^{++} ion.* 2. *Test for the Fe^{+++} ion.* Suppose a few drops of $K_4Fe(CN)_6$ solution is added to a solution of iron(III) chloride, the characteristic dark blue precipitate, $KFeFe(CN)_6 \cdot H_2O$, forms.

$$Fe^{+++} + 3\ Cl^- + 4\ K^+ + Fe(CN)_6^{\equiv} + H_2O \rightarrow$$
$$KFeFe(CN)_6 \cdot H_2O \downarrow + 3\ K^+ + 3\ Cl^-$$

Three potassium ions and three chloride ions are spectators in this reaction. The *formation of a blue precipitate when $K_4Fe(CN)_6$ is added to a solution suspected of containing iron(III) ions serves as a test for the Fe^{+++} ion.*

Potassium thiocyanate, KCNS, provides another excellent test for the Fe^{+++} ion. It is often used to confirm the $K_4Fe(CN)_6$ test. A blood-red solution results from the formation of the complex $FeCNS^{++}$ ion.

22. The blueprint process. In making blueprints, a solution of iron(III) ammonium citrate is mixed with $K_3Fe(CN)_6$. This forms a brown solution, with which a well-sized paper is coated, and then permitted to dry. All of this is done in a dark room.

When the paper is placed under a negative or other transparency and exposed to light, reduction occurs and an iron(II) salt is formed wherever the light strikes the sensitive paper. The print is then developed by dipping it in water. Any iron(II) salt formed during the reduction reacts with the $K_3Fe(CN)_6$ and forms an intense blue color.

At those places where no light strikes the paper, no reduction occurs and the water washes away the mixture of unchanged iron compounds, thus fixing the print. The exposed portions are blue in color, and the unexposed portions are white.

4. COBALT

23. Occurrence and uses of cobalt. Cobalt is found in nature in numerous minerals, together with iron, nickel, copper, silver, and arsenic. It is ordinarily recovered as a by-product of the smelting of various ores. Both cobalt and nickel often remain as oxides after the roasting and reduction processes have been carried out. Cobalt is usually found combined with arsenic and sulfur. The principle ores are *cobaltite*, CoAsS; *smaltite*, $CoAs_2$; and *linnalite*, Co_3S_4. Metallic cobalt may be produced by the reduction of its oxide with aluminum.

This metal so closely resembles nickel that the two metals are often spoken of as "twins." Cobalt has been used to plate iron, but its most important uses are in the making of alloys.

Stellite, a very hard alloy of cobalt and chromium, is used for making metal-cutting lathe tools. *Carboloy* is made by combining cobalt with a carbide of tungsten. It is one of the hardest materials manufactured; hard enough to bore holes through glass or porcelain, or to cut threads on glass. It is a tough alloy, not easily broken, and is used for high-speed cutting tools. *Alnico* is a very strongly ferromagnetic alloy composed of aluminum, cobalt, iron, and nickel. It is used extensively for making small permanent magnets used in loudspeakers, telephones, and hearing aids.

24. Compounds of cobalt. Cobalt forms cobalt(II) and cobalt(III) compounds, in which the oxidation numbers are +2 and +3, respectively. The cobalt(II) compounds, which exist as red crystals and form pink-colored solutions, are more common than cobalt(III) compounds.

Cobalt(II) chloride, $CoCl_2 \cdot 6\ H_2O$, is red when it exists as the hydrate, but turns blue when dehydrated. Paper covered with a solution of cobalt(II) chloride may be used as a crude *hygrometer* to tell how much moisture the air contains. In damp weather, the paper appears pink, changing to violet, and then to blue, as the air becomes less moist. Since the blue color is more intense than the pink, a solution of cobalt(II) chloride may be used as an invisible ink. A message written on paper with the dilute pink solution can hardly be seen. If the paper is heated, the intense blue appears. This color change is frequently used in conjunction with silica gel to indicate when the gel is spent as a desiccant.

Cobalt(II) nitrate, $Co(NO_3)_2$, is used to some extent in analytical work. Cobalt compounds impart a blue color to glass. This metal can be made radioactive and is used in treating the victims of certain types of cancer (see Chapter 39, Section 9).

25. Cobalt nitrate tests. Cobalt(II) nitrate provides a test for the identification of aluminum, magnesium, and zinc by a method of blowpipe analysis. The test is based on the fact that the nitrate, when heated strongly, decomposes to the oxide and combines with the oxides of these metals to form distinctly-colored complexes. A compound of the unknown metal is first heated in the oxidizing flame of the blowpipe on charcoal or plaster of Paris. A drop of cobalt(II) nitrate is then added and the

mass is heated again. If *aluminum* is present, a blue coloration develops. *Magnesium* yields a pink-colored mass. *Zinc* produces a green color.

5. NICKEL

26. The occurrence and properties of nickel. Very little nickel is found in the United States. Almost our entire supply comes from Ontario, Canada, although New Caledonia also produces considerable quantities of the metal.

Nickel is a hard, silver-white metal, capable of taking a high polish. It does not tarnish easily. Its chemical properties resemble those of iron, although it is less active.

27. Some uses of nickel. The uses of nickel for toughening steel, for nickel-plating, and as a catalyst for hardening oils have all been mentioned. Nickel is used in several alloys. The *coin nickel* used in the United States is composed of 25% nickel and 75% copper. *Monel metal* contains about 67% nickel, 28% copper, and small quantities of iron and manganese. It is made directly from a complex ore of nickel and copper, from which neither metal can be satis-

Fig. 35-14. The trim of this motor cruiser was made of monel metal. (International Nickel)

factorily extracted. This alloy is strong and tough, and it resists the action of air, sea water, and acids. Monel metal is used in making valves for steam engines, decorative metal trimmings, and for other purposes requiring a metal that does not tarnish easily. *Nichrome*, an alloy of nickel, chromium, iron, and manganese, melts at a high temperature, and has a high resistance to the passage of an electric current. It is used in making the heating units for electric irons, toasters, and other heating appliances.

28. Compounds of nickel. Nickel forms nickel(II) and (rarely) nickel(III) salts, in which the oxidation numbers are +2 and +3, respectively. Nickel(II) salts, which are more common, usually crystallize as beautiful green crystals. The most common salts are nickel(II) chloride, nickel(II) nitrate, and nickel(II) sulfate. Nickel(II) sulfide, when prepared by precipitation, is a black, amorphous powder. Nickel flake and nickel(II) oxide are used for making the active mixture inside the positive plates of the Edison storage battery. When such a battery is charged, *the nickel(II) compound is oxidized to the nickel(III)*, being reduced again as the battery is discharged. Nickel(II) ammonium sulfate, a double salt, is used as the electrolyte for nickel plating. A piece of pure nickel is used as the anode of the plating cell, and the object to be plated is the cathode.

SUMMARY

Iron, cobalt, and nickel have many similarities and compose the Iron Family of metals. Iron exists in both the +2 and +3 oxidation states. Hematite is the most abundant iron ore.

Iron ore is reduced in the blast furnace. Coke is the reducing agent. Calcium carbonate (limestone) is added as a flux to remove the gangue. The products of the blast furnace are pig iron, slag, and flue gas. Wrought iron is the purest form of iron used commercially.

The conversion of cast iron to steel is essentially a purification process in which the impurities are removed by oxidation. There are three important methods in use today: the Bessemer process, in which oxygen is the oxidizing agent; the open-hearth process, in which iron(III) oxide is the oxidizing agent; and the electric-furnace process, in which iron(III) oxide is the oxidizing agent. The open-hearth accounts for about 85% of the steel produced in the United States. By using different alloying metals, steel alloys of many special varieties can be produced.

Iron(II) sulfate is the most important iron(II) compound. Iron(III) chloride is the most important iron(III) compound. The Fe^{++} ion may be identified by using a solution of $K_3Fe(CN)_6$. The Fe^{+++} ion may be similarly identified by using a solution of $K_4Fe(CN)_6$.

Cobalt is used in producing several very hard alloys used as cutting tools. Cobalt(II) compounds, in which cobalt is in the +2 oxidation state, are more common than cobalt(III) compounds.

Nickel is used in producing alloys which are highly resistant to corrosion. Nickel(II) (+2 oxidation state) compounds are common. Nickel(III) compounds, in which nickel has the oxidation number of +3, are rarely encountered.

TEST YOURSELF ON THESE TERMS

alloy steel
beneficiation
Bessemer process
blast furnace
blueprints
carboloy
cast iron
cementation process
copperas

domain
dropforging
flux
high-carbon steel
ingots
invar
low-carbon steel
monel metal
nichrome

nitralloy
open-hearth process
Parkerized
pig iron
slag
spiegeleisen
stellite
tempering
wrought iron

QUESTIONS

Group A

1. Name four common iron ores.
2. What is the difference between *white cast iron* and *gray cast iron?*
3. Which process is most used for making steel in this country?
4. What are five methods of protecting the surface of iron against rusting?
5. What is monel metal, and what are some of its properties?
6. What is an advantage and a disadvantage of the Bessemer steel process?
7. How is wrought iron made?
8. Explain how a steel knife blade is tempered.
9. (*a*) What is nichrome? (*b*) Why is it used in electric toasters?
10. What was the old cementation process for making steel?
11. Explain why iron inks write blue and dry black.
12. What fortunate situation favors the iron and steel industry in Alabama?

Group B

13. Why does impure iron rust more rapidly than pure iron?
14. Name four advantages of the open-hearth process for steelmaking over the Bessemer process.
15. Give the common names of two oxides of iron that are used as pigments.
16. What steel process would probably be used for making a batch of steel for the blades of kitchen knives?
17. (*a*) How can "sympathetic ink" be made from a cobalt compound? (*b*) Why does it turn blue when the paper is heated?
18. What are the advantages of the duplex process for making steel?
19. How do the percentages of carbon in *low-carbon, medium-carbon,* and *high-carbon* steel compare?
20. Mention a use for which each of the following is particularly suitable: (*a*) permalloy; (*b*) invar; (*c*) silicon steel; (*d*) stainless steel; (*e*) manganese steel; (*f*) chrome-nickel steel; (*g*) tungsten steel.
21. (*a*) What chemical change occurs when blueprint paper is exposed to the light? (*b*) What is the chemical formula for the blue compound that is formed on the blueprint paper?
22. How can you detect an iron(II) and an iron(III) compound, if both are present in the same solution?

PROBLEMS

Group A

1. How much iron(II) chloride can be made by adding 165 g of iron to an excess of hydrochloric acid? Compute to 3 significant figures.
2. How much iron(III) chloride can be prepared from the iron(II) chloride in the preceding problem if more hydrochloric acid is added and air is blown through the solution?

Group B

3. A sample of hematite ore contains Fe_2O_3 87.0%, silica 8.0%, moisture 4.0%, other impurities 1.0%. What is the percentage of iron in the ore?
4. What will be the loss in mass when 1.0×10^6 metric tons of the ore in the preceding problem are heated to 200° C?
5. How much limestone will be needed to combine with the silica in 1.0×10^6 metric tons of the ore of Problem 3?
6. (*a*) How much carbon monoxide is required to reduce 1.0×10^6 metric tons of the ore of Problem 3? (*b*) How much coke must be supplied to meet this requirement? (Assume the coke to be 100% carbon.)
7. Iron(II) sulfate is oxidized to iron(III) sulfate in the presence of sulfuric acid using nitric acid as the oxidizing agent. Nitrogen monoxide and water are also formed. Balance the equation.

SOME THINGS FOR YOU TO DO

1. Collect samples of different kinds of steel from a machine shop. Low-carbon steel, medium-carbon steel, high-carbon steel, tool steel, and various alloy steels should be available. Note the difference in appearance, hardness, resistance to corrosion, etc. of the samples.
2. Prepare some iron tannate ink. To a solution of freshly reduced iron(II) sulfate, add a solution of tannic acid. If the iron(II) salt is not contaminated by iron(III) salt, the iron(II) tannate that results will be nearly colorless. Separate the iron(II) tannate solution into three parts. Use one portion to write a message on paper. Note that the result is nearly colorless writing. Add a few drops of a blue dye solution to the second portion and write with this liquid. Note that the solution "writes blue." To the third solution add a few drops of hydrogen peroxide solution to serve as an oxidizing agent. Note that the iron(II) tannate is immediately changed to iron(III) tannate, a black, insoluble substance. The writing with iron(II) tannate solution will gradually turn black as the iron(II) compound is oxidized by the air. The blue writing of the second portion will change to black, also, as the iron(II) tannate oxidizes.

Chapter 36 · THE COPPER FAMILY

1. The Copper Family of transition elements. The Copper Family consists of *copper*, *silver*, and *gold*, the copper subgroup of transition metals. All three metals appear below hydrogen in the electrochemical series. They are not easily oxidized and may be found in nature in the free, or native, state. Because of their pleasing appearance, durability, and relative scarcity, these metals have been used for ornamental and coinage purposes since the time of their discovery.

The atoms of copper, silver, and gold have a single electron in their outermost energy levels. Thus they form compounds in which they exhibit the +1 oxidation state. To this extent, they resemble the Group I metals of the Sodium Family.

Each metal of the Copper Family has 18 electrons in the next-to-outermost shell and, because the *d* electrons in this shell have energies that differ only slightly from the energy of the outer *s* electron, one or two of these electrons can be removed with comparative ease. Thus copper and gold commonly form compounds in which they exhibit respectively the +2 and +3 oxidation states. In the case of silver the +2 oxidation state has been achieved only under extreme oxidizing conditions.

Copper, silver, and gold are very dense, ductile, and malleable. They are classed as heavy metals along with the other transition metals in the central region of the Periodic Table. Some important properties of each metal are shown in the table below.

THE COPPER FAMILY

Element	Atomic Number	Atomic Weight	Electron Configuration	Oxidation Numbers	Melting Point, °C	Boiling Point, °C	Density, g/cm³
Copper	29	63.54	2, 8, 18, 1	+1, +2	1083	2336	8.9
Silver	47	107.870	2, 8, 18, 18, 1	+1	960.8	1950	10.5
Gold	79	196.967	2, 8, 18, 32, 18, 1	+1, +3	1063	2600	19.3

528

1. COPPER

2. The occurrence of copper. Copper, alloyed with tin in the form of bronze, has been in use over 5000 years. The first copper mines were probably located in northern Africa. The Romans obtained copper from Cyprus and Spain.

Today the United States produces more than one-quarter of the world's output. Chile, Canada, the Congo, and Northern Rhodesia are other large producers of copper. Prior to 1940, the United States exported copper. Over 1 million tons of copper are now produced each year from domestic ores. However, American industries consume approximately 1.5 million tons each year notwithstanding a growing use of aluminum and plastics for products formerly made of copper.

For many years Michigan was the leading copper-producing state. Native copper, mixed with rock, or present in large masses, is found there. Now the deposits lie deep underground, which increases the cost of the mining. The shaft in the famous Calumet and Hecla mine leads underground more than 8500 feet in vertical depth. Arizona, Utah, Montana, New Mexico, and Nevada are today the five largest copper-producing states.

Sulfide ores of copper yield most of our supplies of this metal. *Chalcocite*, Cu_2S, *chalcopyrite*, $CuFeS_2$, and *bornite*, Cu_3FeS_3, are the principal sulfide ores. *Malachite*, $Cu_2(OH)_2CO_3$, and *azurite*, $Cu_3(OH)_2(CO_3)_2$, are beautiful minerals that are basic carbonates of copper. Malachite is a rich green, and azurite is a deep blue. Besides serving as ores of copper, fine specimens of these minerals are sometimes polished for ornamental purposes or jewelry.

3. The extraction of copper. The native ore is crushed in a stamp mill, which is like a huge mortar and pestle, and the rock is washed away by water. The remaining metal is then melted with a flux to remove any gangue that was not washed away, and is cast into large plates.

The carbonate ores of copper are leached with dilute sulfuric acid forming a solution of copper(II) sulfate. The copper is then recovered by electrolysis. High grade carbonate ores may be roasted to convert them into copper(II) oxide, the oxide then being reduced with coke to yield the metallic copper.

The sulfide ores, particularly when iron is present as well as copper, present a more difficult refining problem. These are usually low-grade and require concentrating before they can be smelted profitably. The concentration is accomplished by oil-flotation. Earthy gangue is wetted by water and the ore is wetted by oil. A froth is produced and the oil-wetted ore is floated to the surface of the flotation cell in the froth (see Chapter 33, Section 7, for a detailed description of the flotation process). After flotation, the ore is thickened and filtered.

VOCABULARY

Amalgam (a-*mal*-gam). An alloy of mercury with another metal or metals.

Calcine (*kal*-syne). A partially roasted copper ore.

Matte (*mat*). A crude mixture of sulfides produced in a partially refined ore.

These treatments concentrate the ore from 1 to 2% copper content to as high as 25 to 30% copper.

The concentrated ore is partially roasted to form a mixture of Cu_2S, FeS, FeO, and SiO_2 known as *calcine*. Newly developed techniques in the roasting process involve the use of oxygen-enriched air that saves fuel and yields sulfur dioxide of high quality which is converted directly into sulfuric acid. Calcine is fused with limestone as a flux in a furnace. Part of the iron is removed as a silicate slag, while the rest of the iron, together with the copper, forms a mixture of sulfides known as *matte*. Copper matte contains approximately 40% copper. The melted matte is then poured into a converter much like that used in the Bessemer steel process. A blast of air is blown through the converter for about five hours. Sulfur from the sulfides, as well as arsenic and antimony which are present as impurities, are oxidized and escape as volatile oxides. Iron forms a slag which is poured off at intervals. The blast of air converts some of the copper(I) sulfide into copper(I) ox-

Fig. 36-2. **A copper converter in action. Molten metal is being withdrawn for further refinement by electrolysis.** (Anaconda)

ide which then reacts with more copper(I) sulfide and forms metallic copper and sulfur dioxide.

$$2 Cu_2S + 3 O_2 \rightarrow 2 Cu_2O + 2 SO_2 \uparrow$$
$$2 Cu_2O + Cu_2S \rightarrow 6 Cu + SO_2 \uparrow$$

The use of oxygen-enriched air in the converter stages is under development and shows considerable promise for large savings of fuel.

The molten copper is cast as *blister* copper of 98.5 to 99.5% purity. As the copper cools, dissolved gases escape forming blisters, hence the name. Impurities present are iron, silver, gold, and perhaps zinc.

After smelting, the copper is ready for fire refining. Blister copper is melted in the fire-refining furnace and streams of compressed air are blown in to oxidize some of the impurities. Silica is then added to form a slag that floats above the molten copper.

After all the slag has formed, copper(I) oxide begins to form. For many

Fig. 36-1. **Low-grade copper ores are concentrated in froth-flotation cells.** (Copper and Brass Research Association)

years the reduction of this oxide was effected by thrusting sticks of green wood into the molten metal, an operation known as *poling.* The hydrocarbons of the wood react with the copper(I) oxide to form carbon dioxide. The poling operation is now being replaced by the use of *reformed* gas made by superheating steam and natural gas. The reformed gas is piped into the molten copper to reduce the copper(I) oxide that forms during the process.

4. The electrolytic refining of copper. Crude copper is usually refined before it is marketed. It contains appreciable amounts of silver and gold, the value of which when recovered, is enough to pay the cost of refining. Copper is largely used for making electric conductors, and very small amounts of impurities greatly increase the electric resistance.

In the refining process, sheets of pure copper are used as the cathodes in electrolytic cells, and large plates of impure copper are used as the anodes. The electrolyte is a solution of copper(II) sulfate in sulfuric acid. A direct current at low voltage is used to operate the cell. During the electrolysis, copper and other metals above it in the electrochemical series, which compose the anode, are oxidized and enter the solution as ions.

$$Cu^0 - 2\ e^- \rightarrow Cu^{++}$$
$$Fe^0 - 2\ e^- \rightarrow Fe^{++}$$
$$Zn^0 - 2\ e^- \rightarrow Zn^{++}$$

At the low voltages used, the less active silver and gold are not oxidized and so do not go into solution. As the anode is used up they fall to the bottom of the cell as a sludge, from which they are easily recovered.

We might expect the various positive ions of the electrolyte to be reduced at the cathode. However, H_3O^+ ions, Fe^{++} ions, and Zn^{++} ions all require higher voltages than Cu^{++} ions to be discharged. At the low potential maintained across the cell, only Cu^{++} ions are reduced at the cathode.

$$Cu^{++} + 2\ e^- \rightarrow Cu^0$$

Thus of all the metals present, only

Fig. 36-3. **New technology in the copper refining process.**

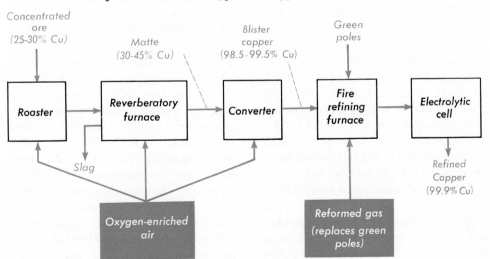

Fig. 36-4. **The principle of electrolytic refining of copper is illustrated by the action in this simple electroplating cell.** (Fritz Goro, Life Magazine)

copper plates out on the cathode. Electrolytic copper is over 99.9% pure.

5. The properties of copper. Copper is a soft, ductile, malleable, red metal with a specific gravity of 8.9. Next to silver, it is the best conductor of electricity.

Heated in air, copper forms a black coating of copper(II) oxide, CuO. A copper wire, and most copper compounds, color a Bunsen flame green. The copper halogenides produce a blue flame as do other copper compounds when moistened with hydrochloric acid.

Copper forms copper(II) salts which dissociate in water to form blue solutions. The color is characteristic of the hydrated copper(II) ion, $Cu(H_2O)_4^{++}$. The addition of an excess of ammonia to solutions containing this ion produces the deeper blue $Cu(NH_3)_4^{++}$ ion.

An excess of sulfur vapor forms a blue-black coating of copper(I) sulfide on hot copper. In moist air, copper tarnishes and forms a protective coating of a green basic carbonate, $Cu_2(OH)_2CO_8$. Sulfur

dioxide in the air may also combine with copper to produce a green basic sulfate, $Cu_4(OH)_6SO_4$. The green color seen on copper roofs is due to the formation of these compounds.

Both copper(I) and copper(II) compounds are known, although copper(II) compounds are much more common. Copper(II) oxide is used in current rectifiers to change alternating current to direct current. It is also used as an oxidizing agent in chemical laboratories.

Hydrated copper(II) sulfate, $CuSO_4 \cdot 5 H_2O$, commonly called *blue vitriol*, is the most important copper compound. It is used to kill algae in reservoirs, for making the agricultural spray known as Bordeaux mixture, for electroplating, and for making other copper compounds.

Because copper stands below hydrogen on the replacement series, it does not replace hydrogen from acids. Thus it is not acted on by nonoxidizing acids such as hydrochloric and dilute sulfuric except very slowly when oxygen is present. The oxidizing acids, nitric and hot concentrated sulfuric, react vigorously with copper to produce the corresponding copper(II) salts. These are typical oxidation-reduction reactions.

CAUTION: *All the soluble compounds of copper are poisonous.*

★ **6. Tests for the Cu⁺⁺ ion.** A dilute solution of a copper(II) salt changes to a very deep-blue color when ammonia is added. This is caused by the formation of the complex $Cu(NH_3)_4^{++}$ ion. The addition of $K_4Fe(CN)_6$ to a solution containing the Cu^{++} ion produces a red precipitate of $Cu_2Fe(CN)_6$, copper(II) hexacyanoferrate(II), also known as copper(II) ferrocyanide. If copper is present in a borax bead formed in the *oxidizing* flame, a clear blue color appears on cooling. The hot bead is green. A bead formed in the *reducing* flame is colorless while hot and an opaque red when cool.

7. Important uses of copper. More electric conductors are made from copper than from any other metal. Copper is also used for sheathing the bottoms of ships, for making electrotypes used in printing, for making water pipes, tanks, and hot water coils. Large quantities are used for making alloys, especially brass. Sheet copper is used for a permanent roofing material, flashings around chimneys, gutters, and rain conductors.

Brass is an alloy of copper and zinc. *Bronze* contains copper and tin, and sometimes zinc. *German silver* contains copper, zinc, and nickel. All our coins contain copper, the penny having as high as 95%. Both silver and gold coins contain 10% copper to increase the hardness. Some silver and gold jewelry also contains copper for the same reason.

Fig. 36-5. Electric conductors are made of electrolytically refined copper. (Consolidated Edison)

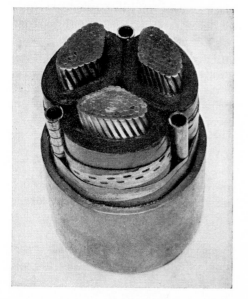

Fig. 36-6. Brass, an alloy of copper and zinc, has excellent working properties for cutting and machining. (Anaconda American Brass)

2. SILVER

8. The occurrence of silver. Utah, Montana, Idaho, Arizona, Nevada, and Colorado have valuable silver mines. Mexico is the largest silver-producing country, followed by the United States, Canada, Peru, and Bolivia.

Silver is obtained as a by-product in the refining of silver-bearing lead and copper ores. Silver is also found free in nature. Silver sulfide, Ag_2S, and silver chloride, $AgCl$, are common silver ores.

9. The extraction of silver.
1. By-product silver. The residue that falls to the bottom of the electrolytic tank in which copper is refined is treated with dilute sulfuric acid to remove impurities more active than silver. By treating the residue with concentrated sulfuric acid, the silver is separated from the gold as silver sulfate. Scrap copper is then added to the silver sulfate solution to precipitate the silver.

$$Ag_2SO_4 + Cu \rightarrow CuSO_4 + 2\,Ag \downarrow$$

Fig. 36-7. **Ancient silver coins.**
(Life Magazine)

2. *Cyanide process.* Crushed silver ore is roasted with common salt to convert the silver to silver chloride. It is added to a huge wooden tank with a large volume of water. Sodium cyanide, NaCN, is then added, and the mixture is allowed to stand for two weeks. The cyanide ions form complex argenticyanide, $Ag(CN)_2^-$, ions which are soluble.

$$AgCl + 2\,NaCN \rightarrow NaAg(CN)_2 + NaCl$$

Silver is precipitated from the filtered sodium argenticyanide solution by adding metallic zinc:

$$2\,NaAg(CN)_2 + Zn \rightarrow$$
$$Na_2Zn(CN)_4 + 2\,Ag \downarrow$$

3. *Parkes process.* Crude lead which contains silver and gold as impurities is melted in a large kettle. Pieces of zinc are then added, and the mixture is stirred. Both silver and gold are much more soluble in molten zinc than in lead. The zinc rises to the surface, carrying with it almost all of the silver and gold. The zinc alloy is scraped off, and the zinc is vaporized in a retort. The residue which is left consists of silver, gold, and a little lead. It is heated in a crucible made of bone ash, called a *cupel.* The lead oxidizes, and the lead

oxide is absorbed by the cupel, leaving a button of silver and gold. Nitric acid reacts with silver but does not react with gold. In this way, the silver is separated from the gold.

10. The properties of silver. Silver is a soft, white, lustrous metal. Its specific gravity is 10.5, and it is the best conductor of heat and electricity known.

Silver is an inactive metal. It does not unite with oxygen in the air, even at elevated temperatures. Traces of hydrogen sulfide in the air cause a brownish-black coating of silver sulfide to form on the surface of silver. The sulfur compounds present in such foods as mustard and eggs cause silverware to tarnish readily.

Tarnished silverware may be cleaned easily by putting it in an aluminum pan, covering it with water, adding a teaspoonful of baking soda (sodium hydrogen carbonate) per quart of water, and boiling the solution. This arrangement forms an electrochemical cell in which the aluminum pan is the cathode and the silverware is the anode. The silver sulfide is reduced by hydrogen which forms at the anode. The silverware should be thoroughly rinsed in hot and then cold water after the process.

Silver reacts readily with oxidizing acids such as nitric acid and hot concentrated sulfuric acid. Hydrochloric acid does not react with it, nor does fused sodium hydroxide or potassium hydroxide.

11. The uses for silver. Much silver is used in making coins and jewelry. United States coins contain 90% silver and 10% copper. Sterling silver contains 92.5% silver and 7.5% copper. Silver plate tableware and other silver plate articles are widely used. In the silvering of mirrors, a solution of a silver compound mixed with a reducing agent such as formaldehyde is poured on the clean glass. A film of metallic silver is deposited on the glass as the reduction occurs. Next to coinage, the principal use for silver is in photography.

12. Important compounds of silver. *Silver nitrate*, $AgNO_3$, crystallizes in colorless scales. It is sometimes used, under the name *lunar caustic*, for cauterizing wounds and bites. *Argyrol* is a compound of silver with a protein, silver vitellin, that is used in medicine as an antiseptic.

The halogen compounds of silver, *silver chloride*, $AgCl$, *silver bromide*, $AgBr$, and *silver iodide*, AgI, are sensitive to light, especially if organic matter is present. The chemical action which occurs is one of reduction. Finely divided silver, which is black in color, is formed. Silver bromide is the most sensitive to light, although all three are used in photography.

13. The principal steps in photography.

1. Making the film or plate. A film of cellulose acetate, or a glass plate, is coated with a light-sensitive emulsion. This consists of finely divided silver bromide colloidally dispersed in gelatin. The process is carried out in a dark room. Light must not fall on the film or plate until it is ready for exposure.

2. Making the negative. This consists of four steps. (*a*) *Exposure*. The film (or

Fig. 36-8. Silver and gold are recovered from crude lead by the Parkes process. (American Smelting and Refining)

Fig. 36-9. Left, a photographic negative. Right, a positive print made from the same negative. (Eastman Kodak)

plate) is exposed to light, which is focused on it by the camera lens, just long enough to start the reduction of the sensitive silver salt. (*b*) *Developing*. The exposed film is developed in a dark room by immersing it in a solution of an alkaline reducing agent. Hydroquinone, pyrogallol, and other organic compounds are used as developers. The developer does not readily start the reduction of any unchanged silver salt, but it continues the reduction started by the exposure to light. (*c*) *Fixing*. After the developing has continued long enough to bring out the picture, the film must be fixed. Fixing consists of immersing the film (still in the dark room) in a solution of sodium thiosulfate, called *hypo*. The sodium thiosulfate dissolves any unchanged silver salts leaving metallic silver wherever the light struck the silver salt. (*d*) *Washing*. The film must then be thoroughly washed in water to remove excess chemicals. Light and dark shades of the original object

are reversed now on the film, and it is called a *negative*.

3. *Making the print*. A *positive print* is made by placing the negative over a sheet of paper that has been sensitized in the same manner as the film or plate. The paper with the negative superposed is exposed to light for a brief interval. The paper is then developed, fixed, and washed in a dark room.

14. Test for the silver ion. Certain solubility characteristics of the silver, Ag^+, ion enable us to recognize its presence in solutions. The chlorides of silver, mercury(I), and lead are very slightly soluble. If a soluble chloride is added to a test solution containing silver ions, silver chloride forms as a white precipitate. If lead and mercury(I) ions are present they too precipitate as chlorides. Certain other metallic oxy-chloride complexes, which otherwise might precipitate, may be prevented from doing so by first making the test solution acid with HNO_3.

Since lead chloride is soluble in hot water, it may be removed from the precipitate by washing with hot water. The silver chloride may be separated from the mercury(I) chloride in the precipitate by washing it with an ammonia-water solution. This produces the soluble complex, the $Ag(NH_3)_2^+$ ion. The basic filtrate contains these silver-ammonia ions and chloride ions. By neutralizing the hydroxide ions of the basic filtrate with nitric acid, silver chloride again precipitates. *The formation of a white precipitate when this filtrate is made acidic in the manner described indicates the presence of silver.*

3. GOLD

15. The occurrence of gold. Gold was probably the first metal known to man. Primitive people collected gold for its ornamental value before any metallurgical processes were known.

California, South Dakota, and Alaska have valuable gold mines. Gold is also mined in a number of other states. Much of the metal produced in the United States is obtained as a by-product from copper and lead mining. The Union of South Africa, the Soviet Union, Canada, and the United States, in that order, are the greatest gold-producing countries. Australia produces a considerable amount.

Gold occurs in *alluvial* deposits as fine particles mixed with sand. It is also found in veins mixed with quartz. While it is usually found as the native metal, compounds of gold with tellurium sometimes occur. Sea water contains 0.1 mg to 0.2 mg per metric ton, but it would cost many times its value to extract it.

16. The extraction of gold. When the gold is in alluvial sand deposits, *hydraulic mining* is used. Powerful streams of water wash the sand into inclined troughs, called *sluices*. The dense particles of gold fall to the bottom, where they are retained by crosswise strips known as *riffles*.

Gold-bearing quartz ores are crushed to a fine powder in a stamp mill. As the powdered ore is carried away by running water it comes in contact with mercury, which forms an amalgam with the gold. The gold amalgam is then distilled to get the gold, and to recover the mercury. This is called the ***amalgamation process.***

Fig. 36-10. **Gold is extracted from low-grade ores by the cyanide process.** (Homestake Mining)

Low-grade gold ores are pulverized and mixed with a large volume of water in a tank. Sodium cyanide is added and, in the presence of air, a soluble *sodium aurocyanide*, $NaAu(CN)_2$, is formed. Metallic zinc is used to precipitate the gold from the aurocyanide.

2 NaAu(CN)$_2$ + Zn →

Na$_2$Zn(CN)$_4$ + 2 Au ↓

This method, known as the *cyanide process*, has made it possible to extract gold profitably from ores that contain very little gold.

Gold is sometimes extracted from pulverized ore with moist chlorine gas. Gold unites with the chlorine to form *gold(III) chloride*, $AuCl_3$, which is soluble in water. The solution of gold(III) chloride is reduced by iron(II) sulfate to metallic gold, which precipitates.

17. The properties of gold. Gold is a soft, yellow metal that is very ductile. It is so malleable that it can be hammered into sheets so thin that 250 of them would be required to equal the thickness of this page. Gold is an excellent conductor of heat and electricity. It has a specific gravity of 19.3.

Gold does not tarnish when exposed to the air, even at elevated temperatures. Hydrofluoric acid reacts with it slowly. Such strong acids as hydrochloric, nitric, and sulfuric do not react with it, if used singly, but *aqua regia* ($HNO_3 + 3\,HCl$) does react with it readily forming gold(III) chloride.

18. The uses of gold. Gold is used in coins and jewelry. Pure gold is too soft to wear well, hence copper is almost always alloyed with it. Its purity is expressed in *carats*, pure gold being 24 carats fine. Jewelry that is 18 carat is stamped 18K, and contains 18 parts by weight of gold mixed with 6 parts by weight of copper. Less expensive, but more durable jewelry is made from 14-carat and 10-carat gold.

Considerable quantities of gold are used in dentistry. Gold leaf is used for lettering and window decorating. Some gold is used for decorating expensive china tableware and in gold plating.

19. Gold forms two series of compounds. In some compounds gold exhibits the +1 oxidation state, but those with gold in the +3 oxidation state are more common. *Gold(III) chloride* is used in photography to give the prints a more pleasing shade. *Sodium aurocyanide* is used for gold plating.

Colloidal gold may be produced by the electric arc method (see Chapter 33, Section 3) or by the reduction of gold(III) chloride. If a solution of tin(II) chloride and stannic acid is added to a dilute solution of gold(III) chloride, the gold is reduced to the free metal by tin(II) chloride. Colloidal stannic acid may be formed by heating the mixture, and the gold particles are absorbed on the stannic acid dispersion. A purple structural color results which is known as *purple of Cassius*.

SUMMARY

Native copper is mined in certain areas; however, the principal ores are sulfides. Crude copper is usually refined by electrolysis, as most of the uses of the metal require a very high degree of purity. Copper is a red metal that ranks next to silver as a conductor of electricity. In combined form it may display an oxidation number of +1 or +2, the latter being more common. In moist air copper forms a protective coating of a basic carbonate or sulfate.

Silver is a white, lustrous metal found in the native state, as silver sulfide, and as silver chloride. It is recovered as a by-product in the refining of lead and copper ores. Silver does not unite with oxygen, but forms black silver sulfide readily. Silver halogenides are sensitive to light, a property that is the basis for the photographic process.

Gold usually occurs as the native metal. It is a soft, lustrous metal and is almost always alloyed with copper to increase its hardness. Gold reacts readily with aqua regia to form gold(III) chloride.

TEST YOURSELF ON THESE TERMS

alluvial	calcine	matte
amalgam	cupel	Parkes process
amalgamation process	cyanide process	poling
blister copper	18K	purple of Cassius
blue vitriol	electrolytic copper	riffles
brass	hypo	sluices
bronze	lunar caustic	sterling

QUESTIONS

Group A

1. What are the uses of blue vitriol?
2. What are five points of similarity between copper, silver, and gold?
3. What are the two most important uses for silver?
4. What type of copper ores provides the bulk of the copper produced in the United States today?
5. A gold ring is stamped 14K. What does this mean?
6. What are the uses for copper?
7. (*a*) What is blister copper? (*b*) How did it get its name?
8. What are four uses for gold?
9. How is copper obtained from the native ore?
10. (*a*) Have you ever seen any silver oxide? (*b*) What is the tarnish on a piece of old silverware?
11. Describe the aluminum process for cleaning silverware.
12. What happens to the halogen compounds of silver when they are exposed to light?
13. Why does the copper trim on roofs frequently acquire a green surface?
14. How is crude copper refined?

Group B

15. How can silver be obtained from the *anode mud* that collects in a tank used for the electrolysis of copper?
16. Explain the process of making photographic film.
17. What metals are alloyed in German silver?
18. How is photographic film developed?

19. How may lead chloride be separated from silver chloride?
20. How is a piece of glass silvered to make a mirror?
21. Why is a developed film placed in a fixing bath?
22. How is gold obtained by hydraulic mining?
23. What are the formulas for the two known chlorides of gold?
24. Why does it usually pay to refine copper by electrolysis?
25. How is the silver, present as an impurity in crude lead, extracted?
26. What is the cyanide process of extracting gold?
27. Describe the cyanide process of extracting silver from silver ore.
28. How is crude copper obtained from chalcopyrite ore?

PROBLEMS

Group A

1. What is the percentage of copper in $CuSO_4 \cdot 5 H_2O$?
2. How many grams of silver nitrate can be obtained by adding 100. g of pure silver to an excess of nitric acid?

Group B

3. Silver reacts with dilute nitric acid to form silver nitrate, water, and nitrogen monoxide. Balance the equation.
4. Copper reacts with hot concentrated sulfuric acid to form copper(II) sulfate, sulfur dioxide, and water. Balance the equation.

SOME THINGS FOR YOU TO DO

1. Plate some copper from solution by electrolysis. Use a solution of copper(II) sulfate, to which a little sulfuric acid has been added, as the electrolyte. The anode can be a piece of scrap copper. The cathode should be a piece of sheet copper. Use a direct current.
2. Make a "silver tree" from sheet zinc and silver nitrate solution. Cut a piece of sheet zinc into a more or less triangular shape, like an evergreen tree. Cut horizontal slits in the zinc toward the center and bend the zinc so as to give it a three-dimensional effect. Immerse the zinc in a solution of silver nitrate (about 1%).
3. Dissolve gold leaf in aqua regia. Mix one volume of concentrated nitric acid with three volumes of concentrated hydrochloric acid. Add a bit of gold leaf to the mixed acids, and stir. Gold reacts with the aqua regia, forming gold(III) chloride. Try to prepare a gold hydrosol from this solution.

Chapter 37 · ZINC, CADMIUM, MERCURY, TIN, AND LEAD

1. The zinc subgroup of transition elements. The last subgroup of transition elements is composed of the metals *zinc, cadmium,* and *mercury.* Like the metals of the copper subgroup and a few other transition metals, these metals have 18 electrons in their next-to-outermost shells. Zinc and cadmium form ions in which they exhibit the +2 oxidation state. Mercury exhibits both the +1 and +2 oxidation states. The mercury(I) ion is known to have the $(Hg:Hg)^{++}$ structure rather than Hg^+ as it is commonly written in empirical formulas. The Hg^+ ion has a single electron remaining in the valence shell. Two such ions share their odd electrons to form a covalent bond and attain greater

stability, resulting in the structure Hg_2^{++}.

Ions of mercury are much more difficult to form than those of zinc and cadmium. In fact, mercury has a strong tendency to form covalent bonds. In some respects it resembles metals of the Copper Family more closely than zinc and cadmium.

Tin and *lead* occupy the last two positions in Group IV of the Periodic Table. Together with *germanium* they constitute the metals of this group. The properties of tin and lead are similar to those of the metals of the zinc subgroup of transition metals and thus are presented along with these elements. Both tin and lead have 4 electrons in their

VOCABULARY

Diluent (*dil*-yoo-ent). A diluting agent.

Dross. A powdery scum that floats on top of molten metals.

Lithopone. A white paint base composed of barium sulfate and zinc sulfide.

Sacrificial metal. The metallic electrode of an electrochemical cell that is oxidized.

Spelter. Commercial zinc.

541

outer shells and exhibit the oxidation number +4. However, the oxidation state of +2 is more common for these metals. Each has the characteristic shell of 18 electrons just under the valence shell. The properties of these five metals are listed in the table below.

1. ZINC

2. The occurrence of zinc. Zinc ores were used for making brass for centuries before the discovery of zinc as a metal. It is thought to have been produced first in 1746 from a silicate ore by heating the ore with charcoal.

The United States produces nearly one half of the world supply of zinc. Missouri, Kansas, and Oklahoma have large mineral deposits in the region where these three states join. Zinc sulfide is found there mixed with *galena*, a lead ore. New Jersey is also an important zinc-producing state. Montana, Colorado, and Arkansas produce considerable amounts of this metal. British Columbia, in Canada, is also an important zinc-producing area.

Zinc does not occur as the native metal because of its chemical activity. The principal ore of zinc is *sphalerite*, ZnS, which is also called *zinc blende*. Zincite, ZnO, and *smithsonite*, $ZnCO_3$, are also important ores. *Willemite*, Zn_2SiO_4, and *calamine*, $Zn_2SiO_4 \cdot H_2O$,

are silicate ores of zinc. At Franklin, New Jersey, the mineral *franklinite*, a complex mixture of oxides of zinc, iron, and manganese, is found.

3. The metallurgy of zinc.
1. *By reduction with coal.* The zinc ores are first roasted to convert them into oxides, for example:

$$2\ ZnS + 3\ O_2 \rightarrow 2\ ZnO + 2\ SO_2 \uparrow$$

The oxides are mixed with powdered coal and heated in earthenware retorts:

$$ZnO + C \rightarrow Zn + CO \uparrow$$

Because of the low boiling point of zinc (907° C) it is distilled from the retorts as a vapor. It is then condensed in iron or earthenware receivers. Some of the zinc is deposited as *zinc dust* in the upper part of the receivers. Liquid zinc collects at the bottom of the receivers where it is drawn off and cast in molds. Such *spelter*, as it is called, may contain arsenic, cadmium, and carbon as impurities, but may be purified by redistillation.

2. *By electrolysis.* In the newer electrolytic process, the ore is first roasted, and then extracted with sulfuric acid to produce a solution of zinc sulfate. Iron and manganese are removed as impurities by adding lime and blowing air through the solution. Sheets of aluminum are used as cathodes in the electrolytic cells. By passing an electric current through the cell, zinc ions are reduced at the

THE ZINC SUBGROUP OF TRANSITION ELEMENTS

Element	Atomic Number	Atomic Weight	Electron Configuration	Oxidation Numbers	Melting Point, °C	Boiling Point, °C	Density g/cm³
Zinc	30	65.37	2, 8, 18, 2	+2	419.5	907	7.14
Cadmium	48	112.40	2, 8, 18, 18, 2	+2	320.9	767	8.64
Mercury	80	200.59	2, 8, 18, 32, 18, 2	+1, +2	−38.87	356.6	13.55
Tin	50	118.69	2, 8, 18, 18, 4	+2, +4	231.9	2270	7.28
Lead	82	207.19	2, 8, 18, 32, 18, 4	+2, +4	327.4	1620	11.34

Fig. 37-1. **Zinc of high purity is now recovered by the electrolytic process. Here we see cathodes being lifted from a cell in the tank house of a zinc recovery plant.** (American Smelting and Refining)

cathode and metallic zinc plates out on the aluminum. Zinc that is 99.9% pure is then stripped off the cathodes. Electrolytic zinc is now preferred for making brass and other alloys because of its higher purity.

4. The properties of zinc. Metallic zinc is bluish-white in color. At room temperature it is somewhat brittle, but above 100° C it becomes malleable and ductile. It can be rolled into sheets or drawn into wire at this higher temperature, after which it does not become brittle again when it cools. It is a moderately hard metal with a density slightly less than that of iron.

Zinc burns in air with a bluish-white flame and forms white clouds of zinc oxide. At room temperature dry air does not affect zinc, but moist air reacts with it and forms a coating of basic zinc carbonate, $Zn_2(OH)_2CO_3$. The tarnish which forms is adherent and somewhat impervious. Hence zinc is a self-protective metal.

Zinc stands well above hydrogen in the electrochemical series (see Chapter 23, Section 6) and may be expected to react readily with acids replacing the hydrogen. *Mossy* zinc, produced by pouring molten zinc dropwise into water, is commonly used in the laboratory to displace hydrogen from nonoxidizing acids. It is found, however, that pure zinc reacts only very slowly with acids. Thus spelter, rather than electrolytic zinc, is used in preparing mossy zinc for ordinary laboratory use.

The active hydroxides, such as sodium hydroxide, react with zinc and set free hydrogen gas. Soluble zincates, which may be considered as the salts of zincic acid, are formed.

$$Zn + 2 NaOH \rightarrow Na_2ZnO_2 + H_2 \uparrow$$

From this behavior, it is evident that the hydroxide of zinc is amphiprotic, acting as a hydroxide, $Zn(OH)_2$, in the presence of a strong acid, but acting as an acid, H_2ZnO_2, in the presence of a strong hydroxide. Thus:

$$2 HCl + Zn(OH)_2 \rightarrow ZnCl_2 + 2H_2O$$
$$2 NaOH + H_2ZnO_2 \rightarrow Na_2ZnO_2 + 2 H_2O$$

Zinc hydroxide dissolves readily in ammonia water because of the strong tendency of zinc to form complex ions, a common property of transition metals. With NH_3-Aq, a stable zinc-ammonia complex, $Zn(NH_3)_4{}^{++}$, is formed. Similarly, with cyanide solutions, a very stable zinc-cyanide complex, $Zn(CN)_4^=$, is formed.

$$Zn^{++} + 4\ NH_3 \rightleftarrows Zn(NH_3)_4^{++}$$
$$Zn^{++} + 4\ CN^- \rightleftarrows Zn(CN)_4^=$$

5. Zinc is a very useful metal. Large quantities are used for making *galvanized iron*. This process protects iron from rusting by covering it with a thin coating of zinc. The iron is first cleaned by pickling it in an acid bath. It is then coated with zinc by dipping it into molten zinc or by electroplating. *Sherardizing* is a process in which iron is galvanized by condensation of zinc vapor on the surface of the iron.

CAUTION: *All soluble salts of zinc are poisonous. Acid foods must not be stored in galvanized iron containers.*

From the electrochemical series, it is evident that zinc is a strong reducing agent and is well suited for use as the negative electrode in an electrochemical cell. Here electrolytic zinc is used, because particles of impurities in the cathode, such as carbon, would cause local electrochemical action between the impurities and the zinc. The metal cylinder, or can, of the dry cell is made of electrolytic zinc which acts as the cathode. The anode is made of carbon (see Fig. 23-4).

6. Zinc is used to make alloys. The most important alloy of zinc is *brass*, which contains zinc and copper. The proportions vary, but ordinary brass contains about 60% copper and 40% zinc. *Bronze* contains copper and tin; usually some zinc is added.

German silver, sometimes called *nickel silver,* is an alloy containing copper, nickel, and zinc. The name *silver* is a misnomer, since there is no silver in the alloy.

7. The cobalt nitrate test for zinc. To test for zinc, a slight depression is made in a block of charcoal or plaster of Paris. The metal, or its compound, is then placed in this depression and heated strongly with the oxidizing flame of a blowpipe. If zinc is present, its oxide will be canary yellow when hot, and white when cold. The residue is then moistened with a drop or two of cobalt nitrate solution, and again heated. If the residue is *dark green,* the presence

Fig. 37-2. Control station for one of the galvanizing lines in a large mill. In the left background is the galvanizing pot containing the molten zinc through which steel sheets are passed. Emerging from the pot, the zinc-coated sheets are deposited on the wire-mesh conveyor, where they cool. (Cal-Pictures)

Fig. 37-3. After small parts are electroplated with cadmium, they are dipped into an acid solution of hydrogen peroxide to increase their brightness. (Food Machinery and Chemical)

of zinc is indicated. When tested in the same manner, magnesium compounds give a delicate *flesh (pink)* color; aluminum compounds give a *blue* color.

8. Important compounds of zinc. Enormous quantities of zinc are burned to form zinc oxide, a white solid used as a paint base, as a filler in rubber for automobile tires, in oilcloth, in linoleum, and for glazes and enamels. Zinc ointment contains zinc oxide and zinc stearate in an ointment base. It is used for treating various skin eruptions.

Zinc chloride, a white, deliquescent solid, is used in preserving wood which comes into contact with the earth, such as railroad ties and fence posts. It may be used alone or with creosote. Such doubly treated wood is very resistant to decay. A solution of zinc chloride is sometimes used as a soldering flux. The fluxing action is produced by the hydrolysis of the zinc chloride to form hydrochloric acid. The acid converts the metallic oxides to soluble chlorides, and thus leaves a clean, metallic surface.

Zinc chloride converts wood fiber into cellulose hydrate, a product which can be pressed into any desired shape and then dried. This strong, tough product, which is called *fiberboard*, or *vulcanized fiber*, is used for making boxes, trunks, washers, pails, wastebaskets, and insulating materials.

Hydrated zinc sulfate, $ZnSO_4 \cdot 7\,H_2O$, is a white, crystalline solid used in making *lithopone*, a white paint base. Zinc sulfate is used in preserving hides, and as a mordant in calico printing.

The sulfide of zinc is the only ordinary sulfide that is white in color. It is present in lithopone, which is made by mixing solutions of barium sulfide and zinc sulfate. In this reaction, barium sulfate and zinc sulfide are precipitated together.

$$BaS + ZnSO_4 \rightarrow BaSO_4 \downarrow + ZnS \downarrow$$

This mixture of precipitates is heated, plunged into cold water, and ground with linseed oil to make lithopone. Lithopone does not darken on exposure to air containing hydrogen sulfide as does white lead.

2. CADMIUM

9. The occurrence and uses of cadmium. Cadmium was discovered in 1817 as an impurity in zinc carbonate. It is usually found in nature associated with zinc. It also occurs as the sulfide, CdS, in the rather rare mineral known as *greenockite*. It is a bluish-white metal which resembles zinc and magnesium in its chemical properties. Cadmium is used as one ingredient of an amalgam for filling teeth, and in the making of some fusible alloys. It forms a more durable coating for iron and steel than zinc does. For that reason, a considerable amount of cadmium is used for plating screws, nuts, bolts, and other objects made of iron or steel. Cadmium metal is used for making the negative plates of the *nickel-cadmium storage battery*. Cadmium sulfide is a fine yellow pigment used as an artist's color, called cadmium yellow. *The soluble salts of cadmium are poisonous.*

Cadmium is becoming increasingly important industrially. Because of its low coefficient of friction and resistance to fatigue, it is used in bearing alloys. Production of cadmium in the United States has been stimulated by its use in control rods for nuclear reactors.

3. MERCURY

10. The occurrence of mercury. Mercury was known in ancient China and India. It has been found in the tombs of Egypt built nearly 3500 years ago.

The bulk of the world's supply of mercury comes from California and Texas in the United States, and from Spain and Italy. It may occur as tiny globules scattered through rock, although the chief ore of mercury is a red mineral known as *cinnabar*, which is mercury(II) sulfide, HgS. The metal can be obtained by simply heating the ore:

$$HgS + O_2 \rightarrow Hg + SO_2 \uparrow$$

11. Mercury is an unusual metal. Mercury, sometimes called *quicksilver*, is the only metal that is a liquid at room temperatures, although gallium metal has a melting point of 29.8° C. It is sil-

ver-white, lustrous, and about 13.6 times as dense as water. It freezes to a hard, brittle solid at approximately −39° C, and boils at a temperature of nearly 357° C.

12. Chemical properties of mercury. Neither dry nor moist air will react with mercury at ordinary temperatures. If heated in air, it slowly changes to a red oxide, HgO. Hydrochloric acid does not react with mercury since hydrogen is above mercury in the replacement series. Nitric and hot concentrated sulfuric acids, however, react with it to form mercury(II) nitrate and mercury(II) sulfate, respectively, in typical oxidation-reduction reactions.

Mercury is found far down on the electrochemical series. Thus most metals replace it from its compounds. It is a poor reducing agent, which accounts for its reluctance to combine with oxygen and its inability to displace hydrogen from nonoxidizing acids.

13. The uses of mercury. Mercury is used in thermometers, barometers, and other pieces of scientific equipment. It is used in mercury-vapor lamps and in arc rectifiers for changing alternating current into direct current.

An alloy of mercury with one or more other metals is known as an *amalgam*. Mercury forms amalgams with most metals, although platinum and iron are exceptions. An amalgam consisting of silver, tin, cadmium, and mercury is used for fillings in teeth. When freshly prepared, it is soft enough to be pressed into the cavity of a tooth, but it hardens in a very short time.

14. Important compounds of mercury. Mercury forms two series of compounds, one in which the oxidation number is +1 and the other in which the oxidation number is +2.

Mercury(I) chloride, a white solid

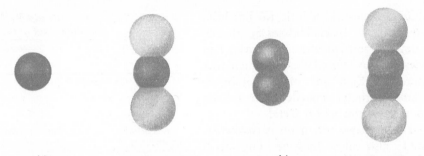

| Hg^{++} ion | $HgCl_2$ molecule | Hg_2^{++} ion | Hg_2Cl_2 molecule |

Fig. 37-4. Mercury(II) chloride and mercury(I) chloride are formed as covalent molecules. The mercury(I) ion is also a covalent structure.

with the molecular formula Hg_2Cl_2, is insoluble in water. It is used in medicine as a laxative under the name of *calomel*. Exposure to sunlight causes mercury(I) chloride to change slowly to mercury and mercury(II) chloride:

$$Hg_2Cl_2 \rightarrow Hg + HgCl_2$$

Mercury(I) nitrate, $Hg_2(NO_3)_2$, is fairly soluble in water. Mercury(I) chloride is precipitated when chloride ions are added to a solution of mercury(I) nitrate. Ammonia reacts with this precipitate forming insoluble white *mercury(II) aminochloride*, and *metallic mercury* as a black dispersion. *The mixture of these two products gives a gray residue which serves as a test for the* Hg_2^{++} *ion.*

$$Hg_2Cl_2 + 2\,NH_3 \rightarrow$$
$$HgNH_2Cl \downarrow + Hg \downarrow + NH_4Cl$$
$$\text{white} \qquad \text{black}$$

CAUTION: *All the soluble salts of mercury are extremely poisonous.* The white of eggs, or milk, may be used as an antidote because the albumin in egg whites or milk forms an insoluble mercury albuminate. The use of Hg_2Cl_2 (calomel) in medicine is safe even though the Hg_2^{++} ion is very poisonous, be-

cause the compound is only very slightly soluble.

Mercury(II) chloride is usually called *bichloride of mercury* or *corrosive sublimate.* It is essentially covalent and has the molecular formula $HgCl_2$. It forms white crystals that can be purified by sublimation. One part of mercury(II) chloride added to 1000 parts of water forms an antiseptic solution that is sometimes used in hospitals. Great care should be exercised in handling bichloride of mercury because it is extremely poisonous.

Mercury(II) oxide, HgO, is used as an antiseptic under the name *red precipitate*. Priestley obtained oxygen by heating this compound. Sublimed *mercury(II) sulfide*, HgS, forms a red pigment known as vermilion. It is used as a paint to prevent the growth of barnacles on the bottoms of ships.

4. TIN

15. The metallurgy of tin. The Malay States, Indonesia, Thailand, Bolivia, and Nigeria supply almost all of the tin mined in the world. For many centuries, tin ore was mined in Cornwall, England, but these deposits have now become almost exhausted. A little tin has been mined in the Black Hills of South Dakota, and some has been discovered in Alaska. The United States, which uses more tin than any other nation, is almost entirely dependent on foreign sources for this useful metal.

The principal ore of tin is *cassiterite*, SnO_2, also called *tinstone*. The ore is usually concentrated by the froth-flotation process prior to shipment to the smelters. The crude metal is recovered in a furnace by reduction with carbon.

$$SnO_2 + 2 C \rightarrow Sn + 2 CO \uparrow$$

It is purified by heating on a sloping hearth where the tin, which has a melting point of approximately 232° C, melts and drains away from the impurities, and is refined by electrolysis.

16. The properties of tin. Tin is a soft, white metal that is not quite so dense as iron. It is so malleable that it can be rolled into very thin sheets known as *tin foil*. The pure metal is called *block tin*.

Tin exists in three allotropic forms. At low temperatures it changes to a gray powder with a cubic crystal structure. This is the stable form below 18° C. At ordinary temperatures it forms a tetragonal crystal structure, while at temperatures just under the melting point it forms rhombic crystals. The crumbling of tin to a gray powder in very cold climates is sometimes called "tin disease."

Air and water do not react with tin at ordinary temperatures. When heated strongly, the metal burns to form tin(IV) oxide, SnO_2. Carbonated water has no effect on it, hence the use of tin pipes in soda fountains.

Tin reacts slowly with dilute acids to replace hydrogen. If dilute hydrochloric acid is used, tin(II) chloride and hydrogen are the products.

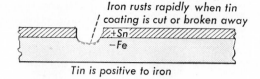

Iron rusts rapidly when tin coating is cut or broken away

Tin is positive to iron

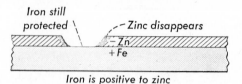

Iron is positive to zinc

Fig. 37-5. Tin accelerates the corrosion of iron when the tin coating is broken. Zinc continues to offer some protection to iron after the zinc coating is broken.

$$Sn + 2 HCl \rightarrow SnCl_2 + H_2 \uparrow$$

With *dilute* nitric acid, tin(II) nitrate is formed and nitrogen is reduced to ammonia which forms ammonium nitrate.

$$4 Sn + 10 HNO_3 \rightarrow$$
$$4 Sn(NO_3)_2 + NH_4NO_3 + 3 H_2O$$

The reaction with concentrated acids is quite vigorous. Tin and hot concentrated sulfuric acid produce tin(II) sulfate, sulfur dioxide, and water.

$$Sn + 2 H_2SO_4 \rightarrow$$
$$SnSO_4 + SO_2 \uparrow + 2 H_2O$$

Concentrated nitric acid reacts with tin to form a hydrated tin(IV) oxide, $SnO_2 \cdot H_2O$, which is usually called metastannic acid, with the formula written as H_2SnO_3.

Hot alkali hydroxides react readily with tin to release hydrogen and form the corresponding *stannites*.

$$2 NaOH + Sn \rightarrow Na_2SnO_2 + H_2 \uparrow$$

This action is similar to that of zinc and aluminum. We would expect tin(II) hydroxide to be amphiprotic.

17. Uses of tin. Tin foil has long been used for wrapping chocolate and other foods, but is rapidly being replaced by aluminum foil. Tin pipes are used as conduits for slightly acid liquids.

More tin is used for making tinware or tin plate than any other use. "Tin cans" are made from sheet steel that has been cleaned in acid, and then dipped in molten tin. If the coating is thick enough, it protects the iron very well. However, if the tin is scratched through at any place, the iron underneath rusts much more readily than would unprotected iron. In such a case, the tin and iron form an electrochemical cell in which the tin is the anode, the iron is the cathode, and the moist air acts as the electrolyte. Iron becomes the "sacrificial metal" since it is more active than tin, and is oxidized rapidly. (The metal which is attacked in such a cell is often called the *sacrificial metal.*) With galvanized iron, zinc is the sacrificial metal because iron is less active electrochemically than zinc. Foods are packed in tin cans because tin does not affect the quality of the foods.

18. Alloys of tin. Type metal, antifriction metals, bronze, and fusible alloys have been mentioned previously. *Solder* is an alloy of tin and lead. Soft solder contains 50% tin and 50% lead, but other solders may contain these metals in other proportions. Plumbers use a solder containing 67% lead for *wiping* the joints of lead waste pipes because it becomes plastic before it hardens to a rigid solid. *Terne plate* is sheet iron coated with an alloy of tin and lead that is used for roofing. *Pewter* is an alloy of variable composition but often contains 80% tin and 20% lead.

19. Tin forms two groups of compounds. If tin and hydrochloric acid react, *tin(II) chloride* is formed. It is used in mordant dyeing and produces brilliant colors with some dyestuffs. It is also used for weighting silk.

Tin(II) chloride is a good reducing agent. When added to a solution of mercury(II) chloride, it provides an interesting example of an oxidation-reduction reaction. By varying the amount used, the mercury(II) chloride is reduced to mercury(I) chloride, or even to metallic mercury.

$$SnCl_2 + 2\ HgCl_2 \rightarrow SnCl_4 + Hg_2Cl_2$$
$$SnCl_2 +\ \ HgCl_2 \rightarrow SnCl_4 + Hg$$

Fig. 37-6. **When a sheet of steel is plated with tin by electrolysis it is heated by high frequency coils as it passes through this machine. The tin melts and flows to form a lustrous coat.**

In each case the mercury(II) chloride acts as an oxidizing agent, and the tin(II) chloride as a reducing agent. The tin, which has an oxidation number of +2 in tin(II) chloride, is oxidized to the +4 state as tin(IV) chloride. At the same time, the mercury(II) chloride is reduced from the +2 oxidation state to the +1 state or to the 0 oxidation state in metallic mercury. The electronic changes may be expressed as follows:

$$Sn^{++} - 2\ e^- \rightarrow Sn^{++++}$$
$$2\ Hg^{++} + 2\ e^- \rightarrow Hg_2^{++}$$

or

$$Hg^{++} + 2\ e^- \rightarrow Hg^0$$

Tin(IV) sulfide, SnS_2, is used as a yellow pigment under the name of *mosaic gold*. Metastannic acid is used sometimes to make cotton cloth nonflammable. Tin(IV) chloride, like tin(II) chloride, is also used for weighting silk and in mordant dyeing.

5. LEAD

20. The occurrence of lead. Lead was known to the ancients. It is mentioned in the book of Exodus. Lead pipes bearing the insignia of Roman emperors are still in use in Rome.

The principal ore of lead is *galena*, PbS, which occurs as grayish-black cubic crystals. It is widely distributed, both in this country and in other parts of the world. Missouri, Colorado, Utah, Idaho, Montana, and Oklahoma are our most important lead-producing states. British Columbia and Mexico also produce large amounts of lead.

21. The metallurgy of lead. Lead ore is first concentrated by the froth-flotation process. This operation not only concentrates the ore, but also separates it from zinc sulfide which commonly occurs mixed with it. Concentrated ore is then carefully roasted to convert the lead(II) sulfide into *lead(II) oxide* and *lead(II) sulfate*.

$$2\ PbS + 3\ O_2 \rightarrow 2\ PbO + 2\ SO_2 \uparrow$$
$$PbS + 2\ O_2 \rightarrow PbSO_4$$

The roasted ore is then heated with unroasted ore, coke, and limestone in a blast furnace. The lead(II) sulfide in the unroasted ore acts as a reducing agent on the lead(II) oxide and lead(II) sulfate of the roasted ore.

$$2\ PbO + PbS \rightarrow 3\ Pb + SO_2 \uparrow$$
$$PbSO_4 + PbS \rightarrow 2\ Pb + 2\ SO_2 \uparrow$$

The coke provides necessary fuel, and may also assist in the reduction. The limestone of the charge reacts with silica, present as an impurity, and forms a calcium silicate slag.

The crude lead contains arsenic, antimony, bismuth, and copper as impurities, as well as the precious metals, silver and gold. When heated and stirred, the impurities, other than the precious metals, form oxides which rise to the surface and are skimmed off as *dross*. The precious metals are removed from the lead by the Parkes process, described in Chapter 36, Section 9.

22. The properties of lead. Lead is a soft, bluish-white metal that has a specific gravity of 11.3, and a melting point of approximately 327° C. It is malleable, but not ductile. Lead wire may be made by *extruding* the heated metal through a die. Lead pipe is made in a similar manner by forcing the lead through a ring-shaped opening.

Lead oxidizes rapidly on exposure to air, forming a surface coating of oxides and carbonates which protects the metal underneath from further oxidation. Hydrochloric and sulfuric acids have little effect on lead, but nitric acid reacts with it vigorously. Acetic acid and some other organic acids react with lead, and water which contains carbon dioxide in solution reacts slowly with this metal.

CAUTION: *All soluble lead compounds are very poisonous.* They are particularly dangerous because they are not excreted, but tend to accumulate in the body. Painters and others who handle lead compounds should use great care so as not to contract lead poisoning.

23. The uses of lead. *Sheet lead* is used for making the lead chambers of sulfuric acid plants, and has other uses for which its chemical inactivity makes it suitable. It is sometimes used as a roofing material. *Lead foil* is used for lining tea chests, and as a substitute for tin foil. *Lead shot* usually has 1% arsenic added to make the lead harder. *Lead pipe* is used for waste pipes and sink traps. It is easily cut, and it can be

bent into any desired shape. Telephone cables are protected by a lead covering in underground wire systems. Large quantities of lead are used to make lead compounds, such as white lead, litharge, and red lead. About 30% of all the lead consumed in the United States is used in lead storage batteries.

The table below summarizes the properties and uses of some of the more important lead compounds.

★ **24. The lead storage battery.** The six-volt battery consists of three cells connected in series. Twelve-volt batteries are made up of six cells. As the name implies, the *storage* battery is a *storehouse* of energy. As the battery is charged, electric energy is converted to chemical energy by an oxidation-reduction reaction in which each cell acts as an *electrolytic cell*. While the battery is being discharged, the reverse oxidation-reduction reaction occurs. Chemical

IMPORTANT LEAD COMPOUNDS

Chemical Name	Common Name	Chemical Formula	Color	Important Uses
Lead(II) oxide	Litharge	PbO	Yellow	In making glass; in the paint and varnish industries
Lead(IV) oxide	Lead peroxide (a misnomer)	PbO_2	Brown	Forms the active material of the positive plate of storage batteries
Lead(II, II, IV) oxide	Red lead	Pb_3O_4	Red	To make a protective paint for iron and steel
Lead(II) acetate	Sugar of lead	$Pb(C_2H_3O_2)_2$	White, crystalline	For making white lead; as a mordant; to treat ivy poisoning
Lead(II) chromate	Chrome yellow	$PbCrO_4$	Yellow	As a yellow pigment
Lead(II) arsenate	Arsenate of lead	$Pb_3(AsO_4)_2$	White	As an insecticide
Basic Lead(II) carbonate	White lead	$Pb_3(OH)_2(CO_3)_2$	White	As a paint base

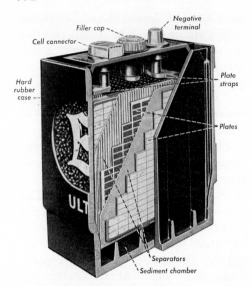

Fig. 37-7. **A cutaway view of one cell of an automobile storage battery.** (Electric Storage Battery)

water in the process. Reaction with sulfuric acid will then produce lead(II) sulfate and water. Lead(II) sulfate precipitates on the anode.

$$2 H_3O^+ + 2 e^- \rightarrow 2 H_2O \quad + 2 H^0$$
$$2 H^0 \quad + PbO_2 \rightarrow PbO \quad + H_2O$$
$$PbO + 2 H_3O^+ + SO_4^= \rightarrow PbSO_4 \downarrow + 3 H_2O$$

The anode reduction is not fully understood, so the above reactions may be an oversimplification of the actual process. The action may be summarized:

$$4 H_3O^+ + 2 e^- + PbO_2 + SO_4^= \rightarrow$$
$$PbSO_4 \downarrow + 6 H_2O$$

The overall oxidation-reduction reaction of the cell during discharge is shown in the series of equations below.

During the discharging process, electrons released by oxidation at the cathode flow through the external circuit of the battery to the anode, where the reduction occurs. This constitutes an electric current which operates the devices connected to the battery circuit.

In the discharged condition, both electrodes consist of lead(II) sulfate, and the electrolyte is a more dilute solution of sulfuric acid. The cell may be made electrochemically active again by recharging. This is accomplished by supplying a direct current from an external source in the opposite direction to the discharging current. The action at the electrodes is reversed and the cell is restored to its charged condition.

During the *charging cycle*, lead(II) sulfate at the cathode is reduced to the element, lead.

$$PbSO_4 + 2 e^- \rightarrow Pb^0 + SO_4^=$$

energy is converted to electric energy and the cells act as *electrochemical cells*.

A fully-charged lead storage cell consists of an anode of lead(IV) oxide, a cathode of spongy lead, and an electrolyte of moderately dilute sulfuric acid. During the *discharging cycle*, the lead at the cathode is oxidized to Pb^{++} ions which then form lead(II) sulfate, $PbSO_4$, as a precipitate on the cathode:

$$Pb^0 \quad - 2 e^- \rightarrow Pb^{++}$$
$$Pb^{++} + SO_4^= \rightarrow PbSO_4 \downarrow$$

This oxidation may be summarized:

$$Pb^0 - 2 e^- + SO_4^= \rightarrow PbSO_4 \downarrow$$

Simultaneously at the anode, H_3O^+ ions may be reduced and may then, in turn, reduce the PbO_2 to PbO forming

(cathode)	$Pb^0 - 2 e^- + SO_4^= \rightarrow PbSO_4 \downarrow$
(anode)	$4 H_3O^+ + 2 e^- + PbO_2 + SO_4^= \rightarrow PbSO_4 \downarrow + 6 H_2O$
(cell)	$Pb^0 + PbO_2 + 4 H_3O^+ + 2 SO_4^= \rightarrow 2 PbSO_4 \downarrow + 6 H_2O$

(cathode)　　　　　　　$PbSO_4 + 2\ e^- \rightarrow Pb^0 + SO_4^=$

(anode)　　　$PbSO_4 + 6\ H_2O - 2\ e^- \rightarrow PbO_2 + 4\ H_3O^+ + SO_4^=$

(cell)　　　　　$2\ PbSO_4 + 6\ H_2O \rightarrow Pb^0 + PbO_2 + 4\ H_3O^+ + 2\ SO_4^=$

Simultaneously at the anode, lead(II) sulfate is oxidized forming lead(IV) oxide.

$$PbSO_4 - 2\ e^- + 6\ H_2O \rightarrow$$
$$PbO_2 + 4\ H_3O^+ + SO_4^=$$

The overall oxidation-reduction reaction of the lead storage cell during the charging cycle is shown in the series of equations at the top of this page.

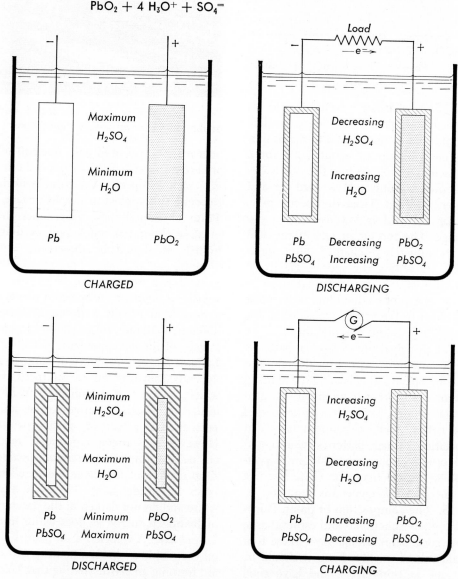

Fig. 37-8. **Diagrams illustrating the essential action in a storage cell.**

During the charging process, electrons are supplied to the cathode, and are removed from the anode, by the external source of electric energy. Electric energy is thus stored as chemical energy in the cell through the mechanism of the oxidation-reduction action. Observe that the last equation is the reverse of the overall equation for the discharging action.

$$\xrightarrow{\qquad \text{charging} \qquad}$$
$$2\ PbSO_4 + 6\ H_2O \rightleftarrows$$
$$\qquad Pb + PbO_2 + 4\ H_3O^+ + 2\ SO_4^=$$
$$\xleftarrow{\qquad \text{discharging} \qquad}$$

During charging, sulfuric acid is formed and water is decomposed. The specific gravity of the acid increases during charging up to about 1.300 for a fully-charged cell. While the cell is discharging, sulfuric acid is used up and water is formed. Thus, the specific gravity of the acid is lowered during discharge. The specific gravity of the acid in a completely discharged cell is about 1.100. By testing the specific gravity of the cell, we can gain information as to its condition of charge. Pure water must be added to the cell to replace that lost by electrolysis and evaporation.

The principal use of storage batteries is in automobiles to provide ignition, and to operate the headlights, starting motor, and other equipment. A generator connected with the engine charges the battery while the automobile is in operation. Storage batteries are also used for other purposes that require a portable source of energy, or where a source of energy in emergencies is required.

⋆ **25. The composition of paint.** Paints have many functional and esthetic uses. Any good paint should meet these four standards of quality. First, it should be opaque in thin layers, and have good covering power to conceal the surface

Fig. 37-9. **Paint products are tested and evaluated under all weather conditions.**

beneath. Second, it should not rub off or become excessively chalky, and should not crack and peel. (Any paint is likely to peel if it is applied to a moist surface.) Third, it should work well under the brush without too much pull or drag. Fourth, it should be impervious and durable.

Paint is a mixture of *a paint base, a vehicle, a pigment* (for colored paints), *a drier,* and usually *a thinner.* Several different materials are available to serve as each of these components.

1. *Paint bases.* The choice of paint base depends primarily on the purpose for which a paint is formulated. *White lead,* a basic lead(II) carbonate, has long been used as a base for outside paints. However, it is largely replaced in modern paint formulas by *titanium dioxide. Zinc oxide* and *lithopone* are excellent bases for inside paint. These are very white and do not darken in the presence of hydrogen sulfide as does white lead.

2. *Vehicles.* A vehicle for oil paint is an oil that oxidizes slowly when exposed to air, forming an elastic coating that holds the paint firmly in place. *Linseed oil* is

the most common paint vehicle. *Tung oil* is an excellent vehicles for use under severe weather conditions. *Fish oils* and *soybean oil*, with proper treatment, may be used as paint vehicles.

3. *Pigments.* All paint bases are white and small quantities of pigments are blended into the base when colored paints are required. Pigments include certain lakes, the oxides and sulfides of certain metals, complex cyanides, and other insoluble substances of high coloring power.

4. *Driers.* Paint driers are catalysts which promote the oxidation of the oil vehicle. They are made by boiling the oxides of lead and manganese in linseed oil. Excessive amounts of a drier in paint produces an inelastic protective film of inferior quality.

5. *Thinners.* Turpentine, alcohol, and certain mineral spirits are used as paint thinners. They are *diluents* used to make paint easier to spread. They dry by evaporation, and thus are distinguished from vehicles.

The use of *latex emulsion paints* for both inside and outside application has grown steadily in the United States in recent years. These paints consist of latex emulsions in water, the most commonly used bases being *styrene-butadiene*, *vinyl acetate*, and *acrylic* emulsions. They are easy to apply, comparatively durable, fast drying, and practically odorless.

SUMMARY

Zinc is extracted from sulfide, carbonate, silicate, and oxide ores. It is a bluish-white metal that becomes malleable above 100° C and burns with a bluish-white flame forming zinc oxide. Pure zinc reacts slowly with acids, but impure zinc reacts readily.

Zinc is used to coat iron, forming galvanized iron, and to make alloys such as brass. Zinc oxide is used as a paint base, as a filler for rubber to make automobile tires, and for making glazes and enamels. Zinc chloride is used for preserving wood against decay. Zinc sulfate is used in making lithopone, a paint base.

Cadmium is used for coating iron and steel, for making the negative plates of the nickel-cadmium storage battery, and for making fusible alloys. Cadmium sulfide is used as a yellow paint pigment.

Mercury is a very dense metal and is liquid at ordinary temperatures. It is used for various scientific instruments. Alloys of mercury are called amalgams. Mercury forms two series of compounds.

Tin oxide is easily reduced with carbon. Metallic tin is soft, white, very malleable, and has a low-melting point. In very cold climates it is sometimes changed to a powdered allotropic form. Tin foil is used for wrapping foods. Block tin is used for piping. Some tin compounds are used in mordant dyeing and for weighting silk.

The principal ore of lead is lead(II) sulfide. The concentrated ore is carefully roasted and then reduced in a blast furnace. Lead is a soft, bluish-white metal that is very dense and has a low melting point. All soluble lead compounds are poisonous. Storage batteries use much lead. Lead compounds are components of many paints.

TEST YOURSELF ON THESE TERMS

amalgam	foil	self-protective
block tin	galvanized iron	sherardizing
brass	lithopone	solder
bronze	paint base	spelter
cinnabar	pewter	terne plate
diluent	pigment	tinstone
drier	red lead	vehicle
dross	sacrificial metal	white lead

QUESTIONS

Group A

1. What are three methods of protecting sheet iron with zinc?
2. Why is so much zinc metal burned to form zinc oxide?
3. What are some uses for the metal cadmium?
4. Starting with zinc sulfide, how is metallic zinc obtained?
5. Where are the most important deposits of tin located throughout the world?
6. What are the uses of tin?
7. What five ingredients does a mixed house paint usually have?
8. (*a*) Why does paint "dry"? (*b*) What oils are used as vehicles in paint?
9. What is meant by "tin disease"?
10. What are the physical properties of tin?
11. What are the uses for lead?
12. What is the difference between *tin plate, block tin,* and *tin foil?*
13. Suggest two objections to the use of sheet lead for a roofing material.
14. Why are pipes for conducting distilled water often made of block tin?
15. What is an amalgam?
16. What mixture of metals is used for *silver* fillings in teeth?
17. How is the mercury recovered from the amalgam formed in the amalgamation process?

Group B

18. How is *spelter* purified?
19. Would galvanized iron containers be suitable for holding milk and other dairy products? Explain.
20. How can the brittleness of zinc be overcome so that it can be rolled into sheets?
21. Mention three uses for zinc chloride.
22. What is meant when we say that zinc hydroxide is amphiprotic?
23. What is the general composition of these substances: (*a*) zinc blende; (*b*) sphalerite; (*c*) zincite; (*d*) smithsonite; (*e*) calcimine?
★24. Explain why the term *storage battery* is appropriate in reference to an automobile battery.
★25. What constitutes the anode, cathode, and electrolyte of a fully-charged lead storage cell?

26. (*a*) What action occurs at the cathode of a lead storage cell during the discharge cycle? (*b*) Write the equation for this cathode action.
27. (*a*) What action occurs at the anode of a storage cell during the discharge cycle? (*b*) Write the equation for this anode action.
28. (*a*) What is the action at the cathode of a lead storage cell during the charging cycle? (*b*) What action occurs at the anode? (*c*) Write the equation for the reversible oxidation-reduction reaction which occurs in the lead storage battery during its normal use.

SOME THINGS FOR YOU TO DO

1. Galvanize a piece of clean sheet iron. First melt some zinc in an iron dish. Dip the sheet iron that is to be galvanized in dilute hydrochloric acid to remove any coating of oxide. Then dip the sheet iron in the melted zinc. Observe the coating of zinc that forms on the iron.
2. Prepare some test strips of different kinds of house paint, both white and colored. The pieces of wood used should have as nearly the same grain characteristics as possible. Plan a series of controlled tests which will enable you to compare the quality of the paints used. See if you can show any correlation between the constituents and the quality of the paint.

CHECK YOUR PROGRESS IN CHEMISTRY

Write the equations for reactions 1–12.

1. The roasting of zinc sulfide ore.
2. The reaction between limestone and silica in a blast furnace.
3. The reduction of iron(III) oxide with carbon monoxide.
4. The thermite reaction with aluminum and iron(III) oxide.
5. The reaction when dry sodium hydrogen carbonate is heated.
6. The reduction of zinc oxide with carbon.
7. Sodium hydroxide solution and zinc metal.
8. Zinc hydroxide and hydrochloric acid.
9. Zinc hydroxide (zincic acid) and sodium hydroxide solution.
10. Barium sulfide and zinc sulfate.
11. Hydrogen sulfide and a solution of cadmium nitrate.
12. The discharge of a lead storage cell.
13. What is the mass of 1 mole of Prussian blue?
14. What is the percentage of iron in a sample of limonite, $2 Fe_2O_3 \cdot 3 H_2O$?
15. What is the mass of a liter of carbon monoxide at S.T.P.?
16. How would you make a molal solution of methanol, CH_3OH?
17. When 46 g of a certain organic compound are added to 500. g of water, the boiling point is raised 0.52 C°. What is the molecular weight of the compound?
18. A certain hydrocarbon has the following composition: C = 92.3%, H = 7.7%. The mass of 224 ml of the gas is 0.26 g. (*a*) What is the empirical formula? (*b*) What is the molecular weight of the gas? (*c*) What is the correct formula?

19. How much basic lead(II) carbonate, $Pb_3(OH)_2(CO_3)_2$, can be made from 621 kg of lead?
20. When 239 g of lead(II) sulfide are roasted, what quantity of lead(II) oxide, PbO, will be produced?
21. When 150.7 kg of tin(IV) oxide, SnO_2, are reduced with carbon, what mass of tin is produced?
22. One molecule of nitrogen unites with three molecules of hydrogen in the *Haber* process. If one million liters of nitrogen are used, what volume of ammonia is produced?
23. How much barium hydroxide, $Ba(OH)_2$, is needed to make 1.00 liter of 0.0100-N solution?
24. By titration, 8.3 ml of 0.010-N hydrochloric acid neutralized 17.4 ml of an unknown basic solution. What is the normality of the hydroxide?
25. If the basic solution in the previous problem is potassium hydroxide, how many grams of potassium hydroxide are dissolved in 100. ml of the solution?

CHALLENGING YOUR KNOWLEDGE

1. Why is it necessary to devise a special treatment for each different kind of ore in order to extract the metal from it?
2. Why did man have some metals in very early times, yet many metals have been obtained only within the last century?
3. Explain the chemistry of the process for making blueprints.
4. Why do all three steel processes, the *open-hearth*, the *Bessemer*, and the *electric furnace*, continue to be used for producing steel in this country?
5. Suppose you have a powdered mixture that contained 90% gold and 10% silver. How could you obtain pure gold from such a mixture?
6. How would you plate a small silver ornament with gold? What would you use as the electrodes in the cell, and what would you use as the electrolyte?

Unit 13 · NUCLEAR
REACTIONS

Natural Radioactivity
Artificial Radioactivity

Chapter 38 · NATURAL RADIOACTIVITY

1. The discovery of radioactivity. In 1896 the French scientist Henri Becquerel (bek-*rel*) (1852–1908) was studying the properties of certain minerals. He was particularly interested in their ability to *fluoresce*, or give off visible light, after they had been exposed to sunlight. Among these minerals was a sample of uranium ore. By accident, Becquerel found that uranium ore gives off certain invisible rays without exposure to the sun. These invisible rays affect an unexposed photographic plate in the same way that light does when the plate is exposed. Substances which emit such invisible rays are *radioactive,* and the property is called *radioactivity.*

2. The discovery of radium. Becquerel was intensely interested in the source of radioactivity. At his suggestion, Pierre Curie (1859–1906) and his wife Marie (1867–1934) started to investigate the properties of uranium and its ores. They soon learned that uranium and uranium compounds are mildly radioactive, but that one uranium ore had unexpected properties. It was four times more radioactive than the amount of

uranium warranted. This ore, *pitchblende,* was mined in Bohemia.

It was a tremendous task to process several tons of pitchblende, but in 1898 the Curies discovered in it two new radioactive elements, *polonium* and *radium.* These accounted for the excess radioactivity of pitchblende. The Curies separated only a few milligrams of radium chloride, $RaCl_2$. Even this tiny amount involved more than 10 000 crystallizations and recrystallizations. Radium is about 1,000,000 times as radioactive as the same weight of uranium.

The metal radium was not isolated by Madame Curie until 1910. What is today marketed as radium usually consists of one of its salts, the bromide, the chloride, or the carbonate. Radium is radioactive both as the element and as a part of a compound. The Curies and Becquerel received the Nobel Prize for physics jointly in 1903 for their work on radioactivity.

3. The sources of radium. Radium is always found in uranium ores. However, it cannot occur in such ores in a greater proportion than 1 part of radium

560

to 3,000,000 parts of uranium. The reason for these conditions will be explained in Section 8. The extraction of radium is a long, tedious, and costly procedure. Formerly, ores from Europe and Africa were used. Now, however, ore deposits near Great Bear Lake in northern Canada are utilized for the production of radium.

4. The properties of radium. Radium is the element of highest atomic weight in Group II of the Periodic Table. Its physical properties were listed in the table at the beginning of Chapter 25. It is the least electronegative member of its group, with chemical properties similar to those of barium.

Radium is an important element not because of its physical or chemical properties, but because of its radioactivity. It is one of the most highly radioactive elements known. Because of this radioactivity, radium and radium compounds have several unusual properties which are also observed in other radioactive materials.

1. It affects the light-sensitive emulsion

Fig. 38-1. **Mme. Marie Curie, a Polish scientist, who together with her French husband, Pierre, discovered the elements polonium and radium.** (Culver Service)

on a photographic plate. Even though a photographic plate is wrapped in opaque paper and kept in the dark, the invisible rays from radioactive materials affect the plate in the same way that light does

VOCABULARY

α **(alpha) particle.** Particle identical with a helium nucleus emitted from the nucleus of a radioactive element.

β **(beta) particle.** Particle identical with an electron emitted from the nucleus of a radioactive element.

γ **(gamma) ray.** High energy X ray emitted from the nucleus of a radioactive element.

Half-life. The length of time required for the disintegration of one-half of a given number of atoms of a radioactive element.

Nuclear equation. An equation representing changes in the nuclei of atoms.

Radioactivity. The spontaneous, uncontrollable disintegration of the nucleus of an atom with the emission of particles and rays.

Transmutation reaction. A reaction in which the nucleus of an atom undergoes a change in its positive charge, and consequently in its identity.

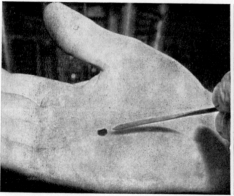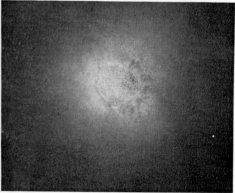

Fig. 38-2. Left, a fragment of metallic uranium, one of the radioactive elements; and right, a photograph produced when radiation from the same fragment of uranium penetrated the light-tight wrappings of a photographic plate. (Matt Grimaldi and Mark Schupack)

when the plate is exposed. When the plate is developed, a black spot shows up on the negative where the invisible radiation struck it. The rays from radioactive materials penetrate paper, wood, flesh, and *thin* sheets of metal.

2. *Radium and its compounds discharge an electroscope and affect a Geiger counter.* The radiation from radium ionizes the molecules of the gases in the air. These ionized molecules conduct the electric charge away from the knob of an electroscope. The activity of a sample of a radium compound may be measured by the speed with which it discharges an electroscope. In a similar way, the radiation given off by radium ionizes the low pressure gas in the tube of a Geiger counter. Electricity can thus momentarily pass through the tube. The passage of electricity may be registered as a "click" by a loudspeaker.

3. *Radium compounds produce fluorescence with certain other compounds.* A small quantity of radium bromide added to zinc sulfide causes the zinc sulfide to glow in the dark. Such a mixture is used in making a luminous paint for

coating the dials of airplane instruments and the hands and dials of clocks and watches.

4. *The physiological effects of radium.* The radiation from radium may destroy the germinating power of seeds, kill bacteria, or even small animals. Those who work with radium may be severely burned by the rays which it emits. Such frightful burns require a long time to heal, and may sometimes prove fatal. Because the radiations from radium destroy tissue, it is used in the treatment of cancer and certain skin diseases.

5. *Radium salts emit energy continuously.* Part of this energy is light energy which causes radium salts to glow in the dark with a pale phosphorescence. This glow is so pale, however, that in the daylight the salts resemble common table salt in their appearance. Radium salts also emit heat continuously. In one hour, one gram of radium gives off 120 calories of heat, enough to melt 1.5 times its own mass of ice. The source of this energy is the transformation of matter into energy which occurs as a radium atom disintegrates into a slightly simpler

atom and simultaneously emits radiation. One half of any number of radium atoms will disintegrate into simpler atoms in about 1600 years. One half of what remains, or one-fourth of the original atoms, will disintegrate in the next 1600 years. One half of what yet remains, or one-eighth of the original atoms, will disintegrate in the next 1600 years, and so on. This process continues until all the radium atoms have disintegrated. This period of 1600 years is called the *half-life of radium.* Each radioactive isotope has its own characteristic half-life.

5. Other natural radioactive elements. The radioactive elements known to Becquerel were uranium and thorium. We have already learned how the Curies discovered two more, polonium and radium. Since that time, several more natural radioactive elements have been discovered. All the elements beyond bismuth in the Periodic Table are radioactive. Several artificial radioactive elements have also been prepared, but a description of that work will be given in Chapter 39. One of the important natural radioactive elements is the inert gas *radon*, which is given off when radium atoms disintegrate. While it is chemically inert, it is quite radioactive. It is collected in tubes and used in place of radium for the treatment of disease.

Fig. 38-3. **An electroscope is used to measure the intensity of an electric charge.**

6. The nature of radioactivity. The radiation emitted by such radioactive elements as uranium, thorium, and radium has been carefully studied. Sir Ernest Rutherford, an English scientist, discovered that such radiation is complex, consisting of two types of particles and one type of ray.

1. The α particles, alpha particles, are helium nuclei. They form helium atoms when they gain two electrons. Their mass is nearly four times that of the hydrogen atom, and they have a speed of from 10,000 to 20,000 miles per second. They do not have so great a penetrating power as the other types of radiation. A thin sheet of aluminum foil or of paper will stop them. However, they burn flesh and ionize air quickly.

2. The β particles, beta particles, are electrons. They are negatively-charged particles each $\frac{1}{1837}$ as heavy as the

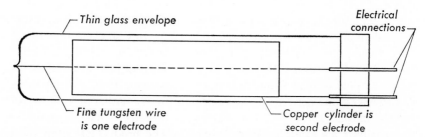

Fig. 38-4. **This cutaway view shows the structure of a Geiger-Müller counter tube. Such tubes are used to detect radioactive materials.**

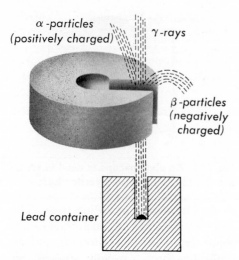

α-particles
(positively charged)

γ-rays

β-particles
(negatively
charged)

Lead container

Fig. 38-5. **The effect of a magnet on the different types of radiations. The north pole of the magnet is toward the reader and the south pole is away from the reader.**

hydrogen atom. They travel at a speed of from 60,000 to 160,000 miles per second. Their penetrating power is much greater than that of alpha particles.

3. The γ rays, gamma rays, are high-energy X rays. *X rays* are the same kind of radiation as light, but with much shorter wave length and higher frequency. Gamma rays are believed to be caused by transitions in energy levels in the nucleus. They are the most penetrating of the radiations given off by radioactive elements.

Figure 38-5 shows the effect of a powerful magnetic field, perpendicular to the plane of the paper, on the complex radiation emitted from a small particle of radioactive material. Note that the north pole is toward the reader and the south pole is away from the reader. The heavier alpha particles are deflected slightly in one direction. The lighter beta particles are deflected more markedly in the opposite direction. The gamma rays are not affected by the magnet.

By the use of such a magnetic field, Rutherford learned much about radiations from radioactive material.

7. The disintegration of atoms of radioactive elements. Radioactive atoms disintegrate spontaneously, yielding heat and light energy. At first it was believed that they did not lose mass and would give off heat and light forever. However, more careful investigation shows that radioactive materials do lose mass slowly.

A long series of experiments has shown that the source of this energy is the disintegration of nuclei of radium and other radioactive elements. The alpha and beta particles are the products of such nuclear disintegration. Spontaneously, certain heavy nuclei break down into simpler and lighter nuclei, releasing enormous quantities of energy by this disintegration.

8. A series of related radioactive elements. All naturally-occurring radioactive elements belong to one of three series of related elements. The heaviest or "parent" elements of these series are the uranium isotope with mass number 238, the uranium isotope with mass number 235, and the thorium isotope with mass number 232. Since radium is in the family which has the uranium isotope with mass number 238 as its parent, let us trace this series of disintegrations.

The nucleus of a uranium atom contains 92 protons, since its atomic number is 92, and has a mass number of 238. As this nucleus disintegrates, it ejects an alpha particle which becomes an atom of helium when its positive charge is neutralized. An alpha particle has a mass number of 4. Since it contains two protons, it has an atomic number of 2. The residue left from the uranium nucleus will thus have an atomic number of 90 and a mass number of 234. It is an isotope of thorium, sometimes designated Uranium X_1. The *nuclear equation* for this transmutation reaction may be written:

$$_{92}U^{238} \rightarrow _{90}Th^{234} + _2He^4$$

A *transmutation* is the change in the identity of a nucleus because of a change in the number of its protons. Since the above equation is a nuclear equation, only nuclei are represented. The superscript is the mass number. The subscript is the atomic number. Alpha particles are represented as helium nuclei, $_2He^4$. The total of the mass numbers on the left must equal the total of the mass numbers on the right. The total of the atomic numbers on both sides of the equation must also be equal.

The half-life of Uranium X_1 is about 24 days. It disintegrates by emitting a beta particle. The loss of a beta particle from the nucleus increases the number of positive charges in the nucleus, the atomic number, by one. The beta particle is believed to be formed by the transformation of a neutron into a proton and beta particle (electron). Since the mass of the lost beta particle is negligible, the mass number of the resulting atom stays the same.

$$_{90}Th^{234} \rightarrow _{91}Pa^{234} + _{-1}e^0$$

The symbol $_{-1}e^0$ represents an electron with an atomic number of -1 and a mass number of 0. $_{91}Pa^{234}$ is an isotope of protactinium, sometimes designated

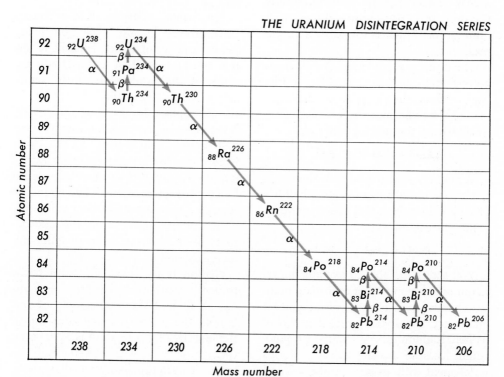

THE URANIUM DISINTEGRATION SERIES

Fig. 38-6. The parent element of the Uranium Disintegration Series is $_{92}U^{238}$. The final element of the series is $_{82}Pb^{206}$.

Uranium X_2. This isotope disintegrates by emitting a beta particle and producing $_{92}U^{234}$, sometimes designated Uranium II.

$$_{91}Pa^{234} \rightarrow {}_{92}U^{234} + {}_{-1}e^0$$

The disintegration of Uranium II is by alpha particle emission.

$$_{92}U^{234} \rightarrow {}_{90}Th^{230} + {}_2He^4$$

The isotope of thorium produced also emits an alpha particle, forming the element radium.

$$_{90}Th^{230} \rightarrow {}_{88}Ra^{226} + {}_2He^4$$

Now we can see why ores of uranium must contain radium, since radium is one of the products of the disintegration of uranium atoms. The rates of disintegration of $_{92}U^{238}$, the intervening elements, and of radium itself, determine the proportion of uranium atoms to radium atoms which is found in uranium ores.

The disintegration of radium proceeds according to the chart shown in Fig. 38-6. Radium disintegrates by the emission of an alpha particle forming radon as shown by the nuclear equation:

$$_{88}Ra^{226} \rightarrow {}_{86}Rn^{222} + {}_2He^4$$

While radon is chemically inert, its nuclei are unstable and after a half-life of almost four days, they disintegrate by alpha particle emission.

$$_{86}Rn^{222} \rightarrow {}_{84}Po^{218} + {}_2He^4$$

You should be able to explain the remaining atomic number and mass number changes shown on the disintegration chart in terms of the emitted particles. When Radium F, an isotope of polonium, loses an alpha particle, it forms an element with atomic number 82 and mass number 206. This is a stable, non-radioactive, isotope of lead. These spon-taneous transmutations, beginning with $_{92}U^{238}$, passing through $_{88}Ra^{226}$, on down to $_{82}Pb^{206}$, occur continuously at a rate which scientists have never been able to alter.

9. Applications of natural radioactivity. The age of minerals containing radioactive substances can be estimated. Since radioactive substances disintegrate at a known rate, an analysis of the mineral is made to determine the amount of long-lived "parent" element and the amounts of the "descendent" elements in the sample. Then by calculation, scientists can determine how long it must have taken for these amounts of "descendent" elements to be produced. This is assumed to be the age of the mineral. One of the oldest minerals has been estimated to be over two billion years old.

The carbon atoms involved in the oxygen-carbon dioxide cycle of living plants and animals are kept at a low but constant level of radioactivity because of the production of the radioactive $_6C^{14}$ isotope from $_7N^{14}$ atoms in the atmosphere by the action of cosmic rays. (Cosmic rays are protons of very high energy which come to the earth from outer space.) When living things die, the oxygen-carbon dioxide cycle no longer operates in them. They no longer replace carbon atoms in their cells with other carbon atoms. Thus the radioactivity of the carbon atoms in nonliving materials slowly diminishes.

Carbon from a wooden beam taken from the tomb of an Egyptian pharaoh has about half the radioactivity of carbon in the wood of living trees. Since the half-life of a $_6C^{14}$ atom is 5570 years, the age of wood with half the radioactivity of currently-living wood is about 5570 years. Objects up to 24,000 years old have been dated by this method.

SUMMARY

Substances which give off rays which affect photographic plates the same way light does are radioactive.

Radium was discovered by Pierre and Marie Curie in 1899. It is a very radioactive element which is always found in uranium ores. It resembles the element barium in its chemical properties. Because of its radioactivity, it has several unusual properties either as the element, or in compounds: *1.* It affects a photographic plate; *2.* it discharges an electroscope and affects a Geiger counter; *3.* it produces fluorescence with certain compounds; *4.* its radiation destroys living tissue; *5.* it emits energy in the form of light and heat continuously.

The radiation from radioactive substances is of three types: *1.* alpha particles, or helium nuclei; *2.* beta particles, or electrons; and *3.* gamma rays, or high-energy X rays. The discharge of these particles from the nuclei of radioactive elements causes them to disintegrate into simpler elements.

All naturally-occurring radioactive elements belong to one of three series of related elements. Uranium-238 is the parent element of the radioactive series which contains radium.

The age of certain minerals and of carbon-containing materials can be estimated by the radioactive isotopes they contain.

TEST YOURSELF ON THESE TERMS

α particle	nuclear equation	radium
β particle	parent element	radon
electroscope	pitchblende	subscript
γ ray	polonium	superscript
Geiger counter	radioactive	transmutation reaction
half-life	radioactivity	uranium

QUESTIONS

Group A

1. (*a*) Who discovered radioactivity? (*b*) How was the discovery made?
2. What evidence led Pierre and Marie Curie to suspect that there were radioactive elements other than uranium in pitchblende?
3. How does the radioactivity of radium compare with that of uranium?
4. What are the sources of radium ore?
5. What practical use is made of the fluorescence produced in zinc sulfide by a radium compound?
6. What is meant by the *half-life* of a radioactive element?
7. What inert gas is radioactive?
8. How many kinds of radiation are given off by radioactive materials?
9. From what part of a radioactive atom do the alpha and beta particles come?
10. What change in identity and mass number occurs when a radioactive atom gives off an alpha particle?

11. What change in identity and mass number occurs when a radioactive atom gives off a beta particle?
12. How is the age of a radioactive mineral estimated?

Group B

13. Why is radium studied separately rather than with the other elements of Group II?
14. Is the radioactivity of an element affected by the other elements with which it may be chemically combined?
15. Why can the radiation from a radioactive material affect photographic film, even though the film is well wrapped in black paper?
16. How does a radioactive material affect the rate of discharge of an electroscope?
17. Where are most of the natural radioactive elements found in the Periodic Table?
18. Give the mass, nature, and speed range of: (*a*) alpha particles; (*b*) beta particles.
19. What do scientists believe gamma rays to be?
20. Write the nuclear equation for the emission of an alpha particle by $_{88}Ra^{226}$.
21. Write the nuclear equation for the emission of a beta particle by $_{82}Pb^{214}$.
22. Write nuclear equations for successive emissions of an alpha particle and a beta particle from $_{84}Po^{214}$.

SOME THINGS FOR YOU TO DO

1. Examine the luminous dial on a watch or clock in the dark with a magnifying glass. You will find that the glow is really a series of tiny flashes caused by the impact of alpha particles with zinc sulfide.
2. Determine the rate of discharge of an electroscope. Then bring some radioactive material, such as a uranium compound, close to the electroscope. How is the rate of discharge affected? Explain.
3. Read *Madame Curie*, written by Eve Curie. This is the biography of the famous woman scientist written by one of her daughters.

Chapter 39 · ARTIFICIAL RADIOACTIVITY

1. **The stability of a nucleus.** In Chapter 38 the nuclei of certain naturally-occurring heavy atoms were described as unstable. These nuclei break down at a definite rate into simpler nuclei and simultaneously emit particles and rays. Let us now consider what conditions promote such instability in the nuclei of atoms.

On the atomic mass scale, the isotope of carbon with six protons and six neutrons in its nucleus is defined as having an *atomic mass* of exactly 12 (see Chapter 4, Section 19). On this scale, a $_2\text{He}^4$ nucleus has a mass of 4.0015, while the mass of a proton is 1.0073 and the mass of a neutron is 1.0087. Since a $_2\text{He}^4$ nucleus contains two protons and two neutrons, we might expect its mass to be the combined mass of these four particles, 4.0320. [2(1.0073) + 2(1.0087) = 4.0320]. Note that there is a difference of 0.0305 atomic mass unit between the actual mass, 4.0015, and the calculated mass, 4.0320, of a $_2\text{He}^4$ nucleus. *This difference in mass is called the mass defect. The mass defect, converted according to Einstein's equation, $E = mc^2$,* (see Chap. 1, Sec. 11), *is the energy released when the helium nucleus is formed from its component particles. This energy is called the binding energy.*

If the binding energies of the atoms of the elements are calculated, it is

Fig. 39-1. Albert Einstein, a theoretical physicist, was the first man to predict the interrelationship of matter and energy. (Wide World Photos)

found that the lightest and the heaviest elements have the smallest binding energies while the elements of intermediate atomic weights have the greatest binding energies. The elements with the greatest binding energies are the ones with the most stable nuclei. Therefore, we see that the nuclei of the lightest and heaviest atoms are less stable than the nuclei of the elements of intermediate atomic weight.

★ There seem to be factors other than mass that are associated with the stability of atomic nuclei. These are the ratio of neutrons to protons and the even-odd nature of the number of neutrons and protons.

★ In the most stable nuclei, the ratio of neutrons to protons is 1:1; that is, there is an equal number of neutrons and protons. Nuclei with a greater number of neutrons than protons (and the ratio increases to 1.6 : 1 in the heavier elements) have lower binding energies and are less stable. In nuclei with an equal number of protons and neutrons, these particles occupy what appear to be the lowest energy levels in the nucleus. Scientists believe that many properties of nuclear particles indicate that in a nucleus there are energy levels, just as there are electron energy levels in atoms. When there is an excess of neutrons over protons, the neutrons must occupy levels of greater energy. This lowers the binding energy, and consequently lowers the stability of the nucleus.

VOCABULARY

Binding energy. The energy released when an atom is formed from its component particles. The energy equivalent of the mass defect.

Chain reaction. A reaction in which the material or energy which initiates the reaction is also one of the products.

Critical size. The amount of radioactive material required to sustain a chain reaction.

Cyclotron. An electromagnetic device for accelerating protons or deuterons in a spiral path.

Electron-volt. The energy required to move an electron across a potential difference of one volt.

Fission. The break-up of a nucleus into medium-weight parts.

Fusion. The combination of two light-weight nuclei to form a heavier, more stable nucleus.

Mass defect. The difference between the mass of a nucleus and the sum of the masses of its constituent particles.

Nuclear disintegration. The emission of a proton or neutron from a nucleus as a result of bombarding the nucleus with alpha particles, protons, deuterons, or neutrons.

Nuclear reactor. A device in which the controlled fission of radioactive material produces new radioactive substances and energy.

Radioactive fall-out. The showering down of radioactive particles which were originally carried high into the air by a nuclear explosion.

1. What is carbon
   a) Why is it important
2. Why is petroleum
3. Where and how it formed
4. First distillation to crude oil.

answer:

1. There are millions of compound
   that have derived from carbon
   important
   organic   gives no more
   Ch. no. 1 of carbon compound

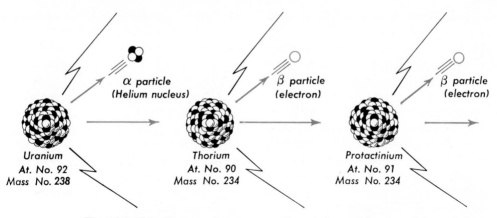

Fig. 39-2. **This diagram shows successive alpha and beta particle emissions in the disintegration of $_{92}U^{238}$.**

★ On the basis of frequency of occurrence alone, the even-odd nature of the number of protons and of the number of neutrons appears to affect the stability of a nucleus. By far the greatest number of stable nuclei have an even number of protons and an even number of neutrons. Less frequent in occurrence are the nuclei with an even number of protons and an odd number of neutrons, or vice versa. Only a few stable nuclei with an odd number of protons and an odd number of neutrons are known.

Because of the difference in stability of the different nuclei, there are four types of nuclear reactions in which nuclear energy is liberated. In each case a small amount of the mass of the reactants is converted into energy and products of greater stability result.

1. A nucleus undergoes *radioactive decomposition*, forming a slightly lighter, more stable nucleus, and emitting an alpha particle or a beta particle, and gamma rays.

2. A nucleus is bombarded with alpha particles, protons, deuterons (deuterium, $_1H^2$, nuclei), or neutrons. The unstable nucleus that is formed emits a proton or a neutron and becomes more stable. This is called *nuclear disintegration*.

3. A very heavy nucleus is split and forms medium-weight nuclei. This process is known as *fission*.

4. Light-weight nuclei combine to form heavier, more stable nuclei. This process is known as *fusion*.

We have already described natural radioactivity. In this chapter we shall review radioactive changes in terms of nuclear stability. Then we shall go on to describe the other three types of nuclear reactions.

2. Radioactive changes produce more stable nuclei. The emission of an alpha particle from a radioactive nucleus decreases the mass of the nucleus. The resulting nucleus of lower mass has a higher binding energy, and is for that reason more stable.

Alpha particle emission decreases the number of protons and neutrons in a nucleus equally and also by an even number. Beta particle emission, by transforming a neutron into a proton, brings the neutron-proton ratio nearer to 1:1. Both of these changes thus promote an increase in the stability of the nucleus undergoing such change.

3. Rutherford produced the first nuclear disintegration. When scientists discovered how uranium and radium undergo natural disintegration and transmutation, they wondered if man-made transmutations could be produced by adding extra protons to the nucleus to make new elements. In 1919 Rutherford produced the first nuclear disintegration by bombarding nitrogen with alpha particles from radium. He obtained protons (hydrogen nuclei) and an isotope of oxygen.

$$_7N^{14} + _2He^4 \rightarrow _8O^{17} + _1H^1$$

4. Experiments with another nuclear disintegration verified Einstein's equation. In 1932 two English scientists, J. D. Cockcroft (1897–   ), and E. T. S. Walton (1903–   ), experimentally verified Einstein's equation, $E = mc^2$. They bombarded lithium with high speed protons. Alpha particles and a very large amount of energy were produced.

$$_3Li^7 + _1H^1 \rightarrow _2He^4 + _2He^4 + energy$$

There is a loss of matter in this reaction. One lithium nucleus, having a mass of 7.0143, was hit by a proton having a mass of 1.0073. These formed two alpha particles (helium nuclei) each having a mass of 4.0015. Simple arithmetic, $(7.0143 + 1.0073) - 2(4.0015)$, shows that there is a loss of 0.0186 atomic mass unit. Cockcroft and Walton found that the energy emitted in the reaction agreed very well with that predicted by Einstein for such a loss in mass. Subsequent experiments have offered further proof for Einstein's equation for the conversion of matter into energy.

5. Neutrons are emitted in some nuclear disintegrations. We have already stated that neutrons were discovered by Chadwick in 1932. He first detected them during the bombardment of beryllium by alpha particles:

$$_4Be^9 + _2He^4 \rightarrow _6C^{12} + _0n^1$$

The symbol for a neutron is $_0n^1$, indicating a particle with zero atomic number (no protons) and a mass number of 1. This reaction offered proof that neutrons were the second type of particle in the nuclei of atoms.

6. The cyclotron and other "atom smashers." Radium, the natural source

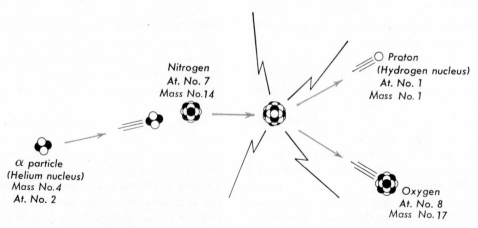

Fig. 39-3. **This diagram shows the historic nuclear disintegration performed by Rutherford.**

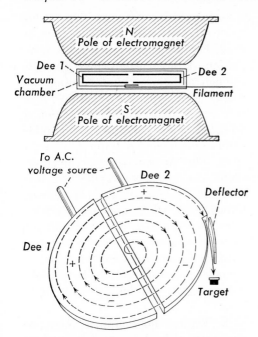

Fig. 39-4. **A diagram of the cyclotron used to produce "atomic bullets" of very high energy.**

of alpha particles used in many early experiments, is rather inefficient in producing nuclear changes. As a result, scientists sought more efficient ways of producing high-energy particles for nuclear bombardment. This search resulted in the development of many large electric devices for the acceleration of charged particles.

The *cyclotron* is the invention of Dr. E. O. Lawrence (1901–1958) of the University of California. It consists of a cylindrical box placed between the poles of a huge electromagnet and exhausted until a high vacuum is produced. The "bullets" used to bombard nuclei are usually protons or deuterons. They are introduced into the cylindrical box through its center.

Inside the box are two hollow, D-shaped electrodes called *dees*. These are connected to a source of very high volt-

age through an oscillator. When the cyclotron is in operation, the electric charge on these dees is reversed very rapidly by the oscillator. The combination of the high voltage alternating potential and the action of the field of the electromagnet causes the protons or deuterons inside to move in a spiral course. They move faster and faster as they near the outside of the box and acquire more and more energy. When they reach the outer rim of the box, they are deflected toward the target. The energy of the particles accelerated in a cyclotron may reach 15,000,000 *electron-volts*. This is the energy an electron would have if it were accelerated across a potential difference of 15,000,000 volts. By studying the fragments of atoms formed by bombardment, scientists have learned a great deal about atomic structure. They also have discovered many things about the products formed by the disintegration of atoms. Other machines for bombarding atomic nuclei are the *betatron*, the *synchrotron*, and the *linear accelerator*.

The betatron is a device which accelerates electrons rather than positively-charged particles as does the cyclotron. The accelerated electrons may be used as "bullets" for bombardment, or for producing high-energy X rays. The synchrotron operates in principle like the cyclotron. But by varying both the oscillating voltage and the magnetic field, the particles can be accelerated in a circular path rather than in a spiral path. A synchrotron can impart an energy of more than 30 billion electron-volts to the protons which it accelerates. Still another type of particle accelerator is the linear accelerator. In this device the particles travel in a straight line through many stages of small potential difference which act to accelerate the particles.

Fig. 39-5. **The 60-inch cyclotron of the Brookhaven National Laboratory.** (Brookhaven National Laboratory)

7. Neutrons make better "bullets." Prior to the discovery of neutrons in 1932, alpha particles and protons were used in studying atomic nuclei. However, alpha particles and protons are charged particles. It requires great quantities of energy, such as are imparted to these particles by cyclotrons and synchrotrons, to "fire" these charged "bullets" into a nucleus. Their positive charge causes them to be repelled by the positive nuclear charge.

Since neutrons have no charge, they can easily penetrate the nucleus of an atom because there is no force of repulsion. Fast neutrons may go right through an atom without causing any change in it. Some fast neutrons, however, may produce the disintegration of a nucleus. Slow neutrons, on the other hand, are sometimes trapped by a nucleus. This nucleus then becomes unstable, and may disintegrate. Fast neutrons may be slowed down by passage through materials composed of elements of low atomic weight such as deuterium oxide or graphite. Neutrons are produced by an atom smasher when the accelerated positively-charged particles strike a target material, possibly beryllium.

8. Neutron bombardment may produce man-made elements. When $_{92}U^{238}$, the most plentiful isotope of uranium, is bombarded with slow neutrons, a $_{92}U^{238}$ nucleus may capture a neutron. An unstable isotope of uranium, $_{92}U^{239}$, is formed. This emits a beta particle (electron) and forms a man-made radioactive element, neptunium. Neptunium has the atomic number 93.

Fig. 39-6. **A portion of the huge synchrotron at the Brookhaven National Laboratory. This view shows the conjunction of the linear accelerator, which produces a beam of protons, with the massive ring magnet of the synchrotron.** (Brookhaven National Laboratory)

Fig. 39-7. The interior of the heavy ion linear accelerator of "Hilac" at the University of California Radiation Laboratory. Hilac is designed to accelerate the nuclei of atoms ranging up to argon in mass. It may thus be possible to add large fragments of matter to the nuclei of uranium atoms and produce elements with atomic numbers higher than 103. (University of California)

$$_{92}U^{238} + _0n^1 \rightarrow _{92}U^{239}$$

$$_{92}U^{239} \rightarrow _{93}Np^{239} + _{-1}e^0$$

Neptunium is an unstable element, also. Its nucleus ejects a beta particle, forming still another man-made element, plutonium, atomic number 94.

$$_{93}Np^{239} \rightarrow _{94}Pu^{239} + _{-1}e^0$$

Neptunium and plutonium were the first man-made *transuranium* elements. *Transuranium elements* are those with more than 92 protons in their nuclei. As this is written, there are eleven artificially prepared transuranium elements. In addition to neptunium and plutonium, there are americium, curium, berkelium, californium, einsteinium, fermium, mendelevium, element 102, and lawrencium.

These have been prepared by bombardment of the nuclei of uranium or more complex elements with neutrons, alpha particles, or other "nuclear bullets."

9. Radioactive atoms can be made artificially. In 1934 Madame Curie's daughter Irene (1897–1956), working with her husband, Frederic Joliot (1900–1958), discovered that stable atoms can be made artificially radioactive. This occurs when they are bombarded with deuterons or neutrons. Now radioactive isotopes of all the elements have been prepared. Many new radioactive isotopes are manufactured by slow-neutron bombardment in the nuclear reactor at Oak Ridge, Tennessee. The equation showing the formation of radioactive $_{27}Co^{60}$ from naturally-occurring nonradioactive $_{27}Co^{59}$ by slow-neutron bombardment is:

$$_{27}Co^{59} + _0n^1 \rightarrow _{27}Co^{60}$$

The radiation from $_{27}Co^{60}$ consists of beta particles and gamma rays.

Radioactive $_{15}P^{32}$ is prepared by bombardment of $_{16}S^{32}$ with slow neutrons:

$$_{16}S^{32} + _0n^1 \rightarrow _{15}P^{32} + _1H^1$$

The radiation from $_{15}P^{32}$ consists only of beta particles.

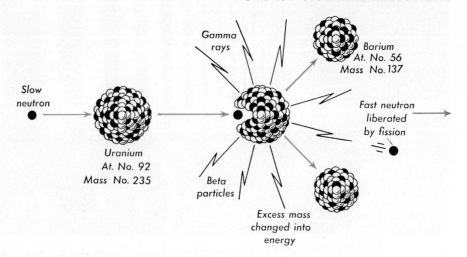

Fig. 39-8. Neutrons from the fission of $_{92}U^{235}$, when slowed down by a carbon moderator,

Radioactive phosphorus and radioactive cobalt are used in the treatment of various forms of cancer. Radioactive iodine may be used as part of the treatment of persons suffering from thyroid gland disorders.

Radioactive cobalt, cesium, or iridium, in specially designed apparatus, produces an intense beam of radiation for the treatment of deepseated tumors. Radioactive arsenic is helpful in locating brain tumors, while neutron-irradiated boron may be used for treatment.

Radioactive cobalt may be added to a fluid flowing through a pipeline. By means of a Geiger counter, it is possible to trace the path of the pipeline or to determine the position of an obstruction or leak in it. This is an example of the use of a radioactive isotope as a *tracer.*

Radioactive tracer materials are used to study the wear of machine parts. For example, a radioactive material may be applied to a bearing, and a shaft turned in the bearing. Then the radioactivity of the shaft is measured. In this way the amount of bearing metal rubbed off by the shaft can be accurately known. In a similar way the wear of automobile tires can be measured. A radioactive tracer may be included in the tire tread. Then, after the tire has been driven over a road surface, the radioactivity of the surface is measured and the amount of rubber rubbed off on it may be determined. The utilization of fertilizer elements by plants is shown by using radioactive tracer elements. Radioactive phosphorus compounds may be added to the soil with the fertilizer. Then the amount taken up by the plants is measured to learn how well the plant is making use of the phosphorus added to the soil in the fertilizer.

Radioactive isotopes make it possible to study the life processes of plants, particularly photosynthesis. The radiation of seeds and of plants is producing new, more desirable varieties.

10. $_{92}U^{235}$ **undergoes fission.** The element uranium exists as three naturally-occurring isotopes; $_{92}U^{238}$, $_{92}U^{235}$, and $_{92}U^{234}$. Most uranium is the isotope $_{92}U^{238}$. Only 0.7% of natural uranium is $_{92}U^{235}$. $_{92}U^{234}$ is found only in insignifi-

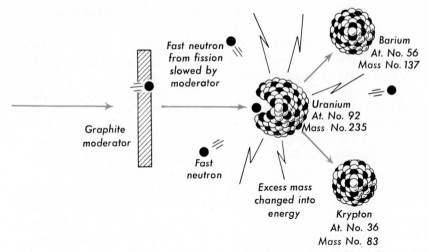

Fast neutron
from fission
slowed by
moderator

Barium
At. No. 56
Mass No. 137

Graphite
moderator

Uranium
At. No. 92
Mass No. 235

Fast
neutron

Excess mass
changed into
energy

Krypton
At. No. 36
Mass No. 83

can cause fission in a second $_{92}U^{235}$ atom. This process makes a chain reaction possible.

cant traces. We have already stated that transuranium elements may be produced when $_{92}U^{238}$ is bombarded with slow neutrons. However, when $_{92}U^{235}$ is bombarded with slow neutrons, each atom may capture one of the neutrons. This additional neutron in the nucleus makes it very unstable. Instead of emitting an alpha particle, or beta particle, as in other radioactive changes, the nucleus splits into two parts of medium weight. *This break-up of a heavy nucleus into medium-weight parts is called fission.* Neutrons are usually given out during this fission. There is a small loss of mass, which appears as emission of a great amount of energy. One equation for the fission of $_{92}U^{235}$ is:

$$_{92}U^{235} + _{0}n^{1} \rightarrow$$
$$_{56}Ba^{141} + _{36}Kr^{92} + 3_{0}n^{1} + \text{energy}$$

The atomic mass of $_{92}U^{235}$ is slightly greater than 235. The atomic masses of the unstable isotopes of barium and krypton are slightly less than 141 and 92. So instead of the masses of the reactants equalling the masses of the products, there is a conversion of about 0.2 atomic

mass unit into energy during the fission process.

11. A nuclear chain reaction. A *chain reaction is one in which the material or energy which initiates the reaction is also one of the products.* The fission of $_{92}U^{235}$ can produce a chain reaction. It requires a neutron to initiate the fission of one $_{92}U^{235}$ nucleus. Two or three neutrons are given out when this fission occurs. These neutrons can start the fission of other $_{92}U^{235}$ nuclei. Again neutrons are emitted. These can cause the fission of still other $_{92}U^{235}$ nuclei. This is a chain reaction. It will continue until all the $_{92}U^{235}$ atoms have split or until the neutrons fail to strike $_{92}U^{235}$ nuclei.

12. The action in a nuclear reactor. A *nuclear reactor,* sometimes called an atomic pile, *is a device in which the controlled fission of radioactive material produces new radioactive substances and energy.* One of the earliest types built at Oak Ridge, Tennessee, in 1943, contains natural uranium. It has a lattice-type construction with blocks of graphite forming the framework. Spaced between the blocks of graphite, and encased in aluminum cans for protection, are rods of uranium. *Control rods* of neutron-absorbing boron steel are inserted into the lattice to regulate the number of free neutrons. This reactor is air cooled.

The rods of uranium or uranium oxide are the *nuclear fuel* for the reactor, since the energy released in the reactor comes from changes in the uranium nuclei. Graphite is said to be the *moderator*, because it slows down the fast neutrons produced by fission and makes them more effective for producing additional nuclear changes. The amount of uranium in such a reactor is important, too. Enough uranium must be present to sustain a chain reaction. This quantity of uranium is called the **critical size.**

Two types of reactions occur in the fuel in such a reactor. Neutrons cause the nuclei of $_{92}U^{235}$ to undergo fission. The fast neutrons from this fission are slowed down by passage through the graphite. Some strike other $_{92}U^{235}$ nuclei and continue the chain reaction. Other neutrons strike $_{92}U^{238}$ nuclei, and initiate the changes which finally produce plutonium. Great quantities of energy are liberated so the reactor has to

be cooled continuously by blowing air through tubes in the lattice. The rate of the reaction is controlled by the insertion or removal of the neutron-absorbing control rods. This type of reactor is now being used to produce radioactive isotopes, using the excess neutrons that are not needed to maintain the chain reaction. Other types of reactors are described in Sections 15, 16, and 17.

13. The separation of uranium isotopes. The intensity of the chain reaction in a nuclear reactor is controlled by the absorption of neutrons by $_{92}U^{238}$ nuclei and by the control rods. But if the critical size of $_{92}U^{235}$ could be obtained in *pure* form, a rapidly accelerating chain reaction would start. This reaction would liberate a tremendous amount of energy in an incredibly short time. Such a liberation of energy would occur with explosive violence. This would be an atomic bomb. However, the problem of separating the isotopes of uranium to get pure $_{92}U^{235}$ presents great difficulty. Chemical methods of separation are not possible because these isotopes have the same chemical properties. The only practical difference be-

Fig. 39-9. **A cutaway view of the Oak Ridge Reactor.**

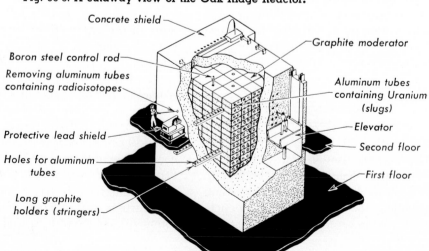

Fig. 39-10. **The atomic bomb which was dropped on Hiroshima, Japan, on August 6, 1945. The bomb was 28 inches in diameter, 120 inches in length, and weighed about 9000 pounds.** (Brookhaven National Laboratory)

tween istopes is their mass which, in the case of $_{92}U^{235}$ and $_{92}U^{238}$, amounts to approximately three atomic mass units.

Scientists working on atomic bomb research discovered several methods for separating uranium isotopes. One method involves gaseous diffusion. This depends on the slight difference in the rate of diffusion through a porous membrane of two hexafluorides of uranium $_{92}U^{235}F_6$ and $_{92}U^{238}F_6$. Another method is electromagnetic. The slight difference in mass causes the two nuclei to follow different paths when deflected by a strong electromagnetic field. This effects a separation.

14. The atomic bomb. $_{92}U^{235}$ undergoes fission when bombarded with neutrons. Plutonium also undergoes fission when bombarded with neutrons. These are the two active materials which have been used in atomic bombs.

We have already described how $_{92}U^{235}$ is separated from $_{92}U^{238}$. Plutonium, being a new element with different properties, can be separated from uranium by chemical means.

When critical sizes of either of these materials are brought together to sustain a rapidly accelerating chain reaction, the atoms undergo fission almost instantaneously. They liberate tremendous energy in a violent explosion which produces terrible and widespread devastation.

Atomic bomb tests have been conducted by the United States to determine the destruction wrought by these bombs. The effects of the radioactivity produced in the target area have also been studied. These topics are discussed more fully in Section 20.

15. Other types of nuclear reactors. *1. Hanford Reactors.* These reactors are located on the Columbia River at Hanford, Washington, and are primarily used for producing $_{94}Pu^{239}$ from $_{92}U^{238}$ by neutrons from the fission of $_{92}U^{235}$ in natural uranium. They are called *converter reactors* because they use one type of fissionable material to produce a nearly equal quantity of another fissionable material. The fuel is natural uranium. The moderator is graphite. Because of some difficulties in air cooling encountered in the construction of the Oak Ridge reactor, which was to serve as a model for the Hanford reactors, the Hanford reactors use water as the coolant. At Hanford are also located the facilities for remote control processing to recover the plutonium being produced in gram quantities, from tons of material including uranium and numerous fission products. The plutonium is being stockpiled for use in nuclear weapons.

Fig. 39-11. **An aerial view of one of the Hanford reactors which produce** $_{94}Pu^{239}$ **from** $_{92}U^{239}$**. These reactors are cooled with water from the Columbia River.** (Johnson)

2. Savannah River Reactor. The Savannah River reactor is a high-power reactor fueled with natural uranium, but using deuterium oxide D_2O, as a moderator. This is a better moderator than either graphite or water because it absorbs fewer neutrons, yet a small amount slows down neutrons effectively. Because of this, deuterium oxide moderated reactors require less uranium and may be made much smaller. However, the high cost of deuterium oxide limits its use.

3. Materials Testing Reactor. This reactor, located near Arco, Idaho, uses $_{92}U^{235}$ as fuel, and water as moderator and coolant. It is controlled by cadmium rods. It produces neutrons at a very high rate. This reactor is used for testing the behavior of various materials under very high radioactivity.

4. Experimental Breeder Reactor. This reactor is also located near Arco, Idaho. It contains a central core of $_{92}U^{235}$ surrounded by natural uranium metal. The coolant is a liquid alloy of sodium and potassium. No moderator is used. The purpose of a breeder reactor is to make fissionable material, $_{94}Pu^{239}$, for example, at a greater rate than the $_{92}U^{235}$ used as fuel is consumed. This can be done by cutting down the loss of neutrons by using fast neutrons and eliminating the moderator which would absorb some neutrons. Since only 2.5 neutrons, on an average, are released by the fission of one $_{92}U^{235}$ nucleus, and 1.0 of these neutrons is needed to carry on the chain reaction, only 1.5 neutrons, on an average, remain to produce plutonium. If there were no loss of neutrons, 1.5 $_{94}Pu^{239}$ atoms, on an average, would be formed from the fission of 1.0 $_{92}U^{235}$ nucleus— a production of fissionable material at a rate greater than the consumption of the fissionable $_{92}U^{235}$ fuel. It has been reported that such a breeder reaction is feasible, though not with this theoretical efficiency. The use of $_{94}Pu^{239}$ to produce more $_{94}Pu^{239}$ from $_{92}U^{238}$ is a more promising breeder reaction since each $_{94}Pu^{239}$ nucleus which undergoes fission produces, on an average, 3.0 neutrons. But, of course, $_{94}Pu^{239}$ can only be made at first by the bombardment of $_{92}U^{238}$ by slow neutrons that result from the fission of $_{92}U^{235}$ nuclei.

5. *Raleigh Reactor.* The Raleigh reactor at North Carolina State College is an example of a *homogeneous reactor,* in which the fuel is dissolved in the moderator. The fuel for the reactor is UO_2SO_4, uranyl sulfate, in which all the uranium is the $_{92}U^{235}$ isotope. The uranyl sulfate is dissolved in water which acts as a moderator. Boron carbide rods are used to control the reactor, which is operated at about 80° C. It is cooled by circulation of water through stainless-steel coils placed in the uranyl sulfate solution. This reactor is used for research purposes.

16. Power production from nuclear reactors. A nuclear reactor can serve as a source of heat energy, just as a coal, oil, or gas fire does. Moreover, the relatively greater amount of energy available from the world supply of nuclear fuels as compared with the diminishing supply of coal and petroleum makes nuclear fuels worth developing for future use.

Several nuclear power plants for the generation of electricity are planned or in operation in the United States, as well as in Canada, Great Britain, Russia, and several other countries. The first large nuclear power plant in the United States is located at Shippingport, near Pittsburgh, Pennsylvania.

This power plant uses a reactor containing natural uranium enriched with $_{92}U^{235}$ as fuel. The fuel rods are surrounded by a blanket of rods of natural uranium oxide. The control rods are of hafnium metal. The moderator and heat transfer fluid is pressurized water, which is circulated between the reactor core and the steam generators. The operating temperature of the reactor is approximately 525° F, with a pressure of about 2000 lb/in².

The hot pressurized water from the reactor is pumped through the steam generators where the heat of the pressurized water converts other water to steam under pressure. The pressurized water, cooled by the transfer of its heat to produce steam, is returned to the reactor for reheating. The steam formed in the heat exchangers drives the turbines, which in turn, drive the generators. The steam, after passage through the turbines, is condensed, and returned to the steam generators to be converted to steam once again.

17. The atomic submarine. The first practical use of a reactor for power production was in the atomic submarine, U.S.S. *Nautilus.* The heat generated by this reactor is used to increase the temperature of water which is kept under pressure to prevent it from changing into steam. This superheated, pressurized water is pumped to a heat exchanger where it gives up some of its heat to other water, converting it into steam. The pressurized water returns to the reactor for reheating. The steam produced in the outer jacket of the heat exchanger drives the steam turbine which runs the propellers. The spent steam from the turbine is condensed and pumped back to the heat exchanger. Using atomic power, submarines may cruise rapidly for long distances without surfacing. The United States has a rapidly growing fleet of atomic submarines and atom-powered surface vessels.

18. Fusion reactions—the sun. Earlier in the chapter (Section 1) we indi-

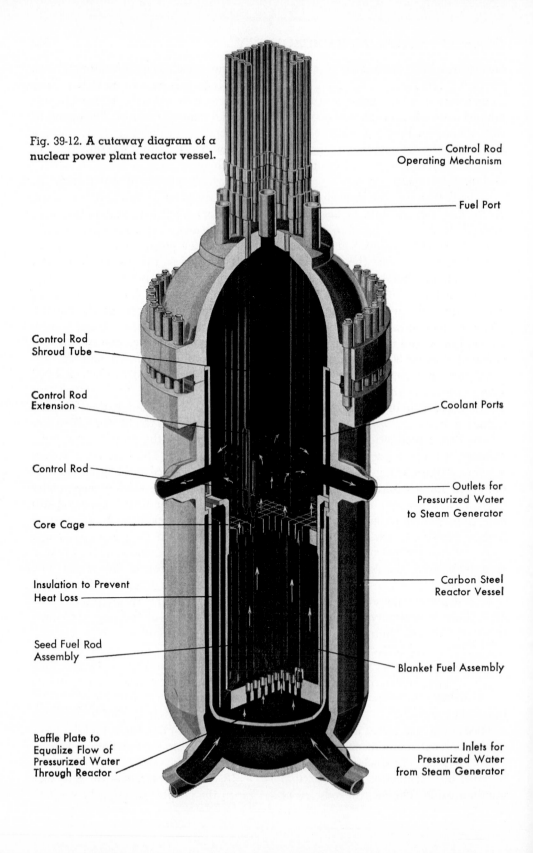

Fig. 39-12. **A cutaway diagram of a nuclear power plant reactor vessel.**

Control Rod Operating Mechanism

Fuel Port

Control Rod Shroud Tube

Control Rod Extension

Control Rod

Core Cage

Insulation to Prevent Heat Loss

Seed Fuel Rod Assembly

Baffle Plate to Equalize Flow of Pressurized Water Through Reactor

Coolant Ports

Outlets for Pressurized Water to Steam Generator

Carbon Steel Reactor Vessel

Blanket Fuel Assembly

Inlets for Pressurized Water from Steam Generator

cated that increased nuclear stability could be produced by combining lightweight nuclei to form heavier nuclei. This process was defined as *fusion.*

Fusion reactions are undoubtedly the source of the sun's energy. There are probably two such reactions going on in the sun, one at the very hot central region of the sun's interior, and another in the larger portion of the sun which is at a slightly lower temperature. Although these two reactions have a different sequence of intermediate reactions, their net effect is the combination of four hydrogen nuclei to form a helium nucleus, with a loss of mass and corresponding production of energy.

19. The hydrogen bomb. The thermonuclear bomb, sometimes called the hydrogen bomb, or H-bomb, produces energy by a fusion reaction. It can be made much more destructive than an atomic bomb because more energy is liberated in a fusion reaction than in a fission reaction, and the quantities of reacting materials may be made much larger, in fact they are theoretically unlimited.

One possible reaction in a hydrogen bomb is the formation of alpha particles and tremendous energy from a compound of lithium and hydrogen. This compound may be formed of the particular isotopes $_3Li^6$ and $_1H^2$. Such a fusion reaction can be started only by subjecting $_3Li^6{}_1H^2$ to extremely high temperature and pressure. These conditions are met by using an atomic bomb as the detonator to set off the hydrogen bomb.

Current research indicates that fusion reactions may be carried out at lower temperatures. If so, this may be another possible source of energy for power generation.

20. The destructive effects of nuclear weapons. The destructive effects of an atomic bomb may be roughly divided into four types. The extent of the damage produced by the explosion of an atomic bomb equivalent to 20,000 tons of T.N.T. in air at the height required to produce maximum damage is given for each type.

1. The shock wave, or blast effect. The shock wave produces virtually complete destruction over an area 0.5 mile in radius from the target zone. Severe damage extends for about 1 mile from the target, while partial damage is found up to about 2 miles from the target.

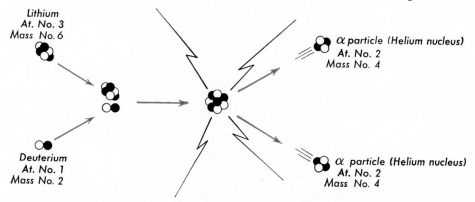

Fig. 39-13. **This diagram shows the reaction in which lithium and deuterium undergo fusion and form helium nuclei. This process yields large amounts of energy.**

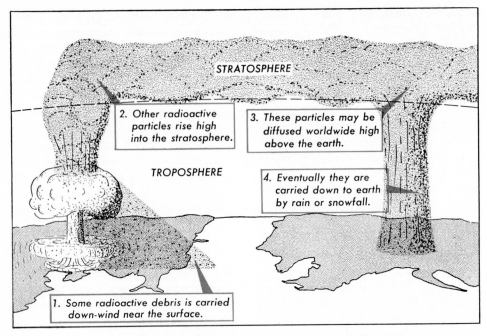

STRATOSPHERE

2. Other radioactive particles rise high into the stratosphere.

3. These particles may be diffused worldwide high above the earth.

TROPOSPHERE

4. Eventually they are carried down to earth by rain or snowfall.

1. Some radioactive debris is carried down-wind near the surface.

Fig. 39-14. **The radioactive fall-out pattern from a large nuclear weapon.**

2. *The thermal radiation,* or flash effect. The thermal (heat) radiation heats the surface of materials in the direct target area to about 3000° C. Serious skin burns and fires are found up to a radius of about 1 mile, while significant amounts of heat are received as far as 2 miles from the target. Even at 30 to 40 miles from the explosion, the light given out temporarily blinds a person if he looks directly at it.

3. *The nuclear radiations.* Nuclear radiations such as gamma rays and neutrons destroy living tissues. This type of damage is severe within a 0.5-mile radius of the target area, and significant out to a 1-mile radius of the target area.

4. *The residual radioactivity.* For a 20,000 ton T.N.T. equivalent bomb, detonated in the air, the residual radioactivity is negligible. However, for a surface bomb detonation, this would be a hazard of only temporary duration.

More powerful hydrogen bombs, equivalent to between 10 and 20 million tons of T.N.T., produce the same types of destructive effects. They are, however, more serious. The shock wave produces damage or partial damage to structures up to 10 miles from the target area. The thermal radiation from such a bomb extends up to 20 miles from the target area. The nuclear radiations from the blast itself produce destructive effects a few miles from the blast scene. A much more serious threat to people far from the scene of the blast may be produced by a hydrogen bomb. This threat is *radioactive fall-out.*

A powerful hydrogen bomb explosion can blow radioactive particles high into the stratosphere, over 30,000 feet above the surface of the earth. Because of atmospheric conditions in the strato-

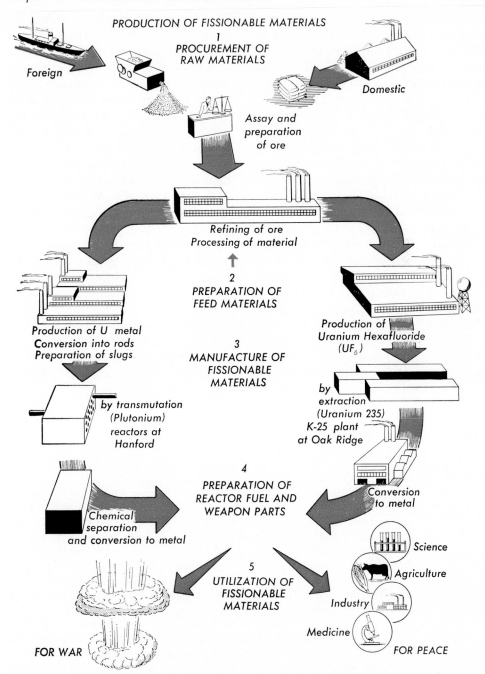

PRODUCTION OF FISSIONABLE MATERIALS

1
PROCUREMENT OF
RAW MATERIALS

Foreign

Domestic

Assay and
preparation
of ore

Refining of ore
Processing of material

2
PREPARATION OF
FEED MATERIALS

Production of U metal
Conversion into rods
Preparation of slugs

3
MANUFACTURE OF
FISSIONABLE
MATERIALS

Production of
Uranium Hexafluoride
(UF$_6$)

by transmutation
(Plutonium)
reactors at
Hanford

by
extraction
(Uranium 235)
K-25 plant
at Oak Ridge

4
PREPARATION OF
REACTOR FUEL AND
WEAPON PARTS

Conversion
to metal

Chemical
separation
and conversion to metal

5
UTILIZATION OF
FISSIONABLE
MATERIALS

Science

Agriculture

Industry

Medicine

FOR WAR

FOR PEACE

Fig. 39-15. **This flow chart shows how fissionable materials are produced.**

sphere, small particles of radioactive material may remain there for as long as ten years. During this time, the particles can become thoroughly mixed and be uniformly distributed in the stratosphere over all parts of the earth. Eventually the particles fall back to the surface of the earth.

A shower of intensely radioactive particles may produce severe, or perhaps fatal, burns. If radioactive particles are eaten with food, internal damage may be produced in the body. Some of the most serious types of internal damage are those which prevent the production of blood corpuscles or of disease-fighting antibodies. Radiation damage may also affect the hereditary characteristics transmitted from one generation of living things to the next.

One of the radioactive isotopes which may be produced in a nuclear explosion is $_{38}Sr^{90}$, sometimes called strontium-90.

This is a fairly long-lived radioactive isotope with a half-life of about 27 years. If it is showered down on the earth, even in very small concentrations, it is taken up from the soil by plants. Animals eating these plants collect more and more $_{38}Sr^{90}$ in their bodies. Then when a person drinks milk, eats meat, or uses other animal products, he may take into his body a much greater quantity of $_{38}Sr^{90}$ than would be showered down on him as an aftermath of a nuclear explosion. The $_{38}Sr^{90}$ accumulates in his bones because it is chemically similar to calcium, an important element in the materials forming the body skeleton. As it becomes more concentrated in the bones, $_{38}Sr^{90}$ can cause cancer, destroy tissues, and ultimately produce death. While estimates differ, many scientists believe that the amount of $_{38}Sr^{90}$ already produced by nuclear explosions is so small as not yet to become a serious hazard.

SUMMARY

The binding energy of a nucleus holds the protons and neutrons together in the nucleus. The lightest and heaviest elements have the smallest binding energies, and their nuclei are least stable. Elements of intermediate mass have larger binding energies, and their nuclei are more stable. There are four ways in which nuclei may become more stable: 1. by radioactive decomposition; 2 by nuclear disintegration; 3. by fission; and 4. by fusion.

The cyclotron is an electromagnetic device for accelerating protons and deuterons in a spiral path. Other particle accelerating devices are the betatron, the synchroton, and the linear accelerator.

When bombarded with slow neutrons, a $_{92}U^{238}$ nucleus may capture a neutron, and ultimately be transformed into $_{94}Pu^{239}$. Stable atoms may be made artificially radioactive by bombardment with deuterons or neutrons. Artificial radioactive isotopes are used as tracers, in medicine, and in research.

When $_{92}U^{235}$ is bombarded with slow neutrons, it undergoes fission. Fission is the break-up of a heavy nucleus into medium-weight parts. A chain reaction is one in which the material or energy which initiates the reaction is also one of the products. Uranium isotopes may be separated by gaseous diffusion and by electromagnetic methods.

A nuclear reactor is a device in which the controlled fission of radioactive material produces new radioactive substances and energy. Scientists have devised various types of reactors using different kinds of fuels, moderators, and cooling agents. Nuclear reactors furnish heat energy for power.

A fusion reaction is one in which two light nuclei combine to form a heavier, more stable nucleus. Fusion reactions produce the sun's heat and light, and produce the destructive effects of hydrogen bombs. The destructive effects of atomic bombs may be due to the shock wave, to thermal radiation, to nuclear radiations, and to the residual radioactivity. Hydrogen bombs present the added hazard of radioactive fall-out because they blow radioactive materials high into the stratosphere. Radioactive fall-out is the showering down of radioactive particles which were carried high into the air by a nuclear explosion.

TEST YOURSELF ON THESE TERMS

artificial radioactivity	electron-volt	nuclear reactor
atomic bomb	fission	radioactive decomposi-
atomic mass	fusion	tion
atomic submarine	homogeneous reactor	radioactive fall-out
betatron	hydrogen bomb	radioactive tracer
binding energy	linear accelerator	residual radioactivity
breeder reactor	mass defect	shock wave
chain reaction	materials testing reactor	stability of a nucleus
control rod	moderator	strontium-90
converter reactor	nuclear disintegration	synchroton
critical size	nuclear fuel	thermal radiation
cyclotron	nuclear radiations	transuranium element

QUESTIONS

Group A

1. Name the four types of nuclear reactions which produce more stable nuclei.
2. In what ways do natural radioactive decompositions produce more stable nuclei?
3. How were neutrons first detected as nuclear particles?
4. Why are neutrons better particles than protons or alpha particles for bombarding atomic nuclei?
5. What may happen to a neutron that is fired at the nucleus of an atom?
6. What are the names and atomic numbers of the transuranium elements?
7. For what purposes are radioactive isotopes used?
8. (*a*) What are the naturally-occurring isotopes of uranium? (*b*) What is their relative abundance?
9. (*a*) What is fission? (*b*) How is it produced in $_{92}U^{235}$?

10. What is meant by the *critical size* of a reactor?
11. Why must a nuclear reactor be continually cooled?
12. Why is it difficult to separate isotopes?
13. What is the principal difference between the action in a nuclear reactor and in an atomic bomb?
14. What distinguishing feature is characteristic of a homogeneous reactor?
15. What reaction produces the sun's energy? To what man-made reaction is this similar?
16. What is radioactive fall-out?

Group B

17. (*a*) Which kinds of elements have the smallest binding energy? (*b*) Which kind has the largest binding energy? (*c*) How does the binding energy affect the stability of a nucleus?
18. (*a*) Who produced the first nuclear disintegration? (*b*) Write the equation for this reaction.
19. How was Einstein's equation for the relationship between matter and energy, $E = mc^2$, proved to be correct?
20. (*a*) Describe the path of the accelerated particles in a cyclotron. (*b*) What causes them to take this path?
21. Explain the changes occurring in the nucleus by which $_{94}Pu^{239}$ is produced from $_{92}U^{238}$.
22. (*a*) How are artificially-radioactive isotopes prepared? (*b*) Write a nuclear equation to show the preparation of such an atom. (*c*) What use is made of the atom whose preparation you have shown in this nuclear equation?
23. (*a*) Describe a chain reaction. (*b*) How does the fission of $_{92}U^{235}$ produce a chain reaction?
24. How is a uranium-graphite reactor constructed?
25. (*a*) What materials are used as coolants for nuclear reactors? (*b*) As moderators? (*c*) As control rods?
26. (*a*) What ways have been devised for separating uranium isotopes? (*b*) Are any of these chemical methods? (*c*) Why?
27. Give two reasons why plutonium is a more desirable fissionable material than $_{92}U^{235}$.
28. (*a*) What is the function of a converter reactor? (*b*) Of a breeder reactor?
29. Describe the energy transformations and transfers which occur in a nuclear power plant.
30. Give two reasons why a hydrogen bomb may be more powerful than an atomic bomb.
31. Describe the various types of destructive effects produced by atomic bombs.
32. In what way is $_{38}Sr^{90}$ a menace to civilization?
33. Why is the radiation from a nuclear weapon dangerous?
★ 34. What factors affect the stability of a nucleus?
★ 35. How does each type of nuclear reaction produce more stable nuclei?

SOME THINGS FOR YOU TO DO

1. Make a mousetrap model to show a chain reaction. You will need about 20 small mousetraps, and twice as many rubber stoppers. Set the mouse-traps, and place two rubber stoppers over each trap wire, so they will be shot off when that trap is sprung. Start the chain reaction by setting off one trap. The rubber stoppers shot off from this trap should set off the other traps in ever increasing numbers until they are all sprung.
2. Prepare a report on new nuclear power developments.
3. From recent newspaper and magazine articles compile a list of uses of radioactive isotopes.

CHECK YOUR PROGRESS IN CHEMISTRY

1. What are five statements that summarize the atomic theory?
2. What do we mean when we say that barium has an atomic weight of 137.36?
3. Define the following terms: (*a*) proton; (*b*) electron; (*c*) neutron; (*d*) nucleus; (*e*) the L shell; (*f*) valence electrons; (*g*) isotopes.
4. Explain the difference between *electrovalence* and *covalence*.
5. How do the three isotopes of hydrogen differ?
6. Explain how $_{92}U^{235}$ can be separated from $_{92}U^{238}$ by the gaseous diffu-sion process.
7. Explain why calcium has an oxidation number of $+2$ and fluorine an oxidation number of -1.
8. What do we mean by a negative radical, such as sulfate?
9. How do the nuclei of elements above number 83 differ from most of the nuclei of lower atomic number?
10. What is the nature of the radiation emitted by radium?
11. What is the source of at least some of the atoms of lead in the ground?
12. Rutherford bombarded nitrogen with alpha particles and obtained pro-tons and an isotope of oxygen. Write the equation for this transmuta-tion.
13. Explain why it is impossible to find a chunk of pure radium compound in the ground.
14. What is the word equation for the relation between matter and energy?
15. Write three nuclear equations to show how plutonium is obtained from $_{92}U^{238}$.
16. Write the equation to show the fission of $_{92}U^{235}$ into barium and krypton.
17. Why is it unlikely that element 98, californium, will ever be a common element?
18. Assuming that the seventh period of the Periodic Table, like the sixth, would be complete with 32 elements, how many elements would then be theoretically possible?
19. Why do the elements of the lanthanide series have very similar prop-erties?
20. What do we mean by amphiprotic elements?

CHALLENGING YOUR KNOWLEDGE

1. A sample of radium ore contained 1,000,000,000 atoms of radium 16,000 years ago. Assuming the half-life of radium to be 1600 years, how many of these atoms are still radium atoms today?

2. Why is there, at present, a poor prospect for using nuclear fission for providing the necessary power for driving our automobiles?

3. Do you think there is a possibility that the seventh period of elements in the Periodic Table was complete at some time in the history of the world? If so, why do we not usually find elements above number 92 now in the world?

4. Indicating the isotopes of hydrogen and oxygen as $_1H^1$, $_1H^2$, $_1H^3$, and $_8O^{16}$, $_8O^{17}$, $_8O^{18}$, write the formulas for the different kinds of water molecules theoretically possible.

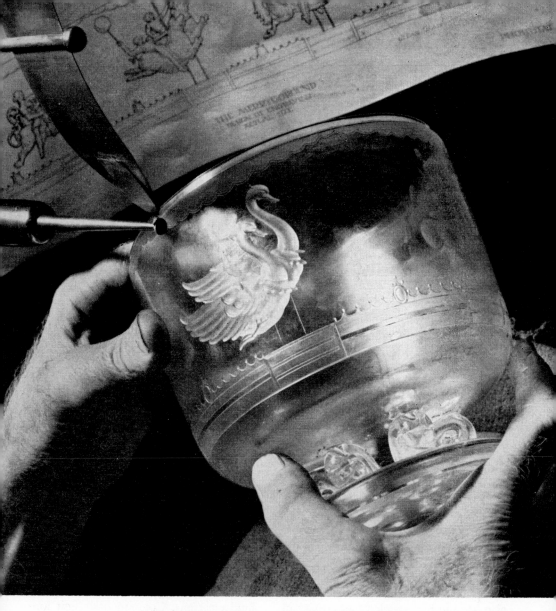

Unit 14 · BORON AND SILICON

Boron, Silicon, and Glass

Chapter 40 · BORON, SILICON, AND GLASS

1. Boron and silicon are used in glass. The rather similar small radii of the atoms of boron and silicon enables them to be used somewhat interchangeably in glass even though boron is a member of Group III of the Periodic Table and silicon belongs in Group IV. A situation similar to this was described in Chapter 34 in connection with beryllium and aluminum.

Boron atoms are small, their atomic radii being only 0.80Å. Their valence electrons are quite tightly bound, giving boron a relatively high ionization energy for a Group III element. Boron also has the highest electronegativity of any element in Group III. A consideration of these characteristics indicates that boron is a metalloid which forms only covalent bonds with other atoms. At low temperatures boron is a poor conductor of electricity; but as the temperature is raised and its electrons have more kinetic energy, the conductivity of boron increases. This behavior is typical of a *semiconductor*.

Silicon atoms, with four valence electrons, crystallize with a tetrahedral bond arrangement similar to that of carbon atoms in diamond. Atoms of silicon also have small atomic radii and tightly held electrons. Consequently their ion-

VOCABULARY

Annealing. The process of heating a material above a certain temperature and then slowly cooling it in order to decrease its hardness and brittleness.

Flux. A substance used to remove the oxide coating from a metallic surface prior to soldering or welding.

Glass. An amorphous material, usually transparent, consisting ordinarily of a mixture of silicates.

Silicone. A compound containing a chain of alternate silicon and oxygen atoms, with organic groups attached to the silicon atoms.

Fig. 40-1. **A view of Searles Lake, California. This dry lake bed is 30 square miles in area and is a source of borax as well as many other chemical raw materials. These materials are extracted from the brine pumped from deposits beneath.** (General Electric)

ization energy and electronegativity are fairly high. Silicon is a metalloid which forms covalent bonds when combining with all other elements, except possibly the halogens. The electric conductivity of silicon is similar to that of boron; it, too, is a semiconductor. Unlike carbon, silicon forms only single bonds, and forms silicon-oxygen bonds in preference to silicon-silicon or silicon-hydrogen bonds.

1. BORON AND ITS COMPOUNDS

2. The occurrence and preparation of boron. Boron is not found as the free element, but it can be isolated in reasonably pure form by reducing boron trichloride with hydrogen at a high tem-

perature. Elementary boron has little commercial value; hence chemists seldom separate it from its compounds.

Colemanite, a hydrated borate of calcium which is given the formula $Ca_2B_6O_{11} \cdot 5 H_2O$, is found in the desert regions of California and Nevada. Sodium tetraborate, $Na_2B_4O_7 \cdot 4 H_2O$, is found as the mineral *kernite* in California, also. The salt brines of Searles Lake, California, yield most of the commercial supply of boron compounds today. When calcium borate is treated with sodium carbonate, sodium tetraborate, or *borax*, is produced. Some hot springs contain small amounts of boric acid, H_3BO_3, in solution.

3. Useful compounds of boron. Boron carbide, B_4C, known as Norbide, is an extremely hard abrasive made by combining boron with carbon in an elec-

CHARACTERISTICS OF BORON AND SILICON

Element	Atomic Number	Atomic Weight	Electron Configuration	Oxidation Numbers	Melting Point, °C	Boiling Point, °C	Density, g/cm³
Boron	5	10.811	2, 3	$+3$	2300	2550	2.33
Silicon	14	28.086	2, 8, 4	$+2, +4, -4$	1420	2355	2.42

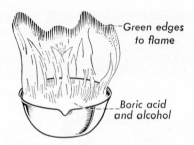

Fig. 40-2. **An alcohol flame has green edges when boric acid is present. This serves as a test for boric acid.**

tric furnace. The form of boron nitride called Borazon, made by combining boron and nitrogen under extreme heat and pressure, is the hardest synthetic material known. It is equal in hardness to the diamond. Alloys of boron with iron or manganese are used to increase the hardness of steel.

Boric acid can be prepared by adding sulfuric acid to a concentrated solution of sodium tetraborate in water. The acid is only moderately soluble and separates as colorless, lustrous scales. It is such a weak acid that 4% solutions of it may be introduced into the eye with safety. It is a mild antiseptic. A test for boric acid depends on the fact that boric acid colors an alcohol flame green (see Fig. 40-2).

Borax is sodium tetraborate with the formula $Na_2B_4O_7 \cdot 10\ H_2O$. It is used alone and in washing powders as a water softener. Because it dissolves metallic oxides leaving a clean metallic surface, it is also used as a *flux* for welding metals. The borates of certain metals are used in making glazes and enamels. Large amounts of boron compounds are used to make borosilicate glass, of which Pyrex is an example.

Boron combines with hydrogen to form several boron hydrides such as B_2H_6, diborane, and B_4H_{10}, tetraborane.

Methyl and ethyl groups may be substituted for the hydrogen atoms in these compounds. These boron compounds have negative heats of formation. Thus, when they are oxidized, they liberate unusually large amounts of energy.

4. Borax beads are used to identify some metals. If a platinum wire with a loop on one end is dipped in powdered borax and held in a flame, the borax swells and then fuses to a clear, glass-like bead. If such a bead is further heated in an oxidizing blowpipe flame with a tiny speck of metal or metallic compound, the metallic oxide formed reacts with the borax bead, and may impart to the bead a characteristic color. The color depends on the kind of metal used. For example, cobalt colors such a bead *blue*; chromium produces a *green* bead; and nickel yields a *brown* bead. This borax bead test is useful in identifying certain metals. The chemical reactions involved and the structure of the colored compounds formed are not well understood.

2. SILICON AND ITS COMPOUNDS

5. The occurrence and preparation of silicon. Silicon ranks second in abundance by weight among the elements of the earth's crust; but, as in the case of boron, it does not occur free in nature. Silicon dioxide is reduced to elementary silicon by carbon in an electric furnace. The chief use for elementary silicon is in an alloy with iron, called *ferrosilicon*, for making silicon steel. Silicon is used in the production of silicones and specially purified silicon is used in heavy-duty transistors and current rectifiers.

The compounds of silicon, such as

sand, sandstone, quartz, and many different silicate rocks are widely distributed in nature. It is the abundance of these compounds that gives silicon its high rank among the elements of the earth's crust.

6. Silica is a common mineral compound. Silicon dioxide, SiO_2, commonly called *silica*, is one of the most widely distributed mineral compounds in the world. It is found in many forms, four of which are given below.

1. As sand. Ordinary sand is silicon dioxide. Layers of sand of varying thickness lie under the topsoil of a large portion of all the continents. Great quantities of sand are used in making glass. It is mixed with lime and water to make mortar, and with crushed stone and cement in making concrete. It is also used for lining molds into which molten iron is poured in making castings.

Scouring soaps or powders usually contain powdered soap, washing soda, and powdered silica, which is gritty enough for scouring purposes.

Fig. 40-3. **Quartz apparatus such as this can be heated red hot and then plunged into cold water without breaking.** (Corning Glass Works)

2. In the mineral sandstone. This mineral is a sedimentary rock formed under water by particles of sand which are bound together by a kind of natural cement. It is used as a building stone.

3. As quartz. The transparent crystalline variety of silica is known as quartz. Quartz crystals consist of tetrahedra with a central silicon atom bonded to four oxygen atoms at the corners. Each oxygen atom serves as the corner of two such tetrahedra. Quartz is a fairly hard mineral because in order to break it, some strong silicon-oxygen bonds must be broken. Pure *rock crystal* is colorless, but traces of impurities impart different colors to such forms of quartz as amethyst, smoky quartz, rose quartz, and milky quartz.

4. As amorphous silica. Such common minerals as flint, jasper, chalcedony, sard, carnelian, onyx, and agate consist largely of silica. Onyx and agate are made up of bands of different colors. Fine specimens of crystallized and amorphous silica are used as semiprecious gems.

7. The production of quartzware. Quartz may be softened in an oxyhydrogen blowtorch and fashioned into tubing, crucibles, and other laboratory apparatus. Quartz is also melted in a graphite crucible in an electric furnace and then extruded from the furnace under high pressure. This material is no longer crystalline because the regularity of the silicon-oxygen tetrahedra has been somewhat disturbed by the heating. The randomness of this arrangement resembles that of a liquid. Thus such fused quartz is a super-cooled liquid, or a glass.

Quartz transmits ultraviolet rays much better than glass does. It is not so easily acted upon by acids and alkalies as ordinary glassware. Because it has a very low coefficient of expansion, about one-

Fig. 40-4. **Resistance electric furnaces used for producing silicon carbide.** (Carborundum)

eighteenth that of glass, it is not likely to break even if it is heated or cooled suddenly.

8. The properties of silica. Silicon dioxide is a hard solid which can be fused with difficulty at a high temperature. It is insoluble in water and ordinary acids, but hydrofluoric acid reacts with it, as follows:

$$SiO_2 + 2 H_2F_2 \rightarrow SiF_4 \uparrow + 2 H_2O$$

The silicon tetrafluoride, SiF_4, which is formed by the reaction, is volatile and escapes into the air. Sodium carbonate reacts with silica at high temperatures and forms sodium silicate.

$$Na_2CO_3 + SiO_2 \rightarrow Na_2SiO_3 + CO_2 \uparrow$$

9. Silicic acid and silica gel. Many acids of silicon are known but none are important compounds. Many of the salts of the different silicic acids are found in natural minerals. The simplest silicic acid has the formula H_2SiO_3, or $SiO_2 \cdot H_2O$. It is formed as a jelly-like precipitate when an acid such as hydrochloric acid is added to a solution of sodium silicate, Na_2SiO_3. If this jelly-like precipitate is carefully heated, a porous solid, called *silica gel*, is produced. Silica gel is used for adsorbing various gases. When saturated, the adsorbed gases can be driven off by heating, and the silica gel is ready for use again. Silica gel is also used in the refining of petroleum. Although silicic acid yields silicon dioxide and water when it is heated, the reaction is not reversible. It is not possible to add water to silicon dioxide and form silicic acid.

10. Water glass. Sodium silicate and potassium silicate are the only water-soluble silicates. A water solution of sodium silicate, Na_2SiO_3, is called *water glass*. As usually prepared for the market, water glass is a thick, syrupy solution about 1.3 times as dense as water. It is used as a filler in laundry soap, as a binder in abrasive wheels and furnace linings, for fireproofing materials, and as an adhesive in the manufacture of wallboards and corrugated paper boards for cartons.

11. Silicones. Silicon resembles carbon in the ability of its atoms to link together to form chains. A group of compounds, called *silicones*, has alternate silicon and oxygen atoms, with hydrocarbon groups attached to the silicon atoms. Thus the silicones are part organic and part inorganic. By using different hydrocarbon groups, a variety of silicones can be produced. One silicone chain has the structure

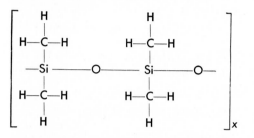

The silicones are not much affected by heat, have excellent electric insulating properties, and are water repellents. Some silicones are oils or greases which may be used as lubricants. Silicon varnishes are used to coat wires for the windings of electric motors. This permits the electric motor to operate at high temperatures without short circuits. Cloth that has been treated with a silicone repels water. Silicones are used in automobile and furniture polishes.

12. Silicon carbide. This compound, SiC, is made by heating sand and coke in an electric furnace. Salt is usually added to the mixture to facilitate fusion, and sawdust is also used to make it more porous. The main reaction is:

$$SiO_2 + 3\,C \rightarrow SiC + 2\,CO \uparrow$$

The charge is heated for about 36 hours. Then the furnace is allowed to cool. Beautiful, iridescent crystals of silicon carbide are formed surrounding the central core. The crystals are crushed, graded to size by sifting through fine sieves, mixed with a binder, and manufactured into grinding wheels and sharpening stones. Silicon carbide has a structure resembling diamond but with alternate carbon atoms replaced by silicon atoms. The rigid structure and strong covalent bonds give it great hardness.

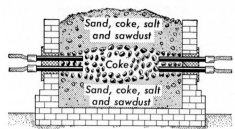

Fig. 40-5. **A sectional view of an electric furnace which is used for making carborundum.**

Carborundum is a crystalline form of silicon carbide with extreme hardness. It is one of the hardest artificial compounds and is an excellent abrasive used for grinding and polishing metals. *Crystolon*, a similar abrasive, is made into hones, polishing cloths, and grinding wheels.

3. GLASS MANUFACTURE

13. The nature of glass. Glass was made by the Egyptians many centuries before the Christian era. It is hard and very brittle when cold but softens when heated. It becomes so plastic when very hot that it can be blown, rolled, or pressed into any shape. It is transparent and almost entirely insoluble in water.

Fig. 40-6. **Crystals of silicon carbide. (Carborundum)**

Ordinary glass is composed of the silicates of sodium and calcium. It is often spoken of as a mixture of these compounds, but it is probably a solid solution of these silicates in each other. In making the many different kinds of glass, potassium may be substituted for sodium. Barium, lead, aluminum, boron, and even zinc may be substituted for all or part of the calcium or silicon.

14. The manufacture of glass.

1. The raw materials. For making *ordinary glass*, the raw materials are sand, limestone, and sodium carbonate. A certain proportion of old, broken glass, known as *cullet*, is added to the batch when it is available. The cullet uses up what would otherwise be a waste material, and it also makes the whole batch melt more rapidly. The mixture is heated in a long, tank-like furnace to a temperature of about 2500° F by the combustion of fuel gas. The process is continuous, raw materials being dumped in at one end and liquid glass being withdrawn from the farther end. Some of the sand reacts with the limestone forming calcium silicate and carbon dioxide, as follows:

$$CaCO_3 + SiO_2 \rightarrow CaSiO_3 + CO_2 \uparrow$$

The rest of the sand reacts with the sodium carbonate according to the following equation:

$$Na_2CO_3 + SiO_2 \rightarrow Na_2SiO_3 + CO_2 \uparrow$$

The material passes through the furnace very slowly. Several days elapse from the time the raw materials are added before the liquid glass is ready to be withdrawn. This insures the elimination of all bubbles of carbon dioxide which were produced in the glass-making reactions and which would make flaws in the finished glass.

Optical glass is made by heating sand, potassium carbonate, and lead oxide in pots made of fire clay. Such glass is

Fig. 40-7. These workmen are using long steel bars to push sand, limestone, sodium carbonate, and cullet from the hoppers into the melting tank during the production of glass. (Libbey Owens Ford)

made in small batches of a few hundred pounds each. Glass for cut glass tableware is also made in small batches from the same raw materials in a fire-clay pot.

Pyrex glass is made in a tank furnace by fusing sand, borax, and aluminum oxide. It is a sodium aluminum borosilicate glass and has a coefficient of expansion only one-third that of ordinary, soda-lime glass. While soda-lime glass may be softened in a Bunsen burner flame, Pyrex glass has a much higher softening temperature and can be worked only in the flame of a blast lamp.

2. *The working of glass.* In making hand-blown glass, the glass-blower inserts one end of a long metal blowpipe into a pot of molten glass. He rolls the blowpipe around until the required amount of glass has adhered to the end of the pipe. Then he blows a bubble in the glass and fashions it into the desired shape. Sometimes he blows the bubble into a mold to give the object its finished form. However, experienced glassblowers make water goblets and other objects without the aid of a mold. They use a few simple tools, such as a paddle and a rounded rod, to shape the article. The surplus glass is cut off by shears while it is still plastic. Certain types of laboratory glassware and the better grades of table glass are still made by the hand-blown process.

The greatest tonnage of products in the glass industry is now machine made. Bottles are produced in large numbers by an intricate machine that duplicates hand-blowing in molds. Compressed air is used to blow the bubbles. Window glass is made by lowering a horizontal rod into the molten glass in the furnace. As the rod is drawn vertically upward, the glass clings to the rod and forms a sheet. The thickness of the sheet of glass can be regulated by controlling the rate

Fig. 40-8. **Glassblowers are skilled craftsmen who with a few simple tools fashion glass articles very accurately.** (Corning Glass Works)

at which the rod is elevated and the temperature of the molten glass in the furnace. Plate glass is made by extruding a wide strip of glass directly from the furnace. In one continuous operation, the glass is cooled, cut, ground, and polished. The surfaces of plate glass are smooth and parallel. Objects are viewed

Fig. 40-9. **This man is grinding a large glass cylinder, used in blueprinting, to remove minor imperfections.** (Corning Glass Works)

through plate glass without distortion. 3. *The annealing of glass.* After glass has been formed into a sheet or a finished article, it must be cooled very slowly. Otherwise the glass would be so brittle as to be worthless. The slow cooling of glass is called *annealing,* and is accomplished by passing the glass through a long, narrow chamber called a *lehr.* The temperature in the lehr is regulated carefully so that it is hot at one end and room temperature at the other end. Blown glass objects, for example, travel very slowly through the lehr on a moving belt. So slowly does the belt move through the lehr that several days elapse before the glass objects reach the unloading end.

15. **There are many kinds of glass.** Besides ordinary *soda-lime glass* which is used for window glass and bottles, *lead-potash glass* is used when a more lustrous product is desired. *Sodium aluminum borosilicate glass* is used for baking dishes and laboratory glassware which must stand wide changes in temperature. *Ultraviolet glass* is composed mostly of silica because glass of this composition transmits ultraviolet rays which cannot pass through ordinary glass. *Quartz glass* is made from pure silica and has such a low coefficient of expansion that it can be plunged red-hot into cold water without cracking or breaking.

16. **Metals impart colors to glass.** Even a small quantity of iron compounds as impurities in sand impart a pale-green color to finished glass. Consequently, glass makers try to secure as pure sand as possible. Manganese gives an amethyst or red color when added to glass, so small quantities of a manganese compound are sometimes added to a batch of glass to neutralize the pale-green color imparted by iron compounds. Chromium in glass gives it a deep-green color. Cobalt produces a deep blue. Silver is used to make yellow glass. Selenium is added to the batch to make red glass. White, or opalescent glass is made by adding calcium fluoride to the raw materials. It takes only a small amount of a metallic compound to color a large batch of glass vividly and uniformly.

SUMMARY

The small sized and tightly-bound electrons of boron and silicon atoms give them some similar chemical properties.

Elementary boron has little commercial value. Calcium borate occurs in California and Nevada. Sodium tetraborate (borax) and boric acid are the most important boron compounds. Borates are used for making glazes, enamels, and Pyrex glass. Boron carbide and boron nitride are extremely hard substances.

Elementary silicon is prepared in an electric furnace. Its chief use is in making silicon steel. Silicon compounds are found as sand and silicate rocks in great abundance in the earth's crust. Silica, SiO_2, occurs in nature as sand, sandstone, quartz, and in several amorphous varieties. Fused silica is used in making silica glass for laboratory glassware and ultraviolet lamps.

Silicic acid is a weak acid that is not an important compound; but its salts, the silicates, are abundant natural minerals. Talc, mica, asbestos, clay, granite, feldspar, and pumice stone are common silicates. Water glass is a concentrated solution of sodium silicate. Silicones are compounds that have hydrocarbon groups attached to the silicon atoms. Silicon carbide is used as an abrasive.

Glass may be considered to be a solid solution of two or more silicates. Ordinary glass is made from sand, limestone, and sodium carbonate. Optical glass and high grade glass for tableware may be made from sand, lead oxide, and potassium carbonate. Pyrex glass is a sodium aluminum borosilicate glass. It stands sudden changes in temperature without breaking better than ordinary glass. Small quantities of mineral compounds are used to color glass.

TEST YOURSELF ON THESE TERMS

annealing	ferrosilicon	semiconductor
borax	flux	silica
borax bead test	glass	silica gel
Borazon	lehr	silicate
boric acid	optical glass	silicon carbide
Carborundum	Pyrex glass	silicone
Crystolon	quartz	soda-lime glass
cullet	rock crystal	water glass

QUESTIONS

Group A

1. What is the main source of boron compounds in the United States?
2. Why may borax be used as a flux in welding metals?
3. What is the chief use for elementary silicon?
4. Give some uses for sand.
5. Name some of the varieties of amorphous silica.
6. (*a*) How is silica gel prepared? (*b*) For what purpose is it used?

7. (*a*) How does silicon rank in abundance among the elements? (*b*) What accounts for this rank?
8. (*a*) From what raw materials is silicon carbide made? (*b*) Write the equation for the reaction by which it is prepared.
9. (*a*) Of what is ordinary glass composed? (*b*) How are these materials believed to be related in glass?
10. What are the raw materials used in making ordinary glass?
11. (*a*) How does Pyrex glass differ in composition from ordinary glass? (*b*) How does it differ in properties?
12. (*a*) How is window glass made? (*b*) How is plate glass made?

Group B

13. Describe the properties characteristic of metalloids such as boron and silicon in terms of (*a*) atomic radius; (*b*) ionization energy; (*c*) electronegativity; (*d*) type of bonds formed; (*e*) electric conductivity.
14. (*a*) How can elementary boron be prepared? (*b*) Why is it seldom seen in school laboratories?
15. Explain how the test for boric acid is performed.
16. (*a*) What is the structure of a quartz crystal? (*b*) What characteristic of this structure gives quartz its hardness? (*c*) How does fused quartz differ in structure from quartz crystals?
17. Write the balanced formula equation for the reaction of hydrofluoric acid on silica.
18. Why do you suppose *water glass* was given that name?
19. (*a*) What is a silicone? (*b*) What are some of the important uses for silicones?
20. Compare the structure of silicon carbide and diamond.
21. Why is sand of very high purity desired by glass manufacturers?
22. What is a *lehr* and for what is it used?
23. How is glass of different colors obtained for use in "stained glass" windows in churches and public buildings?
24. Why is quartz not damaged by rapid temperature changes?
25. Write equations for the reactions of limestone and sodium carbonate with sand in glass manufacture.
26. When a red crystalline compound was tested by means of a borax bead, the bead turned blue. What metal was probably present in the compound?
27. Boron nitride and diamond have similar crystal structures. Is there any relationship between this fact and their similar hardness?

PROBLEMS

Group A

1. Calculate the percentage of boron in colemanite, $Ca_2B_6O_{11} \cdot 5 H_2O$.
2. How many grams of sodium silicate can be prepared from 1.000 kg of sodium carbonate by reacting it with an excess of silica?
3. What volume of carbon dioxide is liberated in Problem 2?

Group B

4. Boric acid, H_3BO_3, is produced when sulfuric acid is added to a water solution of borax, $Na_2B_4O_7$. How much boric acid can be prepared from 5.00 lb of borax?

5. What weight of silicon dioxide and what weight of carbon are needed in order to prepare 1.00 ton of silicon carbide in an electric resistance furnace.

SOME THINGS FOR YOU TO DO

1. Put some borax in an evaporating dish and moisten it with sulfuric acid. Then add a few teaspoonfuls of denatured alcohol and ignite it. Note the green flame that is characteristic of boric acid. This is a qualitative test for boric acid.

2. Make some borax beads in loops on the ends of platinum wires, and color them with tiny traces of cobalt, chromium, and manganese compounds. Dip the hot wire loop in powdered borax and heat it. The borax will swell, then shrink to a glassy bead. Then dip the hot bead in the speck of mineral compound and reheat it rather strongly to produce the colored bead.

3. Make a "silica garden" in a tall glass cylinder. Add one volume of 40% water glass solution to seven volumes of water and mix well. Pour this diluted water glass in a tall glass cylinder. Drop in a tiny crystal of cobalt chloride, manganese sulfate, or nickel sulfate. Watch the crystals "grow." Pretty color effects can be obtained by using different colored salts in the same "silica garden."

CHECK YOUR PROGRESS IN CHEMISTRY

1. Give examples of each of the eight types of colloidal dispersions.
2. What are the four principal properties of suspensoids?
3. What two factors contribute to the stability of emulsoids?
4. Draw a labeled diagram of the apparatus used for preparing aluminum from purified bauxite.
5. Write an equation for the preparation of magnesium by electrolysis of fused magnesium chloride.
6. Describe the tests for the presence of Fe^{++} and Fe^{+++} ions.
7. Why is crude copper refined before being marketed?
8. (*a*) What do the subscripts in a nuclear equation represent? (*b*) What do the superscripts represent?
9. Why are neutrons more successful for nuclear bombardment than protons or electrons?
10. Describe the use of boric acid as an antiseptic.
11. For what purpose may borax be used in the laundry?
12. How is elementary silicon produced?
13. How is quartzware fashioned?

CHALLENGING YOUR KNOWLEDGE

1. (*a*) In what form does boric acid principally exist in water solution, as molecules, or as hydronium and borate ions? (*b*) What experimental evidence supports your answer?
2. How does borax act as a water softener?
3. (*a*) Why isn't nearly pure silica glass used more frequently in school laboratories? (*b*) What advantage does such a glass have over aluminum borosilicate glass?
4. Why do we not usually classify silicon dioxide as an acid anhydride?
5. Why would you expect silicones to be water-repellant?

Unit 15 · COMMON ORGANIC COMPOUNDS

Fuels and Petroleum
Hydrocarbon Substitution Products
Textiles and Paper
Rubber and Plastics

Chapter 41 · FUELS AND PETROLEUM

1. THE NATURE OF FUELS

1. Fuels provide heat. A fuel may be a solid, a liquid, or a gas. Most fuels come directly or indirectly from the plant kingdom; they either are plants of the present, or are derived from extinct plants. A *fuel is any substance which is burned to provide heat.* The table in Fig. 41-1 shows that the common fuels contain large percentages of carbon. This carbon may be present as the free element or as compounds of carbon and hydrogen.

VOCABULARY

Alkylation. The combining of simple hydrocarbons with unsaturated hydrocarbons under the influence of heat, pressure, and the presence of a catalyst.

Calorimeter. An apparatus for measuring quantities of heat.

Catalytic cracking. The breaking-up of large molecules into smaller ones by the use of a catalyst and high temperature and pressure.

Explosive range of a gas. A pair of percentages, representing the proportions of a gas mixed with air, between which the mixture of the gas and air will explode if ignited.

Fuel. A material which is burned to provide heat.

Hydroforming. The forming of ring compounds by heating straight chain hydrocarbons together with hydrogen in the presence of a catalyst.

Petroleum. A liquid mixture of hydrocarbons obtained from beneath the surface of the ground.

Polymerization. The combining of simple molecules of the same kind to form more complex molecules.

Thermal cracking. The breaking-up of large molecules into smaller ones by the combined use of high temperature and pressure.

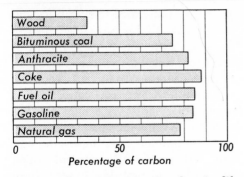

Fig. 41-1. **The percentage of carbon in different fuels.**

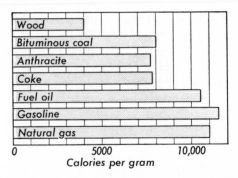

Fig. 41-2. **The amount of heat in equal masses of different fuels shows considerable variation.**

When a fuel burns, the carbon in it forms carbon dioxide, and the hydrogen forms water vapor. If the fuel contains a high percentage of carbon, there may be difficulty in supplying sufficient oxygen to burn it completely. In such a case, both carbon dioxide and carbon monoxide may be produced. Sometimes dense clouds of carbon, or soot, escape into the air. This not only pollutes the atmosphere, but also wastes tremendous quantities of fuel.

2. **Measuring the heat content of a fuel.** The amounts of heat produced by one-gram samples of various common fuels is shown in Fig. 41-2. The heat content of a fuel is determined by burning a sample of the fuel of known mass and measuring how much it warms a known mass of water. For example, a sample of coal is powdered, dried, and its mass determined. Then it is mixed with an oxidizing agent, such as sodium peroxide, Na_2O_2, to insure complete combustion in a closed vessel called a *bomb*. The bomb is surrounded with a known mass of water in a cylindrical container called a *calorimeter* (see Fig. 41-3). The temperature of this water is carefully measured just before the burning begins. A loop of wire dips into the mixture in the bomb. When a switch is

closed, an electric current passes through the loop and ignites the fuel. As the fuel burns, the bomb is rotated slowly by means of an electric motor. Paddles fastened to the rotating bomb stir the water, causing the heat to be distributed uniformly. The increase in temperature of the water is observed by reading a very sensitive thermometer.

Fig. 41-3. **The bomb calorimeter is used by chemists to measure the amount of heat in a given mass of a sample of fuel.**

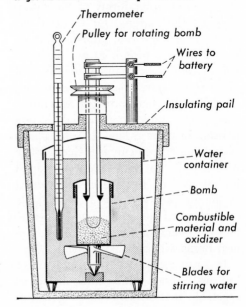

If the mass of the sample of fuel, the mass of water used, and the increase in temperature of the water are known, the heat value of the fuel can be computed. A sample of high-grade coal may yield at much as 14,500 Btu per pound (see Chapter 10, Section 4).

2. SOLID FUELS

3. Wood, peat, and lignite. Probably no fuel is more widely distributed than wood. In those places where the cost is not too high, wood meets the demand for a good fuel. Where some other fuel is the main source of heat, wood is frequently used for kindling the fire. Compared with coal and some other fuels, the heat content per pound of wood is not very high.

Several million years ago, plants grew more luxuriantly than today. Possibly there was more carbon dioxide in the atmosphere and this may have stimulated the growth of vegetation. In the carboniferous age, tree ferns, giant club mosses, and other forms of vegetation supplied the material for our coal deposits. Peat bogs were probably formed first. Extensive peat bogs are found in Pennsylvania, Michigan, Wisconsin, and other states. The bogs contain mosses, sedges, and other forms of vegetation which have undergone partial decomposition in swampy land. In some places such deposits are many feet thick. Sedge peat may be cut into blocks and dried for use as fuel. Even after being dried in the air, peat contains a considerable percentage of moisture. The heat content per pound of fuel is rather low, and peat burns with a smoky flame.

In some areas, upheavals of parts of the earth's crust buried thick masses of vegetable matter. Once buried, it was subjected to increased temperatures and pressures. At a fairly early stage in these changes, *lignite* was formed. Lignite is sometimes called *brown coal* because of its brownish-black color. It is common in some of the western states. Lignite burns with a smoky flame and yields less heat than bituminous coal.

4. Bituminous coal, anthracite, and coke. *Bituminous coal,* commonly called soft coal, was probably formed from the remains of prehistoric plants. It appears to have been subjected to greater heat and pressure than lignite, and may be considered to be a third step in the evolution of coal. Bituminous coal has a higher percentage of carbon and a higher heat content than lignite.

Anthracite, or hard coal, is believed to have been subjected to greater temperatures and pressures than the other forms of coal. Anthracite contains the least amount of volatile matter of all coals. It has the highest percentage of carbon and leaves very little ash after it is burned. Pennsylvania supplies most of the anthracite although small deposits are scattered through some of the western states.

Coke is left as a residue from the destructive distillation of bituminous coal. Most of the coke produced is used as a reducing agent in the production of pig iron and other metals, but some is consumed as a household fuel. It burns with a clean, smokeless flame, has a high heat content per pound, and leaves little ash.

3. LIQUID FUELS

5. The source of liquid fuels. Petroleum supplies almost all the liquid fuels used in the United States. This valuable natural resource is separated by

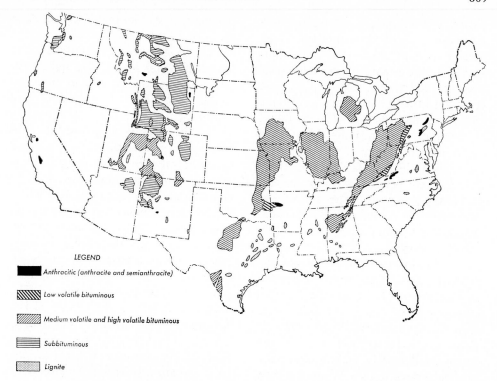

LEGEND

Anthracitic *(anthracite and semianthracite)*

Low volatile bituminous

Medium volatile and high volatile bituminous

Subbituminous

Lignite

Fig. 41-4. Coal is widely distributed throughout the United States.

refining into a variety of fuels and lubricants. Gasoline is the liquid fuel produced in greatest volume. Kerosene, a liquid fuel with a somewhat higher boiling point than gasoline, is used for oil lamps, for some oil stoves, and as a jet aircraft fuel. Diesel oil, another product resembling kerosene, is used in Diesel locomotives and trucks. New installations of oil burners in homes have increased the consumption of fuel oil greatly in recent years. Heavier grades of fuel oil are used for oil burners in factories and for oil-burning ships.

6. The nature of petroleum. Petroleum, sometimes called *crude oil*, is obtained from beneath the surface of the ground. It is a complex mixture of many hydrocarbons, and varies greatly in composition. Oil from some fields yields *paraffin wax* as one of the end products of distillation. Such oil is called a *paraffin-base oil.* Oil from other fields may contain certain ring compounds called *naphthenes.* Such an oil is known as *naphthene-base oil.* Some oils are mixtures of both types.

7. The origin of petroleum. Petroleum is believed to be a material resulting from the partial decomposition of animals and plants that lived in the sea. Changes in the earth's crust have buried this material underground, sometimes at great depths.

In certain areas, upward bulging of impervious rocks has produced dome-like formations under which *natural gas, petroleum,* and *salt water* are frequently found. The natural gas, having the lowest density, rises to the top of the dome. Here it is confined by the impervious rock above, and may collect under great pressure. Below the natural gas, the crude oil saturates a porous sandstone, called the *oil-bearing sand*, or is found in dolomite or sandstone formations. Salt water commonly accumulates in a layer below these sands (see Fig. 41-5). When a drill penetrates the oil-bearing sands, the pressure of the natural gas may force the oil upward. As the pressure of the gas diminishes, the oil is obtained by pumping.

8. The location of petroleum deposits. In the United States, petroleum was first produced at Titusville, Pennsylvania, in 1859. Later, oil fields were opened in Ohio and West Virginia. Texas is now far in the lead in oil production, followed by California, Louisiana, Oklahoma, Kansas, Wyoming, New Mexico, Illinois, Colorado, Mississippi, Arkansas, and Montana. Several other states produce smaller amounts.

Canada, Mexico, and Venezuela also have rich oil deposits. The richest deposits yet found are located in Saudi Arabia, Iran, and other Middle East countries.

9. The refining of petroleum. The refining of petroleum is the separation of crude oil into fractions with properties suitable for certain uses. It is accomplished by **fractional distillation**. No attempt is made to separate the petroleum into individual hydrocarbons. Instead, fractions that distill over between certain temperature ranges are collected in separate receivers. *Gasoline* is mostly a mixture of hexane, C_6H_{14}; heptane, C_7H_{16}; and octane, C_8H_{18}. *Kerosene* contains hydrocarbons that distill over at higher temperatures. Decane, $C_{10}H_{22}$, and dodecane, $C_{12}H_{26}$, are two of the hydrocarbons found in kerosene. Still higher boiling mixtures are known

Fig. 41-5. Petroleum, natural gas, and salt water commonly saturate the oil-bearing sands under domes of cap rock in some favored locations.

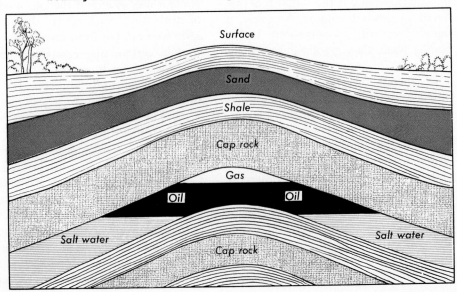

Surface

Sand

Shale

Cap rock

Gas

Oil   Oil

Salt water   Salt water

Cap rock

as *fuel oil* or *gas oil. Lubricating oils* have even larger molecules and still higher boiling points. *Greases, petroleum jelly, paraffin wax,* and *petroleum coke* are products obtained near the end or at the end of the heating.

A continuous process employing a *pipe still* and a *fractionating tower* is in general use. These are large structures that have a capacity for distilling 10,000 barrels of crude oil a day. The fractionating towers are about 100 feet tall. In operation, the crude oil is heated to a temperature of about 700° F in the coiled pipes of the pipe still. The vapors are then discharged into the fractionating tower at a point near its base. Here the fractions with the highest boiling points condense and are drawn off to collecting vessels. Inside the tower are platforms or shallow troughs on which liquids from the condensed vapors collect. Those fractions that have the lowest boiling points, and consequently are the most difficult to condense as liquids, pass up through the tower. Pipes that project through the tower at different heights lead off the overflow of condensed liquids from the platforms. Gasoline, together with other more volatile portions of the petroleum, passes over as a gas from the top of the tower. The gasoline fraction, and the more volatile naphtha fraction, are liquefied in separate condensers. The uncondensed gases may be piped to the polymerizer (see Section 11) or be used as fuel in the refinery. Each of the liquid fractions may be redistilled to effect a better separation. Each fraction is also treated with chemicals to remove impurities.

10. Characteristics of a good motor fuel. A good gasoline should contain enough volatile matter to make starting of the engine easy. It should be free of gummy residues that cause valves to

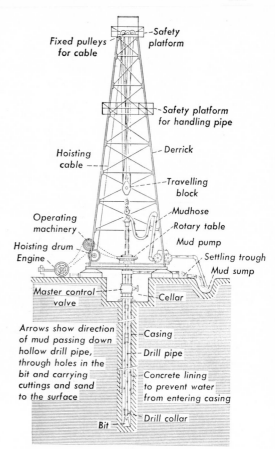

Fig. 41-6. A cross-section of a rotary rig used in drilling for petroleum.

stick and also form carbon in the combustion chamber. It should also give good mileage per gallon and not "knock," particularly on hills.

"Knocking" in an automobile engine is caused by too rapid burning of the mixture of gasoline vapor and air within the cylinders. Instead of a smooth, steady push, the top of the piston is given a sudden, hammer-like blow when the fuel burns too rapidly. This causes a loss in power, may be harmful to the engine, and is noticed as a succession of knocking sounds.

Knocking may be prevented by using a fuel that has less tendency to knock

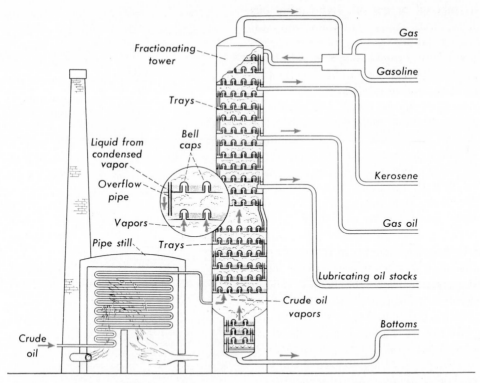

Fig. 41-7. A cross-section of a pipe still and fractionating tower used in refining petroleum.

and by adding a catalyst to the gasoline. Gasoline that is made up principally of straight chain hydrocarbons tends to knock badly in automobiles. Such a hydrocarbon is normal heptane, C_7H_{16}, with the structural formula:

$$\begin{array}{ccccccc} H & H & H & H & H & H & H \\ \vdots & \vdots & \vdots & \vdots & \vdots & \vdots & \vdots \\ H:C:C:C:C:C:C:C:H \\ \vdots & \vdots & \vdots & \vdots & \vdots & \vdots & \vdots \\ H & H & H & H & H & H & H \end{array}$$

Hydrocarbons with side chains burn less rapidly and give smoother operation in an automobile engine. Ring compounds, such as benzene, C_6H_6, also have less tendency to knock than straight chain hydrocarbons. To improve the antiknock properties of gasoline, refiners try to produce gasoline that con-

tains a large proportion of side chain hydrocarbons or ring compounds.

Certain compounds, when added to gasoline in small amounts, improve the antiknocking properties by slowing the rate of combustion. The best known of these is *lead tetraethyl*, $Pb(C_2H_5)_4$. Gasoline to which lead tetraethyl is added is known as *leaded gasoline.* It should not be used for purposes other than as a motor fuel because of the poisonous nature of this compound.

The *octane rating* of a gasoline is a number which indicates the tendency of a gasoline to knock in a high compression engine. The higher the number, the less the tendency of the gasoline to knock. To determine the octane rating, the gasoline is burned in a standard test engine. Its performance in the test engine is compared with a fuel of known octane rating. The fuels used as standards are *normal heptane* and 2,2,4-trimethylpentane, which is also called **iso-octane**. This hydrocarbon has side chains, as shown by the structural formula:

$$
\begin{array}{c}
\text{H} \\
\text{H H:C:H H} \quad \text{H} \quad \text{H} \\
\text{H : C : C : C : C : C : H} \\
\text{H H:C:H H H:C:H H} \\
\text{H} \qquad \text{H}
\end{array}
$$

Iso-octane has excellent antiknock properties and is given an arbitrary rating of 100. Normal heptane knocks very badly and is given a rating of zero. A gasoline with the characteristics of a mixture of 90% iso-octane and 10% heptane would have an octane rating of 90. Good gasolines have a rating of 95 or higher. Chemists have produced gasolines with even better antiknock properties than pure iso-octane. Thus it is possible to have gasolines, such as those used for aviation fuels, with an even higher rating than 100.

11. Increasing the yield of gasoline from petroleum. Crude oil contains only a small percentage of gasoline. The yield of gasoline is increased by a number of methods.

1. Thermal cracking. When crude oil is heated to a high temperature under high pressure, the bonds of some of the larger molecules are weakened so that the molecules are "cracked," or split up into simpler molecules which are more easily vaporized. For example, a molecule of $C_{16}H_{34}$ may be cracked to yield a molecule of C_8H_{18}, octane, and a molecule of C_8H_{16}, octene. This increases the amount of gasoline obtained from the crude oil.

2. Catalytic cracking. This process is more efficient than thermal cracking. It also uses heat and pressure, but in addition employs a catalyst to increase the rate at which cracking occurs and to enable the process to be carried out at a lower temperature than that needed for thermal cracking. Many different substances may be used as catalysts. The choice of the catalyst depends on the products desired, since different catalysts favor the production of different products from the cracking process. Aluminum chloride and zirconium dioxide are two catalysts which have been used. Catalytic cracking produces better quality gasoline and greater quantities of home heating oil than thermal cracking.

3. Polymerization. Polymerization is the opposite of cracking. In this process, simple molecules such as methane, CH_4,

Fig. 41-8. An exterior view of a pipe still (right) and fractionating tower (left). (Standard Oil of New Jersey)

Fig. 41-9. **A catalytic cracking unit breaks up large molecules found in petroleum and produces more molecules of the size required for gasoline.** (Shell Oil)

ethane, C_2H_6, and others, are polymerized, or "bunched," to make molecules of the proper size for gasoline. This is accomplished by heating the hydrocarbon with a suitable catalyst such as aluminum silicate. An example of a polymerization reaction is that between two molecules of isobutene, C_4H_8, to form an isomer of octene, C_8H_{16}, which may then be hydrogenated to form an isomer of octane.

4. Casing-head gasoline. Natural gas consists mostly of methane, but it also contains some other hydrocarbons. If it is cooled and compressed, these other hydrocarbons may be extracted from the natural gas. They form a volatile liquid, called *"casing-head"* gasoline, which is blended with other gasolines to help make the fuel quick-starting.

12. Hydroforming and alkylation improve the quality of gasoline. Both of these processes result in a rearrangement of the molecules to produce more side chain or ring compounds and thus increase the antiknock properties.

Hydroforming consists of heating gasoline of poor quality with hydrogen in the presence of a catalyst. Ring compounds are formed from straight chain hydrocarbons by causing the ends of the chains to join. Hydroformed gasoline, rich in ring compounds, has excellent antiknock properties.

Alkylation produces gasoline with extremely high octane numbers. In this process, simpler hydrocarbons are made to unite with unsaturated hydrocarbons such as ethene C_2H_4, by heat and pressure in the presence of a catalyst. Aviation gasoline is made by this process.

13. Synthetic petroleum. A petroleum-like mixture can be made by synthesis from carbon monoxide and hydrogen with the aid of a catalyst by the *Fischer-Tropsch process.* From this mixture gasoline, kerosene, Diesel fuel, and paraffin wax have been extracted.

Another process for producing synthetic petroleum, the **Bergius process,** involves hydrogenation of low grade coal at high temperature and high pressure. Gasoline and lubricating oils of high quality have been produced by this method. Both of these processes are now much more expensive than the refining of natural petroleum. However, they do offer possibilities for the time when the natural petroleum supply dwindles.

14. Petroleum yields many products. More than 25 billion gallons of gasoline are produced each year in the United States. In addition, other products of petroleum are important commodities.

1. *Benzine and naphtha* are volatile flammable mixtures that have a lower boiling range than gasoline. They are used to some extent as solvents for oil or grease. Painters sometimes use benzine as a substitute for turpentine.

2. *Kerosene* is used as a fuel for oil stoves, or as an illuminant in oil lamps and lanterns. It is less volatile than gasoline. A kerosene-like fuel is now being used in some types of jet aircraft.

3. *Fuel oil* is used in tremendous amounts for heating. The lighter grades are used for household oil burners, while the heavier grades are burned in factories or aboard ships.

4. *Dieselene,* a fuel for Diesel engines, resembles fuel oil in composition. *Normal cetane,* $C_{16}H_{34}$, is used for rating dieselene just as octane is used as a standard for gasoline.

5. *Dry cleaning solvent* is much less volatile than gasoline and thus is much safer to use for dry cleaning garments. It is a purified, deodorized product with a boiling range near that of kerosene.

6. *Lubricating oils* vary in viscosity from thin, mobile fluids for lubricating sewing machines to thick, viscous liquids for heavy trucks. Some automobile lubricat-ing oils now have added detergents which keep carbon particles and dirt in suspension in the oil. This helps to keep the automobile engine clean.

7. *Greases* are solids, or semisolids, at ordinary temperatures. Some greases have added graphite. They are used on bearings that are not easily lubricated by oil.

8. *Petroleum jelly* is a refined petroleum grease used for making medicinal ointments.

9. *Petroleum coke* is a decomposition product obtained in refining petroleum. It is used for making carbon electrodes because it leaves no ash.

10. *Paraffin wax* is used in making candles and waxed paper, and as an electric insulator.

An expanding field for the petroleum industry is the making of chemicals from petroleum as a raw material. From petroleum a variety of commercially pure hydrocarbons may be prepared. In Chapter 18 we described how some of these hydrocarbons, such as methane, ethene, and ethyne, may be used as starting materials for the production of other organic compounds. In the following chapters we shall learn how other chemicals derived from petroleum are used in the production of alcohols, detergents, insecticides, plastics, synthetic rubber, textiles, and many other products.

4. GASEOUS FUELS

15. Natural gas. When vegetable matter decomposes under water, *marsh gas,* or *methane,* CH_4, is formed. This gas may form as much as 90% of the natural gases that are found in tremendous volumes in West Virginia, Texas, Oklahoma, Pennsylvania,

California, Kansas, Indiana, Louisiana, and some other states.

Natural gas is widely used as a fuel for cooking and home heating in many parts of our country. It furnishes about 1100 Btu per cubic foot, an amount considerably greater than that furnished by other fuel gases. It is one of our most valuable natural resources.

16. Coal gas. In the manufacture of coke, coal gas is a useful by-product. Even though natural gas has largely replaced coal gas for household use, coke must be produced for the iron and steel industry. Thus the making of coal gas will continue, though usually only for immediate industrial use. Bituminous coal is heated in iron retorts until most of the volatile matter has been driven off (Chapter 16, Section 14). From the retorts, the gas passes to the condensers in which it is cooled and where most of the vaporized tar is condensed to a liquid. The gas is then purified by re-

moving ammonia and the last portions of tar by forcing it upward against a countercurrent flow of water in a scrubbing tower loosely filled with large pieces of coke. In large plants, the ammonia in the scrubbing water is recovered and converted into ammonium sulfate for use as fertilizer.

The gas still contains compounds of sulfur, especially hydrogen sulfide, H_2S. The *purifiers*, which are used to remove the sulfur compounds, are large boxes with shelves containing a porous mixture of iron(III) oxide (rusted iron) and wood shavings. Hydrogen sulfide is removed from the gas as it passes through several of these boxes in turn by reacting with the iron(III) oxide according to the following equation:

$$Fe_2O_3 + 3 H_2S \rightarrow Fe_2S_3 + 3 H_2O$$

The purified gas then goes to the storage holder.

From a ton of high-volatile coal it is

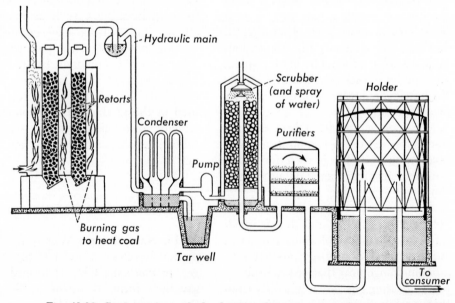

Fig. 41-10. **Coal gas is made by heating bituminous coal in vertical retorts. Tar, ammonia, and sulfur compounds must be removed from the gas before it is used as a fuel.**

possible to obtain from 10,000 to 12,000 cubic feet of gas. The other products include 1200 to 1400 lb of coke, about 120 lb of coal tar, and a smaller quantity of ammonia.

17. Water gas. If a blast of steam is forced up through a white-hot bed of coke or anthracite, hydrogen and carbon monoxide are produced, as shown in the equation:

$$C + H_2O \rightarrow H_2 \uparrow + CO \uparrow$$

Because water in the form of steam is used to make this mixture of gases, it is commonly known as **water gas.** The reaction takes place efficiently only when the coke is very hot. The blast of steam cools the glowing coke after a few minutes to a temperature at which the reaction does not take place efficiently. Consequently, the making of water gas must be interrupted while a blast of air is used to heat the coke to the required temperature.

Although water gas has been replaced by natural gas as a household fuel in most communities, the manufacture of water gas for industrial purposes is still important. Carbon monoxide and hydrogen can be produced at much lower costs by this process than by any other method. These gases are of increasing value in the chemical industry for the synthesis of organic chemical compounds.

18. Bottled gas is available for rural homes. Bottled gas, delivered in steel cylinders, provides gas of high fuel value at a reasonable cost. Bottled gas is liquefied propane, butane, or a mixture of these compounds. The steel cylinders containing the liquefied fuel are usually mounted outside the building (in case of a possible leak). Copper tubing leads the gas through the wall to the stove or heater. A delivery service provides full cylinders to replace the empty ones as needed. In a newer method, the smaller cylinders at homes are filled from a large tank of liquefied gas on the delivery truck.

19. The explosive range of a gas. Not all proportions of a combustible gas and air will explode. A mixture that contains too much gasoline vapor to explode when ignited is called *too rich.* Similarly, a mixture of gasoline vapor and air may contain so much air that it is *too lean* to explode. To secure the greatest mileage from a gallon of motor fuel, the mixture should be adjusted to give the most violent explosion.

The explosive range of a gas is a pair of percentages, representing the proportions of a gas mixed with air, between which the mixture of the gas and air will explode if ignited. For example, any mixture that contains *between* 2.5% and 80.0% of ethyne (acetylene), C_2H_2, mixed with air will explode when ignited. The equation for the combustion of ethyne is as follows:

$$2 C_2H_2 + 5 O_2 \rightarrow 4 CO_2 \uparrow + 2 H_2O \uparrow$$

Hence the most violent explosion occurs when two volumes of ethyne are mixed with five volumes of oxygen, or with about twenty-five volumes of air.

Hydrogen has a wide explosive range when mixed with air. Any mixture of hydrogen and air which contains from 4.0% to 74.2% of hydrogen will explode if ignited. The explosion is most violent when the mixture contains about 29% of hydrogen. The explosive range of mixtures of gas and air should be kept in mind when gas leaks occur in a closed space. To search for the leak with a lighted match may result in a violent explosion. A soap solution which bubbles at the leak is safer.

SUMMARY

A fuel is any substance which is burned to provide heat. Its heat content may be determined by means of a calorimeter.

The solid fuels include: wood, peat, lignite, bituminous coal, anthracite, and coke. They are all obtained from plants, either directly, or as the fossil remains of plants that lived in past geologic ages.

Practically all of the liquid fuels used in the United States are obtained from petroleum. Petroleum is a complex mixture of many hydrocarbons, believed to result from the partial decomposition of marine animal and vegetable organisms. Petroleum is separated by fractional distillation into gasoline, kerosene, fuel oil, lubricating oil, grease, paraffin wax, and petroleum coke. Too rapid combustion of gasoline in an automobile engine results in knocking. Straight chain hydrocarbons knock badly in an automobile engine while branch chain and ring hydrocarbons have much better antiknock properties. Catalysts, such as lead tetraethyl, increase the antiknock quality of gasoline. The octane rating is a number that indicates the antiknock quality of gasoline. The yield of gasoline may be increased by thermal cracking, catalytic cracking, polymerization, and the addition of casinghead gasoline. Hydroforming and alkylation improve the quality of gasoline.

Natural gas is an excellent fuel that has a very high heat content. Coal gas is made by the destructive distillation of bituminous coal. Water gas is composed almost entirely of carbon monoxide and hydrogen. Bottled gas is used extensively in rural homes. The explosive range of a gas is a pair of percentages, representing the proportions of a gas mixed with air, between which the mixture of the gas and air will explode if ignited.

TEST YOURSELF ON THESE TERMS

alkylation	fractional distillation	lubricating oil
anthracite	fractionating tower	natural gas
Bergius process	fuel	octane rating
bituminous coal	gasoline	paraffin wax
calorimeter	grease	peat
casing-head gasoline	heat content of a fuel	petroleum
catalytic cracking	hydroforming	pipe still
coal gas	kerosene	polymerization
coke	"knocking"	thermal cracking
explosive range of a gas	lead tetraethyl	water gas
Fischer-Tropsch process	lignite	wood

QUESTIONS

Group A

1. (a) What is a fuel? (b) What is the original source of almost all fuels?
2. What objections are there to the use of peat as a household fuel?
3. What are the different probable stages in the evolution of anthracite?
4. From what source are most of our liquid fuels obtained?

5. What is the probable origin of petroleum?
6. Name five main products obtained from crude oil.
7. Describe two ways in which a fuel which knocks may be improved.
8. What is the *octane rating* system used in testing gasolines?
9. (*a*) What is meant by *cracking* crude oil? (*b*) How is this done?
10. Why is petroleum not produced commercially by synthetic methods?
11. (*a*) What is fractional distillation? (*b*) How is it employed in the petroleum industry?
12. What is the principal component of natural gas?
13. What impurity is removed from coal gas by application of the countercurrent principle?
14. Why do we say that water gas is made by an intermittent process?

Group B

15. What explanation is given for the more luxuriant growth of vegetation during the carboniferous age?
16. How is the heating value of a solid fuel measured?
17. Why are large quantities of coke being produced when gaseous and liquid fuels are becoming more popular for home heating?
18. What is the difference in the type of hydrocarbons in a paraffin-base oil and in a naphthene-base oil?
19. Describe the operation of a fractionating tower.
20. What happens in an automobile engine when the engine knocks?
21. (*a*) What is meant by *leaded gasoline*? (*b*) Why must it not be used for any other purpose than as a motor fuel?
22. Draw structural formulas for n-heptane and 2,2,4-trimethylpentane.
23. Give an example of a polymerization reaction used to increase the yield of gasoline from crude oil.
24. Why do petroleum refiners make use of hydroforming and alkylation?
25. Write the chemical equation for the production of water gas.
26. What is the cheapest method for producing hydrogen and carbon monoxide for industrial purposes?

SOME THINGS FOR YOU TO DO

1. Determine the percentage of moisture in various powdered coal samples by heating weighed 1-gram portions in crucibles in an oven for one hour at 105° C. The loss in mass during this heating is assumed to be moisture. Calculate the percentage of moisture in each sample.
2. The dried samples obtained in No. 1 may be slowly heated until the crucibles are at dark red heat and all black particles of carbon have burned off. The material which remains is ash. Calculate the percentage of ash in each sample.
3. Large oil companies distribute literature consisting of charts that describe the different petroleum products which they market. Procure such a chart and study it. Make a report to the class about petroleum products.
4. Visit your local gas works if manufactured gas is distributed in your community.

Chapter 42 · HYDROCARBON SUBSTITUTION PRODUCTS

1. HALOGEN SUBSTITUTION PRODUCTS

1. **Halogen substitution products of methane.** In Chapter 18, Section 6, it was noted that the halogens react with methane to form substitution products. An atom of a halogen may be substituted for an atom of hydrogen in methane. Under certain conditions, halogen atoms can be substituted for each of the four hydrogen atoms in methane. This reaction occurs in four steps:

$$CH_4 + Cl_2 \rightarrow CH_3Cl + HCl$$
$$CH_3Cl + Cl_2 \rightarrow CH_2Cl_2 + HCl$$
$$CH_2Cl_2 + Cl_2 \rightarrow CHCl_3 + HCl$$
$$CHCl_3 + Cl_2 \rightarrow CCl_4 + HCl$$

CH_3Cl, chloromethane, or methyl chloride, is a colorless gas that is widely used in preparing other organic compounds.

CH_2Cl_2, dichloromethane, or methylene chloride, is a volatile, colorless liquid which is very stable and unreactive. It is used in one type of paint remover.

$CHCl_3$, trichloromethane, or chloroform, is a sweet-smelling, colorless liquid used as a solvent, and also as an anesthetic.

CCl_4, tetrachloromethane, or carbon tetrachloride, is a colorless, volatile liquid. It is an excellent agent for removing grease spots from clothing because it is a good solvent and will not burn or explode. Its vapors are toxic, however, and there must be good ventilation

VOCABULARY

Detergent. A substance which removes dirt.

Esterification. The process of producing an ester by reaction of an acid with an alcohol.

Saponification. The process of making a soap by hydrolysis of an ester with an alkali.

Substitution product. A compound in which various atoms or groups have been substituted for one or more atoms.

whenever carbon tetrachloride is used. Its most important use is in the production of Freon refrigerants and aerosol propellants.

2. Commercial preparation of chloroform and carbon tetrachloride. While the direct chlorination of methane does yield chloroform and carbon tetrachloride, this method is not generally used for the commercial preparation of these compounds because of difficulty in controlling the reaction and in separating the products.

Chloroform is manufactured by reducing carbon tetrachloride with moist iron.

Carbon tetrachloride is prepared commercially by the reaction between carbon disulfide, CS_2, and sulfur monochloride, S_2Cl_2, using iron as a catalyst.

$$CS_2 + 2\ S_2Cl_2 \xrightarrow{\text{Fe}} CCl_4 + 6\ S$$

The sulfur produced in this reaction is used to make more sulfur monochloride.

3. Organic groups derived from the alkanes. The compound CH_3Cl is sometimes called methyl chloride, and CH_3— is known as the methyl group. It occurs frequently in organic compounds. It consists of a carbon atom which has shared three of its four valence electrons with hydrogen atoms. The fourth valence electron is available for covalent bond formation with another atom. In methyl chloride this fourth valence electron is shared with a chlorine atom. One of the valence electrons of the chlorine atom is likewise shared with the carbon atom. The electron-dot formulas below illustrate these structures.

Methyl group   Methyl chloride

The name of the methyl group is derived from that of the alkane with the same number of carbon atoms, methane, by replacing the suffix –ane with –yl.

Other alkanes form similar groups. For example, C_2H_5— is the ethyl group, and C_3H_7— is the propyl group.

4. Other halogen substitution products. Chloroethane, or ethyl chloride, C_2H_5Cl, is sprayed on the skin before minor operations. It evaporates so rapidly that it cools and anesthetizes the tissues.

1,2-dibromoethane, $BrCH_2CH_2Br$, is used with lead tetraethyl in antiknock fluid for gasoline. During the combustion of the gasoline, lead tetraethyl is decomposed. 1,2-dibromoethane supplies bromine so the lead may be removed from the engine in the exhaust gases as lead bromide. Otherwise, deposits of lead oxide would foul the spark plugs.

Tri-iodomethane, or iodoform, CHI_3, is a yellow solid that is made by treating ethanol (ethyl alcohol) with iodine in

Fig. 42-1. Freon, made from carbon tetrachloride, is used as a propellant in spray can for paints and lacquers. (E. I. du Pont)

the presence of a mild alkali such as potassium carbonate. Iodoform has such a peculiar, persistent odor that this reaction may be used as a test for ethanol.

Dichlorodifluoromethane, CCl_2F_2, commonly called Freon, is used as a refrigerant in mechanical refrigerators and in air conditioners. It is also used as the propellant in spray cans of various kinds. Freon is nontoxic, nonflammable, and noncorrosive. It is prepared from carbon tetrachloride and hydrofluoric acid with antimony compounds used as catalysts.

$$CCl_4 + 2\ HF \xrightarrow{\text{catalyst}} CCl_2F_2 + 2\ HCl$$

2. ALCOHOLS

5. Alcohols contain hydroxyl groups. Alcohols are a class of compounds which have a hydrocarbon group and one or more −OH, hydroxyl, groups. For example, methanol has the formula CH_3OH. It is also called *methyl alcohol* or *wood alcohol*. Ethanol has the formula C_2H_5OH, and is called *ethyl alcohol* or *grain alcohol*. Glycerol, or glycerin, is a nonpoisonous alcohol that has the formula $C_3H_5(OH)_3$. There are many other alcohols in organic chemistry.

While many alcohols are soluble in water, they are not ionized by water. An alcohol exists in water solution in the form of molecules. Since the hydroxyl group of an alcohol *does not produce* hydroxide ions in water solution, alcohols *do not have* the properties of inorganic hydroxides.

6. Methanol. Methanol is a colorless liquid with a rather pleasant odor. It has a low density, and boils at 64.7° C. It is very poisonous, even when used externally. If taken internally in small quantity it causes blindness by destroying the cells of the optic nerve. Larger amounts may cause death. Methanol is a good fuel, burning with a hot, smokeless flame. Large quantities are used as an automobile radiator antifreeze. It is also used as a vehicle for shellac, a denaturant for ethanol, and as a starting

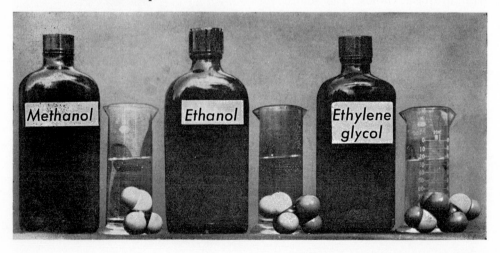

Fig. 42-2. **There are many alcohols in chemistry. These three, methanol, ethanol, and ethylene glycol, are used as antifreeze in automobiles.** (S. E. DeBerry)

Fig. 42-3. **This plant manufactures ethanol from ethene.** (Shell Chemical)

material in the preparation of other organic compounds. Methanol is made from carbon monoxide and hydrogen under pressure, using a catalyst.

7. The preparation of ethanol.
1. From ethene (ethylene). Large quantities of ethene are produced during the cracking of petroleum. Ethene may be hydrated, using sulfuric acid as a catalyst, to produce ethanol.

$$C_2H_4 + H_2O \xrightarrow{H_2SO_4} C_2H_5OH$$

2. By fermentation. If yeast is added to a dilute solution of sugar or molasses at room temperature, chemical action soon begins to occur. Bubbles of carbon dioxide are liberated and ethanol is produced. The equation which summarizes the reaction is:

$$C_6H_{12}O_6 \rightarrow 2\ C_2H_5OH + 2\ CO_2 \uparrow$$

The yeast plants secrete an enzyme, zymase, which acts as a catalyst in changing the sugar into alcohol and carbon dioxide.

Both of these processes are widely used today for the commercial production of ethanol. However, the hydration of ethene is a less expensive method and is gradually accounting for a greater proportion of the total production.

8. The properties of ethanol. Ethanol is a colorless liquid which has a characteristic odor and a sharp, biting taste. It boils at 78° C, freezes at −115° C, and burns with a nearly colorless blue flame. Ethanol is a good solvent for many organic compounds which are insoluble in water. Accordingly, it is used for making tinctures, spirits, and fluid extracts for medicinal use. Ethanol is used as an antifreeze in automobiles, and for making ether and acetaldehyde.

Denatured alcohol is a mixture, composed principally of ethanol, to which poisonous and nauseating materials have been added. These materials are added to make it unfit for beverage purposes.

9. The higher alcohols. Alcohols with a greater number of carbon atoms per molecule than ethanol are sometimes called *higher* alcohols. *Propanol*, propyl alcohol, C_3H_7OH, is used as a solvent. *Butanol*, butyl alcohol, C_4H_9OH, and *pentanol*, amyl alcohol, $C_5H_{11}OH$, are used in making lacquers. *Dodecanol*, lauryl alcohol, $C_{12}H_{25}OH$, is used for manufacturing one type of synthetic detergent. Other higher alcohols are known, but they have very limited uses. The higher alcohols are made by fermentation, using special yeasts.

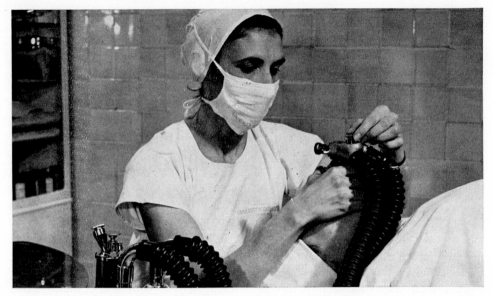

Fig. 42-4. **Ether is used as an anesthetic during a surgical operation.** (E. R. Squibb)

10. Ethylene glycol and glycerol. Ethylene glycol, $C_2H_4(OH)_2$, is an alcohol containing two hydroxyl groups. It is used extensively as a "permanent type" antifreeze in automobile radiators. Its boiling point is so much higher than that of water that it does not readily evaporate or boil away.

Glycerol, or glycerin, $C_3H_5(OH)_3$, is a colorless, odorless, viscous liquid with a sweet taste. It has a low vapor pressure and is hygroscopic. It is used in making synthetic resins for paints, by the tobacco industry to keep cigarettes moist, in the manufacture of cellophane, in making nitroglycerin, and in some toilet soaps. Glycerol is used in some lotions because it keeps the skin from becoming dry and chapped. It is an important pharmaceutical ingredient, and is used, too, in many foods and beverages. Glycerol is a by-product of soap manufacture. Important quantities of glycerol are synthesized from propylene, a product of petroleum cracking.

3. OTHER SUBSTITUTION PRODUCTS

11. Ethers are organic oxides. Ordinary ether or *diethyl ether*, $(C_2H_5)_2O$, is a volatile liquid of characteristic odor that is very flammable. It is made by heating ethanol and sulfuric acid to 140° C.

$$2\ C_2H_5OH \xrightarrow{\ H_2SO_4\ } C_2H_5OC_2H_5 + H_2O$$

Besides its familiar use as an anesthetic, ether is employed as a solvent for fats and oils.

12. There are other ethers besides ethyl ether. By heating methanol instead of ethanol with sulfuric acid, *dimethyl ether*, $(CH_3)_2O$, is formed. With propyl alcohol, *dipropyl ether*, $(C_3H_7)_2O$, can be made by the same process. Since there are many alcohols, it is possible to make many different ethers.

13. Aldehydes. An *aldehyde* is a compound which has a hydrocarbon group and one or more formyl, –CHO, groups. For example, *acetaldehyde* has the formula CH_3CHO, and benzaldehyde has the formula C_6H_5CHO. Both of these aldehydes are important in producing a variety of organic compounds. Aldehydes are made by mild oxidation of alcohols.

14. Formaldehyde is an important compound. If methanol vapor and a regulated amount of air are passed over heated copper, formaldehyde is produced.

$$2\ CH_3OH + O_2 \xrightarrow{Cu} 2\ HCHO + 2\ H_2O$$

At room temperature, formaldehyde is a gas with a suffocating odor. Dissolved in water, it makes an excellent disinfectant. It is sometimes used to treat seeds before they are planted to destroy injurious fungi. Seed potatoes are treated with formaldehyde solution to prevent scab. It is used for preserving anatomical specimens, and for making the embalming fluid used by undertakers. But by far the largest use for formaldehyde is in the making of certain types of plastics, which will be discussed in Chapter 44.

15. Acetone is the simplest ketone. *Ketones* are a class of organic compounds that contain the $>CO$, or *carbonyl* group. They may, like the aldehydes, be prepared by mild oxidation of alcohols. Acetone, CH_3COCH_3, is prepared in this manner by oxidation of 2-propanol, $CH_3CHOHCH_3$. Another common method of preparing acetone is by special bacterial fermentation of molasses.

Acetone, a colorless, volatile liquid, is widely used as a solvent in the manufacture of acetate rayon, and in paint and varnish removers. Tanks for the storage of ethyne gas are loosely filled with asbestos saturated with acetone.

The ethyne dissolves in the acetone and thus increases the amount of ethyne which may safely be compressed into the tank. Acetone and other ketones are used for cleaning metals, removing stains, and for preparing synthetic organic chemicals.

16. The occurrence of organic acids. Many organic acids and their salts occur naturally in sour milk, in unripe fruits, in rhubarb and sorrel, as well as in other plants. All organic acids contain the $-COOH$, or *carboxyl* group.

It is the hydrogen atom bonded to an oxygen atom in the carboxyl group which is ionized in water solution and gives these substances their typical acid properties. The hydrogen atoms bonded to carbon atoms in these acids are *never* ionized in water solution.

Some organic acids are made by oxidizing their corresponding alcohols or aldehydes.

17. Formic acid. Formic acid, $HCOOH$, is prepared from sodium hydroxide and carbon monoxide under

Fig. 42-5. **A chemical plant in which isopropyl alcohol is converted to acetone.** (Standard Oil, N. J.)

pressure. This reaction yields sodium formate, HCOONa.

$$NaOH + CO \rightarrow HCOONa$$

If sodium formate is heated with sulfuric acid, formic acid distills off.

$$HCOONa + H_2SO_4 \rightarrow$$
$$HCOOH \uparrow + NaHSO_4$$

Formic acid is found in nature in stinging nettles, in the sting of bees, wasps, and hornets, and in red ants. Formic acid is used commercially in the textile industry.

18. Acetic acid. Vinegar is made from apple cider which has fermented to form hard cider. The ethanol in hard cider is oxidized slowly to acetic acid by the action of certain bacteria. The equation is:

$$C_2H_5OH + O_2 \rightarrow CH_3COOH + H_2O$$

Good vinegar contains from 4% to 6% acetic acid. Malt vinegar and wine vinegar are made by a similar process of fermentation and oxidation.

Some acetic acid is still obtained as a by-product of the destructive distillation of wood. Pure acetic acid is produced by the catalytic oxidation of acetaldehyde. Concentrated acetic acid is a colorless liquid that is a good solvent for some organic chemicals. It is used for making cellulose acetate, one of the synthetic fibers.

19. Oxalic acid. This organic acid has the formula $(COOH)_2$. It is an active poison. Oxalic acid is used as a reducing agent, in blueprints, in bleaching flax and straw, in cleaning brass and copper, and in removing ink spots and rust stains.

20. Tartaric acid. This acid has the formula $(CHOH)_2(COOH)_2$. It is obtained from potassium hydrogen tartrate, which collects as a sediment in the bottom of wine barrels. Both tartaric acid and potassium hydrogen tartrate, which is commonly known as *cream of tartar*, are used as the acid substance in some baking powders. The double salt, *sodium potassium tartrate*, $NaKC_4H_4O_6$, is used in medicine under the name of *Rochelle salts*.

21. Citric acid. Citric acid is a white, crystalline solid. It occurs in such fruits as raspberries, gooseberries, and currants, and is present also in lemons, limes, and other citrus fruits. The acid is used in soft drinks. A solution of magnesium citrate is used as a laxative.

22. Salicylic acid. Salicylic acid has the following formula:

It is a white, crystalline solid which is made from phenol, C_6H_5OH. If salicylic acid is treated with methanol, in the presence of sulfuric acid, *methyl salicylate*, or synthetic oil of wintergreen is obtained. Salicylic acid treated with acetic acid yields *acetyl salicylic acid*, better known as *aspirin*. Aspirin has the following formula:

It is used for relieving the discomfort of colds, and to help relieve pain from headaches and other conditions.

23. Esters. An *ester* is produced when an acid reacts with an alcohol. For example, *ethyl acetate* is the ester formed when ethanol and acetic acid react.

$$C_2H_5OH + CH_3COOH \xrightarrow{H_2SO_4}$$
$$CH_3COOC_2H_5 + H_2O$$

Such reactions, which result in the formation of esters, are **esterification reactions.** Reactions between acids and alcohols are reversible. Consequently, sulfuric acid is used to absorb the water that is produced in these reactions, thereby forcing them in the direction of ester formation.

It is possible, too, to have an ester formed by the union of an alcohol with an inorganic acid. *Glyceryl trinitrate,* known as nitroglycerin, is an example.

Esters give fruits their characteristic flavor and odor. *Amyl acetate* has an odor somewhat resembling bananas. As "banana oil" this ester is used as the vehicle for some aluminum paints. *Ethyl butyrate* has an odor and flavor that resembles pineapples. Ripe pineapples contain some of this ester, together with smaller amounts of other esters.

4. SOAPS AND SOAPLESS DETERGENTS

24. Saponification means soap making. *Stearin* is the glyceryl ester of stearic acid. If stearin is treated with an alkali, such as sodium hydroxide, soap and glycerol are formed.

$$\text{stearin}$$
$$C_3H_5(C_{17}H_{35}COO)_3 + 3\ NaOH \rightarrow$$
$$\text{soap}$$
$$3\ C_{17}H_{35}COONa + C_3H_5(OH)_3$$

Stearin is obtained from beef and mutton tallow. *Palmitin,* an ester found in palm oil, and *olein,* an ester found in lard, olive oil, and cottonseed oil, are also used in making soap. Coconut oil contains a high content of *lauric acid,* $C_{11}H_{23}COOH$, and *myristic acid,* $C_{13}H_{27}COOH$. It is also an important raw material for making soap.

Fig. 42-6. **The surface of a kettle of soap that is heated by steam from coils in the bottom of the kettle.** (Procter & Gamble)

25. The kettle method of making soap. In this method, the fats and oils are added to giant kettles. Sodium hydroxide solution is poured in, and the mixture then boiled. When the reaction is complete, sodium chloride is added to "salt out" the colloidal soap from the glycerol and water. The soap is next transferred to a *crutching machine,* in which it is thoroughly mixed. Now, it is run into molds which may hold about 1200 lb each, where it is permitted to solidify. The large blocks are next cut into slabs by means of steel wires. The strips or slabs are then ready for the final cutting and stamping that will convert them into cakes of the desired size and shape.

26. The hydrolyzer method of making soap. In this method, fat is pumped into the bottom of the hydrolyzer, which is a stainless steel tube about three feet in diameter and 70 feet high. The fat rises through superheated water which is pumped into the top of the hydrolyzer. The fat, possibly stearin, undergoes hydrolysis forming an acid, such as stearic acid, and glycerol.

Fig. 42-7. The long vertical steel tube in the photograph is the hydrolyzer used in one method of preparing soap. (Proctor & Gamble)

$$C_3H_5(C_{17}H_{35}COO)_3 + 3\ H_2O \rightarrow$$
$$3\ C_{17}H_{35}COOH + C_3H_5(OH)_3$$

Note that this hydrolysis is the reverse of an esterification reaction. The glycerol is drawn off with the water at the bottom of the hydrolyzer. The stearic acid is drawn off the top. After purification, the stearic acid is reacted with sodium hydroxide to form soap.

$$C_{17}H_{35}COOH + NaOH \rightarrow$$
$$C_{17}H_{35}COONa + H_2O$$

The soap is further processed into cakes as in the kettle method.

The advantage of the hydrolyzer method is that it can be operated on a continuous production basis, whereas the kettle method is essentially a "batch" process.

27. Synthetic detergents. *Synthetic detergents* are products which offer real competition to soap as cleaning agents. These substances are *wetting agents* which lower the surface tension of water, permitting it to spread through the fibers of cloth readily, thus loosening the dirt (see Chap. 33, Section 6). They do not hydrolyze to produce the hydroxide ion, so they can be used for delicate fabrics. They work equally well with hard and soft water, an important advantage in areas where the water is hard.

A number of higher alcohols are used for making wetting agents. One type of synthetic detergent is made by treating lauryl alcohol, $C_{12}H_{25}OH$, with sulfuric acid and sodium hydroxide, to make *sodium lauryl sulfate*. A more common type of synthetic detergent is produced from kerosene. The kerosene is chlorinated, caused to combine with an aromatic hydrocarbon, and then treated with sulfuric acid and sodium hydroxide. The product is an alkylaryl sodium sulfonate.

SUMMARY

Hydrocarbon substitution products may be made by substituting for one or more of the hydrogen atoms in a hydrocarbon an atom such as chlorine, or a group such as hydroxyl. Trichloromethane, chloroform, is a sweet-smelling, colorless liquid used as a solvent and anesthetic. Tetrachloromethane, carbon tetrachloride, is a colorless, volatile liquid used as a solvent and starting material for preparing other halogenated hydrocarbons.

CH_3- is the methyl group. Its name is derived from methane by replacing the suffix –ane with –yl. Other groups, similarly named, are C_2H_5-, ethyl group, and C_3H_7-, propyl group.

Alcohols are a class of compounds with an organic group and one or more hydroxyl groups. Methanol and ethanol are important and well-known compounds. Denatured alcohol is principally ethyl alcohol, to which poisonous and nauseating materials have been added to make it unfit for beverage purposes. Some of the higher alcohols are used as solvents. Ethylene glycol, an alcohol with two hydroxyl groups, is used as "permanent type" antifreeze. Glycerol is a nonpoisonous alcohol that has three hydroxyl groups.

Ethers are organic oxides. Ethyl ether is used as a solvent and as an anesthetic. Aldehydes are organic compounds with one or more –CHO groups. Formaldehyde is the best-known aldehyde. Ketones contain the $>CO$ group. Acetone is well-known ketone. Organic acids have the –COOH, or carboxyl group. Acetic acid is a common organic acid that is present in vinegar. An ester is produced by the reaction of an acid and an alcohol. Many esters have pleasant fruity odors.

Soap is made by the reaction between fats or oils and sodium hydroxide. Synthetic detergents are wetting agents which lower the surface tension of water. They produce no hydroxide ions in solution and may be used with delicate fabrics.

TEST YOURSELF ON THESE TERMS

acetic acid	ester	glycerol
acetone	esterification	hydrolyzer method
alcohol	ethanol	ketone
aldehyde	ether	kettle method
aspirin	ethylene glycol	methanol
carbon tetrachloride	ethyl group	methyl group
carbonyl group	formaldehyde	saponification
carboxyl group	formic acid	stearin
chloroform	formyl group	substitution product
denatured alcohol	Freon	synthetic detergents

QUESTIONS

Group A

1. What are the names and formulas for the four chlorine substitution products of methane?
2. (*a*) What are the uses of carbon tetrachloride? (*b*) What precaution must be exercised in its use?
3. How are the names of the alkyl groups, such as methyl, ethyl, and propyl, derived?
4. What is an important use for 1,2-dibromoethane?
5. What compound is produced in the test for ethanol?
6. How do alcohols differ from inorganic hydroxides?
7. What is the effect of methanol on the human body?

8. How is ethanol produced by the fermentation of molasses?
9. Why is alcohol denatured?
10. What is meant by the term *higher alcohol?*
11. How are ethers prepared?
12. How is formaldehyde used in a biology laboratory?
13. Give several uses for acetone.
14. Where is formic acid found in nature?
15. What is the function of sulfuric acid in an esterification reaction?
16. Why are the common names of esters associated with certain fruits?
17. (*a*) What are synthetic detergents? (*b*) What advantages do they have over soap?

Group B

18. Write the equation for the commercial production of CCl_4.
19. What method is used for preparing dichlorodifluoromethane?
20. What is the characteristic group in: (*a*) an alcohol; (*b*) an ether; (*c*) an aldehyde; (*d*) a ketone; (*e*) an acid?
21. Write the equation for the preparation of ethanol from ethene.
22. What alcohol is used as "permanent type" antifreeze?
23. What property of glycerol makes it useful for keeping tobacco moist?
24. By what method is formaldehyde prepared from methanol?
25. In what three ways may acetic acid be prepared?
26. (*a*) What is the formula for oxalic acid? (*b*) What are its uses?
27. What is unusual about the formula for salicylic acid?
28. Write an equation showing the formation of the ester, butyl acetate.
29. When benzoic acid, C_6H_5COOH, containing O^{16} atoms, reacts with methanol, CH_3OH, containing radioactive O^{18}, each methyl benzoate molecule, $C_6H_5COOCH_3$ contains one O^{18} atom, while the liberated water contains only O^{16} atoms. (*a*) How is the liberated water formed? (*b*) How does this water formation compare with the formation of water in a neutralization reaction?
30. What is the principal advantage of the hydrolyzer method for preparing soap?
31. Why is only one hydronium ion produced when a molecule of acetic acid ionizes, even though there are four hydrogen atoms in the molecule?

SOME THINGS FOR YOU TO DO

1. Ask your instructor to show you the supply of organic chemicals in the laboratory stockroom. Look especially for alcohols, ether, formaldehyde, chloroform, carbon tetrachloride, acetone, benzene, toluene, xylene, phenol, acetic acid, citric acid, and salicylic acid.
2. Prepare synthetic oil of wintergreen, the methyl ester of salicylic acid. Add 0.5 g of salicylic acid to a small Erlenmeyer flask. Pour in 5 ml of methanol, and then cautiously add 2 ml of concentrated sulfuric acid. Warm the flask gently, and note the odor of wintergreen.
3. Make up 1% solutions of various synthetic detergents in water. Determine the pH of such solutions using a suitable indicator.

Chapter 43 · TEXTILES AND PAPER

1. NATURAL FIBERS

1. The nature of textiles. *Textiles* is a collective term for the different fabrics produced by weaving. Threads or yarns are interlaced according to a pattern. The threads or yarns may be derived from vegetable, animal, mineral, or synthetic sources. The yarn is made by combing the fibers so that they lie parallel, and then twisting them together to make a continuous strand. Cotton and linen are frequently bleached with chemicals to produce "white goods." Silk and wool are not so frequently bleached. Some fibers may be dyed before they are made into cloth; others after they are woven.

2. Cotton is our most important fiber. *Cotton fibers* used in textiles vary in length from $\frac{3}{4}$ inch to $2\frac{1}{2}$ inches. The longer the fibers, the better the quality, and the longer the cloth made from them will wear. Under the microscope, individual cotton fibers appear like flattened, twisted tubes. They are nearly pure cellulose, $(C_6H_{10}O_5)_n$. The exact molecular weight is not known, but it is believed that "n" is probably a large number. Cotton absorbs moisture readily and is a poor conductor of heat. When immersed in a concentrated

VOCABULARY

Chromophor. An atom or group of atoms in a molecule which is believed to be responsible for the color of an organic dye.

Mercerizing. The treatment of stretched cotton fibers with concentrated sodium hydroxide.

Spinneret. A metal plate with many small holes used in forming a synthetic fiber.

Textile. A fabric produced by weaving.

Weighting. The repeated dipping of raw silk into a solution of tin chloride or iron chloride.

631

solution of sodium hydroxide, stretched cotton fibers swell, become rounded, more lustrous, and stronger. This process is called *mercerizing.* Cotton burns readily, leaving almost no ash. While alkalies do not injure cotton, acids react with it very readily.

3. Linen is a textile of permanence. *Linen fibers* are obtained from the stem of the flax plant before the seeds mature. Individual fibers are soft, lustrous, and about two feet long. Under the microscope, they appear as transparent tubes, with junctions at intervals. Linen, like cotton, is nearly pure cellulose and has similar chemical properties.

Linen absorbs moisture faster than any other fiber, a property that adapts it for summer garments. The fibers leave no lint on other objects, a property that recommends it for dish towels. Linen fibers are strong, and linen thread is used for sewing when strength is required. Linen lacks *resiliency*; that is, it does not spring back after being folded. This property causes linen garments to wrinkle or crease quite easily.

4. Wool is a fiber for warmth. *Wool* is the curly hair of sheep, and of the mammals such as goats, llamas, alpacas, and camels. It is a good heat insulator because it tends to mat together, enclosing much "dead air." Wool is a protein composed of carbon, hydrogen, oxygen, nitrogen, and sulfur. It burns poorly, with an unpleasant odor, forming a black, charred mass. Under the microscope, wool fibers appear to be made up of tiny, scalelike plates that overlap like shingles. Alkalies damage wool. Concentrated solutions of alkalies, especially when hot, convert wool to soluble materials. Soaps that contain much free alkali injure it. Wool has resiliency and the fibers spring back to their original position after bending or folding. Woolen garments tend to hold their shape better than those made of other natural fibers.

The quality of wool is determined by length of fiber, fineness, luster, and texture. *Virgin wool* is wool that has not previously been woven into cloth. Scraps of unworn woolen cloth are shredded

Fig. 43-1. Cotton fibers (left) and linen fibers (right) as they appear under the microscope. (S. E. DeBerry)

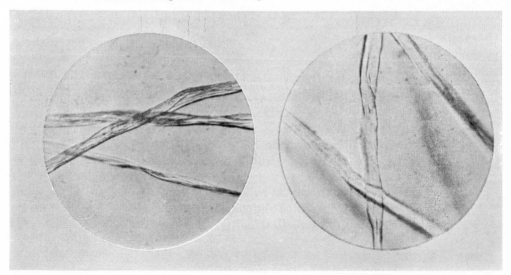

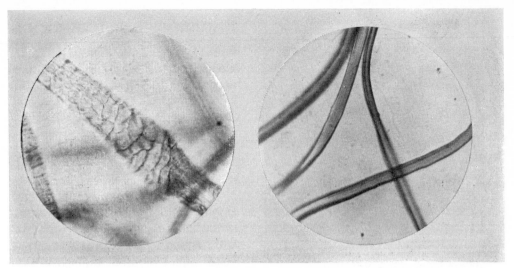

Fig. 43-2. The appearance of wool fibers (left) and silk fibers (right) as viewed through a microscope. (S. E. DeBerry)

into fibers to form *reprocessed wool.* Old, worn, woolen rags are shredded into fibers to form *shoddy.* The shredding operation breaks some of the fibers, so reprocessed wool and shoddy do not wear as well as virgin wool with its greater fiber length.

5. Silk is a luxury fiber. Silk is used to make luxurious fabrics which are admired for their soft luster. Raw silk, obtained by unwinding the cocoons of the silkworm, consists of two proteins, *fibroin* and *sericin.* The fibers are very fine, about 1/2500 inch in diameter, and remarkably strong. They are lustrous, semitransparent, free of joints or scales, and thus smooth to the touch. Silk is elastic and resilient. It burns poorly, swelling to form a gummy mass. Alkalies destroy silk, and acids also injure this fiber. Silk is more readily affected by chemicals than many other textile fibers. It unites with dyes easily, forming brilliantly colored fabrics with a beautiful sheen. Silk unites with the chlorides of tin and iron. Raw silk is dipped repeatedly in solutions of these compounds to form *weighted silk.* Such weighted fabrics tend to crack, particularly when the silk is exposed to light and perspiration. *Pure dye silk* is silk which has not been weighted.

6. Mineral fibers are fireproof. Asbestos is the name given to the fine, silky fibers obtained from *chrysotile*, a hydrated magnesium silicate rock. The peculiar, fibrous nature of this mineral was probably produced by the action of steam on the hot, volcanic rock. It is fireproof, and most acids do not affect it, so it is valuable for making fireproof curtains and pads. It is also used as insulation in the walls and ceilings of houses.

Glass wool, a fluffy mass of very fine fibers of glass, is produced by directing a blast of high pressure steam against molten glass as it issues under pressure from small openings. Glass wool will not burn, does not rot, and is vermin-proof. It makes an excellent heat insulator that is used in the walls of refrigerators. Glass wool can be spun into yarn and woven into cloth which is suitable for filtering corrosive solutions that would destroy ordinary cloth or filter paper. Glass cloth is used for other purposes for which it is adapted because it is nonflammable.

Fig. 43-3. Asbestos is a mineral fiber that will not burn. (Johns Manville)

2. SYNTHETIC FIBERS

7. The production of synthetic fibers. Synthetic fibers are made by forcing a suitable liquid through tiny holes in a metal plate. The plates, called *spinnerets*, are about the size of a dime and have from 10 to 150 holes, depending on the desired size of the fiber. This process imitates that of the silkworm which has two silk-spinning glands located just below the mouth. Some synthetic fibers are ejected directly into an acid bath to convert them from a liquid to a solid. Others are hardened by exposure to warm, dry air.

8. Rayon is regenerated cellulose. Two processes for producing rayon in the United States today are the *viscose process* and the *cuprammonium process*. Wood pulp or cotton linters (fibers of cotton too short for spinning) are the raw materials.

1. *Viscose process.* Sodium hydroxide solution is used to convert wood pulp or cotton linters into a compound called *alkali cellulose.* This is changed to *cellulose xanthate* by treatment with carbon disulfide. The cellulose xanthate is then dissolved in sodium hydroxide to form *viscose solution* which is carefully filtered and then forced through a spinneret into a bath of dilute sulfuric acid. The sulfuric acid reconverts the viscose solution into a continuous glossy transparent filament of cellulose. Several filaments are twisted to form rayon thread. More than 80% of the rayon used in this country is now made by this process.

2. *Cuprammonium process.* In the cuprammonium process, cellulose is dissolved in a mixture of copper(II) sulfate solution and ammonia water. The bluish liquid is forced through a spinneret, first into water, and then into a bath of dilute acid. This process produces Bemberg rayon. Like viscose, it is a *regenerated cellulose;* that is, cellulose which was converted into a liquid, and then back into a solid again. Viscose and cuprammonium rayon lose considerable strength when wet. Perspiration and light gradually weaken them. They burn readily.

9. Cellulose acetate fiber. This type of fiber, formerly called acetate rayon, is made by treating cellulose with acetic

Fig. 43-4. As viscose solution is forced through the spinneret holes into a dilute acid bath, the acid solidifies the viscose streams into rayon filaments. (American Viscose)

Fig. 43-5. **In one process of rayon manufacture, wood fibers (left) are converted into a syrupy liquid called viscose (center). The viscose solution is converted into threads of rayon (right) by passing it through spinnerets.** (American Viscose)

acid, acetic anhydride, and sulfuric acid. When the reaction is complete, the batch is added to water. Cellulose acetate separates as solid, white flakes. The flakes are dissolved in acetone to make a spinning liquid. A cellulose acetate filament is formed by forcing the liquid through a spinneret into a tube through which dry air circulates.

Cellulose acetate loses less strength when wet and is not injured by perspiration and light. A hot iron destroys cellulose acetate fabric because of its low decomposition temperature. Since cellulose acetate is also soluble in some organic solvents, certain dry cleaning fluids will dissolve it.

10. Nylon is a versatile synthetic fiber. *Nylon* is made by a series of complex reactions using coal, air, and water as basic raw materials. It is a strong, elastic fiber that is made by forcing a melted solid through a spinneret. From the basic raw materials, two complex compounds, *adipic acid* and *hexamethylene diamine* are produced. Combination of these chemicals forms molecules of a solid called *nylon salt*, which polymerize to form giant molecules. The polymerized nylon salt is melted and forced through a spinneret. The filaments are stretched to about four times

their original length, thus increasing the strength and elasticity of the finished product. The elasticity of nylon has made it a popular fiber for use in hosiery.

Nylon is lustrous, very strong, wears well, shrinks little, can be washed easily, and is not injured by water or dry cleaning solvents. Mildew and clothes moths do not affect it. The melted nylon salt can be colored before spinning, or the finished yarn can be dyed. Thus nylon can appear in a variety of attractive colors.

11. Other synthetic fibers. Many other synthetic fibers are being used today. Each of them has some special property or use to recommend it. *Acrilan, Orlon,* and *Dynel* are fibers which are made from acrylonitrile. Acrilan is used to make synthetic furs and sturdy carpeting. Orlon yarn is knitted into fine sweaters. Dynel is good for suits; it withstands rain well. *Dacron* is a polyester fiber used for curtains. Alone, or blended with long-fiber Egyptian cotton, it makes a quick-drying fabric for shirts, blouses, and suits, that requires no ironing. *Vinyon* is made by polymerizing vinyl chloride and vinyl acetate. It withstands acids, water, and chemicals. *Velon* is a polymerized vinylidene chloride. It is not affected by sun or perspiration. *Saran* is another vinylidene chloride textile that is strong and wears well. It is used for outdoor furniture. V*icara* is made from zein, which comes from corn. Vicara is not strong but it is a fiber which can be blended easily. Further research promises more useful synthetic fibers.

3. BLEACHING AND DYEING

12. The common bleaching agents. Natural fibers are commonly bleached when white yarn or white fabrics are desired. Cotton and linen have for many years been bleached with sunlight, but sunlight bleaches so slowly that chemicals are usually used today. Chlorine and hydrogen peroxide are used for bleaching vegetable fibers. Sulfur dioxide, hydrogen peroxide, and sodium "perborate," actually sodium peroxyborate, $NaBO_2 \cdot 3 H_2O \cdot H_2O_2$, are used for bleaching animal fibers.

13. The bleaching of cotton. Chlorine bleaches cotton *indirectly*, because

Fig. 43-6. Ropes of Dacron polyester fiber greatly outlast ordinary ropes.

it is the oxygen set free from the bleaching solution that actually decolorizes the cloth. Several methods for utilizing chlorine for bleaching are in use. One method uses chlorine gas dissolved in water. A second method uses a solution of sodium hypochlorite. *Clorox*, for example, is prepared by dissolving chlorine in sodium carbonate solution. A third method uses H.T.H. (high test hypochlorite), a triple salt of sodium hypochlorite, calcium hypochlorite, and sodium chloride. In a fourth method, a new heavy-duty dry bleach, *Halane*, may be dissolved in water to produce a solution of sodium hypochlorite. Hydrogen peroxide is used in increasing amounts for industrial bleaching of cotton, now that a cheaper method of producing hydrogen peroxide by electrolysis is available.

14. The bleaching of wool and silk. Wool and silk are animal fibers that are destroyed by chlorine. Hence other chemicals must be used to bleach them. Sulfur dioxide gas has long been used as the bleaching agent, but it does not give permanent results because the fibers regain their color slowly when exposed to air. Hydrogen peroxide is now favored for bleaching these textiles.

New powdered bleaches containing sodium "perborate" may also be used for bleaching silk and wool, as well as rayon, nylon, and other synthetic fibers. The mild bleaching action of the oxygen released by sodium "perborate" in water whitens the fabric without chemically injuring it.

15. Optical bleaches make cloth appear whiter. Some manufacturers of detergents include an optical bleach in their product. Optical bleaches are also used by those who weave cloth from various synthetic fibers. An *optical bleach* is a substance which remains in

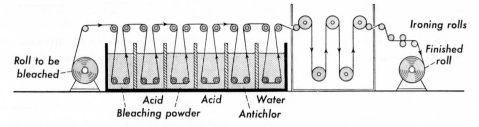

Fig. 43-7. **A commercial method of bleaching cotton goods.**

the cloth after washing or rinsing. Optical bleaches have the property of absorbing ultraviolet light from sunlight and converting it into visible blue light. The restoration of this blue light in the light reflected from white cloth makes it appear whiter, as though it had been more thoroughly bleached.

16. Dyes are produced from coal tar. Formerly, dyers used extracts from leaves, roots, berries, and barks for dyeing cloth. A few animal products and some mineral compounds were also used. Good dyes were expensive and the variety of colors limited. The discovery of synthetic *mauve* in 1856 by William H. Perkin (1838–1907) began a new industry, the manufacture of coal tar dyes. *There are no dyes in coal tar,* but when coal tar is fractionally distilled, benzene, naphthalene, and anthracene are separated from the black, sticky liquid. These serve as raw materials for the preparation of more complex materials called **intermediates.** From the intermediates, by a series of reactions, still more complex compounds are produced which have brilliant colors. These colored substances are often called *coal tar dyes* because coal tar furnishes the basic raw materials. All of the dyes have complex structures and long chemical names. Whether an organic compound will be a bright dye or a colorless compound seems to depend on the presence of certain groups called **chromophors.** One of the common chromophors is the *azo group* $(-N=N-)$. The molecules of many dyes contain this group. For example, the structural formula of methyl orange, a dye which is often used as an indicator, is given below:

Notice the presence of the azo group in the formula above. The chemical name for methyl orange is *sodium dimethyl-aminoazobenzene sulfonate.* This name and formula are given merely to show the complexity of composition of coal tar dyes. Other dyes have similarly complex structures.

17. Several classes of dyes are used. There are hundreds of different dyes in common use. Some are adapted for wool and silk, others are used for cotton and linen. Special dyes are used for acetate fabrics. In general, the animal fibers are easier to dye than the vegetable fibers. Some of the common classes of dyes are:

1. Direct dyes. Direct dyes can be used for all the natural fibers. The fabric is immersed in a solution of the dye and allowed to simmer until the dye has been absorbed.

2. *Acid dyes.* Acid dyes are the alkaline salts of complex color acids. They give bright, fast colors with wool and silk but do not cling to cotton and linen. Acid dyes do not fade in light. Fabrics that have been dyed with acid colors must not be washed with alkali because the dye is removed as the alkali reacts with the color acid.

3. *Mordant dyes.* Mordant dyes are those which require a preparatory chemical to make the dye cling to cotton and linen. There are different groups of mordant dyes. One such group is the *basic dyes*, of which methyl violet, methylene blue, fuchsine, and malachite green are well-known examples.

To dye cotton with one of these dyes, the cloth is first soaked in a solution of aluminum sulfate. Then the cloth is dipped in ammonia water without rinsing. The sticky precipitate of aluminum hydroxide is the **mordant** that fills the flattened tubes of the cotton fibers. The cloth is then immersed in the dye bath. The basic dye unites with the mordant held by the fiber, coloring it with a bright, fast color. Salts of iron, chromium, and tin are used in the same manner as aluminum sulfate. By using different chemical compounds with the same dye, it is often possible to get a variety of shades of color.

4. *Vat dyes.* Indigo is a good example of a vat dye. In the presence of a reducing agent, indigo white is produced. It is soluble in alkalies. When cotton is saturated with indigo white solution, and then exposed to air, oxidation takes place. The indigo white changes to *insoluble indigo blue*, which is firmly deposited within the fibers. It is a very fast (permanent) dye which is popular for overalls because it is fast to light and washing. It is also used to dye wool yarn for men's suits.

4. PAPER

18. Paper is a fibrous material. Paper is made from cellulose. The principal raw materials are wood pulp and the fibers of cotton and linen. To make paper, the fibers are separated by chipping, shredding, and beating the raw material. Bleaching is usually necessary when making white paper. The fibers are mixed with a large volume of water to make a thin suspension called "soup" by the papermaker. This soup is forced through a thin slit onto a moving wire screen. As the water drains through the wire screen, the fibers become tangled together to form a fibrous sheet. The fibrous sheet then passes over rollers that squeeze out the excess water and iron the surface to a smooth finish. Finely-divided materials are added to the paper stock in the beater, a machine that disintegrates the cellulose into fibers. These materials add weight and body to the

Fig. 43-8. Poplar, spruce, and certain kinds of pine are the source of pulp for ordinary paper. (International Paper)

Fig. 43-9. **In this beater, wood pulp is separated into individual fibers for papermaking.** (International Paper)

paper, and prevent ink from running. The surface of some paper is coated with casein or gelatin to add gloss to the sheets.

19. Mechanical pulp. *Pulp* is the name given to the crude sheets of tangled fibers first produced from logs of poplar, spruce, or certain kinds of pine. Wood contains *lignin* in addition to cellulose. If the wood is merely ground to fibers, and formed into sheets, the product is called **mechanical pulp**. Newspapers are printed on bleached mechanical pulp because it it cheap and can be produced in quantity.

20. Chemical pulp. *Chemical pulp* is also made from wood, but the wood chips are *digested*, or boiled under pressure, with a chemical solution to remove the lignin. Three processes for making chemical pulp are in use at the present time.

1. Sulfite process. The wood chips are digested with a solution of calcium hydrogen sulfite, $Ca(HSO_3)_2$, and sulfur dioxide, SO_2, in large boilers under pressure. After digestion, the fibrous mass is bleached with chlorine to make white stock. Sulfite pulp is of good quality and

is the principal component of book paper and the white paper used in schools.
2. Soda process. Poplar logs are commonly converted into pulp by the soda process. The chips are digested with a solution of sodium hydroxide to get rid of the lignin. The digested material is bleached with chlorine, as in the sulfite process.
3. Sulfate process. The sulfate process produces "Kraft" paper from southern pine trees. The chips are digested with sodium sulfate and sodium hydroxide. The resin and lignin are removed by the digesting operation.

21. The difference between pulp and paper. *Pulp* is the crude, fibrous material obtained from wood, and formed into sheets. *Paper* is a refined product made by blending different kinds of pulp, adding weighting chemicals, and again forming into sheets. Most paper is also given a surface coating so that it will take ink better.

22. Rag paper. Cotton and linen rags make paper of the highest quality. The rags are disintegrated into fibers in a beater. The beater is an elliptical-shaped tank that is fitted with revolving knives

Fig. 43-10. **This huge paper-making machine produces a sheet of paper 16 feet in width and weighing about 10 tons. (West Virginia Pulp and Paper)**

that tear the fibers apart. The rag stock is mixed with a large volume of water, and circulates around and around through the beater, passing through the knives at each revolution. Finely-divided barium sulfate, calcium carbonate, and other powders are added to the stock in the beater as weighting agents. After the stock has been completely disintegrated in the beater, it passes through the papermaking machine. The papermaking, or **Fourdrinier** (for-*drin*-ih-err) *machine* converts the stock into sheets.

Paper that contains no other fibers than those from cotton and linen is called 100% rag content. It is the most expensive paper and is used for important documents. Rag paper will stand folding and creasing many times without breaking. It does not become brittle,

even after many years. United States paper money is printed on rag paper that has a few colored fibers of silk or nylon scattered through it to prevent counterfeiting. By mixing rag stock with different percentages of wood pulp, many different qualities of paper are made for particular purposes.

23. Cellophane is regenerated cellulose. *Cellophane* is not paper because it is not a sheet of tangled fibers. It is made from cotton linters by a process similar to that for making viscose rayon. The viscose solution, however, instead of being extruded through a spinneret to form fibers, is extruded through a narrow slit. The viscose is solidified into transparent sheets by passage through an acid bath. It may be waterproofed with transparent lacquer.

SUMMARY

Cotton is the most important natural fiber. It is nearly pure cellulose. Alkalies do not injure cotton, but acids react with it readily. Linen is a fiber of permanence. It is also cellulose and is derived from the flax plant. Linen absorbs moisture faster than other fibers. Wool is the fiber for warmth. It is a protein which has a scaly appearance under the microscope. Alkalies damage wool. Silk is a luxury fiber, composed of two proteins.

Asbestos is a fireproof mineral fiber obtained from a silicate rock. Glass wool makes an excellent, fireproof heat insulator. It is sometimes woven into glass cloth.

Synthetic fibers are made by forcing a suitable liquid through tiny holes in a metal plate called a spinneret. Rayon, regenerated cellulose, is made from cellulose by the viscose process and the cuprammonium process. Cellulose acetate is made by treating cellulose with acetic acid, acetic anhydride, and sulfuric acid. Nylon is a versatile synthetic fiber. Many other synthetic fibers are produced.

Sunlight, chlorine, and hydrogen peroxide are used for bleaching cotton and linen. Sulfur dioxide, hydrogen peroxide, and sodium peroxyborate are used for bleaching animal fibers.

Dyes were formerly derived from plant sources but today they are synthesized as complex organic chemicals. Cotton and linen require dyes that are different from those used to dye wool and silk. Some dyes are made fast to the cloth with the aid of mordants.

Paper is a fibrous material that is made from wood pulp or the fibers of cotton and linen. Mechanical pulp is made from wood, ground to fibers. Chemical pulp is digested with chemicals to remove the lignin from the wood chips. Rag paper is the strongest, most lasting, and the most expensive paper. Cellophane is regenerated cellulose.

TEST YOURSELF ON THESE TERMS

asbestos	dye intermediate	paper
bleaching	glass wool	pulp
cellophane	linen	rayon
cellulose acetate	mechanical pulp	silk
chemical pulp	mercerizing	spinnerets
chromophor	mordant	textile
cotton	nylon	weighting
dye	optical bleach	wool

QUESTIONS

Group A

1. What are four sources of textile fibers?
2. (*a*) How is cotton mercerized? (*b*) How does this improve the cotton?
3. Why is linen fiber preferred for dish towels?
4. Why are winter suits and overcoats made of wool?
5. What are the differences between *virgin wool, reprocessed wool,* and *shoddy?*
6. How do linen and cotton differ in composition from silk and wool?
7. What are the uses for glass wool?
8. What raw material is used for making rayon?
9. Why are nylon filaments stretched after being formed?
10. Which synthetic fiber is used for making synthetic furs?

11. Of which synthetic fiber is the seating material of outdoor furniture commonly made?
12. Why do we call certain dyes *coal tar dyes?*
13. What are the main classes of dyes?
14. What is the difference between pulp and paper?
15. How is newsprint made?
16. What is the difference between viscose rayon fiber and cellophane?

Group B

17. What are the physical and chemical properties of cotton?
18. What would be likely to happen if a wool sweater were washed with laundry soap?
19. Why is asbestos fireproof?
20. How are fibers formed from synthetic substances?
21. What chemical is now being used to bleach all the natural fibers?
22. What types of fibers can be successfully bleached with sodium "perborate"?
23. How do "optical bleaches" make white cloth appear whiter?
24. What is the function of a mordant in dyeing?
25. What are the three kinds of chemical pulp?
26. What is the appearance under the microscope of: (*a*) cotton fiber; (*b*) linen fiber; (*c*) wool fiber; (*d*) silk fiber; (*e*) rayon fiber?
27. Describe the chemical changes which occur during the viscose process for making rayon.
28. How does cellulose acetate fiber differ from rayon?
29. Why do we say that chlorine bleaches cotton *indirectly?*
30. What is H.T.H.?
31. What is meant by a chromophor in a dye molecule?

SOME THINGS FOR YOU TO DO

1. Unravel threads of cotton, linen, silk, wool, rayon, and nylon so that they are separated into individual fibers. Examine each kind separately under a compound microscope. Make a sketch of each fiber.
2. Procure a sample of cloth that is about half wool and half cotton. Gently boil a two-inch square of the cloth for 5 minutes in 5% solution of sodium hydroxide. The wool will dissolve completely, leaving the cotton. Examine the rinsed, dried residue of cotton.
3. Pluck apart the silky fibers from a piece of asbestos rock. Twist some of the fibers into a thread. See if it will burn.
4. Examine the labels of the powdered bleaches on your grocer's shelves to learn the active bleaching ingredient in each.

Chapter 44 · RUBBER AND PLASTICS

1. RUBBER

1. The nature of rubber. *Rubber* is a plastic hydrocarbon obtained from the sap of rubber trees. A milky fluid, called *latex*, drips from V-shaped gashes in the trunks of the trees. Each tree gives about an ounce of latex a day. Latex contains about 35% rubber in colloidal suspension. When acetic acid is added to latex, the rubber *coagulates*, or gathers into a mass. After being washed and dried, it is shipped to market in large sheets of crude rubber.

The simplest formula for rubber is $(C_5H_8)_x$. The C_5H_8 unit is presumed to have this structure:

The "x" is believed to be a large number. Consequently, rubber molecules are giants when compared with many simpler molecules. C_5H_8 is called a *monomer* (single part). When many monomers join, the giant molecule is called a *polymer* (many parts). Rubber is thus a polymer of C_5H_8. The monomers in rubber are joined in a zigzag chain that accounts for its elasticity.

VOCABULARY

Monomer. A simple molecule, or single unit of a polymer.

Plastic. A natural or synthetic material which can be shaped while soft into a required form and then hardened to produce a durable finished article.

Polymer. A compound formed by two or more simpler molecules or radicals.

Vulcanization. The heating of rubber with other materials to improve its properties.

643

Fig. 44-1. **Rubber for coating tire fabrics being fed into a rubber mill.** (U. S. Rubber)

2. The compounding of rubber. Raw rubber is mixed with a number of powdered solids between heavy rollers in a machine called a *mill*. The rubber, sulfur, and other powders forming the batch are squeezed through the rollers over and over again until they are thoroughly mixed. The formula for the batch varies according to the products to be made. Sulfur is always one of the many ingredients used in making rubber. Automobile tires contain considerable amounts of carbon black. This increases the wearing qualities of the tires by forming bonds between the rubber molecules. Zinc oxide is added to many batches to produce white rubber. Diantimony trisulfide yields red rubber. Organic catalysts, known as *accelerators*, are added to speed the vulcanization process. **Anti-oxidants** are also organic chemicals that prevent the rubber from becoming hard and brittle. A certain percentage of reclaimed rubber from old automobile tires is usually added to the batch. Very cheap rubber goods may have various fillers, such as whiting or clay, added. After mixing, the product is shaped either in a mold or from thin sheets. The whole mass is then vulcanized. *Vulcanization is the heating of the rubber mixture to a definite temperature for a definite time.* It gives the article a permanent shape, makes the rubber more elastic, and causes it to lose its sticky qualities. The changes which occur during vulcanization are many and complex. It is believed, however, that the sulfur atoms form cross-linkages between adjacent rubber molecules.

Foam rubber is used as an upholstery material for cushions and mattresses. One process for making foam rubber is to mix ammonium carbonate with the batch in the mill. The heat of vulcanization forms bubbles of ammonia, carbon dioxide, and water vapor within the rubber. In another process, air is whipped into latex in a mixing machine. The air expands during vulcanization, forming bubbles within the rubber.

3. Thiokol, the first commercial synthetic rubber. Thiokol was developed in the late 1920's by J. C. Patrick, who discovered it while experimenting to find a cheaper antifreeze solution. It is made from 1,2-dichloroethane, $ClCH_2CH_2Cl$, and sodium polysulfide, Na_2S_x. It is vulcanized by using zinc oxide. The structural unit of Thiokol is:

$$-S-S-\underset{\underset{H}{|}}{\overset{\overset{H}{|}}{C}}-\underset{\underset{H}{|}}{\overset{\overset{H}{|}}{C}}-S-S-$$

Thiokol does not swell, rot or change its physical properties when in contact with gasoline, chemicals, or air. It remains firm and rubbery over a wide temperature range. Thiokol is used for lining fuel and paint spray hose, for printing rollers, and as a sealant in airplane fuel

Fig. 44-2. **Tires are formed and vulcanized in "watchcase" molds.** (U. S. Rubber)

tanks. When Thiokol is mixed with an oxidizing agent, it produces a solid fuel which is used in rockets and missiles.

4. Neoprene, a hydrocarbon synthetic rubber. Scientists produced hydrocarbon synthetic rubber about 1910 by polymerizing isoprene, C_5H_8. However, the cost was too high to compete with natural rubber from plantations in the East Indies. In 1931 *neoprene*, a successful hydrocarbon synthetic rubber, appeared on the market. The research work of Dr. J. A. Nieuwland of the University of Notre Dame made neoprene possible. Ethyne (acetylene) is converted into vinyl acetylene using copper salts as catalysts.

$$H—C\equiv C—H \xrightarrow{catalyst} \overset{\displaystyle H \quad H}{\underset{\displaystyle H}{C=C—C\equiv C—H}}$$

acetylene   vinyl acetylene

When treated with hydrochloric acid, vinyl acetylene yields chloroprene:

$$\overset{\displaystyle H \quad H}{\underset{\displaystyle H}{C=C—C\equiv C—H}} + HCl \rightarrow \overset{\displaystyle H \quad H \qquad H}{\underset{\displaystyle H \quad Cl \ H}{C=C—C=C}}$$

vinyl acetylene   chloroprene

The catalytic polymerization of chloroprene yields neoprene. The structural unit of neoprene is:

Fig. 44-3. **A foam rubber cushion being removed from its mold.** (U. S. Rubber)

is made by cracking petroleum, or from alcohol. Styrene,

Fig. 44-4. **Neoprene is used for the tube and cover of gasoline hoses at filling stations.** (E. I. du Pont)

is made from benzene, or from petroleum. Churning in soapy water at 41° F, using cumene hydroperoxide as a catalyst, causes the chemicals to polymerize to form GR–S rubber. The addition of an acid causes the rubber to separate in curd-like masses, which are washed and dried. The structural unit of GR–S is:

GR–S is a good all-purpose synthetic rubber. It can be used in place of natural rubber for most purposes. GR–S is excellent for tire treads because it resists wear better than other synthetic rubbers. More than three-quarters of a million tons have been produced in one year in synthetic rubber factories in the United States.

Oils and greases, which act on natural rubber, causing it to swell and rot, have little effect on neoprene. Hence this synthetic material is used for gasoline hoses at filling stations.

5. GR–S, the synthetic for tires. GR–S (Government Rubber-Styrene), formerly called *Buna S*, is used for automobile tires. It is made by churning *butadiene* and *styrene* together in soapy water. Butadiene,

6. Other synthetic rubbers. GR–I, or butyl rubber, is made from *isobutylene* and *isoprene*. These materials react at −140° F with aluminum chloride used as a catalyst. GR–I holds air better than natural rubber and is used for inner tubes. It also resists the action of ozone and many other chemicals.

Nitrile rubber is produced from acrylonitrile and butadiene. While produced in much smaller quantities than GR–S and GR–I, nitrile rubber is important because it does not swell on contact with oils and greases.

Silicone rubber has the remarkable property of being usable over the wide temperature range of −130° F to +500° F. The long-chain molecules of silicone rubber consist of alternate silicon and oxygen atoms, with some carbon groups as side chains. This rubber is colorless and not readily affected by solvents.

Hypalon synthetic rubber is produced by reacting polyethylene with chlorine and sulfur dioxide. Hypalon can be colored in an unlimited range of colors which do not fade. It has high resistance to weather and chemicals.

A process has been developed for producing a synthetic rubber of the same composition as natural rubber by polymerization of isoprene at 104° F, using finely-divided lithium as a catalyst. This material is expected to supplant natural rubber in increasing amounts. Many new rubber-like materials are rapidly being developed by the laboratories of rubber, petroleum, and chemical companies. Some of these are halogenated hydrocarbons, polymerized alkenes, and organometallic polymers.

2. PLASTICS

7. The nature of plastics. The term *plastics* was originally applied to those substances that could be formed or shaped by molding. In its broadest meaning, it includes such diverse materials as glass, steel, rubber, and rosin, as well as the familiar celluloid and Bakelite. A more limited meaning has come

Fig. 44-5. **This picture diagram shows the relative amounts of the raw materials used to produce GR–S synthetic rubber. The nine ingredients at the left form a milklike latex after about 12 hours in the steel pressure kettle. The finished rubber at the right is produced after the removal of water from the latex by coagulation and drying. GR–S rubber is composed only of butadiene and styrene. The other ingredients serve to regulate and accelerate the chemical changes.** (U. S. Rubber)

into general use, so that we usually understand plastics to be hard, gummy solids. Chemists think of plastics as **synthetic resins,** as distinguished from such natural resins as rosin and shellac. Plastics may be made from the raw materials of nature, or from synthetic chemicals. The number of different plastics that can be produced and the different useful products which can be made from them seem to be limitless.

8. There are two general types of synthetic plastics. Synthetic plastics may be divided into two groups, *thermoplastic* and *thermosetting.* Those which are **thermoplastic** may be softened and changed in shape by gentle heating. Plastic eyeglass frames are thermoplastic. By careful heating, the optician adjusts the length of the bows to fit the wearer. The **thermosetting plastics,** once heated, set into a hard mass which cannot be softened. Bakelite is a good example of a thermosetting plastic. Radio cabinets and the outer cases of telephone sets are made from thermosetting plastics and cannot be changed in shape after they are formed.

The nature of the reaction that produces the plastic seems to be the factor that determines whether a plastic will be thermoplastic or thermosetting. Thermoplastic resins are *polymerization* products. That is, molecules join other similar molecules to form a large cluster. Lucite and Krene are two thermoplastic materials. Thermosetting plastics are produced by *condensation* reactions. When the two chemicals used to form them unite, water is set free. For example, when phenol and formaldehyde solution are heated together, water and Bakelite resin are produced.

9. Properties determine the uses for individual plastics. The uses for a particular plastic depend on its properties.

Such properties as resistance to acids, bases, water, oils, and organic solvents have been carefully determined and catalogued for each of the commercial plastics. Combustibility, electric insulating properties, hardness, resistance to scratching, strength, toughness, ease of machining, and solubility in oils are other important properties.

Phenolic plastics are excellent insulators and are used for making parts of electric appliances. Polystyrene plastics are not affected by water and are used for bathroom tiles. Urea-formaldehyde plastics are hard and tough. They are used for making the cases of computing scales which must withstand hard knocks. Methyl methacrylate plastics are transparent, adapting them for lenses or full-view airplane nosepieces. Polyethylene is semiflexible and resists the action of water and many other liquids. Consequently, it is used for nonbreakable containers for these liquids. Plastics which are soluble in oils can be used to make enamel paints. A plastic that may be excellent for one purpose may be entirely unfitted for another. Hence the study of the properties of plastics is very important in this industry.

10. The uses of plastics. Plastics may appear on the market in the form of sheets, rods, or blocks, from which various objects can be fabricated. Thermosetting plastics are sold by the manufacturers in the form of "molding powders." Wood flour or asbestos may be mixed with the plastic material as a filler. A weighted quantity of molding powder is placed between two heated dies in a powerful hydraulic press. By heat and pressure, the molding powder is converted into a plastic that takes the shape of the die. After a short time interval that varies according to the thickness of the piece, the press opens and

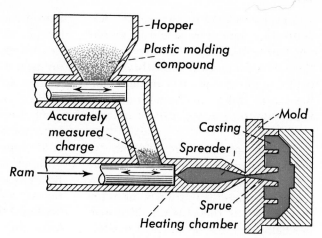

Fig. 44-6. **This diagram shows how plastic articles are manufactured by injection molding.**

the finished article pops out. Radio cabinets and small kitchen articles are made in this manner. The material that composes the molding powder undergoes condensation during heating.

Thermosetting plastics are used to make many laminated articles. *Laminated* means built up in layers or plates. Sheets of cotton cloth or paper are dipped in Bakelite varnish, and then piled one on top of another until the desired thickness is secured. When the pile is placed in a hydraulic press, and heat and pressure are applied, a hard plastic sheet is the result. Laminated plastics are used for making gears, electric distribution panels, and such articles as airplane propellers.

Plasticizers such as camphor and castor oil are sometimes mixed with the plastic substance to make it easier to work, or to increase the hardness of the final product. *Lubricants* such as wax or stearic acid are sometimes added to free the plastic from the mold easily. *Accelerators* like calcium oxide, zinc chloride, and oxalic acid are used to speed up the polymerization process. Coloring materials may be added so as to produce any desired shade in the finished product.

11. Some well-known synthetic plastics.

1. Cellulose nitrate. Cellulose nitrate is made by the reaction between cotton and nitric acid. Sulfuric acid is mixed with the nitric acid to absorb the water produced in the reaction. The nitrated cotton is dissolved in a mixture of alcohol and ether. When the solvent evaporates, a jelly-like mass is left. *Celluloid* is a cellulose nitrate plastic to which camphor has been added to serve as a plasticizer. First produced in 1869, it is the oldest of the synthetic plastics. Celluloid is highly flammable and, if ignited, burns with a flash, a disadvantage that limits its uses.

2. Phenolic plastics. When phenol is boiled with a solution of formaldehyde in the presence of a catalyst, a hard, gummy residue is produced. Bakelite is a thermosetting plastic produced in this manner. Cresol, C_7H_7OH, can be used instead of phenol, and other aldehydes can be used in place of formaldehyde. Thus a group of plastics can be made from these related chemicals. The phenolic plastics are incombustible and resist the action of chemicals and solvents well and thus can be used for a variety of products.

3. *Urea-formaldehyde.* Synthetic urea, $CO(NH_2)_2$, and formaldehyde heated together with a catalyst produce a plastic notable for its great strength. Articles made from this plastic include "unbreakable" dishes and water tumblers, besides buttons and a variety of novelties.

4. *Vinylite plastics.* Krene resins are mixtures of polymers of vinyl chloride and vinyl acetate. Ethyne is the raw material used as the starting point in the manufacture of these plastics. Transparent belts are made of this plastic, while the textile known as Vinyon has a similar composition. Vinylite phonograph records are popular because they are nonbreakable.

5. *Polystyrene.* Styrene, C_8H_8, was mentioned during the description of rubber, earlier in this chapter. Styrene is polymerized to form a plastic known as *polystyrene.* This plastic is unaffected by water, a property that adapts it for certain uses.

6. *Methacrylates.* One of the most popular of the plastics is the group known as the methacrylate resins. Ethyne is the raw material for making this group, just as it was for making Vinylite resins. Methyl methacrylate is the best known of the group. It is marketed under the names Lucite and Plexiglas. It is particularly notable for its clear transparency. It machines well and is strong and shatterproof. Some of the uses for the plastic are: lenses, toilet articles, fancy jewel boxes, costume jewelry, and, when colored pink, imitation gums in which false teeth are mounted in making dental plates.

7. *Polyethylene* and *polypropylene.* Ethylene may be polymerized at high pressure, with a catalyst, to form a soft, semi-flexible plastic which is molded into bottles or produced in sheet form for making bags. Polyethylene bottles are the familiar "squeeze" bottles in which toiletries are marketed. Polyethylene bags are used by laundries for wrapping clean shirts, dresses, and blankets. These bags may also be used for packing new merchandise, such as shoes or purses. Polypropylene is another polymerized alkene synthetic plastic which is finding significant use in injection-molded housewares, in sheeting, and in rope and webbing.

8. *Tetrafluorethylene.* Ethene (ethylene) with four fluorine atoms substituted for the hydrogen atoms, may also be polymerized to form a useful plastic. It may be produced in the form of fibers for making chemical-resistant fabrics, or as rods from which small parts may be machined. Tetrafluorethylene plastic has a very low coefficient of friction, and is used in applications where heat-resistant, nonlubricated moving parts are needed.

These examples of types of plastics which are being manufactured today are not to be considered as a complete

Fig. 44-7. Cabinets for portable television sets made of polystyrene. (Union Carbide)

list of all plastic materials available. In fact, it has been possible to give here only a few of the main types of plastics. However, enough have been listed to show that the field of plastics is large and still growing. It is possible to make many types of plastics related to these we have discussed, by using slightly different, but related, chemical starting materials.

SUMMARY

Latex is a milky fluid that is obtained from the sap of the rubber tree. When acetic acid is added to latex, the rubber, which is dispersed in the fluid, coagulates into a solid mass. Rubber is a polymer of a hydrocarbon whose simplest formula is C_5H_8. Rubber is compounded in a mill with sulfur and other powders. Carbon black added to the batch makes a rubber that wears well, especially for automobile tires. Zinc oxide is used for making white rubber, and diantimony trisulfide for red rubber. After mixing, the batch of raw rubber is formed into shape, and is then vulcanized by heating it to a definite temperature for a definite time. Vulcanization gives the article a permanent shape, makes the rubber more elastic, and causes it to lose its sticky qualities.

Thiokol was the first commercial synthetic rubber. Thiokol is used for lining fuel and paint spray hoses, and as a sealant in airplane fuel tanks. Neoprene is a hydrocarbon synthetic rubber. It is used for gasoline hoses at filling stations. GR–S is a synthetic rubber used for tires. GR–I is used for inner tubes. A synthetic rubber having the same composition as natural rubber is also being produced.

Plastics are substances that can be formed by molding. They may be made from raw materials of nature, or from synthetic chemicals. Synthetic plastics may be divided into two classes, thermoplastic and thermosetting. The uses for individual plastics are determined by the set of properties that pertain to each. There are many different synthetic plastics, including the following: 1. cellulose nitrate; 2. phenolic; 3. urea-formaldehyde; 4. vinylite; 5. polystyrene; 6. methacrylates; 7. polyethylene and polypropylene; and 8. tetrafluorethylene.

TEST YOURSELF ON THESE TERMS

accelerators	lubricant	polymerization
anti-oxidant	methacrylates	polystyrene
cellulose nitrate	monomer	tetrafluorethylene
coagulate	neoprene	thermoplastic
foam rubber	phenolic plastic	thermosetting
GR–I	plastic	Thiokol
GR–S	plasticizer	urea-formaldehyde
laminated	polyethylene	vinylite
latex	polymer	vulcanization

Group A

1. What is the difference between a monomer and a polymer?
2. What probably accounts for the elasticity of rubber?
3. How is rubber compounded?
4. What is *vulcanization?*
5. What property of Thiokol makes it useful in airplane fuel tanks?
6. What advantage does neoprene have over natural rubber?
7. What does the chemist usually mean by the term *plastics?*
8. What are some of the properties of a plastic that determine whether or not it is suitable for a particular purpose?
9. How are laminated articles made?
10. (*a*) What is celluloid? (*b*) What disadvantage does it have?

Group B

11. How is rubber coagulated from its colloidal suspension in latex?
12. Why are accelerators and anti-oxidants used in making rubber goods?
13. How may foam rubber be made?
14. (*a*) What materials are polymerized to produce GR–S rubber? (*b*) What is an important use for GR–S rubber? (*c*) Why is it used for this purpose?
15. (*a*) What is an important use for GR–I rubber? (*b*) Why is it used for this purpose?
16. What atoms comprise the long-chain molecules of silicone rubber?
17. What substances are included in the broadest meaning of *plastics?*
18. (*a*) What is the difference between a *thermoplastic* and a *thermosetting* plastic? (*b*) Give an example of each.
19. What do the following terms mean in the plastics industry: (*a*) *plasticizers;* (*b*) *accelerators;* (*c*) *lubricants;* (*d*) *pigments?*
20. Give an outstanding characteristic of each of the following plastics: (*a*) urea-formaldehyde; (*b*) phenolic; (*c*) polystyrene; (*d*) methacrylate; (*e*) vinylite; (*f*) polyethylene; (*g*) tetrafluorethylene.

SOME THINGS FOR YOU TO DO

1. Procure a blowout repair kit from an automobile supply store. The sheet rubber in the repair kit is unvulcanized stock. Note how sticky it is. Get an old inner tube and apply a patch, following the directions that come with the repair kit. Note how vulcanization of the sheet rubber is accomplished. Is the patch still sticky?
2. Test the difference between thermoplastic and thermosetting plastics under the influence of heat. An old pair of eyeglass frames will serve as a thermoplastic substance. Bakelite objects are thermosetting. Other plastic objects that are no longer useful may be used for the test. Immerse each in hot water in a beaker and observe which ones can be changed in shape by gentle heating.

CHECK YOUR PROGRESS IN CHEMISTRY

1. What factors should be considered in choosing a fuel?
2. What evidence do we have that coal was once vegetation?
3. What is bottled gas?
4. By what process is petroleum separated into the various useful products?
5. What are the substances used as standards in rating gasoline?
6. For what purpose is petroleum coke used?
7. Draw an electron-dot formula for an ethyl group.
8. By what two processes is ethanol made?
9. Write equations to show the preparation of formic acid from sodium hydroxide and carbon monoxide.
10. What kind of chemical reaction is utilized in the production of soap?
11. Why do linen garments crease and wrinkle easily?
12. For what purposes is glass cloth used?
13. What property of Dacron-cotton fabrics makes them useful for shirts and suits?
14. What fabrics may be dyed with acid dyes?
15. What is the empirical formula for the structural unit in natural rubber?
16. What is an important property of Hypalon synthetic rubber?
17. Of what type of plastic is Lucite or Plexiglas an example?

CHALLENGING YOUR KNOWLEDGE

1. Why is it impossible to separate completely a mixture of methanol and ethanol by ordinary distillation?
2. Why are all the solutions from which synthetic fibers are prepared filtered so carefully?
3. How does the paper used for printing dollar bills differ from newspaper?

TABLE 1.—METRIC–ENGLISH EQUIVALENTS

1 inch = 2.54 centimeters.
1 quart (U.S. liquid) = 0.946 liter.
1 ounce = 28.35 grams.
1 pound = 453.6 grams.
1 ton = 0.907 metric ton.
1 meter = 39.37 inches.
1 liter = 1.06 quarts (U.S. liquid).
1 gram = 0.035 ounce.
1 kilogram = 2.2 pounds.
1 metric ton = 1.10 tons.

TABLE 2.—TEMPERATURE CONVERSION FORMULAS

In these formulas C is Centigrade temperature, F is Fahrenheit temperature, and K is Kelvin temperature.

$$C = \tfrac{5}{9}(F - 32)$$

$$F = \tfrac{9}{5}C + 32$$

$$K = C + 273$$

TABLE 3.—ISOTOPES OF SOME ELEMENTS

(Naturally occurring nonradioactive isotopes are given in ordinary type. Naturally occurring radio-active isotopes are in bold-face italics. All other radioactive isotopes are in italics. Naturally occurring isotopes are listed in order of their abundance. All other isotopes are listed in order of length of half-life).

Elements	Isotopes
H	1, 2, *3*
He	4, 3, *6*
Li	7, 6, *8, 9*
Be	9, *10, 7, 8*
B	11, 10, *8, 12*
C	12, 13, *14, 11, 10, 15*
N	14, 15, *13, 16, 17, 12*
O	16, 18, 17, *15, 14, 19*
F	19, *18, 17, 20, 21*
Ne	20, 22, 21, *23, 19, 18*
Na	23, *22, 24, 25, 21, 20*
Mg	24, 26, 25, *28, 27, 23*
Al	27, *26, 29, 28, 25, 24*
Si	28, 29, 30, *32, 31, 27*
P	31, *33, 32, 30, 34, 29, 28*
S	32, 34, 33, 36, *35, 37, 31*
Cl	35, 37, *36, 39, 38, 33, 34, 32*
A	40, 36, 38, *39, 42, 37, 41, 35*
K	39, 41, *40, 43, 42, 44, 38, 37*
Ca	40, 44, 42, 48, 43, 46, *41, 45, 47, 49, 39*
Ti	48, 46, 47, 49, 50, *44, 45, 51*
Cr	52, 53, 50, 54, *48, 51, 49, 55*
Mn	55, *54, 52, 56, 51, 57*
Fe	56, 54, 57, 58, *55, 59, 52, 53*
Co	59, *60, 57, 56, 58, 55, 61, 62, 54*
Ni	58, 60, 62, 61, 64, *59, 63, 66, 57, 65, 56*
Cu	63, 65, *67, 64, 61, 60, 62, 58, 66, 68*
Zn	64, 66, 68, 67, 70, *65, 72, 62, 71, 69, 63*
As	75, *73, 74, 71, 77, 76, 72, 78, 70, 79*
Br	79, 81, *77, 82, 76, 83, 75, 74, 84, 78, 85, 87, 88*
Kr	84, 86, 82, 83, 80, 78, *81, 85, 79, 76, 88, 87, 77, 89, 90, 91, 92, 93, 94, 95, 97*
Rb	85, *87, 83, 84, 86, 82, 81, 88, 89, 90, 91*
Sr	88, 86, 87, 84, *90, 85, 89, 82, 83, 91, 92, 81, 93, 94*
Mo	98, 96, 92, 95, 100, 97, 94, *93, 99, 90, 91, 101, 105*
Ag	107, 109, *105, 106, 111, 113, 112, 103, 104, 115, 108, 114, 110*
Cd	114, 112, 111, 110, 113, 116, 106, 108, *109, 115, 107, 104, 105, 117, 118*
Sn	120, 118, 116, 119, 117, 124, 122, 112, 114, 115, *123, 113, 125, 121, 108, 127, 126, 111, 109*
Sb	121, 123, *125, 124, 122, 127, 119, 126, 118, 129, 117, 131, 120, 116, 133, 132, 134, 135*
I	127, *129, 125, 126, 131, 124, 133, 123, 130, 135, 132, 121, 134, 128, 122, 137, 138, 139*
Xe	132, 129, 131, 134, 136, 130, 128, 124, 126, *127, 133, 122, 125, 135, 123, 121, 138, 137, 139, 140, 141, 143, 144*
Cs	133, *135, 137, 134, 136, 131, 132, 129, 127, 125, 138, 130, 139, 123, 128, 126, 140*
Ba	138, 137, 136, 135, 134, 130, 132, *133, 140, 131, 128, 129, 126, 141, 142, 143*
W	184, 186, 182, 183, 180, *181, 185, 188, 178, 187, 177, 176*
Pt	195, 194, 196, 198, 192, **190**, 191, 197, 189, *187, 199*
Au	197, *195, 196, 199, 198, 194, 193, 192, 191, 200, 189, 201, 187, 203*
Hg	202, 200, 199, 201, 198, 204, 196, *203, 197, 195, 192, 193, 191, 189, 205*
Pb	208, 206, 207, 204, *202, 210, 203, 200, 212, 201, 209, 199, 211, 214, 198*
Bi	*209, 210, 207, 205, 206, 204, 203, 201, 202, 212, 213, 200, 199, 214, 215, 198, 211*
Rn	*222, 211, 210, 209, 221, 212, 208, 220, 219, 218, 217, 216, 215*
Ra	*226, 228, 225, 223, 224, 227, 213, 222, 221, 220, 219*
U	***238, 235, 234,*** *236, 233, 232, 230, 237, 231, 240, 229, 239, 228, 227*
Np	*237, 235, 234, 239, 238, 241, 231, 233, 240*
Pu	*244, 242, 239, 240, 238, 241, 236, 237, 246, 245, 234, 243, 232, 235*
Am	*243, 241, 242, 240, 239, 238, 245, 237, 244, 246*
Cm	*248, 245, 246, 243, 244, 242, 247, 241, 240, 238*
Bk	*247, 249, 245, 246, 248, 244, 243, 250*
Cf	*251, 249, 250, 252, 248, 254, 253, 246, 247, 245, 244*
E	*254, 252, 253, 251, 246*
Fm	*252, 254, 253, 256*
Mv	*256*

TABLE 4.—ELECTRONIC ARRANGEMENT OF THE ELEMENTS

Shells		K	L		M			N				O				P				Q
	Sub-Levels	1s	2s	2p	3s	3p	3d	4s	4p	4d	4f	5s	5p	5d	5f	6s	6p	6d	6f	7s
1	Hydrogen	1																		
2	Helium	2																		
3	Lithium	2	1																	
4	Beryllium	2	2																	
5	Boron	2	2	1																
5	Carbon	2	2	2																
7	Nitrogen	2	2	3																
8	Oxygen	2	2	4																
9	Fluorine	2	2	5																
10	Neon	2	2	6																
11	Sodium	2	2	6	1															
12	Magnesium	2	2	6	2															
13	Aluminum	2	2	6	2	1														
14	Silicon	2	2	6	2	2														
15	Phosphorus	2	2	6	2	3														
16	Sulfur	2	2	6	2	4														
17	Chlorine	2	2	6	2	5														
18	Argon	2	2	6	2	6														
19	Potassium	2	2	6	2	6		1												
20	Calcium	2	2	6	2	6		2												
21	Scandium	2	2	6	2	6	1	2												
22	Titanium	2	2	6	2	6	2	2												
23	Vanadium	2	2	6	2	6	3	2												
24	Chromium	2	2	6	2	6	5	1												
25	Manganese	2	2	6	2	6	5	2												
26	Iron	2	2	6	2	6	6	2												
27	Cobalt	2	2	6	2	6	7	2												
28	Nickel	2	2	6	2	6	8	2												
29	Copper	2	2	6	2	6	10	1												
30	Zinc	2	2	6	2	6	10	2												
31	Gallium	2	2	6	2	6	10	2	1											
32	Germanium	2	2	6	2	6	10	2	2											
33	Arsenic	2	2	6	2	6	10	2	3											
34	Selenium	2	2	6	2	6	10	2	4											
35	Bromine	2	2	6	2	6	10	2	5											
36	Krypton	2	2	6	2	6	10	2	6											
37	Rubidium	2	2	6	2	6	10	2	6			1								
38	Strontium	2	2	6	2	6	10	2	6			2								
39	Yttrium	2	2	6	2	6	10	2	6	1		2								
40	Zirconium	2	2	6	2	6	10	2	6	2		2								
41	Niobium	2	2	6	2	6	10	2	6	4		1								
42	Molybdenum	2	2	6	2	6	10	2	6	5		1								
43	Technetium	2	2	6	2	6	10	2	6	6		1								
43	Ruthenium	2	2	6	2	6	10	2	6	7		1								
45	Rhodium	2	2	6	2	6	10	2	6	8		1								
46	Palladium	2	2	6	2	6	10	2	6	10										
47	Silver	2	2	6	2	6	10	2	6	10		1								
48	Cadmium	2	2	6	2	6	10	2	6	10		2								
49	Indium	2	2	6	2	6	10	2	6	10		1	2							
50	Tin	2	2	6	2	6	10	2	6	10		2	2							
51	Antimony	2	2	6	2	6	10	2	6	10		2	3							
52	Tellurium	2	2	6	2	6	10	2	6	10		2	4							

TABLE 4.—ELECTRONIC ARRANGEMENT OF THE ELEMENTS (cont'd)

Shells		K	L		M			N				O				P				Q
Sub-Levels		1s	2s	2p	3s	3p	3d	4s	4p	4d	4f	5s	5p	5d	5f	6s	6p	6d	6f	7s
53	Iodine	2	2	6	2	6	10	2	6	10		2	5							
54	Xenon	2	2	6	2	6	10	2	6	10		2	6							
55	Cesium	2	2	6	2	6	10	2	6	10		2	6			1				
56	Barium	2	2	6	2	6	10	2	6	10		2	6			2				
57	Lanthanum	2	2	6	2	6	10	2	6	10		2	6	1		2				
58	Cerium	2	2	6	2	6	10	2	6	10	2	2	6			2				
59	Praseodymium	2	2	6	2	6	10	2	6	10	3	2	6			2				
60	Neodymium	2	2	6	2	6	10	2	6	10	4	2	6			2				
61	Promethium	2	2	6	2	6	10	2	6	10	5	2	6			2				
62	Samarium	2	2	6	2	6	10	2	6	10	6	2	6			2				
63	Europium	2	2	6	2	6	10	2	6	10	7	2	6			2				
64	Gadolinium	2	2	6	2	6	10	2	6	10	7	2	6	1		2				
65	Terbium	2	2	6	2	6	10	2	6	10	9	2	6			2				
66	Dysprosium	2	2	6	2	6	10	2	6	10	10	2	6			2				
67	Holmium	2	2	6	2	6	10	2	6	10	11	2	6			2				
68	Erbium	2	2	6	2	6	10	2	6	10	12	2	6			2				
69	Thulium	2	2	6	2	6	10	2	6	10	13	2	6			2				
70	Ytterbium	2	2	6	2	6	10	2	6	10	14	2	6			2				
71	Lutetium	2	2	6	2	6	10	2	6	10	14	2	6	1		2				
72	Hafnium	2	2	6	2	6	10	2	6	10	14	2	6	2		2				
73	Tantalum	2	2	6	2	6	10	2	6	10	14	2	6	3		2				
74	Tungsten	2	2	6	2	6	10	2	6	10	14	2	6	4		2				
75	Rhenium	2	2	6	2	6	10	2	6	10	14	2	6	5		2				
76	Osmium	2	2	6	2	6	10	2	6	10	14	2	6	6		2				
77	Iridium	2	2	6	2	6	10	2	6	10	14	2	6	7		2				
78	Platinum	2	2	6	2	6	10	2	6	10	14	2	6	8		2				
79	Gold	2	2	6	2	6	10	2	6	10	14	2	6	10		1				
80	Mercury	2	2	6	2	6	10	2	6	10	14	2	6	10		2				
81	Thallium	2	2	6	2	6	10	2	6	10	14	2	6	10		2	1			
82	Lead	2	2	6	2	6	10	2	6	10	14	2	6	10		2	2			
83	Bismuth	2	2	6	2	6	10	2	6	10	14	2	6	10		2	3			
84	Polonium	2	2	6	2	6	10	2	6	10	14	2	6	10		2	4			
85	Astatine	2	2	6	2	6	10	2	6	10	14	2	6	10		2	5			
86	Radon	2	2	6	2	6	10	2	6	10	14	2	6	10		2	6			
87	Francium	2	2	6	2	6	10	2	6	10	14	2	6	10		2	6			1
88	Radium	2	2	6	2	6	10	2	6	10	14	2	6	10		2	6			2
89	Actinium	2	2	6	2	6	10	2	6	10	14	2	6	10		2	6	1		2
90	Thorium	2	2	6	2	6	10	2	6	10	14	2	6	10		2	6	2		2
91	Protactinium	2	2	6	2	6	10	2	6	10	14	2	6	10	2	2	6	1		2
92	Uranium	2	2	6	2	6	10	2	6	10	14	2	6	10	3	2	6	1		2
93	Neptunium	2	2	6	2	6	10	2	6	10	14	2	6	10	5	2	6			2
94	Plutonium	2	2	6	2	6	10	2	6	10	14	2	6	10	6	2	6			2
95	Americium	2	2	6	2	6	10	2	6	10	14	2	6	10	6	2	6	1		2
96	Curium	2	2	6	2	6	10	2	6	10	14	2	6	10	7	2	6	1		2
97	Berkelium	2	2	6	2	6	10	2	6	10	14	2	6	10	9	2	6			2
98	Californium	2	2	6	2	6	10	2	6	10	14	2	6	10	10	2	6			2
99	Einsteinium	2	2	6	2	6	10	2	6	10	14	2	6	10	11	2	6			2
100	Fermium	2	2	6	2	6	10	2	6	10	14	2	6	10	12	2	6			2
101	Mendelevium	2	2	6	2	6	10	2	6	10	14	2	6	10	13	2	6			2
102		2	2	6	2	6	10	2	6	10	14	2	6	10	14	2	6			2
103	Lawrencium	2	2	6	2	6	10	2	6	10	14	2	6	10	14	2	6	1		2

TABLE 5.—PRESSURE OF WATER VAPOR IN MILLIMETERS OF MERCURY

°C	mm	°C	mm	°C	mm	°C	mm
0.0	4.6	17.5	15.0	22.5	20.4	30.0	31.8
5.0	6.5	18.0	15.5	23.0	21.1	35.0	42.2
7.5	7.8	18.5	16.0	23.5	21.7	40.0	55.3
10.0	9.2	19.0	16.5	24.0	22.4	50.0	92.5
12.5	10.8	19.5	17.0	24.5	23.1	60.0	149.4
15.0	12.8	20.0	17.5	25.0	23.8	70.0	233.7
15.5	13.2	20.5	18.1	26.0	25.2	80.0	355.1
16.0	13.6	21.0	18.7	27.0	26.7	90.0	525.8
16.5	14.0	21.5	19.2	28.0	28.3	95.0	633.9
17.0	14.5	22.0	19.8	29.0	30.0	100.0	760.0

TABLE 6.—HEAT OF FORMATION OF COMPOUNDS

Name of Compound	Heat of Formation K-cal/mole	Name of Compound	Heat of Formation K-cal/mole
Aluminum oxide	389.5	Lead monoxide	52.5
Ammonia	10.9	Lead(II) nitrate	100.7
Barium sulfate	345.3	Lead(II) sulfide	22.2
Calcium chloride	190.7	Magnesium chloride	153.2
Calcium hydroxide	236.1	Magnesium oxide	145.8
Calcium oxide	151.7	Mercury(II) chloride	53.4
Carbon dioxide	94.4	Mercury(II) fulminate	−64.5
Carbon disulfide	−22.0	Mercury(II) nitrate	58.1
Carbon monoxide	26.4	Mercury(II) oxide	21.7
Carbon tetrachloride	33.2	Nitrogen dioxide	−7.4
Copper(II) nitrate	72.4	Nitrogen monoxide	−17.0
Copper(II) oxide	34.9	Potassium bromide	94.0
Copper(II) sulfate	178.7	Potassium chloride	104.3
Dinitrogen monoxide	−21.5	Potassium hydroxide	102.0
Dinitrogen pentoxide	14.6	Potassium nitrate	118.8
Dinitrogen tetroxide	−1.9	Potassium sulfate	338.6
Diphosphorus pentoxide	365.8	Silver chloride	30.6
Ethyne (acetylene)	−54.9	Silver nitrate	30.1
Hydrogen bromide	8.6	Silver sulfide	5.0
Hydrogen chloride	22.0	Sodium chloride	98.4
Hydrogen fluoride	64.0	Sodium hydroxide	101.9
Hydrogen iodide	−5.9	Sodium nitrate	112.5
Hydrogen oxide (water)	68.4	Sodium sulfate	326.3
Hydrogen peroxide	44.5	Sulfur dioxide	69.3
Hydrogen sulfide	5.3	Sulfur trioxide	103.2
Iron(II) sulfate	217.2	Tin(IV) chloride	127.4
Iron(II,III) oxide (magnetic)	266.9	Zinc oxide	84.4
Iron(III) oxide	190.7	Zinc sulfide	45.9

TABLE 7.—TABLE OF SOLUBILITIES

S, soluble in water. A, soluble in acids, insoluble in water. P, partially soluble in water, soluble in dilute acids. I, insoluble in dilute acids and in water. a, slightly soluble in acids, insoluble in water. d, decomposes in water.

	Acetate	Bromide	Carbonate	Chlorate	Chloride	Chromate	Hydroxide	Iodide	Nitrate	Oxide	Phosphate	Silicate	Sulfate	Sulfide
Aluminum	S	S		S	S		A	S	S	a	A	I	S	d
Ammonium	S	S	S	S	S	S		S	S		S		S	S
Barium	S	S	P	S	S	A	S	S	S	S	A	S	a	d
Calcium	S	S	P	S	S	S	S	S	S	P	P	P	P	P
Copper(II)	S	S		S	S		A		S	A	A	A	S	A
Iron(II)	S	S	P	S	S		A	S	S	A	A		S	A
Iron(III)	S	S		S	S	A	A	S	S	A	P		P	d
Lead(II)	S	S	A	S	S	A	P	P	S	P	A	A	P	A
Magnesium	S	S	P	S	S	S	A	S	S	A	P	A	S	d
Manganese(II)	S	S	P	S	S		A	S	S	A	P	I	S	A
Mercury(I)	P	A	A	S	a	P		A	S	A	A		P	I
Mercury(II)	S	S		S	S	P	A	P	S	P	A		d	I
Potassium	S	S	S	S	S	S	S	S	S	S	S	S	S	S
Silver	P	a	A	S	a	P		I	S	P	A		P	A
Sodium	S	S	S	S	S	S	S	S	S	S	S	S	S	S
Strontium	S	S	P	S	S	P	S	S	S	S	A	A	P	S
Tin(II)	d	S		S	S	A	A	S	d	A	A		S	A
Tin(IV)	S	S		S	S	S	P	d		A			S	A
Zinc	S	S	P	S	S	P	A	S	S	P	A	A	S	A

TABLE 8.—SOLUBILITY OF COMPOUNDS

The numbers give the number of grams of anhydrous compound that can be dissolved in 100 grams of water at the given temperatures.

Compound	0° C	20° C	60° C	100° C
Calcium hydroxide	0.19	0.17	0.12	0.08
Calcium sulfate (gypsum)	0.18	0.19	0.20	0.16
Cerium sulfate	17.35	9.16	3.73	
Copper(II) sulfate	14.3	20.7	40.0	75.4
Mercury(II) chloride	3.6	6.5	16.3	61.3
Potassium bromide	53.5	65.2	85.5	104.0
Potassium chlorate	3.3	7.4	24.5	57.0
Potassium chloride	27.6	34.0	45.5	56.7
Potassium nitrate	13.3	31.6	110.0	246.0
Potassium sulfate	7.4	11.1	18.2	24.1
Sodium chloride	35.7	36.0	37.3	39.8
Sodium nitrate	73.0	88.0	124.0	180.0

TABLE 9.—SOLUBILITY RULES

1. Common sodium, potassium, and ammonium compounds are *soluble* in water.
2. Common nitrates, acetates, and chlorates are *soluble*.
3. Common chlorides are *soluble* except silver, mercury(I), and lead(II). (Lead(II) chloride is soluble in hot water.)
4. Common sulfates are *soluble* except calcium, barium, strontium, and lead(II).
5. Common carbonates, phosphates, and silicates are *insoluble* except sodium, potassium, and ammonium.
6. Common sulfides are *insoluble* except calcium, barium, strontium, magnesium, sodium, potassium, and ammonium.

TABLE 10.—DENSITY AND SPECIFIC GRAVITY OF GASES

Gas	Density Grams per Liter S.T.P.	Specific Gravity Air Standard	Gas	Density Grams per Liter S.T.P.	Specific Gravity Air Standard
Ammonia	0.771	0.596	Hydrogen chloride	1.639	1.268
Carbon dioxide	1.977	1.529	Hydrogen sulfide	1.539	1.190
Carbon monoxide	1.250	0.967	Methane	0.717	0.554
Chlorine	3.214	2.486	Nitrogen	1.251	0.967
Dinitrogen monoxide	1.978	1.530	Nitrogen monoxide	1.340	1.037
Ethyne (acetylene)	1.173	0.907	Oxygen	1.429	1.105
Hydrogen	0.0899	0.0695	Sulfur dioxide	2.927	2.264

TABLE 11.—SOLUBILITY OF GASES IN WATER

Volume of gas (reduced to S.T.P.) that can be dissolved in 1 volume of water.

Gas	0° C	10° C	20° C
Air	0.0292	0.0228	0.0187
Ammonia	1298.9	910.4	710.6
Carbon dioxide	1.713	1.194	0.878
Chlorine	4.54	3.148	2.299
Hydrogen	0.0215	0.0196	0.0182
Hydrogen chloride	506.7	473.9	442.0
Hydrogen sulfide	4.670	3.399	2.582
Nitrogen	0.0235	0.0186	0.0155
Oxygen	0.0489	0.0380	0.0310
Sulfur dioxide	79.79	56.65	39.37

TABLE 12.—PROPERTIES OF IMPORTANT ELEMENTS

Name	Specific Gravity		Melting Point ° C	Boiling Point ° C	Common Oxidation Numbers
	Water Std.	Air Std.			
Aluminum	2.70		659.7	2057	+3
Antimony	6.69		630.5	1380	+3, +5
Arsenic	5.73		814 (36 atm)	615 (sublimes)	+3, +5
Barium	3.6		850	1140	+2
Bismuth	9.75		271.3	1560	+3
Boron	3.33		2300	2550 (sublimes)	+3
Bromine	3.12		−7.2	58.8	−1, +5
Calcium	1.55		842	1240	+2
Carbon	1.7–3.5		(sublimes above 3500° C)	4200	+2, +4
Chlorine		2.486	−101.6	−34.6	−1, +5, +7
Chromium	7.1		1890	2480	+2, +3, +6
Cobalt	8.9		1495	2900	+2, +3
Copper	8.9		1083	2336	+1, +2
Fluorine		1.312	−223	−187	−1
Gold	19.3		1063	2600	0, +3
Hydrogen		0.0695	−259	−253	−1, +1
Iodine	4.93		113.5	184.4	−1, +5
Iron	7.86		1535	3000	+2, +3
Lead	11.34		327.4	1620	+2, +4
Magnesium	1.74		651	1107	+2
Manganese	7.2		1260	1900	+2, +4, +7
Mercury	13.55		−38.9	356.6	+1, +2
Nickel	8.90		1455	2900	+2
Nitrogen		0.967	−209.9	−195.8	−3, +3, +5
Oxygen		1.105	−218	−183	−2
Phosphorus	1.8–2.3		44.1	280	+3, +5
Platinum	21.37		1773.5	4300	+2, +4
Potassium	0.86		62.3	760	+1
Radium	5		700	1140	+2
Silicon	2.42		1420	2355	+4
Silver	10.5		960.8	1950	+1
Sodium	0.97		97.5	880	+1
Strontium	2.54		800	1150	+2
Sulfur	2.0		114.5	444.6	−2, +4, +6
Tin	7.28		231.9	2270	+2, +4
Titanium	4.5		1800	(over 3000)	+3, +4
Tungsten	19.3		3370	5900	+6
Zinc	7.14		419.5	907	+2

TABLE 13.—FOUR–PLACE LOGARITHMS OF NUMBERS

n	0	1	2	3	4	5	6	7	8	9
10	0000	0043	0086	0128	0170	0212	0253	0294	0334	0374
11	0414	0453	0492	0531	0569	0607	0645	0682	0719	0755
12	0792	0828	0864	0899	0934	0969	1004	1038	1072	1106
13	1139	1173	1206	1239	1271	1303	1335	1367	1399	1430
14	1461	1492	1523	1553	1584	1614	1644	1673	1703	1732
15	1761	1790	1818	1847	1875	1903	1931	1959	1987	2014
16	2041	2068	2095	2122	2148	2175	2201	2227	2253	2279
17	2304	2330	2355	2380	2405	2430	2455	2480	2504	2529
18	2553	2577	2601	2625	2648	2672	2695	2718	2742	2765
19	2788	2810	2833	2856	2878	2900	2923	2945	2967	2989
20	3010	3032	3054	3075	3096	3118	3139	3160	3181	3201
21	3222	3243	3263	3284	3304	3324	3345	3365	3385	3404
22	3424	3444	3464	3483	3502	3522	3541	3560	3579	3598
23	3617	3636	3655	3674	3692	3711	3729	3747	3766	3784
24	3802	3820	3838	3856	3874	3892	3909	3927	3945	3962
25	3979	3997	4014	4031	4048	4065	4082	4099	4116	4133
26	4150	4166	4183	4200	4216	4232	4249	4265	4281	4298
27	4314	4330	4346	4362	4378	4393	4409	4425	4440	4456
28	4472	4487	4502	4518	4533	4548	4564	4579	4594	4609
29	4624	4639	4654	4669	4683	4698	4713	4728	4742	4757
30	4771	4786	4800	4814	4829	4843	4857	4871	4886	4900
31	4914	4928	4942	4955	4969	4983	4997	5011	5024	5038
32	5051	5065	5079	5092	5105	5119	5132	5145	5159	5172
33	5185	5198	5211	5224	5237	5250	5263	5276	5289	5302
34	5315	5328	5340	5353	5366	5378	5391	5403	5416	5428
35	5441	5453	5465	5478	5490	5502	5514	5527	5539	5551
36	5563	5575	5587	5599	5611	5623	5635	5647	5658	5670
37	5682	5694	5705	5717	5729	5740	5752	5763	5775	5786
38	5798	5809	5821	5832	5843	5855	5866	5877	5888	5899
39	5911	5922	5933	5944	5955	5966	5977	5988	5999	6010
40	6021	6031	6042	6053	6064	6075	6085	6096	6107	6117
41	6128	6138	6149	6160	6170	6180	6191	6201	6212	6222
42	6232	6243	6253	6263	6274	6284	6294	6304	6314	6325
43	6335	6345	6355	6365	6375	6385	6395	6405	6415	6425
44	6435	6444	6454	6464	6474	6484	6493	6503	6513	6522
45	6532	6542	6551	6561	6571	6580	6590	6599	6609	6618
46	6628	6637	6646	6656	6665	6675	6684	6693	6702	6712
47	6721	6730	6739	6749	6758	6767	6776	6785	6794	6803
48	6812	6821	6830	6839	6848	6857	6866	6875	6884	6893
49	6902	6911	6920	6928	6937	6946	6955	6964	6972	6981
50	6990	6998	7007	7016	7024	7033	7042	7050	7059	7067
51	7076	7084	7093	7101	7110	7118	7126	7135	7143	7152
52	7160	7168	7177	7185	7193	7202	7210	7218	7226	7235
53	7243	7251	7259	7267	7275	7284	7292	7300	7308	7316
54	7324	7332	7340	7348	7356	7364	7372	7380	7388	7396

TABLE 13.—FOUR-PLACE LOGARITHMS OF NUMBERS (cont'd)

n	0	1	2	3	4	5	6	7	8	9
55	7404	7412	7419	7427	7435	7443	7451	7459	7466	7474
56	7482	7490	7497	7505	7513	7520	7528	7536	7543	7551
57	7559	7566	7574	7582	7589	7597	7604	7612	7619	7627
58	7634	7642	7649	7657	7664	7672	7679	7686	7694	7701
59	7709	7716	7723	7731	7738	7745	7752	7760	7767	7774
60	7782	7789	7796	7803	7810	7818	7825	7832	7839	7846
61	7853	7860	7868	7875	7882	7889	7896	7903	7910	7917
62	7924	7931	7938	7945	7952	7959	7966	7973	7980	7987
63	7993	8000	8007	8014	8021	8028	8035	8041	8048	8055
64	8062	8069	8075	8082	8089	8096	8102	8109	8116	8122
65	8129	8136	8142	8149	8156	8162	8169	8176	8182	8189
66	8195	8202	8209	8215	8222	8228	8235	8241	8248	8254
67	8261	8267	8274	8280	8287	8293	8299	8306	8312	8319
68	8325	8331	8338	8344	8351	8357	8363	8370	8376	8382
69	8388	8395	8401	8407	8414	8420	8426	8432	8439	8445
70	8451	8457	8463	8470	8476	8482	8488	8494	8500	8506
71	8513	8519	8525	8531	8537	8543	8549	8555	8561	8567
72	8573	8579	8585	8591	8597	8603	8609	8615	8621	8627
73	8633	8639	8645	8651	8657	8663	8669	8675	8681	8686
74	8692	8698	8704	8710	8716	8722	8727	8733	8739	8745
75	8751	8756	8762	8768	8774	8779	8785	8791	8797	8802
76	8808	8814	8820	8825	8831	8837	8842	8848	8854	8859
77	8865	8871	8876	8882	8887	8893	8899	8904	8910	8915
78	8921	8927	8932	8938	8943	8949	8954	8960	8965	8971
79	8976	8982	8987	8993	8998	9004	9009	9015	9020	9025
80	9031	9036	9042	9047	9053	9058	9063	9069	9074	9079
81	9085	9090	9096	9101	9106	9112	9117	9122	9128	9133
82	9138	9143	9149	9154	9159	9165	9170	9175	9180	9186
83	9191	9196	9201	9206	9212	9217	9222	9227	9232	9238
84	9243	9248	9253	9258	9263	9269	9274	9279	9284	9289
85	9294	9299	9304	9309	9315	9320	9325	9330	9335	9340
86	9345	9350	9355	9360	9365	9370	9375	9380	9385	9390
87	9395	9400	9405	9410	9415	9420	9425	9430	9435	9440
88	9445	9450	9455	9460	9465	9469	9474	9479	9484	9489
89	9494	9499	9504	9509	9513	9518	9523	9528	9533	9538
90	9542	9547	9552	9557	9562	9566	9571	9576	9581	9586
91	9590	9595	9600	9605	9609	9614	9619	9624	9628	9633
92	9638	9643	9647	9652	9657	9661	9666	9671	9675	9680
93	9685	9689	9694	9699	9703	9708	9713	9717	9722	9727
94	9731	9736	9741	9745	9750	9754	9759	9763	9768	9773
95	9777	9782	9786	9791	9795	9800	9805	9809	9814	9818
96	9823	9827	9832	9836	9841	9845	9850	9854	9859	9863
97	9868	9872	9877	9881	9886	9890	9894	9899	9903	9908
98	9912	9917	9921	9926	9930	9934	9939	9943	9948	9952
99	9956	9961	9965	9969	9974	9978	9983	9987	9991	9996

THE ELEMENTS, THEIR SYMBOLS, ATOMIC NUMBERS, AND ATOMIC WEIGHTS

The more important elements are printed in blue type.

Name of element	Symbol	Atomic number	Atomic weight	Name of element	Symbol	Atomic number	Atomic weight
Actinium	Ac	89	[227]	Mercury	Hg	80	200.59
Aluminum	Al	13	26.9815	Molybdenum	Mo	42	95.94
Americium	Am	95	[243]	Neodymium	Nd	60	144.24
Antimony	Sb	51	121.75	Neon	Ne	10	20.183
Argon	Ar	18	39.948	Neptunium	Np	93	[237]
Arsenic	As	33	74.9216	Nickel	Ni	28	58.71
Astatine	At	85	[210]	Niobium	Nb	41	92.906
Barium	Ba	56	137.34	Nitrogen	N	7	14.0067
Berkelium	Bk	97	[249*]	(Nobelium)	(No)	102	
Beryllium	Be	4	9.0122	Osmium	Os	76	190.2
Bismuth	Bi	83	208.980	Oxygen	O	8	15.9994
Boron	B	5	10.811	Palladium	Pd	46	106.4
Bromine	Br	35	79.909	Phosphorus	P	15	30.9738
Cadmium	Cd	48	112.40	Platinum	Pt	78	195.09
Calcium	Ca	20	40.08	Plutonium	Pu	94	[242]
Californium	Cf	98	[251*]	Polonium	Po	84	[210*]
Carbon	C	6	12.01115	Potassium	K	19	39.102
Cerium	Ce	58	140.12	Praseodymium	Pr	59	140.907
Cesium	Cs	55	132.905	Promethium	Pm	61	[147*]
Chlorine	Cl	17	35.453	Protactinium	Pa	91	[231]
Chromium	Cr	24	51.996	Radium	Ra	88	[226]
Cobalt	Co	27	58.9332	Radon	Rn	86	[222]
Copper	Cu	29	63.54	Rhenium	Re	75	186.2
Curium	Cm	96	[247]	Rhodium	Rh	45	102.905
Dysprosium	Dy	66	162.50	Rubidium	Rb	37	85.47
Einsteinium	Es	99	[254]	Ruthenium	Ru	44	101.07
Erbium	Er	68	167.26	Samarium	Sm	62	150.35
Europium	Eu	63	151.96	Scandium	Sc	21	44.956
Fermium	Fm	100	[253]	Selenium	Se	34	78.96
Fluorine	F	9	18.9984	Silicon	Si	14	28.086
Francium	Fr	87	[223]	Silver	Ag	47	107.870
Gadolinium	Gd	64	157.25	Sodium	Na	11	22.9898
Gallium	Ga	31	69.72	Strontium	Sr	38	87.62
Germanium	Ge	32	72.59	Sulfur	S	16	32.064
Gold	Au	79	196.967	Tantalum	Ta	73	180.948
Hafnium	Hf	72	178.49	Technetium	Tc	43	[99*]
Helium	He	2	4.0026	Tellurium	Te	52	127.60
Holimum	Ho	67	164.930	Terbium	Tb	65	158.924
Hydrogen	H	1	1.00797	Thallium	Tl	81	204.37
Indium	In	49	114.82	Thorium	Th	90	232.038
Iodine	I	53	126.9044	Thulium	Tm	69	168.934
Iridium	Ir	77	192.2	Tin	Sn	50	118.69
Iron	Fe	26	55.847	Titanium	Ti	22	47.90
Krypton	Kr	36	83.80	Tungsten	W	74	183.85
Lanthanum	La	57	138.91	Uranium	U	92	238.03
Lawrencium	Lw	103	[257]	Vanadium	V	23	50.942
Lead	Pb	82	207.19	Xenon	Xe	54	131.30
Lithium	Li	3	6.939	Ytterbium	Yb	70	173.04
Lutetium	Lu	71	174.97	Yttrium	Y	39	88.905
Magnesium	Mg	12	24.312	Zinc	Zn	30	65.37
Manganese	Mn	25	54.9380	Zirconium	Zr	40	91.22
Mendelevium	Md	101	[256]				

A value given in brackets denotes the mass number of the isotope of longest known half-life, or for those marked with an asterisk, a better known one. The atomic weights of most of these elements are believed to have no error greater than ±0.5 of the last digit given.

absorption. A soaking up of one substance through the entire mass of another.

accelerator. A substance that speeds up a chemical reaction by acting as a positive catalyst.

acid. A substance which gives up protons to another substance.

acid anhydride. (1) An oxide of a nonmetal which unites with water to form a solution which contains an acid. (2) A compound derived from an acid by the removal of water from the acid.

activated. Pertaining to an adsorbent, the surface of which has been freed of adsorbed gases by heating.

activation energy. See *energy, activation.*

activity series. A table of metals or nonmetals arranged in order of descending activity.

adsorbate. A material adsorbed on the surface of another.

adsorbent. A material upon whose surface adsorption occurs.

adsorption. The concentration of a gas, liquid, or solid on the surface of a solid or liquid.

aerosol. A suspensoid in which a gas is the dispersing medium.

alcohol. A compound containing a hydrocarbon group and one or more −OH, hydroxyl, groups.

aldehyde. A compound which has a hydrocarbon group and one or more −CHO, formyl, groups.

alkadiene. A straight or branched chain hydrocarbon with two double covalent bonds between carbon atoms.

alkane. A straight or branched chain hydrocarbon in which the carbon atoms are connected by only single covalent bonds; a member of the paraffin series.

alkene. A straight or branched chain hydrocarbon in which two carbon atoms are connected by a double covalent bond; a member of the olefin series.

alkylation. The combining of simple hydrocarbons with unsaturated hydrocarbons under the influence of heat, pressure, and the presence of a catalyst.

alkyne. A straight or branched chain hydrocarbon in which two carbon atoms are connected by a triple covalent bond; a member of the acetylene series.

allotrope. One of the two or more different forms of an element.

alloy. A material composed of two or more metals.

alloy, anti-friction. An alloy which reduces friction.

alloy, fusible. An alloy which has a low melting temperature.

alluvial. Pertaining to soil, sand, or gravel deposited by running water.

alnico. A strongly ferromagnetic alloy of iron, nickel, aluminum, and cobalt.

alpha particle. Particle identical with a helium nucleus emitted from the nucleus of a radioactive element.

alum. A double salt that is a sulfate of a monovalent and a trivalent metal.

aluminothermy. A thermite or similar reaction.

amalgam. An alloy of mercury with another metal or metals.

amorphous. Without definite shape.

amphiprotic. Capable of acting either as an acid or as a base.

amphoteric. See *amphiprotic.*

analysis. The separation of a material into its component parts to determine the composition.

Ångstrom. A unit of linear measure; 1×10^{-8} cm.

anhydrous. Without water of hydration.

anion. A negative ion.

annealing. The process of heating a material to above a certain temperature and then slowly cooling it in order to decrease its hardness and brittleness.

anode. A positively charged electrode.

antichlor. A substance used to remove traces of chlorine left in bleached goods.

anti-friction alloy. See *alloy, anti-friction.*

anti-oxidant. A substance which retards oxidation.

aqua regia. A mixture of concentrated nitric and hydrochloric acids capable of reacting with gold.

arc-type furnace. A furnace in which the heat is produced by an electric arc between carbon electrodes.

aromatic hydrocarbon. See *hydrocarbon, aromatic.*

atmosphere. The layer of gases which surrounds the earth.

atom. The smallest particle of an element that can enter into combination with other elements.

atomic bomb. An explosive device whose source of energy is a fission reaction.

atomic mass. See *mass, atomic.*

atomic number. The number of protons in the nucleus of an atom.

atomic theory. See *theory, atomic.*

atomic weight. See *weight, atomic.*

Avogadro number. The number of atoms in 1 gram-atom of an element; the number of molecules in 1 mole of a molecular substance; 6.02483×10^{23}.

baking soda. Sodium hydrogen carbonate, $NaHCO_3$.

barometer. An apparatus for measuring atmospheric pressure.

base. A substance which acquires protons from another substance.

basic anhydride. An oxide of a metal which unites with water to form a solution which contains the basic hydroxide ions.

beneficiation. Any process, physical or chemical, which renders an ore more suitable for reduction.

Bessemer converter. An egg-shaped furnace in which iron is converted into steel by burning out impurities with a blast of air.

beta particle. Particle identical with an electron emitted from the nucleus of a radioactive element.

betatron. A device for accelerating electrons.

binary. Pertaining to compounds made up of two elements.

binary compound. See *compound, binary.*

binding energy. See *energy, binding.*

biocolloid. A lyophilic colloidal system existing within plant and animal organisms.

blast furnace. A tall cylindrical chamber in which iron oxide is reduced using coke, limestone, and a blast of hot air.

bleaching. The operation by which color is partially or wholly removed from a colored material.

blister copper. Crude copper as produced in a reverberatory furnace.

block tin. Solid tin, as distinguished from tin plate.

boiling point. The temperature at which the equilibrium vapor pressure of a liquid is equal to the prevailing atmospheric pressure.

borazon. A crystalline form of boron nitride, equal in hardness to a diamond.

brass. An alloy of copper and zinc.

breeder reactor. A nuclear reactor used for making fissionable material.

British thermal unit. The quantity of heat needed to raise the temperature of one pound of water one Fahrenheit degree.

bronze. An alloy of copper and tin.

Brownian movement. The haphazard motion of colloidally dispersed particles as a result of collisions with the molecules of the dispersing medium.

buffer. A substance which, when added to a solution, causes a resistance to any change in pH.

buffered solution. See *solution, buffered.*

calcine. A partially roasted copper ore.

calorie. The quantity of heat needed to raise the temperature of one gram of water one Centigrade degree.

calorimeter. An apparatus for measuring quantities of heat.

carboloy. An extremely hard alloy of cobalt and tungsten carbide.

Carboniferous Age. A geological period in which plants grew luxuriantly.

carbonyl group. The $\rangle CO$ group.

carboxyl group. The $-COOH$ group.

carrier. A substance used to transfer an element or radical from one material to another.

carrier catalyst. See *catalyst, carrier.*

casing-head gasoline. A volatile liquid, containing hydrocarbons other than methane, formed when natural gas is cooled and compressed.

catalyst. An agent which affects a chemical action without itself being permanently altered.

catalyst, carrier. A catalytic agent which influences the speed of a reaction by forming an intermediate compound with one of the reactants.

catalyst, contact. A catalytic agent which influences the speed of a reaction by altering the contact efficiency between the molecules of the reactants.

catalyst, negative. A catalyst which decreases the rate of a chemical reaction.

catalyst, positive. A catalyst which increases the rate of a chemical reaction.

catalytic agent. See *catalyst.*

catalytic cracking. See *cracking, catalytic.*

catalytic poison. A specific material which when preferentially adsorbed on the surface of a contact catalyst retards or stops the catalytic action.

cathode. A negatively charged electrode.

cation. A positive ion.

caustic. (*1*) Capable of converting some types of animal and vegetable matter into soluble materials by chemical action; (*2*) A substance with such properties.

Celsius scale. The Centigrade thermometer scale.

cement. A mixture made from limestone and clay which, after mixing with water, sets to a hard mass.

centi-. Metric prefix meaning 0.01.

Centigrade temperature. Temperature on the Centigrade scale which has the two fixed points as 0° and 100°.

chain reaction. A reaction in which the material or energy which initiates the reaction is also one of the products.

chamber process. A process for making sulfuric acid in large lead chambers, using oxides of nitrogen to promote the necessary reactions.

checkerwork. Loosely stacked firebricks in a chamber, providing a circuitous passage for fuel gas or air.

chemical bond. The linkage between atoms produced by transfer or sharing of electrons.

chemical change. A change in which new substances with new properties are formed.

chemical equilibrium. See *equilibrium, chemical.*

chemical formula. See *formula, chemical.*

chemical properties. Those properties which pertain to the behavior of a material in changes in which its identity is altered.

chemical symbol. Either a single capital letter, or a capital letter and a small letter used together, as an abbreviation for (*1*) an element; (*2*) an atom of an element; (*3*) a gram-atom of an element.

chemistry. The science dealing with the composition of substances and the changes in composition which these substances undergo.

chemistry, organic. The study of carbon compounds.

chlorination. The addition of chlorine to a material.

chromophor. An atom or group of atoms in a molecule which is believed to be responsible for the color of many organic dyes.

coagulate. To form into a compact mass.

coal gas. A fuel gas obtained by the destructive distillation of soft coal.

coke. The residue from the destructive distillation of bituminous coal.

colloidal state. A state of subdivision of matter ranging between the dimensions of ordinary molecules and microscopic particles.

colloidal suspension. A two-phase system having dispersed particles suspended in a dispersing medium.

combustion. Any chemical action which occurs so rapidly that both noticeable heat and light are produced.

combustion, spontaneous. A combustion started by the accumulation of heat from slow oxidation.

common-ion effect. The shift in equilibrium which occurs when a substance is added to a solution of a second substance with which it has a common ion, the volume being kept constant.

composition reaction. A chemical reaction in which two or more substances combine to form a more complex substance.

compound. A substance which can be decomposed into two or more simpler substances by ordinary chemical means.

compound, binary. A compound consisting of only two elements.

compound, stable. A compound that does not decompose easily.

compound, unstable. A compound that decomposes easily.

concentrated. Containing a relatively large amount of solute.

condensation. (*1*) Changing a material such as a vapor to a liquid; (*2*) Increasing the size of very small particles up to colloidal size; (*3*) A reaction between raw materials in the making of a plastic that results in the formation of water as one of the products.

constant. A magnitude that does not change in value.

constant, equilibrium. The product of the concentrations of the substances produced at equilibrium divided by the product of the concentrations of reactants, each concentration raised to that power which is the coefficient of the substance in the chemical equation.

constant, ionization. The equilibrium constant of a reversible reaction by which ions are produced from molecules.

constant, velocity. The speed of a reaction, at a fixed temperature, in which the concentration of each reactant is 1 mole per liter.

contact agent. See *catalyst, contact.*

contact catalyst. See *catalyst, contact.*

contact process. A process for making sulfuric acid in which the sulfur dioxide and oxygen come in contact with a catalyst.

control rod. A rod of neutron-absorbing

material used in regulating the reaction in a nuclear reactor.

converter reactor. A reactor in which one type of fissionable material is used to produce another type of fissionable material.

corrode. (1) To disintegrate slowly. (2) To waste away by chemical action, especially the action of an acid on a metal.

countercurrents. Movement of a gas and liquid in opposition to one another.

covalence. Covalent bonding.

covalent bonding. Bonding in which atoms share a pair of electrons.

C.P. Abbreviation for "chemically pure."

cracking. A process of breaking down complex organic molecules by the action of heat or a catalyst or both.

cracking, catalytic. The breaking-up of large molecules into smaller ones by using a catalyst together with high temperature and high pressure.

cracking, thermal. The breaking-up of large molecules into smaller ones by the use of high temperature and high pressure.

critical pressure. See *pressure, critical.*

critical size. The amount of radioactive material required to sustain a chain reaction.

critical temperature. The highest temperature at which it is possible to liquefy a gas with any amount of pressure.

critical volume. The volume occupied by one mole of a gas at its critical temperature and critical pressure.

crystal. (1) A solid with a definite shape or structure. (2) A homogeneous portion of a substance bounded by plane surfaces making definite angles with each other, giving a regular geometric form.

crystal, ionic. A crystal consisting of ions arranged in a systematic order.

crystal, macromolecular. A crystal consisting of molecular groups or aggregates of these groups arranged in a systematic order.

crystal, metallic. A crystal lattice consisting of positive ions permeated by a cloud of valence electrons.

crystal, molecular. A crystal consisting of molecules arranged in a systematic order.

crystalline. Consisting or made of crystals.

cullet. Old, broken glass.

cupel. A porous crucible or dish of bone ash.

cyclotron. An electromagnetic device for accelerating protons or deuterons in a spiral path.

data. A group of facts or statistics.

decomposition reaction. A chemical reaction in which a complex substance breaks down to form two or more simpler substances.

decrepitation. The loss of mechanically held water when certain crystals are heated.

dehydrating agent. A substance which removes water from a material.

deliquescence. The property of certain substances to take up water from the air to form a solution.

density. The mass per unit volume.

destructive distillation. See *distillation, destructive.*

detergent. A substance which removes dirt.

detonator. A sensitive explosive used to start the main explosion.

deuterium. The isotope of hydrogen having one proton and one neutron in the nucleus.

developing. A process in photography in which the reduction of the silver compound, started by light, is promoted by the action of an alkaline, organic reducing agent.

diatomic. Consisting of two atoms.

diffusion. The process of spreading out spontaneously to fill a space uniformly; the intermingling of the particles of substances.

diluent. A diluting agent.

dilute. Containing a relatively small amount of solute.

dipole. A polar molecule, one region of which is positive and the other region is negative.

diprotic. Referring to an acid with two replaceable hydrogen atoms.

dispersion. A scattering, or state of being scattered.

dissociation. The separation of the ions of an electrovalent substance during the solution process.

distillation. The process of evaporation followed by condensation of the vapors in a separate vessel.

distillation, destructive. The process of decomposing materials by heating them in a closed vessel without access to air or oxygen.

distillation, fractional. The separation of the components of a mixture which have slightly different boiling points by carefully controlled vaporization.

domain. Small magnetized region formed by groups of properly aligned atoms of ferromagnetic substances.

drier. A catalyst, such as an oxide of lead

or manganese, added to paint to promote the drying of the paint.

dross. A powdery scum that floats on top of molten metals.

duralumin. An alloy of aluminum, copper, manganese, and magnesium.

dust explosion. An explosion resulting from the ignition of dust suspended in the air, particularly within a confined space.

Dutch process. A process for making white lead using lead buckles, acetic acid, and decomposing tanbark or manure.

dye. A substance used for coloring textiles.

dynamite. An explosive made by absorbing nitroglycerin in wood pulp mixed with ammonium nitrate.

effervescence. The rapid escape of a gas from a liquid in which it is dissolved.

efflorescence. The property of hydrated crystals to lose water of hydration when exposed to the air.

electrochemical. Pertaining to spontaneous oxidation-reduction reactions used as a source of electric energy.

electrode. A conductor by which the current either enters or leaves an electrolyte.

electrolysis. Separation of a compound into simpler substances by electricity.

electrolyte. A substance whose water solution conducts the electric current.

electrolytic. Pertaining to forced oxidation-reduction reactions which utilize electric energy from an external source.

electron. A negatively-charged particle found in an atom. It has $\frac{1}{1837}$ of the mass of a hydrogen atom.

electron affinity. The energy released when an electron is added to a neutral atom.

electron pair. Two electrons which occupy the same orbital.

electron, valence. One of the electrons in an incomplete outer shell of an atom.

electron-volt. The energy required to move an electron across a potential difference of one volt.

electronegative element. See *element, electronegative.*

electronegativity. The tendency of an atom to attract the electrons forming a bond between it and another atom.

electroplating. Deposition of a metal on a surface by means of an electric current.

electropositive element. See *element, electropositive.*

electroscope. A device for determining the presence of electric charge.

electrovalence. Ionic bonding.

element. A substance which cannot be further decomposed by ordinary chemical means.

element, electronegative. An element having a relatively strong attraction for valence electrons.

element, electropositive. An element having a relatively weak attraction for valence electrons.

element, parent. The heaviest, most complex, naturally-occurring element in a disintegration series of radioactive elements.

element, rare earth. An element which differs in electronic configuration from that of next lower or higher atomic number only in the number of electrons in the second-from-outside shell.

element, transition. An element which differs in electronic configuration from that of next lower or higher atomic number only in the number of electrons in the next-to-the-outside shell.

element, transuranium. Elements with a higher atomic number than uranium, atomic number 92.

empirical formula. See *formula, empirical.*

emulsion. See *emulsoid.*

emulsoid. A colloidal system in which there is a strong attraction between the dispersed substance and the dispersing liquid.

endothermic. Pertaining to a reaction which occurs with the absorption of heat.

end point. That point reached in titration in which the quantities of acid and hydroxide present are chemically equivalent.

end reaction. Reactions between certain ions which run to completion due to the removal of the ions from solution.

energy. The capacity for doing work.

energy, activation. Energy required initially to start a reaction.

energy, binding. The energy released when an atom is formed from its component particles.

energy, free. The energy of a reaction which can be converted to useful work outside the reaction.

energy, kinetic. Energy of motion.

energy level. A region about the nucleus of an atom in which electrons move. A shell.

energy, potential. Energy of position.

enzyme. A catalyst produced by living cells.

equilibrium. A dynamic state in which two opposing processes take place at the same time and at the same rate.

equilibrium, chemical. The state of balance attained in a reversible chemical action in which the speeds of the opposing reactions are exactly equal.

equilibrium constant. See *constant, equilibrium.*

equilibrium, ionic. The state of balance attained in a reversible ionization action between unionized molecules in solution and their hydrated ions.

equilibrium, physical. A dynamic state in which two opposing physical processes in the same system proceed at equal rates.

equilibrium, solution. The physical state attained in which the opposing processes of dissolving and crystallizing of a solute occur at equal rates.

equilibrium vapor pressure. See *pressure, equilibrium vapor.*

equivalent weight. See *weight, equivalent.*

ester. A compound formed by the reaction between an acid and an alcohol.

esterification. The process of producing an ester by reaction of an acid with an alcohol.

ether. An organic oxide.

eudiometer. A gas-measuring tube.

evaporation. The escape of molecules from the surface of liquids and solids.

exothermic. Pertaining to a reaction which occurs with the evolution of heat.

explosive. A compound or mixture which decomposes suddenly with the production of a large volume of gas.

explosive range of a gas. A pair of percentages, representing the proportions of a gas mixed with air, between which the mixture of the gas and the air will explode if ignited.

external phase. The dispersing medium of a colloidal suspension.

feldspar. A complex silicate, usually aluminum silicate with either sodium or potassium silicate.

fermentation. A chemical change produced by the action of an enzyme.

ferrosilicon. An alloy of iron and silicon.

filtration. The process of removing suspended material from a liquid by allowing the liquid to pass through a medium such as filter paper or a layer of sand.

fission. The break-up of a nucleus into medium-weight parts.

fixing. In photography, the operation of removing unchanged silver salts after the picture has been developed, thereby fixing the image on the film or plate.

flame. A burning gas.

flame, oxidizing. The outer cone of a burner flame.

flame, reducing. The inner cone of a burner flame.

flame test. A test to determine the identity of an element in a compound by the color which the compound imparts to a flame.

flammable. Capable of burning readily.

flotation. The process by which low grade ores are separated from gangue as a result of preferential wetting action.

fluid. A material which flows; a liquid or gas.

flux. (1) A material used to promote the fusion of minerals. (2) A substance used to remove the oxide coating from a metallic surface prior to soldering or welding.

formality. The concentration of a solution expressed in gram-formula weights per liter of solution.

formal solution. See *solution, formal.*

formula. A shorthand method of representing the composition of substances using chemical symbols and numerical subscripts.

formula, chemical. A shorthand notation using chemical symbols and numerical subscripts to represent the composition of a substance.

formula, empirical. A chemical formula which denotes the constituent elements of a substance and the relative number of atoms of each.

formula equation. A concise symbolized picture of a chemical change.

formula, molecular. A chemical formula which denotes the constituent elements of a molecular substance and the number of atoms of each composing one molecule.

formula, simplest. See *formula, empirical.*

Formula, structural. A formula which indicates kind, number, arrangement, and valence bonds of the atoms in a molecule.

formula weight. See *weight, formula.*

formyl group. The —CHO group.

fractional distillation. See *distillation, fractional.*

free energy. See *energy, free.*

fuel. A material which is burned to provide heat.

fuller's earth. An aluminum silicate used as an adsorbent.

fungicide. A chemical material that kills non-green, microscopic plants known as fungi.

fusible alloy. See *alloy, fusible.*

fusion. The combination of two lightweight nuclei to form a heavier, more stable nucleus.

galvanize. To coat iron or steel with zinc.

gamma ray. High energy X ray emitted from the nucleus of a radioactive element.

gangue. Worthless rock or vein matter in which valuable minerals occur.

gas. The state of matter characterized by neither a definite volume nor a definite shape.

gas, ideal. The perfect gas; one which conforms exactly to the Gas Laws.

Geiger counter. A device for determining the presence of radiation from radioactive materials.

gel. A jelly-like mass consisting of a colloidal suspension of a liquid in a solid.

generator. In chemistry, the vessel in which a reaction occurs to produce a desired gaseous product.

German silver. An alloy of copper, zinc, and nickel.

glass. An amorphous material, usually transparent, consisting ordinarily of a mixture of silicates.

gram. The metric unit of mass.

gram-atom. One gram-atomic weight of an element.

gram-atomic weight. See *weight, gram-atomic.*

gram-equivalent weight. See *weight, gram-equivalent.*

gram-formula weight. See *weight, gram-formula.*

gram-molecular volume. The volume, in liters, of 1 gram-molecular weight of a gas at S.T.P.; commonly referred to as the molar volume.

gram-molecular weight. See *weight, gram-molecular.*

gram-molecule. One gram-molecular weight of a molecular substance.

group. A vertical column of elements in the Periodic Table.

half-life. The length of time required for the disintegration of one-half of a given number of atoms of a radioactive element.

halogen. The name given to the family of elements having seven valence electrons.

hard water. Water containing ions such as calcium and magnesium which form precipitates with soap.

heat of formation. The quantity of heat energy liberated or consumed when 1 mole of a compound is formed from its constituent elements.

heavy water. Water containing deuterium

atoms in place of ordinary hydrogen atoms.

heterogeneous. Having parts with different properties.

hexagonal. A crystalline system in which 3 equilateral angles intersect at angles of 60° and with a vertical axis of variable length at right angles.

homogenous. Having similar properties throughout.

homogeneous reactor. A reactor in which the fuel, a uranium salt, is dissolved in the moderator, water.

homologous series. A series of similar compound which conform to a general formula.

hydrate. A crystallized substance that contains water of hydration.

hydrated ion. See *ion, hydrated.*

hydration. The attachment of water molecules to particles of the solute.

hydraulic mining. The use of a stream of water to wash away dirt and rock particles, exposing valuable ore.

hydride. A compound of hydrogen and at least one other element of lower electronegativity.

hydrocarbon. A compound containing hydrogen and carbon.

hydrocarbon, aromatic. A hydrocarbon with alternating single and double covalent bonds in six-membered carbon rings.

hydroforming. The forming of ring compounds by heating straight-chain hydrocarbons with hydrogen in the presence of a catalyst.

hydrogen bomb. An explosive device whose source of energy is a fusion reaction.

hydrogen bond. A weak chemical bond between a hydrogen atom in one polar molecule and the negative atom in a second polar molecule of the same substance.

hydrogenation. The addition of hydrogen to a material.

hydrolysis. The reaction of a salt with water to form a solution which is acidic or basic.

hydronium ion. A hydrated proton; the H_3O^+ ion.

hydrosol. A suspensoid in which water is the dispersing medium.

hydrous oxide. See *oxide, hydrous.*

hygroscopic. Absorbing and retaining moisture from the atmosphere.

hypothesis. A possible or tentative explanation.

ice point. 0° C; 32° F.

ideal gas. See *gas, ideal.*

immiscible. Not capable of being mixed.

indicator. A substance which changes in color on the passage from acidity to alkalinity, or the reverse.

inertia. Resistance of matter to change in position or motion.

ingot. A molded block of steel.

inhibitor. A negative catalyst.

inorganic. Pertaining to materials which are not hydrocarbons or their derivatives.

insoluble. Not soluble, or soluble to only a very small extent.

internal phase. The dispersed particles of a colloidal suspension.

ion. An atom or group of atoms with an unbalanced electrostatic charge.

ion exchange resin. A resin which can exchange hydronium ions for positive ions; or one which can exchange hydroxide ions for negative ions.

ion, hydrated. An ion of a solute to which molecules of water are attached.

ionic bonding. Bonding in which one or more electrons are transferred from one atom to another.

ionic crystal. See *crystal, ionic.*

ionic equilibrium. See *equilibrium, ionic.*

ionic reaction. A chemical reaction in which ions in solution combine to form a product that leaves the reaction environment.

ionization. The formation of ions from polar solute molecules by the action of the solvent.

ionization constant. See *constant, ionization.*

ionization energy. The energy required to remove an electron from an atom.

isomer. One of two or more compounds having the same molecular formula, but different structures.

isometric. A crystalline system in which the 3 axes are at right angles, as in a cube.

isotope. One of two or more forms of atoms with the same atomic number but with different atomic masses.

kaolin. A fine white clay composed of hydrated aluminum silicate.

Kelvin temperature. Temperature on the Kelvin scale which is numerically 273° higher than that on the Centigrade scale.

kernel. The portion of an atom, excluding the valence electrons.

ketone. An organic compound that contains the $>$CO, carbonyl, group.

kiln. A type of furnace used for producing quicklime, making glass, baking pottery, etc.

kilo-. Metric prefix meaning 1000.

kilocalorie. The quantity of heat required to raise the temperature of one kilogram of water one Centigrade degree.

kindling temperature. The lowest temperature at which a substance takes fire and continues to burn.

kinetic energy. See *energy, kinetic.*

kinetic theory. See *theory, kinetic.*

knocking. A pounding sound produced in automobile engines by too-rapid combustion of the mixture of gasoline vapor and air.

lake. A pigment made by precipitating a dye with aluminum hydroxide.

laminated. Built up in layers or plates.

law. A statement of scientific fact concerning natural phenomena.

law of octaves. A statement made by Newlands that the properties of any element are repeated in the eighth element beyond when the elements are arranged according to atomic weight.

law, periodic. The chemical properties of elements are periodic functions of their atomic numbers.

leavening agent. A substance which releases carbon dioxide in a dough or batter.

lehr. A cooling oven for annealing glass.

lifting power. The difference between the weight of a given volume of air and that of the same volume of a gas less dense than air.

lignite. A partially mineralized peat.

lime. Calcium oxide, CaO.

linear accelerator. A particle accelerator in which the particles travel in a straight line through many stages of relatively small potential difference.

liquefaction. The process of converting a gas or solid to a liquid.

liquid. The state of matter characterized by a definite volume, but an indefinite shape.

liter. The metric unit of capacity.

lithopone. A white paint base composed of barium sulfate and zinc sulfide.

litmus. A dye extracted from lichens which is used as an indicator.

lunar caustic. Silver nitrate.

lye. A term used for either sodium hydroxide or potassium hydroxide.

lyophilic. Pertaining to a colloidal system of the emulsoid type.

lyophobic. Pertaining to a colloidal system of the suspensoid type.

macromolecular crystal. See *crystal, macromolecular.*

mass. The quantity of matter which a

body possesses; a measure of the inertia of a body.

mass, atomic. The mass of an atom expressed in atomic mass units of 1.660×10^{-24} g.

mass defect. The difference between the mass of a nucleus and the sum of the masses of its constituent particles.

mass number. The whole number closest to the atomic mass of an atom.

materials testing reactor. A reactor used to test the behavior of materials under very high radioactivity.

matte. A crude mixture of sulfides produced in a partially refined ore.

matter. Anything which occupies space and has mass.

mercerizing. The treatment of stretched cotton fibers with concentrated sodium hydroxide.

metal. One of a class of elements which show a luster, are good conductors of heat and electricity, and are electropositive.

metallic crystal. See *crystal, metallic.*

metalloid. An element having certain properties characteristic of a metal, but which is generally classed as a non-metal.

metamorphic. A term applied to rocks that have undergone a change in form due to heat or pressure.

meter. The metric unit of length.

metric system. A decimal system of measurement.

milli-. Metric prefix meaning 0.001.

miscible. Capable of being mixed.

mixture. A material composed of two or more substances each of which retains its own characteristic properties.

moderator. A material which slows down neutrons.

molality. The concentration of a solution expressed in moles of solute per 1000 grams of solvent.

molal solution. See *solution, molal.*

molarity. The concentration of a solution expressed in moles of solute per liter of solution.

molar solution. See *solution, molar.*

molar volume. The volume, in liters, of 1 mole of a gas at S.T.P.; taken at 22.4 liters for ordinary gases; precisely 22.414 liters for the ideal gas.

mole. The gram-molecular weight of a molecular substance. In practice, extended to include the gram-formula weights of nonmolecular substances and gram-atomic weights of elements represented as monatomic.

molecular crystal. See *crystal, molecular.*

molecular formula. See *formula, molecular.*

molecular weight. See *weight, molecular.*

molecule. The smallest portion of an element or compound that retains the properties exhibited by the substance in mass.

molecule, polar. A molecule containing one or more unsymmetrically arranged polar covalent bonds and as a whole having regions of positive and negative charge.

monatomic. Consisting of one atom.

monel metal. A nickel-copper alloy.

monoclinic. A crystalline system in which there are 3 unequal axes, with one oblique intersection.

monomer. A simple molecule, or single unit of a polymer.

mordant. A substance which, by combining with a dye, produces a fast color in a textile fiber.

mortar. A mixture of lime, sand, and water.

mother liquor. The saturated solution remaining after crystals have separated from a solution.

muriatic acid. Technical grade hydrochloric acid.

natural gas. A combustible gas formed in nature by the decomposition of vegetable matter.

negative catalyst. See *catalyst, negative.*

neutralization. The reaction between hydronium ions and hydroxide ions to form water.

neutron. A neutral particle found in the nucleus of an atom. It has about the same mass as a proton.

N.F. The abbreviation for *National Formulary,* a book containing a list of medicinal substances and formulas.

nichrome. An alloy of nickel, chromium, iron and manganese.

nitralloy. An alloy steel that has been treated with ammonia.

nitride. A compound of nitrogen and a less electronegative element.

nitrocellulose. A powerful explosive made by treating cellulose with nitric and sulfuric acids.

nitrogation. The direct addition of nitrogen compounds to the soil.

nitrogen fixation. The process of converting elementary nitrogen into nitrogen compounds.

nitroglycerin. Glyceryl trinitrate, a powerful and sensitive explosive.

nodule. A knob-like swelling on the roots of plants of the bean and pea family in which nitrogen-fixing bacteria grow.

nonelectrolyte. A substance whose water solution does not conduct the electric current appreciably.

nonflammable. Not capable of being burned.

nonmetal. One of a class of elements which are usually poor conductors of heat and electricity and are electronegative.

nonpolar bond. A covalent bond between atoms with negligible difference in electronegativity.

normality. The concentration of a solution expressed in equivalent weights of solute per liter of solution.

normal solution. See *solution, normal.*

nuclear change. A change which involves changes in the identity of the atoms themselves.

nuclear disintegration. The emission of a proton or neutron from a nucleus as a result of bombarding the nucleus with alpha particles, protons, deuterons, or neutrons.

nuclear equation. An equation representing changes in the nuclei of atoms.

nuclear reactor. A device in which the controlled fission of radioactive material produces new radioactive substances and energy.

nucleus. The positively-charged, dense central part of an atom.

occlusion. The adsorption of a gas on a solid.

octane rating. A number indicating how a gasoline behaves with regard to knocking when compared with a test fuel given an arbitrary rating of 100.

octet. An outer shell of an atom containing four electron pairs.

oil of vitriol. Concentrated sulfuric acid.

open-hearth. A large furnace in which steel is made in a shallow pool.

optical bleach. A substance which remains in cloth after washing or rinsing and replaces the blue light waves absorbed by the cloth.

orbital. A possible electron orbit in a shell or energy level.

ore. A mineral containing an element that can be extracted profitably.

organic. Pertaining to carbon compounds, particularly hydrocarbons and their derivatives.

organic chemistry. See *chemistry, organic.*

organosol. A suspensoid in which an organic liquid is the dispersing medium.

orthorhombic. A crystalline system in which there are three unequal axes at right angles.

oxidation. Any chemical action in which an atom, a group of atoms, or an ion loses electrons.

oxidation number. A special valence number assigned to each element to indicate the number of electrons gained, lost, or shared unequally.

oxidation state. See *oxidation number.*

oxide. A compound consisting of oxygen and usually one other element.

oxide, hydrous. A hydrated metallic oxide.

oxidizing agent. The atom, group of atoms, or ion which takes up electrons during a chemical reaction.

oxidizing flame. See *flame, oxidizing.*

ozone. An allotropic form of oxygen containing three atoms per molecule.

parent element. See *element, parent.*

peat. Moss, sedge, or other form of vegetation which has undergone partial decomposition under water.

peptization. The process of preparing colloidal suspensions by the addition of a substance which acts upon the suspended particles reducing them to colloidal dimensions.

peptizing agent. A substance which when added to a suspension causes peptization.

period. A horizontal row of elements in the Periodic Table.

periodic law. See *law, periodic.*

Periodic Table. A tabular arrangement of the chemical elements based on their atomic structure.

permalloy. A high nickel alloy steel that is easily magnetized.

permanent hardness. Hardness, caused by the sulfates of calcium and magnesium, which can be removed by the addition of chemical softeners.

peroxide group. The $^-:\ddot{O}:\ddot{O}:^-$ group.

petroleum. A liquid mixture of hydrocarbons obtained from beneath the surface of the ground.

pH. Hydronium ion index; the common logarithm of the reciprocal of the hydronium-ion concentration.

phenolphthalein. An indicator which is colorless in the presence of excess H_3O^+ ions and red in the presence of excess OH^- ions.

phenomenon. An event or situation of scientific interest susceptible of scientific description and explanation.

phlogiston theory. See *theory, phlogiston.*

photosynthesis. The process by which plants build carbohydrate foods with the aid of sunlight, using carbon dioxide and water as the raw materials, and chlorophyll as the catalyst.

physical change. A change in which the identifying properties of a substance remain unchanged.

physical equilibrium. See *equilibrium, physical.*

physical properties. Those properties which can be determined without causing a change in the identity of a material.

pickling. Removing the surface impurities from a metal by dipping it into an acid bath.

pigment. A coloring agent.

pigment color. Color due to the absorption by pigments of some portions of white light.

plastic. A natural or synthetic material which can be shaped while soft into a required form and then hardened to produce a durable finished article.

plasticizer. A substance which makes plastics easier to work.

polar bond. A chemical bond, essentially covalent, resulting from the unequal sharing of valence electrons between atoms of intermediate difference in electronegativity.

polar molecule. See *molecule, polar*.

poling. The use of green wood to prevent oxidation in the production of crude copper.

polymer. A compound formed by two or more simpler molecules or radicals.

polymerization. The combining of simple molecules of the same kind to form a more complex one.

porcelain. A product made from pure white clay mixed with powdered feldspar and usually fired twice in a kiln.

positive catalyst. See *catalyst, positive*.

potential energy. See *energy, potential*.

precipitate. (1) A substance, usually a solid, which separates from a solution as a result of some physical or chemical change. (2) To produce such a substance.

pressure. Force per unit area.

pressure, critical. The pressure required to liquefy a gas at its critical temperature.

pressure, equilibrium vapor. The pressure exerted by a vapor in equilibrium with its liquid.

pressure, standard. The pressure exerted by a column of mercury 760 mm high at 0° C.

pressure, vapor. Pressure due to the vapor of confined liquids and solids.

product. An element or compound resulting from chemical action.

proportion. The relation of one portion to another; the equality between ratios.

protective agent. A colloidal substance which when adsorbed on suspended particles stabilizes the system.

protein. A complex organic compound necessary for the growth of living things or the repair of worn-out tissue.

proton. A positively-charged particle ✓ found in the nucleus of an atom. It has $\frac{1836}{1837}$ of the mass of a hydrogen atom.

proton acceptor. A base according to the Bronsted concept.

proton donor. An acid according to the Bronsted concept.

pulp. Crude sheets of tangled fibers produced from poplar, spruce, or pine logs.

radical. A group of atoms which usually behaves as if it were a single atom.

radioactive. Having the property of radioactivity.

radioactive decomposition. A radioactive change in which a nucleus emits a particle and rays, forming a slightly lighter, more stable nucleus.

radioactive fall-out. The showering down of radioactive particles which were originally carried high into the air by a nuclear explosion.

radioactive tracer. A radioactive element introduced in small quantities to determine the behavior of chemically similar nonradioactive atoms in various physical or chemical changes.

radioactivity. The spontaneous, uncontrollable disintegration of the nucleus of an atom with the emission of particles and rays.

rare earth element. See *element, rare earth*.

reactant. An element or compound entering into a chemical action.

redox. Pertaining to oxidation-reduction reactions.

reducing agent. The atom, group of atoms, or ion which supplies electrons during a chemical reaction.

reducing flame. See *flame, reducing*.

reduction. Any chemical action in which an atom, a group of atoms, or an ion gains electrons.

refractory. (1) Not readily melted. (2) A substance which is not readily melted.

replacement reaction. A chemical reaction in which one substance is displaced from its compound by another substance.

resistance furnace. A furnace in which the heat is produced by the electrical resistance of loose pieces of coke.

resonance. The property of a molecule of shifting its electronic structure between two or more different patterns.

resonance hybrid. A molecule whose properties show that its structure resonates among several possible covalent bonding arrangements.

respiration. The process by which a plant or animal absorbs oxygen and gives off products of oxidation in the tissues, especially carbon dioxide.

reversible reaction. A chemical reaction in which the products may re-form the original reactants under suitable conditions.

rhombic. See *orthorhombic*.

riffle. A strip laid crosswise in a sluice for retaining gold particles.

roasting. Heating in the presence of air.

sacrificial metal. The metallic electrode of an electrochemical cell that is oxidized.

salt. A compound composed of positive ions of a metal or radical and negative ions produced when certain acids transfer protons to a base.

salting out. The precipitation of a colloidal dispersion by the addition of a soluble salt.

saponification. The process of making a soap by hydrolysis of an ester with an alkali.

saturated. (1) Pertaining to a solution in which the concentration of solute is the maximum possible under existing conditions. (2) Pertaining to an organic compound which has only single covalent bonds between carbon atoms.

scattering. The deflection of rays of light sidewise by particles of suspended matter.

science. A body of systematized knowledge.

scientific notation. A system of writing large and small numbers using the form $M \times 10^n$, where M is a number between 1 and 10 having a single digit to the left of the decimal point and n is a positive or negative integer.

sedimentary. A term applied to rocks formed from sediment that has been deposited in layers.

self-protective metal. A metal which forms a nonporous, nonscaling coat of tarnish.

shell. A region about the nucleus of an atom in which electrons move.

shell-filler. An explosive that requires a severe shock to set it off.

sherardize. To galvanize by the condensation of zinc vapor on a ferrous metal surface.

significant figures. The digits in measurement represent the number of units counted with reasonable assurance.

silicone. One of a group of compounds containing a chain of alternate silicon and oxygen atoms, with hydrocarbon groups attached to the silicon atoms.

simplest formula. See *formula, empirical*.

slag. An easily melted product of the reaction between the flux and the impurities of an ore.

slaking. The addition of water to quicklime, CaO, to produce hydrated lime, $Ca(OH)_2$.

sluice. A trough for washing out gold from gold-bearing gravel.

slurry. A watery mixture.

smokeless powder. A nitrocellulose explosive.

solid. The state of matter characterized by a definite shape.

solubility. The amount of a solute dissolved in a given amount of solvent at equilibrium, under specified conditions.

soluble. Capable of being dissolved.

solute. The dissolved substance in a solution.

solution. A homogeneous mixture of two or more substances. the composition of which may be varied within definite limits.

solution, buffered. A solution containing a relatively high concentration of a buffer salt which tends to maintain a constant pH.

solution equilibrium. See *equilibrium, solution*.

solution, formal. A solution containing 1 gram-formula weight of solute per liter of solution.

solution, molal. A solution containing 1 mole of solute per 1000 grams of solvent.

solution, molar. A solution containing 1 mole of solute per liter of solution.

solution, normal. A solution containing 1 gram-equivalent weight of solute per liter of solution.

solution, standard. A solution that contains a definite concentration of solute which is known precisely.

solvation. The adsorption of molecules of the dispersing liquid by dispersal particles.

solvent. The dissolving medium in a solution.

specific gravity. The ratio of the density of a substance to the density of a standard of reference. Solids and liquids are referred to water; gases are commonly referred to air.

specific surface. The ratio of surface area to volume.

spectroscope. An optical instrument consisting of a collimator tube, a glass prism, and a telescope, used for producing and viewing spectra.

spectrum. The pattern of colors formed by passing light through a prism.

spelter. Commercial zinc.

GLOSSARY

spiegeleisen. Ferromanganese alloy added to iron in the steelmaking process.

spinneret. A metal plate with many small holes used in forming a synthetic fiber.

spontaneous combustion. See *combustion, spontaneous.*

stable compound. See *compound, stable.*

stalactite. An icicle-like mass of calcium carbonate hanging from the roof of a limestone cave.

stalagmite. A mass of calcium carbonate rising from the floor of a limestone cave, formed by the dripping of calcium bicarbonate solution from the cave roof.

standard pressure. See *pressure, standard.*

standard solution. See *solution, standard.*

standard temperature. 0° Centigrade.

steam point. 100° C; 212° F.

steelite. A hard alloy of cobalt and chromium.

sterling. Pertaining to silver which contains 7.5% copper.

stibnite. A sulfide ore of antimony.

stoichiometry. The branch of chemistry pertaining to the numerical relationships of chemical elements and compounds and the mathematical proportions of reactants and products in chemical transformations.

S.T.P. The abbreviation for "standard temperature and pressure."

structural color. Color due to the scattering of white light by colloidally suspended particles.

structural formula. See *formula, structural.*

sublime. To pass from the solid to the gaseous state without liquefying.

subscript. A number written below and to the side of a symbol. If at the left, it represents the atomic number; if at the right it represents the number of atoms of the element.

substance. A homogeneous material consisting of one particular kind of matter.

substitution product. A compound in which various atoms or groups have been substituted for one or more atoms.

superheated water. Water heated under pressure to a temperature above its normal boiling point.

supersaturated. Pertaining to a solution which contains an amount of solute in excess of that normally possible under existing conditions.

superscript. A number written above and to the side of a symbol. If at the right it represents the mass number of the atom represented by the symbol.

suspension. See *suspensoid.*

suspensoid. A colloidal suspension in which there is little attraction between the

dispersed substance and the dispersing liquid.

synchrotron. A particle accelerator in which particles move in a circular path due to the varying of the oscillating voltage and the magnetic field.

synthesis. A combining of simple substances to make a more complex substance.

synthetic. Man-made; artificial.

tartar emetic. Potassium antimonyl tartrate.

tempering. The regulation of the iron carbide, and thus the hardness of steel by a process of heating and sudden cooling.

temporary hardness. Hardness, caused by the bicarbonates of calcium and magnesium, which can be removed by boiling the water.

ternary. Composed of three elements.

tetragonal. A crystalline system in which the three axes are at right angles, but only two, the lateral axes, are equal.

textile. A fabric produced by weaving.

theory. A plausible explanation of a natural phenomenon in terms of a simple model which has familiar properties.

theory, atomic. A theory which explains the definite composition of substances and the way and proportions in which substances react with one another in terms of the atoms of which substances are composed.

theory, kinetic. A theory pertaining to the motion of the ultimate particles of substances, and in particular, of the molecules of gases.

theory, phlogiston. An obsolete theory which explained combustion as being due to the loss of a substance called phlogiston.

thermal cracking. See *cracking, thermal.*

thermite reaction. The reaction by which a metal is prepared from its oxide by reduction with aluminum.

thermoplastic. Refers to a plastic that can be softened by heat.

thermosetting. Refers to a plastic that cannot be softened by heat.

titanium sponge. Powdered titanium.

titration. Determination of the concentration of a solution by comparing it with a standard solution, usually employing burets for the operation.

total valence. See *valence, total.*

toxic. Poisonous.

transition element. See *element, transition.*

transmutation reaction. A reaction in which the nucleus of an atom undergoes a change in its positive charge, and consequently in its identity.

transuranium element. See *element, transuranium.*

triad. A group of three elements, the middle one of which has an atomic weight which is approximately the same as the average of the atomic weights of the other two elements.

triclinic. A crystalline system in which there are three unequal axes and oblique intersections.

triprotic. Referring to an acid with three replaceable hydrogen atoms.

tritium. The isotope of hydrogen having one proton and two neutrons in the nucleus.

trunnion. One of a pair of opposite protruding pivots that provide a means of turning a heavy vessel.

tuyère. A blowpipe in the base of a blast furnace.

Tyndall effect. The diffusion of light by colloidal particles.

type metal. An alloy of antimony, tin, and lead.

ultramicroscope. A microscope in which the object is illuminated at right angles to the optical axis of the microscope.

unsaturated. An organic compound with a double or triple bond between two carbon atoms.

unstable compound. See *compound, unstable.*

U.S.P. The abbreviation for *United States Pharmacopoeia,* an official guide in compounding medicines.

valence. The number of electrons gained, lost, or shared by an atom in bonding with one or more atoms.

valence electron. See *electron, valence.*

valence, total. The product of the valence of an element or radical by the number of atoms of the element or the number of radicals taken.

vapor. The gaseous state of substances which normally exist as liquids or solids.

vapor pressure. See *pressure, vapor.*

vapor pressure, equilibrium. See *pressure, equilibrium vapor.*

velocity constant. See *constant, velocity.*

vermiculite. Mica that has been expanded with steam to make a light, porous material.

volatile. Easily vaporized.

vulcanization. The heating of rubber with other materials to improve its properties.

water gas. A fuel gas made by blowing a blast of steam through a bed of red-hot coke.

water glass. A water solution of sodium silicate.

water of hydration. Water that has united with some chemicals as they form crystals called hydrates.

water softener. A chemical substance which removes hardness from water.

weight. The measure of the earth's gravitational attraction for a body.

weight, atomic. The average relative weight of the atoms of the naturally-occurring mixture of isotopes of an element based on the weight of the atoms of naturally-occurring carbon-12 isotope as exactly 12.0000.

weight, equivalent. A term used to connote equal combining power.

weight, formula. The sum of the atomic weights of all the atoms present in the chemical formula.

weight, gram-atomic. The mass of an element in grams equal to its atomic weight.

weight, gram-equivalent. The mass of a reactant, in grams, which contains, replaces, or reacts with (either directly or indirectly) 1 gram-atom of hydrogen.

weight, gram-formula. The mass of a substance in grams equal to its formula weight.

weight, gram-molecular. The mass of a molecular substance in grams equal to its molecular weight.

weight, molecular. The formula weight of a molecular substance.

weighted silk. Silk that has been dipped in solutions of certain salts.

weighting. The repeated dipping of raw silk into a solution of tin chloride or iron chloride.

white lead. A paint base composed of basic lead carbonate.

word equation. A brief statement which identifies the reactants entering into chemical action and the products formed.

X rays. Radiations similar to light or radio waves but which have a high frequency and a short wave length.

zeolite. A sodium silico-aluminate used to soften water.

Page references for illustrations are print[...]

THE ELEMENTS, THEIR SYMBOLS, ATOMIC NUMBERS, AND ATOMIC WEIGHTS

The more important elements are printed in blue type.

Name of element	Symbol	Atomic number	Atomic weight	Name of element	Symbol	Atomic number	Atomic weight
Actinium	Ac	89	[227]	Mercury	Hg	80	200.59
Aluminum	Al	13	26.9815	Molybdenum	Mo	42	95.94
Americium	Am	95	[243]	Neodymium	Nd	60	144.24
Antimony	Sb	51	121.75	Neon	Ne	10	20.183
Argon	Ar	18	39.948	Neptunium	Np	93	[237]
Arsenic	As	33	74.9216	Nickel	Ni	28	58.71
Astatine	At	85	[210]	Niobium	Nb	41	92.906
Barium	Ba	56	137.34	Nitrogen	N	7	14.0067
Berkelium	Bk	97	[249*]	(Nobelium)	(No)	102	
Beryllium	Be	4	9.0122	Osmium	Os	76	190.2
Bismuth	Bi	83	208.980	Oxygen	O	8	15.9994
Boron	B	5	10.811	Palladium	Pd	46	106.4
Bromine	Br	35	79.909	Phosphorus	P	15	30.9738
Cadmium	Cd	48	112.40	Platinum	Pt	78	195.09
Calcium	Ca	20	40.08	Plutonium	Pu	94	[242]
Californium	Cf	98	[251*]	Polonium	Po	84	[210*]
Carbon	C	6	12.01115	Potassium	K	19	39.102
Cerium	Ce	58	140.12	Praseodymium	Pr	59	140.907
Cesium	Cs	55	132.905	Promethium	Pm	61	[147*]
Chlorine	Cl	17	35.453	Protactinium	Pa	91	[231]
Chromium	Cr	24	51.996	Radium	Ra	88	[226]
Cobalt	Co	27	58.9332	Radon	Rn	86	[222]
Copper	Cu	29	63.54	Rhenium	Re	75	186.2
Curium	Cm	96	[247]	Rhodium	Rh	45	102.905
Dysprosium	Dy	66	162.50	Rubidium	Rb	37	85.47
Einsteinium	Es	99	[254]	Ruthenium	Ru	44	101.07
Erbium	Er	68	167.26	Samarium	Sm	62	150.35
Europium	Eu	63	151.96	Scandium	Sc	21	44.956
Fermium	Fm	100	[253]	Selenium	Se	34	78.96
Fluorine	F	9	18.9984	Silicon	Si	14	28.086
Francium	Fr	87	[223]	Silver	Ag	47	107.870
Gadolinium	Gd	64	157.25	Sodium	Na	11	22.9898
Gallium	Ga	31	69.72	Strontium	Sr	38	87.62
Germanium	Ge	32	72.59	Sulfur	S	16	32.064
Gold	Au	79	196.967	Tantalum	Ta	73	180.948
Hafnium	Hf	72	178.49	Technetium	Tc	43	[99*]
Helium	He	2	4.0026	Tellurium	Te	52	127.60
Holimum	Ho	67	164.930	Terbium	Tb	65	158.924
Hydrogen	H	1	1.00797	Thallium	Tl	81	204.37
Indium	In	49	114.82	Thorium	Th	90	232.038
Iodine	I	53	126.9044	Thulium	Tm	69	168.934
Iridium	Ir	77	192.2	Tin	Sn	50	118.69
Iron	Fe	26	55.847	Titanium	Ti	22	47.90
Krypton	Kr	36	83.80	Tungsten	W	74	183.85
Lanthanum	La	57	138.91	Uranium	U	92	238.03
Lawrencium	Lw	103	[257]	Vanadium	V	23	50.942
Lead	Pb	82	207.19	Xenon	Xe	54	131.30
Lithium	Li	3	6.939	Ytterbium	Yb	70	173.04
Lutetium	Lu	71	174.97	Yttrium	Y	39	88.905
Magnesium	Mg	12	24.312	Zinc	Zn	30	65.37
Manganese	Mn	25	54.9380	Zirconium	Zr	40	91.22
Mendelevium	Md	101	[256]				

A value given in brackets denotes the mass number of the isotope of longest known half-life, or for those marked with an asterisk, a better known one. The atomic weights of most of these elements are believed to have no error greater than ±0.5 of the last digit given.

spiegeleisen. Ferromanganese alloy added to iron in the steelmaking process.

spinneret. A metal plate with many small holes used in forming a synthetic fiber.

spontaneous combustion. See *combustion, spontaneous.*

stable compound. See *compound, stable.*

stalactite. An icicle-like mass of calcium carbonate hanging from the roof of a limestone cave.

stalagmite. A mass of calcium carbonate rising from the floor of a limestone cave, formed by the dripping of calcium bicarbonate solution from the cave roof.

standard pressure. See *pressure, standard.*

standard solution. See *solution, standard.*

standard temperature. 0° Centigrade.

steam point. 100° C; 212° F.

steelite. A hard alloy of cobalt and chromium.

sterling. Pertaining to silver which contains 7.5% copper.

stibnite. A sulfide ore of antimony.

stoichiometry. The branch of chemistry pertaining to the numerical relationships of chemical elements and compounds and the mathematical proportions of reactants and products in chemical transformations.

S.T.P. The abbreviation for "standard temperature and pressure."

structural color. Color due to the scattering of white light by colloidally suspended particles.

structural formula. See *formula, structural.*

sublime. To pass from the solid to the gaseous state without liquefying.

subscript. A number written below and to the side of a symbol. If at the left, it represents the atomic number; if at the right it represents the number of atoms of the element.

substance. A homogeneous material consisting of one particular kind of matter.

substitution product. A compound in which various atoms or groups have been substituted for one or more atoms.

superheated water. Water heated under pressure to a temperature above its normal boiling point.

supersaturated. Pertaining to a solution which contains an amount of solute in excess of that normally possible under existing conditions.

superscript. A number written above and to the side of a symbol. If at the right it represents the mass number of the atom represented by the symbol.

suspension. See *suspensoid.*

suspensoid. A colloidal suspension in which there is little attraction between the dispersed substance and the dispersing liquid.

synchrotron. A particle accelerator in which particles move in a circular path due to the varying of the oscillating voltage and the magnetic field.

synthesis. A combining of simple substances to make a more complex substance.

synthetic. Man-made; artificial.

tartar emetic. Potassium antimonyl tartrate.

tempering. The regulation of the iron carbide, and thus the hardness of steel by a process of heating and sudden cooling.

temporary hardness. Hardness, caused by the bicarbonates of calcium and magnesium, which can be removed by boiling the water.

ternary. Composed of three elements.

tetragonal. A crystalline system in which the three axes are at right angles, but only two, the lateral axes, are equal.

textile. A fabric produced by weaving.

theory. A plausible explanation of a natural phenomenon in terms of a simple model which has familiar properties.

theory, atomic. A theory which explains the definite composition of substances and the way and proportions in which substances react with one another in terms of the atoms of which substances are composed.

theory, kinetic. A theory pertaining to the motion of the ultimate particles of substances, and in particular, of the molecules of gases.

theory, phlogiston. An obsolete theory which explained combustion as being due to the loss of a substance called phlogiston.

thermal cracking. See *cracking, thermal.*

thermite reaction. The reaction by which a metal is prepared from its oxide by reduction with aluminum.

thermoplastic. Refers to a plastic that can be softened by heat.

thermosetting. Refers to a plastic that cannot be softened by heat.

titanium sponge. Powdered titanium.

titration. Determination of the concentration of a solution by comparing it with a standard solution, usually employing burets for the operation.

total valence. See *valence, total.*

toxic. Poisonous.

transition element. See *element, transition.*

transmutation reaction. A reaction in which the nucleus of an atom undergoes a change in its positive charge, and consequently in its identity.

transuranium element. See *element, transuranium.*

triad. A group of three elements, the middle one of which has an atomic weight which is approximately the same as the average of the atomic weights of the other two elements.

triclinic. A crystalline system in which there are three unequal axes and oblique intersections.

triprotic. Referring to an acid with three replaceable hydrogen atoms.

tritium. The isotope of hydrogen having one proton and two neutrons in the nucleus.

trunnion. One of a pair of opposite protruding pivots that provide a means of turning a heavy vessel.

tuyère. A blowpipe in the base of a blast furnace.

Tyndall effect. The diffusion of light by colloidal particles.

type metal. An alloy of antimony, tin, and lead.

ultramicroscope. A microscope in which the object is illuminated at right angles to the optical axis of the microscope.

unsaturated. An organic compound with a double or triple bond between two carbon atoms.

unstable compound. See *compound, unstable.*

U.S.P. The abbreviation for *United States Pharmacopoeia,* an official guide in compounding medicines.

valence. The number of electrons gained, lost, or shared by an atom in bonding with one or more atoms.

valence electron. See *electron, valence.*

valence, total. The product of the valence of an element or radical by the number of atoms of the element or the number of radicals taken.

vapor. The gaseous state of substances which normally exist as liquids or solids.

vapor pressure. See *pressure, vapor.*

vapor pressure, equilibrium. See *pressure, equilibrium vapor.*

velocity constant. See *constant, velocity.*

vermiculite. Mica that has been expanded with steam to make a light, porous material.

volatile. Easily vaporized.

vulcanization. The heating of rubber with other materials to improve its properties.

water gas. A fuel gas made by blowing a blast of steam through a bed of red-hot coke.

water glass. A water solution of sodium silicate.

water of hydration. Water that has united with some chemicals as they form crystals called hydrates.

water softener. A chemical substance which removes hardness from water.

weight. The measure of the earth's gravitational attraction for a body.

weight, atomic. The average relative weight of the atoms of the naturally-occurring mixture of isotopes of an element based on the weight of the atoms of naturally-occurring carbon-12 isotope as exactly 12.0000.

weight, equivalent. A term used to connote equal combining power.

weight, formula. The sum of the atomic weights of all the atoms present in the chemical formula.

weight, gram-atomic. The mass of an element in grams equal to its atomic weight.

weight, gram-equivalent. The mass of a reactant, in grams, which contains, replaces, or reacts with (either directly or indirectly) 1 gram-atom of hydrogen.

weight, gram-formula. The mass of a substance in grams equal to its formula weight.

weight, gram-molecular. The mass of a molecular substance in grams equal to its molecular weight.

weight, molecular. The formula weight of a molecular substance.

weighted silk. Silk that has been dipped in solutions of certain salts.

weighting. The repeated dipping of raw silk into a solution of tin chloride or iron chloride.

white lead. A paint base composed of basic lead carbonate.

word equation. A brief statement which identifies the reactants entering into chemical action and the products formed.

X rays. Radiations similar to light or radio waves but which have a high frequency and a short wave length.

zeolite. A sodium silico-aluminate used to soften water.

INDEX

Page references for illustrations are printed in **boldface**.